4. 343.75
2. 2 9 0/0
3. #590
7. $2 508.75

BUSINESS MATHEMATICS
PRINCIPLES AND PRACTICE—COMPLETE

R. ROBERT ROSENBERG is a recognized authority in business mathematics, law, and other areas of business education. He has taught in all types of institutions—high school, university, business school, and adult evening school. He has also been a business consultant in accounting (he is a C.P.A.) and office management. Dr. Rosenberg was President of Jersey City Junior College, Jersey City, New Jersey, and from time to time teaches business subjects at various institutions in the area. He is author of several textbooks in business mathematics and business law on the secondary school and collegiate levels. He received his Ed.D. in administration and supervision of business education from New York University.

HARRY LEWIS is Head of the Mathematics Department of East Side High School, Newark, New Jersey, a position he has held for five years. He has taught mathematics to both business and nonbusiness students in secondary schools and he has also taught methods courses in mathematics in colleges and universities. He is author of numerous magazine articles on the teaching of mathematics. Dr. Lewis received his Ph.D. in mathematics education from New York University.

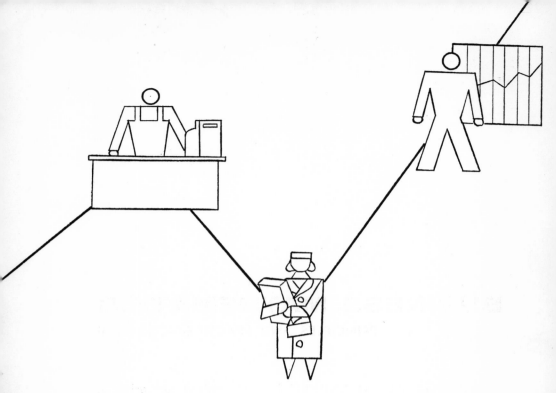

BUSINESS

GREGG PUBLISHING DIVISION
McGraw-Hill Book Company, Inc.

NEW YORK CHICAGO DALLAS CORTE MADERA, CALIF.
TORONTO LONDON

MATHEMATICS

PRINCIPLES AND PRACTICE—COMPLETE

R. ROBERT ROSENBERG, Ed.D., C.P.A.

HARRY LEWIS, Ph.D.

FIFTH EDITION

BUSINESS MATHEMATICS, PRINCIPLES AND PRACTICE, COMPLETE, Fifth Edition

Copyright, © 1958, by McGraw-Hill Book Company, Inc. Copyright, 1953, 1946, 1937, 1934, by McGraw-Hill Book Company, Inc. All rights reserved. This book, or parts thereof, may not be reproduced in any form without permission of the publishers.—

6 7 8 9 10 11   KP-58   9 8 7 6 5 4 3 2 1

53825

Library of Congress Catalog No. 57–10227

PUBLISHED BY GREGG PUBLISHING DIVISION

McGraw-Hill Book Company, Inc.

PRINTED IN THE UNITED STATES OF AMERICA

Preface

BUSINESS MATHEMATICS, PRINCIPLES AND PRACTICE, COMPLETE, has enjoyed wide popularity in its various editions for many years. In a sense, this book has "grown up" with business education. Each edition reflected the thinking of the businessman, the teacher, and the recent graduate of the particular time, concerning the kind of arithmetic needed for job performance. In many ways, too, this book has influenced or led the thinking in business mathematics; many state and city courses of study have been modeled on it.

In its various editions, BUSINESS MATHEMATICS has always been primarily a *vocational* business mathematics text, emphasizing most heavily mathematics as applied to on-the-job situations. But this emphasis has not lessened the *personal-use* aspects of business mathematics, for this book has always been a practical text for the consumer, too.

BUSINESS MATHEMATICS has always been a *thorough* text, covering every phase of business activity in which the student's mathematical knowledge was considered important by the employer. It has always been a *teachable* book; its clear presentation of principles in 1–2–3 steps, its generous illustrations, its abundance of problems, and its concise style of writing all contribute to its reputation for teachableness.

A NEW BOOK

Retaining those features that have made its predecessors so popular with teachers and students, the Fifth Edition claims several new distinctions, too. Most important, it is a *new* book, reflecting the most modern thinking in mathematics content and instruction. The following features are among those that characterize this new Fifth Edition.

1. *Emphasis on the "Why" of Learning.* The student who learns mathematics by rote is often not capable of applying his knowledge to situations outside the textbook. Greater emphasis, therefore, is placed in this new edition on the *why*. Throughout the text, the student is helped to see the *why* through careful and meaningful explanations

v

of principles—not merely a quick rule followed by a rote application. A particularly effective application of the *why* is found at the end of many chapters where the student, thinking of himself as the owner of a business ("You As a Businessman"), a borrower ("You As a Borrower"), or an investor ("You As an Investor"), is asked to make a choice among several courses of action—decisions that people must make in the course of their daily business and personal affairs. The wise businessman or consumer makes such decisions only after carefully weighing the alternatives that are available to him. The afore-mentioned sections are designed to teach the student how to examine the alternatives (see page 207 for an example).

2. *Dramatization of the Fundamental Operations.* Regardless of the student's previous background in mathematics, it is usually worthwhile to review with him at the outset the fundamental operations of addition, subtraction, multiplication, and division. However, rather than present these fundamentals as monotonous "drill for drill's sake," they are made lively and dramatic in this text through the story of Fred Wilson, an executive trainee in a large department store. Here, in his daily work in various departments, Fred really discovers the need for accurate arithmetic computation. Through this approach the student can see the *need* for the study of business mathematics, so that the subject comes to life for him (see pages 1–3 for an example).

3. *Motivation.* BUSINESS MATHEMATICS is designed to motivate the student from beginning to end. For example, to capture the student's interest, most chapters are introduced by a short story (accompanied by drawings or photographs) in which a problem is presented. Immediately following the story is a series of questions aimed at provoking lively class discussion, enabling the teacher to determine the students' background in the subject. In keeping with the fundamental premise of education that the student will learn best when he knows "where he is going and why he is so headed," each chapter preview contains a small segment devoted to a bird's-eye view of what is in store for him and why it is important (see page 161 for examples).

4. *Mathematics in Everyday Living.* Although many students who learn business mathematics may never be engaged in occupations that require a thorough knowledge of the subject, all will need such a knowledge in their everyday lives. For this reason, considerable emphasis has been placed on such topics as installment buying, borrowing money, home ownership and cost of public utilities, life insurance, social security, and income tax. Other topics, such as business graphs, have been given a "new look" that makes them more useful as an everyday

tool while still stressing their business applications. For example, the emphasis is on *interpretation* of graphic data in addition to the highly technical art of graph construction.

5. *Using Tables Intelligently.* The age of the lightning-fast human calculator is rapidly disappearing, and he is being replaced by the electrically driven calculator and the mathematical table. In view of this, a great number of tables of many varieties have been included (see pages 168–169 for examples). The student who is taught to properly use these tables will have no trouble in understanding the tables he will encounter in business and personal affairs. At the same time, the teacher who prefers not to use the tables will find more than ample problem material in these same areas that can be solved by traditional methods.

6. *New Topics.* A new chapter on business records appears in this Fifth Edition. The purpose of this chapter is to help the business teacher correlate the material offered in bookkeeping and accounting courses with the study of business mathematics. Thus, the student can understand more clearly the relationship between accounting practices and business mathematics where often the two subjects appear to be unrelated.

Transportation plays an increasingly important role in business and personal life. In fact, many young people are finding important new careers in the field of transportation and shipping. For these reasons, more emphasis has been placed on this vital activity.

Home ownership and the cost of public utilities often present complicated problems to today's consumer. A new chapter has been added to this revision to help the student understand and cope with these problems more intelligently. The material on weights and measures, included as supplementary material in preceding editions, has now been written as a text chapter with its own "doing" activities.

7. *Special Learning Helps.* Several special learning helps have been incorporated in this new edition. Typical of these aids are the following:

a. There is a large number of problems that will fill the needs of a wide variety of students and classroom situations. For the quicker students, there are "bonus" problems to challenge their ability (see page 199 for an example). At the close of each chapter there is a set of problems covering every topic presented in the chapter. Each problem is followed by the number of the page on which the solution of a similar problem can be found (see pages 157–159 for examples). Following this section is a chapter test with problem material similar to the review preceding it. Great care was taken to insure that these tests would contain no material that was irrelevant to the topics covered within the chapter (see pages 159–160 for an example).

b. Each set of Learning Exercises is preceded by several "business transactions," wherein the student is first shown *why* each step in the solution of the problem is necessary. This is followed by an outline showing *how* the computation should be presented. Thus, the student learns not only the reason for the steps that may be necessary in solving a problem but is given an outline to follow when solving the Learning Exercises (see page 111 for an example). At no time are narrative problems presented before the student has had the opportunity to achieve a reasonable degree of confidence through practice on exercises differing but slightly from the illustrative "business transactions."

c. A general review appears in the last unit of each chapter. It is divided into two sections. The first section is always a drill on the fundamental operations; the second section is a set of simple problems covering all areas of business mathematics that have been covered up to that point in the text (see pages 188–189 for an example).

8. *Supplementary Section.* A Supplementary Section has been included at the end of the book containing material on the English and Metric Systems and on the Language of Business Mathematics. Included in the Supplementary Section is a General Review of Business Mathematics. This review may be used by the teacher for general class review and discussion, or as supplementary problems for the quicker students.

SUPPORTING MATERIALS

The following materials are available to users of this new Fifth Edition:

1. **Workbook.** This completely new Workbook contains supplementary problems closely paralleling those in the text, together with the necessary forms on which they may be worked. The Workbook is correlated chapter by chapter and unit by unit with the text.

2. **Tests.** A set of tests, correlated with the text, is available.

3. **Solutions Manual.** The Solutions Manual contains teaching suggestions, course schedules, and the key to the problems in the text. In most cases, not only the key is given to the problems but the solution is also worked out for the teacher in order to conserve valuable teaching time.

ACKNOWLEDGMENTS

Many people gave suggestions and other help to the authors in this new edition. Some taught portions of the material in manuscript form;

others read parts of the manuscript and offered valuable criticism. For this assistance, the authors hereby express their gratitude to:

Miss Catherine Cleary, East Side High School, Newark, New Jersey

Mr. John H. Feather, Jr., Bellevue High School, Pittsburgh, Pennsylvania

Mr. A. Raymond Jackson, Vice-President, Goldey Beacom School of Business, Wilmington, Delaware

Mr. Ernest A. May, Riverside High School, Milwaukee, Wisconsin

Mrs. Laura Schefter, East Side High School, Newark, New Jersey

Dr. William Selden, Chief of Business Education, Pennsylvania State Department of Public Instruction, Harrisburg

Professor Elwood B. Sheeder, State Teachers College, Indiana, Pennsylvania

Mr. Edwin E. Weeks, Head of Department of Business Education, Syracuse, New York

A special note of appreciation is due the thousands of teachers who taught this text in one or more of its preceding editions. It is they who have made this Fifth Edition possible.

R. ROBERT ROSENBERG
HARRY LEWIS

Contents

1

Improving Addition Skills

PREVIEW

Fred Wilson had just been graduated from school. Even before
he had begun to think seriously about a job, Fred knew that he
should look into the opportunities offered by several different
kinds of business before making a final decision. He also knew that,
in selecting employment that may turn out to be one's life's work,
more should be considered than the beginning salary.

After a thorough investigation, he was offered, and accepted,
the position of executive trainee with R. C. Bond and Company,
a large department store. The title "executive trainee," though
rather impressive-sounding, was far from that at the outset.

As is the practice with many large firms, Fred agreed to spend 3 years in the company's training program. This program was designed to give Fred experience in all phases of the business. Under this plan, Fred was to move from department to department, learning the practices of each unit of the concern. It was the belief of the management of R. C. Bond and Company that, on completion of this 3-year plan, trainees would have a broad understanding of the company procedures and hence be qualified to act as department managers, buyers, sales supervisors, and so on.

As Fred looked back on this training at the close of the 3 years, he was struck by the importance that a knowledge of the four fundamental operations of arithmetic—addition, subtraction, multiplication, and division—seemed to play in every department into which he went. True, he did find computing machines in some sections, but for the large part it was necessary for him to perform the operations manually. It is to these problems in arithmetic that Fred Wilson encountered as a trainee that the first section of this book is devoted.

UNIT 1   **Addition of Whole Numbers**

While working in the Shipping and the Receiving departments, Fred was constantly handling forms called *bin tickets*. It was part of his responsibility to note on these forms all the changes that occurred in the quantity of supplies that were kept in these rooms.

Each department in the store depended on Fred's records, too. Although each department kept its own record of supplies, the records were not always accurate; and often they lacked notations regarding the latest shipments. Sometimes, for example, Fred received calls from the Furniture Department asking about the availability of a special living-room sofa or a certain dining-room suite. If the information that Fred supplied from his records was incorrect—that is, if the records showed sofas in the stock room when they were not actually there—the customer might be promised delivery when it could not be made.

Needless to say, delay in the receipt of merchandise by a customer does not make for a satisfactory relationship between the customer and the store. Hence, though the recording of changes in stock on the bin ticket first appeared to be a rather routine operation, Fred soon came to realize the importance of accuracy in his work, particularly after he became aware of its relationship to the sales picture as a whole.

A copy of a bin ticket appears here.

Item:	Beach Umbrellas		
Month:	June, 19--		

DATE	IN	OUT	BALANCE
2	375		
4		125	
5		64	
17		37	
19	150	83	
23		56	
27	238	98	
Total	763	463	

At the close of each month Fred had to determine the total number of items that had come "In" to his room as well as the total number of those items that had gone "Out." Thus, the bin ticket shows the total for the In column to be **763**; that for the Out column, **463**. Although he also had to find the balance on hand every time that an In or an Out entry was made, this information is not shown on the form.

LEARNING EXERCISES

Complete the following forms.

1

Item: Shirts		
Size 16–35		
Month: Sept., 19—		

Date	In	Out
1	350	68
5		27
17	725	49
19		35
23		94
Total	xxx	xxx

2

Item: Towels		
Size 18 × 26		
Month: June, 19—		

Date	In	Out
2	896	126
7		88
16		375
18	927	416
20	623	68
Total	xxx	xxx

3

Item: Sheets No. 462		
Month: Jan., 19—		
Date	In	Out
1	2,500	1,272
6	620	437
7		684
15	1,275	397
19		103
23	895	756
30		843
Total	xxx	xxx

4

Item: Children's Shoes Style No. 247		
Month: May, 19—		
Date	In	Out
2	4,378	3,276
3	5,294	858
7		496
16	1,768	2,740
18	3,846	962
25		1,584
27		3,688
Total	xxx	xxx

5

Item: Women's Knitted Hats		
Month: Oct., 19—		
Date	In	Out
3	3,567	1,877
4		467
5	4,384	969
10	1,056	2,385
11		741
18	2,973	593
20		1,794
25	3,042	1,248
Total	xxx	xxx

6

Item: Men's Socks		
Month: Sept., 19—		
Date	In	Out
2	7,566	4,384
4	2,978	1,967
12	1,924	858
14		1,382
17		764
20	992	1,272
22	12,756	3,082
24	1,644	8,610
Total	xxx	xxx

UNIT 2   Special Devices for Increasing Speed in Addition

SECTION 1   Increasing Speed by Grouping in Combinations of 10

It soon became apparent to Fred that he could improve both the speed and the accuracy of his addition work by observing certain number combinations. Thus, the simplest and fastest way of adding the following column:

$$
\begin{array}{r}
7 \\
8 \\
\left[\begin{array}{r} 3 \\ 7 \end{array}\right] \\
2 \\
\hline
27
\end{array}
$$

is to note that the **7** and **3** have a sum of 10, and that the **8** and **2** have the same sum. Hence, these two combinations of 10 added to the **7** at the top of the column will give a total of **27**. Notice the combinations of 10 in each of these illustrations.

(1)	(2)	(3)
6	8	1
9	0	7
1	2	2
4	6	5
3	4	5
23	20	20

Practice in quickly spotting groupings that add to 10 greatly increases speed in addition.

LEARNING EXERCISES

Find the sum in each of the following problems by looking for groupings of 10.

A. Add:

1	2	3	4	5	6	7	8	9	10	11	12
5	6	9	7	3	8	34	56	82	27	98	43
3	3	1	4	2	4	74	43	19	53	76	86
1	8	8	5	1	6	53	21	71	35	54	97
9	4	3	8	8	2	87	63	34	86	12	54
6	2	7	9	9	1	12	57	56	47	87	83
4	1	5	1	4	3	68	84	95	34	53	21
2	6	2	3	6	7	31	46	23	32	28	56

B. Add:

1	2	3	4	5	6	7
7	4	57	38	327	583	5,876
8	6	43	42	642	417	4,218
3	3	28	96	897	118	6,596
5	7	86	,13	263	762	4,304
8	6	43	31	574	943	7,985
7	3	27	85	516	155	3,214
3	1	45	73	326	864	6,811
9	8	93	27	875	319	4,976
1	7	17	18	238	782	4,824
4	4	62	92	784	218	3,209

SECTION 2   Increasing Speed by Rapid Sight Reading of the 45 Number "Facts"

If the numbers 1 through 9 are grouped in combinations of two at a time, there would be 45 of these groupings. These would include pairs such as 4 and 7, 5 and 2, and the like. Also, each time a column of numbers is added, the sum is found by combining only two numbers at one time. Therefore, Fred Wilson realized that, if he were able to determine the sum of each of the 45 groupings without hesitation, the speed with which he performed addition would be greatly increased. Reading these combinations—or *addition facts*, as they are sometimes called—at sight is no different from acquiring skill on a musical instrument or on a typewriter. It can only be done through constant practice.

LEARNING EXERCISES

A. The 45 addition facts are listed below. Practice in finding their sums should be continued until all 45 sums can be found orally in 30 seconds.

	1	2	3	4	5	6	7	8	9
a	1	2	3	1	2	3	1	2	3
	9	7	5	8	6	4	7	5	3
	?	?	?	?	?	?	?	?	?
b	1	2	1	2	3	6	3	1	2
	6	4	5	3	9	3	8	1	2
	?	?	?	?	?	?	?	?	?

c
3	9	8	1	7	6	9	6	5
7	2	2	2	6	4	5	6	6
?	?	?	?	?	?	?	?	?

d
3	4	8	4	5	7	5	9	7
1	9	5	1	4	4	7	9	9
?	?	?	?	?	?	?	?	?

e
4	8	5	8	7	8	8	8	6
4	4	5	9	7	6	8	7	9
?	?	?	?	?	?	?	?	?

B. Add:

1	2	3	4	5	6	7
8	32	88	26	318	829	2,341
7	19	37	83	602	781	5,098
5	47	62	91	451	342	3,846
3	63	53	19	836	217	1,732
9	84	49	84	524	642	9,184
2	25	16	53	368	533	5,376
8	16	84	27	915	863	7,264
6	73	97	46	746	498	8,759
5	28	53	38	543	567	3,341
9	92	16	94	194	647	9,836

UNIT 3 Checking Addition by the Reverse-Order Method

Through such devices as observing groups of numbers in combinations of 10, Fred was able to attain greater speed in adding numbers. He soon realized, however, that with greater speed the danger of making errors increased many times. Once, while in school, he had been disturbed when he did not receive partial credit for an answer of $25,496 that should have been $35,496. Now it occurred to him that this was an error of $10,000—a mistake that could have affected his entire future with the store. Though speed was still important to him, accuracy became his first consideration.

To test the accuracy of his answers in addition, he tried and eliminated several checking methods before settling on the technique called the *reverse-order check*. This method merely consists in adding the column of numbers from the topmost number to the bottom number in the usual manner and then repeating the process by starting with the bottommost and adding upward to the top number. Fred found that, when the direction was reversed, different number combinations were added in the first direction from those that were added in the second. Had he checked by adding in the same direction both times, it is possible that he would have made the same error both times.

As an example:

$$
\begin{array}{r}
5 \\
6 \\
+\,8 \\
\hline
\end{array}
$$

Assume that Fred made an error in adding the 5 and the 6, calling the sum 12. By reversing the direction, however, he no longer adds the 5 and the 6, but the 8 and the 6, giving him the sum of 14, to which he must now add the 5. With the new number combinations, likelihood of repeating errors is reduced.

When Fred was checking, in order to avoid looking at the answer at the bottom of the column, which he had found by adding from the top number to the bottom number, he placed a small piece of paper over the answer and wrote the reverse-order sum at the top of the column.

Example

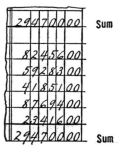

The accuracy of the reverse-order check depends largely on the ability of a person to be honest with himself. If he merely recopies the answer at the top of the column, he is not only defeating the purpose of the check but is also placing himself in an embarrassing position before his employer, particularly if many of his answers are wrong!

LEARNING EXERCISES

In each of the following problems find the sum and check.

1	2	3	4
6,843	8,947	1,798	56,213
4,287	5,365	3,526	32,872
9,182	2,179	7,964	43,346
5,817	4,631	2,637	58,915
6,454	4,345	5,813	64,261

5	6	7	8
92,816	18,614	56,325	87,213
43,294	52,496	42,874	53,814
56,817	48,175	68,235	87,965
28,628	67,816	41,286	52,467
32,935	54,293	24,681	21,643
		35,790	97,426
9	10	51,319	23,671
83,214	81,096	84,986	85,933
56,873	59,074		
58,925	43,597		
42,689	67,513		
13,571	28,678		
57,528	22,432		
36,746	97,815		
74,364	13,285		

UNIT **4** **Horizontal Addition**

At the end of the first week of work in the Receiving Department at R. C. Bond and Company, Fred Wilson was given the form shown on page 10 to complete.

Though Fred had always considered himself to be rather rapid in adding numbers vertically, he found that trying to add horizontally decreased his speed and accuracy to a point that he considered to be in-

Department 542 – Kitchenwares Received Week Beginning Jan. 15, 19–						
Article	Mon.	Tues.	Wed.	Thurs.	Fri.	Total
Can openers	73	48		125		*246*
Steak knives	83	47	56	92		*278*
Rubber bottle stoppers	176			43	154	*373*
Stainless-steel tongs	356		84			*440*
Table mats	128		88		40	*256*

efficient. His first reaction was to rewrite each row of numbers vertically. Thus, the first row would become:

$$73$$
$$48$$
$$\underline{125}$$

It was then possible for him to find the sum in the usual manner, but the time wasted in copying the numbers under one another and then transferring the sum to the Total column was more than the time he lost by adding horizontally.   Hence, he did what most young business-men eventually must come to—he practiced adding horizontally until addition in this direction was as rapid for him as vertical addition. Horizontal addition was quite simple once he had learned to think to himself:

→"First I'll add the units digits—the first digits on the right. Then I'll add the tens digits—the second digits from the right; then the third digits from the right; and so on."

Thus, for the first line on the form:

	Mon.	*Tues.*	*Wed.*	*Thurs.*	*Fri.*	*Total*
Can openers	73	48		125		246

First he combined the units digits: **5 + 8 + 3 = 16** (write **6** carry 1)
Then he added the tens digits: **2 + 4 + 7** + (1 carried) = 14 (write **4** carry 1)
Finally, the hundreds digit: 1 + (1 carried) = 2 (write **2**)
remembering, of course, the numbers that were to be carried. Checking by adding in the reverse direction enabled Fred to determine quickly the accuracy of his work.

LEARNING EXERCISES

During his three years as a trainee, Fred had to complete forms similar to the following. Make copies of these forms and complete them.

1

DEPARTMENT 47—FURNITURE Received Week Beginning March 7, 19—						
Article	Mon.	Tues.	Wed.	Thurs.	Fri.	Total
Sofas	12	23		9		xxx
End tables		56	84		17	xxx
Desks	2	16	7		12	xxx
Rocking chairs	26	43	10	7		xxx
Bookcases	18	26		19	34	xxx
Armchairs	5	8	24	12	7	xxx

2

DEPARTMENT 124—DRUGS AND COSMETICS Received Week Beginning April 4, 19—						
Article	Mon.	Tues.	Wed.	Thurs.	Fri.	Total
Bright Toothpaste	156	342			84	xxx
Carlin Lipstick	65		243	756	163	xxx
Scented soap	424	586		329		xxx
Foamy shampoo	144			384	576	xxx
Dream Make-up Kit	2,304		528		1,728	xxx
Salin's Toothbrush		608		1,468		xxx

3

DEPARTMENTAL SALES Month Ending April 30, 19—					
Department	Cash Sales	Charge Sales	C.O.D. Sales	Approval Sales	Total
Radio-Television	$2,186	$1,416	$1,218	$5,817	$xxx
Furniture	3,642	1,884	2,296	8,293	xxx
Hosiery	1,967	625	984	6,765	xxx
Dresses	987	378	653	3,349	xxx
Children's Wear	854	592	512	2,571	xxx
Jewelry	1,438	919	849	7,882	xxx

UNIT **5**   **Horizontal and Vertical Addition**

Some business forms are so designed that they furnish an automatic checking device for the person completing them without the necessity of resorting to the reverse-order check. As an example, when Fred was working in the Payroll Department, part of a form that he had to complete resembled the following.

Name of Employee	HOURS				Week Beginning	January 5. 19-
	Mon.	Tues.	Wed.	Thurs.	Fri.	Total
A. Alden	8	7	8	6	9	*38*
S. Burke	8	8	8	8	8	*40*
T. Clark	8	4	8	7	8	*35*
B. Dalton	6	8	8	4	8	*34*
Total	*30*	*27*	*32*	*25*	*33*	*147*

The totals in the bottom row are obtained by adding the numbers in each column. The number **30** represents the total number of hours that the four men worked on Monday; **27** on Tuesday; and so on. The numbers in the last column are the sums of each of the rows. Thus, A. Alden worked **38** hours that week; S. Burke, 40 hours; and so on. The sum of the Total *column* and the sum of the Total *row* must be exactly the same number—because each number represents the total number of hours that all men worked during the week. This grand total (**147**) appears in the shaded rectangle. If these two sums are different, it means that an error has been made.

LEARNING EXERCISES

Complete the following business forms. Make certain that the sum of the Total *column* is the same as that of the Total *row*. That is your check.

1

NUMBER OF ARTICLES SOLD							
Dept. 67 Item 743 Week Beginning June 7, 19—							
Sales Girl	Mon.	Tues.	Wed.	Thurs.	Fri.	Sat.	Total
M. Brown		37	64	26	39	42	xxx
S. Carpenter	34	26		56	91	48	xxx
P. Coppola	76		36	52	19	31	xxx
D. Dudek	47	93	85	34		52	xxx
L. Jenkins	68	58	92		56	23	xxx
Total	xxx	xxx	xxx	xxx	xxx	xxx	xxx

2

DEPARTMENTAL SALES Week Ending September 12, 19—				
Department	Cash Sales	Charge Sales	C.O.D. Sales	Total
47—Coats	$2,346	$ 842	$1,684	$xxx
56—Dresses	3,826	1,875	5,685	xxx
85—Hats	752	476	2,343	xxx
134—Hosiery	2,358	927	976	xxx
183—Notions	435	895	104	xxx
Total	$ xxx	$ xxx	$ xxx	$xxx

3

DEPARTMENTAL SALES REPORT						
Department	January	February	March	April	May	Total
Rugs	$5,415	$4,670	$4,216	$6,986	$5,246	$xxx
Furniture	6,732	5,328	5,678	7,695	4,386	xxx
Radio-TV	4,693	3,282	4,108	5,415	5,124	xxx
Pianos	5,987	3,816	3,586	5,870	3,437	xxx
Kitchenware	8,153	5,194	5,881	7,140	6,080	xxx
Yard goods	1,357	1,835	2,074	2,265	1,921	xxx
China	2,548	1,359	2,136	2,843	1,675	xxx
Toys	3,212	3,491	2,917	1,758	2,158	xxx
Total	$ xxx	$ xxx	$ xxx	$ xxx	$ xxx	$xxx

UNIT **6**   **Addition of Decimals**

If Fred Wilson had remained as an employee in the Shipping and the Receiving Departments, or in the stock room, he could have managed very well with the arithmetic so far covered in this book. However, as soon as he moved into the Sales or the Bookkeeping Departments and encountered numbers involving decimals, he had to be somewhat more careful of the manner in which he arranged the numbers before adding them. He knew that it would be possible for him to add numbers no matter how haphazardly they were arranged as long as he was careful to add the units digit to the units digit, the tens digit to the tens digit, and so on. But doing this took too long and left too great a chance for errors. Hence, he devised two rules that he always used whenever adding numbers that involved decimals:

→**1.** If the numbers are arranged in columns, be certain that the decimal points are directly under one another.

→**2.** If the numbers are arranged in rows, then, when adding numbers that involve dollars and cents to numbers representing only dollars, be certain that the decimal point and two zeros follow the numbers representing only dollars.

As an example:

The sum of $438.71 + $832 + $796.65

Should be written $438.71 + $832.00 + $796.65

By following Rule 2, we can avoid the error of adding the 5, the 2, and the 1. In reality, the 5 and the 1 represent cents; whereas the 2 represents 2 dollars.

LEARNING EXERCISES

1. In each of the following problems, arrange the numbers properly in a column and add.

    a. $42.27 + $38.46 + $95.17 + $58.42

    b. $642.12 + $735.43 + $692.86 + $249.17

    c. $804.65 + $673 + $45.87 + $927.48

    d. $2,467 + $824.58 + $3,006 + $258.12

2. In each of the following problems, arrange the numbers in a row and add. Apply Rule **2** wherever necessary.

    a. $2.76 + $8.03 + $6.77 + $4.36
    b. $26.54 + $12.73 + $7.14 + $8.95
    c. $427.42 + $199.98 + $67 + $432.75
    d. $3,562 + $673.45 + $5,000 + $8,795.95

3. Copy and complete the following departmental sales report.

SALES RECORD

Dept. 72—Shoes   Week Beginning July 12, 19—

Employee	Mon.	Tues.	Wed.	Thurs.	Fri.	Sat.	Total
T. Haggerty	$85.76	$123.40		$116.55	$154.12	$210.17	$xxx
F. Hooper	64.27		104.32	96.84	125.19	168.42	xxx
L. Jenkins	69.95	73.85	112.20		132.60	187.56	xxx
J. Lipuma		86.75	93.60	103.46	136.80	174.15	xxx
Total	$xxx	$xxx	$xxx	$xxx	$xxx	$xxx	$xxx

4. The payroll form for the employees of Department **27**—Children's Wear—is given here. Copy and complete this form.

Employee	Mon.	Tues.	Wed.	Thurs.	Fri.	Sat.	Total
A. Coburn	$10.15	$ 9.80	$ 9.95	$11.15	$12.35	$10.95	$xxx
S. Meyers	10.25	10.40	8.95	9.75	9.80	10.85	xxx
W. Newman	11.15	10.85	10.95	10.25	11.35	10.95	xxx
E. Quail	9.70	11.25	10.45	10.55	9.65	8.10	xxx
P. Terrace	9.90	10.85	9.65	9.80	9.95	10.55	xxx
W. Young	9.35	8.85	10.55	9.85	9.20	8.95	xxx
Total	$xxx	$xxx	$xxx	$xxx	$xxx	$xxx	$xxx

U N I T 7   Measuring Your Skill in Addition

How does your skill in addition compare with that of the average business student? In view of the importance of both speed and accuracy in addition, the following sections will help you measure your skill. The time given at the beginning of each section indicates the number of minutes it will take an average student to complete the problems in that group.

TIMED DRILL A   20 Minutes

Find the sum of each of these problems. (Do *not* copy these problems. Place a piece of paper below the last number; then write your sum on this paper.)

1	2	3	4	5
76,436	$75,617.83	$4,586.97	$ 987.16	$62,816.53
37,584	83,463.32	473.82	32,756.84	894.67
53,125	37,574.64	819.38	39.73	59.76
28,972	29,926.58	7,956.73	5,864.79	83.42
42,369	91,785.97	96.98	546.31	8,227.68
19,211	14,320.13	3,124.37	695.42	714.84
65,897	48,298.29	5,842.55	78,344.26	176.39
84,643	69,843.75	637.42	73.95	9,658.93
91,758	52,169.36	68.13	2,765.68	48,294.37
10,312	58,986.84	9,456.48	7,514.76	953.95

6	7	8	9	10
53,816	$37,426.18	$8,974.68	$58,357.64	$ 3,286.95
47,293	64,582.37	465.32	964.25	989.31
64,568	16,137.62	39.19	546.81	82,164.56
38,432	93,893.48	817.85	7,483.97	87.34
92,675	58,218.25	8.97	38.36	412.59
16,329	42,341.74	6,292.13	9,172.78	9,678.43
85,941	75,961.51	9,818.26	825.42	824.15
29,187	23,679.89	56.44	91.19	759.87
71,754	69,455.26	576.71	52,219.53	28,946.44
13,366	81,736.94	639.39	8,683.47	593.78

TIMED DRILL B   10 Minutes

Copy and complete the business form that follows. The time required to copy this form is not to be included in the 10 minutes.

WEEKLY PAYROLL							
Department 56			Week Beginning June 7, 19—				
Employee	Mon.	Tues.	Wed.	Thurs.	Fri.	Sat.	Total
Darwin, T.	$10.50	$ 9.75	$ 9.85	$10.20	$ 9.60	$10.85	$xxx
Hanson, M.	11.30	11.55	10.85	10.50	11.65	11.80	xxx
Lutz, B.	9.90	9.95	10.65	10.35	10.85	9.90	xxx
Verner, A.	12.10	12.80	11.75	13.25	12.95	11.50	xxx
White, L.	15.40	16.70	15.85	16.25	16.40	10.70	xxx
Total	$xxx	$xxx	$xxx	$xxx	$xxx	$xxx	$xxx

TIMED DRILL C   25 Minutes

Solve the following problems.

1. Twelve clerks employed in the Yard Goods Department of R. C. Bond and Company receive the following weekly salaries: $44.18, $47.56, $56, $58, $59.87, $53, $48.17, $53.39, $61.27, $60.50, $59, and $50.75. Find the total of the weekly salaries for this department.

2. The monthly income and expenses for the Furniture Department of R. C. Bond and Company during a recent year are given here. Enter this information on a form similar to the one shown, and find the totals for the year.

Month	Income	Expenses
January	$xxx	$xxx
February	xxx	xxx
March	xxx	xxx
April	xxx	xxx
May	xxx	xxx
June	xxx	xxx
July	xxx	xxx
August	xxx	xxx
September	xxx	xxx
October	xxx	xxx
November	xxx	xxx
December	xxx	xxx
Total	$xxx	$xxx

Income: January, $5,786.58; February, $4,795.40; March, $8,976.38; April, $9,567.11; May, $6,643.87; June, $5,388.76; July, $5,389.97;

August, $9,167.35; September, $8,432.83; October, $4,599.39; November, $9,763.32; December, $7,758.86.

Expenses: January, $2,432.82; February, $2,338.60; March, $6,-426.56; April, $7,312.51; May, $1,866.33; June, $2,654.39; July, $3,538.76; August, $6,288.93; September, $7,456.48; October, $1,649.72; November, $7,458.97; December, $5,238.64.

3. The following table shows the millions of dollars spent on advertising in the United States through the four outlets listed during each of 5 years. Copy and complete this table.

ADVERTISING EXPENDITURES IN THE UNITED STATES (in millions of dollars)					
Year	Daily News-papers	Maga-zines	Radio	Tele-vision	Total
First	$2,075.6	$514.9	$605.4	$170.8	$xxx
Second	2,257.7	573.7	606.3	332.3	xxx
Third	2,472.8	615.8	624.1	453.9	xxx
Fourth	2,644.8	667.4	611.2	606.1	xxx
Fifth	2,695.3	667.9	564.9	803.6	xxx
Five-year total	$ xxx	$ xxx	$ xxx	$ xxx	$xxx

2
Improving
Subtraction Skills

PREVIEW

You may recall that Fred Wilson's first encounter with arithmetic as a trainee with R. C. Bond and Company was in keeping an accurate account of the quantities of merchandise that entered and left the stock room each month. Changes in supply were kept up to date on the form called the "bin ticket," which you studied in the preceding chapter. Emphasis was there placed on the In and Out columns of the bin ticket. A third column, which is probably more important than either of these two, was not discussed. A glance at this third column, the Balance column, would immediately have informed Fred as to the quantity of any article that was in the stock room. A record of merchandise that is constantly changing because of shipments either into or out of the stock room is commonly called a *running inventory*, a *book inventory*, or a *perpetual inventory* of stock. Fred's first few weeks at Bond's reminded him of his study of a foreign language at school, for he was again learning a language that was completely foreign to him. These new words seemed strange to him, but within a short time he found himself using them as though they had been part of his vocabulary for many years.

UNIT 1   **Subtraction of Whole Numbers**

Here is a copy of a bin ticket.

DATE	IN	OUT	BALANCE
Item: Bathroom Mats – Rubber
Month: July, 19--
3	428		428
7		104	324
8		62	262
11		125	137
15	684	61	760
18		209	551
21		93	458
28	124		582
31		176	406
Total	1,236 —	830 =	406

You will remember that the items received are entered in the In column; those that are issued to the Sales Department are entered in the Out column. For example, on July 3, 428 mats were received from the manufacturer; on July 7, 104 mats were issued to the Sales Department. To find the balance on hand, 104 is subtracted from 428. The difference, 324, represents the number of mats still in the stock room. To find the balance on July 8, the 62 that were sent out were subtracted from the balance of 324, leaving a new stock balance of 262. Thus, each new balance is obtained by subtracting the stock that left the stock room from the preceding balance, or, perhaps, by adding to the balance the stock that comes in.

This form, like others you have encountered, includes an automatic checking device within itself. The total number of mats that left the storeroom subtracted from the total that came in must leave the number that still remain. Therefore, if 830, the total of the Out column, is subtracted from 1,236, the total of the In column, the difference of 406 should be the balance on hand on July 31. If these numbers are not the same, an error has been made.

Fred Wilson, in order to overcome errors caused by his inexperience in subtracting when the numbers were not arranged under one another and the fact that it had been many years since he had last performed this operation, resorted to daily practice sessions in subtraction. At first, he dealt only with examples in which the numbers were arranged vertically. Only after he became proficient in performing vertical subtraction, did he attempt to improve his skill at horizontal subtraction.

So you, too, should spend some time in reviewing the operation of subtraction. Because the names for the "upper" number, the "lower" number, and the answer in a subtraction problem are used so frequently, they should be committed to memory. They are:

$$
\begin{array}{rl}
937 & \text{Minuend} \\
-452 & \text{Subtrahend} \\
\hline
485 & \text{Difference}
\end{array}
$$

You may feel that finding the difference between two numbers is a simple operation. You should realize, however, that merely obtaining the answer is not what gives value to this practice. The value results from the fact that practice will increase the speed and accuracy of your work.

LEARNING EXERCISES

Find the difference in each of the following problems.

	a	b	c	d	e	f	g	h
1	97	87	96	69	89	95	98	99
	23	46	53	28	19	64	87	95

	a	b	c	d	e	f	g	h
2	832	586	987	473	935	584	498	732
	567	368	918	325	876	425	187	614
3	481	632	511	763	581	613	943	416
	312	516	243	674	482	417	819	337
4	5,867	6,428	3,211	5,784	3,982	2,645	7,286	9,541
	3,098	2,864	1,987	2,591	1,675	1,869	2,517	3,875
5	3,576	4,881	2,976	3,876	5,936	8,403	2,966	5,864
	1,863	3,296	1,085	1,398	1,878	1,808	1,009	3,958
6	8,708	9,065	8,648	5,960	4,302	8,711	9,645	4,827
	4,569	2,066	7,586	3,869	2,469	8,348	2,816	1,998

UNIT 2   Checking the Accuracy of Subtraction

Unfortunately, there is no such thing in business as being *nearly* right in finding the answer to an arithmetic problem. As Fred soon learned, reporting 14 bedroom suites rather than 15, an error of only 1 suite, meant a mistake of possibly $275—the cost of this suite. To avoid making even the slightest error, he resorted to the practice of checking every arithmetical operation that he had to perform. As he learned from experience (and as you learned in Chapter 1 on addition), the best check is one that does not repeat an operation in the same manner in which it was first performed. Repetition of the same process often leads to a repetition of the error. Of all the checks for subtraction that he was able to find, Fred felt that the one that was most trustworthy, and certainly no more difficult to apply than any of the others, was the one that had been taught him almost the first day he had learned how to subtract. This was the check by addition.

To illustrate:
$$
\begin{array}{rl}
7,518 & \text{Minuend} \\
-1,964 & \text{Subtrahend} \\
\hline
5,554 & \text{Difference}
\end{array}
$$

If the difference (5,554) is added to the subtrahend (1,964), the sum should be equal to the minuend (7,518) if the work was done correctly.

If the sum is not the same as the minuend, then an error has been made in either finding the difference or applying the check. Thus:

Add:
$\begin{cases} 7{,}518 & \text{Minuend} \\ 1{,}964 & \text{Subtrahend} \\ \overline{5{,}554} & \text{Difference} \end{cases}$

Check: $\boxed{7{,}518}$ Minuend

LEARNING EXERCISES

Find the difference in each of the following problems, checking each by adding the subtrahend and the difference to get the minuend.

	a	b	c	d	e	f	g	h
1	5,304	8,296	5,876	4,673	5,376	4,876	5,980	7,645
	2,675	3,897	3,587	2,674	1,849	2,695	1,981	3,798
2	2,863	5,876	4,389	6,408	9,743	8,596	6,687	4,382
	1,985	2,975	1,895	2,463	2,869	5,987	3,895	1,967
3	3,471	5,581	8,881	4,298	1,982	2,453	9,976	5,831
	1,879	2,986	5,897	2,659	1,098	1,839	5,819	2,976
4	2,212	3,598	6,450	8,095	9,246	8,432	4,408	8,843
	1,089	1,589	2,875	3,381	3,958	7,645	1,239	8,189

UNIT 3   **Horizontal Subtraction**

Having achieved a reasonable degree of speed in vertical subtraction, Fred Wilson turned his attention to his immediate problem —improving his skill in horizontal subtraction. He soon realized that, as with horizontal addition, success would come much sooner when he was able to keep the various units distinct. Thus, in the following example:

$$567 - 213 = 354$$

First subtract the units digits: 3 from 7 = **4**
Then the tens digits: 1 from 6 = **5**
Finally, the hundreds digits: 2 from 5 = **3**

It should be remembered that sometimes it may be necessary to "borrow" in order to complete the work. "Borrowing," when the example is written horizontally, is no different than "borrowing" when the example is written vertically.

As part of a weekly check on items in the stock room, Fred filled out a form similar to the following. (Assume that there were no "In" deliveries during the week.)

Children's Wear Week Beginning *June 3*, 19–			
Item	UNITS ON HAND		Sent to Children's Wear Department
	At Beginning of Week	At End of Week	
Pants	375	184	191
Dresses	856	298	558
Socks	2,476	873	1,603
Ties	524	144	380
Undershirts	476	238	238
T shirts	709	347	362

The value of the form rested in the fact that, by simply glancing at the end column of numbers, Fred could see immediately the total number of items that had been sent to the Children's Wear Department. In addition, the form acted as a cross check against the daily deliveries to this department, for the sum of the daily deliveries (recorded on on another form) had to be the same as the numbers appearing in the end column.

The numbers in the Units on Hand columns were found by actually counting the stock on hand. The numbers in the last column were found by subtracting the numbers in the At End of Week column from those in the At Beginning of Week column.

To illustrate for the first item, **375 − 184 = 191**

The number **191** had to agree with the sum of the items in the Out column of the bin ticket for the week of June 3, 19—.

As a check on his subtraction, Fred added the numbers in the last column to those in the At End of Week column. The sum should be the numbers in the At Beginning of Week column.

Check: 191 + 184 = 375

LEARNING EXERCISES

1. In each of the following problems, find the difference by subtracting horizontally. Check each of your answers by covering the first column with a piece of paper and adding the subtrahend and the difference.

a

No.	Minu-end	Subtra-hend	Differ-ence	Check
(1)	936	672	xxx	xxx
(2)	593	289	xxx	xxx
(3)	538	367	xxx	xxx
(4)	829	542	xxx	xxx
(5)	888	582	xxx	xxx
(6)	928	422	xxx	xxx
(7)	509	218	xxx	xxx
(8)	812	619	xxx	xxx
(9)	918	535	xxx	xxx
(10)	753	464	xxx	xxx

b

No.	Minu-end	Subtra-hend	Differ-ence	Check
(1)	671	321	xxx	xxx
(2)	923	871	xxx	xxx
(3)	984	956	xxx	xxx
(4)	586	311	xxx	xxx
(5)	917	424	xxx	xxx
(6)	569	187	xxx	xxx
(7)	833	619	xxx	xxx
(8)	919	523	xxx	xxx
(9)	843	548	xxx	xxx
(10)	917	692	xxx	xxx

2. Copy and complete the following form.

Men's Wear Department Week Beginning December 14, 19—			
Item	In Stock: Monday	In Stock: Saturday	Removed to the Department
Shirts	593	315	xxx
Ties	992	891	xxx
Gloves	863	286	xxx
Socks	954	563	xxx
Belts	911	421	xxx
Sport shirts	863	672	xxx
T shirts	942	523	xxx
Shorts	368	242	xxx
Cuff links	410	321	xxx
Tie pins	815	526	xxx

UNIT **4**   **Application of Horizontal Subtraction to Completion of Bin Tickets**

With the additional knowledge you have just acquired in subtraction, it is now desirable to return to the bin ticket shown on page 20 and examine it again. Below is a partial copy of that form.

DATE	IN	OUT	BALANCE
			324
8		62	262
11		125	137
15	684	61	760
31		176	406
Total	1,236 —	830 =	406

You may recall that, in order to obtain the balance on July 8, the **62** mats that went out that day were subtracted from the **324** mats that had been there, leaving a new balance of **262**. The balance on July 11 was found by subtracting the **125** mats that were removed from the stock room from the **262** that were there. On July 15, the **684** mats that were brought in were added to the balance of **137**. From this total, the **61** mats that were taken out were subtracted. The **760** difference was the balance at the end of the day on July 15. To check the monthly balance of **406** mats, Fred Wilson simply found the totals of the In and Out columns; then he subtracted the second from the first. If his running inventory was correct, this difference will also be **406**.

LEARNING EXERCISES

1. Copy and complete the following bin ticket.

Item: Men's Swimming Trunks Month: July, 19—			
Date	In	Out	Balance
1	876		xxx
2		132	xxx
5	637		xxx
6		587	xxx
8	429		xxx
11	742	359	xxx
15		275	xxx
19	1,384		xxx
23		96	xxx
24		387	xxx
26	275	463	xxx
31		184	xxx

2. Using the following information, fill out bin tickets similar to the one you have just completed for Problem 1.

a

Date	In	Out
3	956	
4		293
12		187
17	468	352
18		475
20		109

b

Date	In	Out
1	2,346	694
3		428
6		287
9	1,529	
14		941
17	618	406
20		379
21		453
28		52

c

Date	In	Out
1	3,758	963
2		547
4	1,476	629
8		754
11		427
14	1,806	292
16		841
17		635
20	593	498
22		306
29		78

d

Date	In	Out
2	4,587	
5		948
6		753
8	1,475	694
10		267
14		548
15	923	
18	638	856
20	2,705	691
23		473
27		907
29	957	869

e

Date	In	Out
1	3,946	849
2		1,205
4	2,585	
7		694
8	976	786
11	1,468	
13		468
16		572
18		293
21	927	385
25	1,650	738
30		456

f

Date	In	Out
2	5,683	1,476
4	548	
5		862
7	2,700	568
10	1,685	
12		457
14		839
17		683
18		394
20	2,845	568
26	738	
28	1,659	965

UNIT 5   Subtraction of Decimals

Fred's need for an understanding of and skill in horizontal subtraction did not end when he left the Shipping and the Receiving departments. In fact, the frequency with which he had to apply this knowledge increased rather than diminished. This was particularly true during the period that he spent as a trainee in the Comptroller's or Accounting Department. Forms such as those that follow were frequently used.

Example 1

Voucher-Check Register – *May, 19—*					
			HOW PAID		
Date	Check No.	Voucher No.	Cost	Discount	Amount of Check
5/16	438	542	576|00	28|16	547|84

This form is a section of a page from a book called a *voucher-check register*. It is designed as a record of payments made by the department store to concerns from whom it purchased merchandise. Thus, R. C. Bond and Company bought $576 worth of table linens from Irish Linens, Inc. Irish Linens allowed Bond a reduction of $28.16 from the price of $576. Check 438 was made out for $547.84 on May 16 to pay this debt. The amount of the check was found by subtracting the discount from the original cost of the articles. Note that a vertical line between the 547 and the 84 is used to separate the dollars from the cents. Such lines frequently appear on business forms because it has been found that the use of these lines prevents errors in computation.

Example 2

A similar form is the following section of a page from a *cash receipts journal.*

Cash Receipts Journal — *September* 19–			
Dept. 53		**Men's Suits and Coats**	
DATE	AMOUNT DUE	DISCOUNT ALLOWED	CASH RECEIVED
9/1	637 54	43 26	594 28
9/2	875 00	67 84	807 16
Total	1,512 54	— 111 10	= 1,401 44

Apparently, R. C. Bond and Company had a sale on men's suits and coats during the month of September. It was part of Fred's work to keep a record of the daily sales. The numbers in the Cash Received column were found by subtracting the discount from the amount that the department would have received had there been no sale. The accuracy of the records on this form can easily be checked by subtracting the total of the Discount Allowed column from the total of the Amount Due column. The difference should be the total of the Cash Received column. Thus:

$$\$1,512.54 - \$111.10 = \$1,401.44$$

Example 3

Records are kept of daily sales made in each department. The day's receipts are immediately compared with the cost of the articles sold, so that the profit on these sales can be found. This is done as shown on this form.

Daily Sales			
June 17, 19--			
Dept. 107	Sporting Goods		
Article	Sales	Cost	Profit
Baseball bats	56.20	37.56	18.64
Baseball gloves	73.92	54.75	19.17
Total	130.12	92.31	37.81

As in the form in Example 2, the numbers in the Profit column were found by subtracting the Cost from the Sales. The check here is the same as that for Example 2.

You have probably noticed that in the foregoing examples the numbers contained decimal points. It is impossible for an employee of a department store or of any other business firm to avoid the use of decimals. Here, again, Fred employed the two rules that he had formulated for adding decimals. They apply equally well in the subtraction of decimals.

→1. If the numbers are arranged in columns, be certain that the decimal points are directly under one another.

→2. If the numbers are arranged in rows, then, when subtracting numbers that involve dollars and cents from numbers containing only dollars, be certain that the decimal point and two zeros follow the numbers containing only dollars.

In keeping with Rule 2, you will notice in Example 2 that $875 was written $875.00 in order to lessen the possibility of adding or subtracting incorrectly.

LEARNING EXERCISES

The following problems are to be completed in the manner described in the examples on the preceding pages.

1. Copy and complete the following sales records.

a

Sales Record			
Dept. 17	June 6, 19—		Women's Accessories
Article	Sales	Cost	Profit Margin
Aprons	$ 3.10	$ 2.64	$xxx
Blouses	8.65	5.87	xxx
Coats	15.85	12.37	xxx
Collars	2.15	1.62	xxx
Dresses	28.75	15.38	xxx
Hats	9.85	5.39	xxx
Pinafores	3.85	1.82	xxx
Shoes	7.85	3.97	xxx
Shorts	2.95	1.09	xxx
Gloves	2.25	1.37	xxx
Suits	35.50	22.86	xxx
Handbags	2.98	1.39	xxx
Total	$xxx	$xxx	$xxx

b

Sales Record			
Dept. 83	March 15, 19—		Musical Instruments
Article	Sales	Cost	Profit Margin
Banjos	$ 15.50	$ 6.98	$xxx
Cellos	97.95	81.39	xxx
Drums	110.00	96.42	xxx
Flutes	9.75	5.87	xxx
Guitars	42.50	24.58	xxx
Harps	350.00	263.89	xxx
Horns	68.85	51.09	xxx
Organs	3,575.00	2,184.53	xxx
Pianos	645.00	339.39	xxx
Radios	187.95	109.08	xxx
Saxo-phones	96.65	65.98	xxx
Violins	94.75	73.57	xxx
Total	$ xxx	$ xxx	$xxx

2. Copy and complete the following page from a voucher-check register.

VOUCHER-CHECK REGISTER June, 19—						
Voucher No.	Date	Check No.	Cost	Discount Allowed	Amount of Check
473	June 1	574	$3,467.42	$298.68	$xxx
474	3	575	826.58	87.64	xxx
475	4	576	394.76	19.58	xxx
481	6	577	8,582.37	586.43	xxx
483	7	578	975.85	196.54	xxx
484	11	579	38.96	1.26	xxx
487	12	580	643.88	296.64	xxx
491	15	581	2,205.65	814.77	xxx
493	18	582	991.36	132.56	xxx
494	19	583	246.78	16.23	xxx
496	24	584	395.84	21.87	xxx
497	30	585	4,567.26	990.82	xxx
	Total		$ xxx	$ xxx	$xxx

3. Copy and complete the following page from a cash receipts journal.

CASH RECEIPTS JOURNAL, September, 19—			
Date	Amount Due	Discount Allowed	Cash Received
September 1	$ 876.42	$ 81.40	$xxx
3	1,717.48	217.68	xxx
4	89.95	1.23	xxx
6	38.76	.97	xxx
7	3,912.58	684.56	xxx
8	2,125.39	517.88	xxx
9	654.67	24.65	xxx
10	1,393.82	386.72	xxx
11	1,027.63	267.85	xxx
17	487.95	58.97	xxx
19	2,771.89	688.24	xxx
20	586.43	23.67	xxx
Total	$ xxx	$ xxx	$xxx

UNIT **6**   **Preparing a Bank Reconciliation Statement**

Training in the Comptroller's Department covered a wide variety of activities, not the least important of which is one that Fred must perform shortly after the first of each month. Checks that R. C. Bond and Company mailed to firms from which it had purchased merchandise were deposited by these firms. Each check eventually finds its way back to the bank at which R. C. Bond and Company deposits its money. The bank then deducts the amount of the check from the amount in Bond's account. At the close of each month, the bank prepares and sends to R. C. Bond and Company a statement listing the checks that have been returned, the deposits that have been made, any service charges, and the balance that is on record for the account of R. C. Bond and Company. Although banks rarely make mistakes in their records because of their excellent system of checking, it was Fred's duty to examine these monthly statements for several reasons:

1. To make a record of those checks that had been issued but that had not as yet reached the bank.

2. To list any late deposits that were made by R. C. Bond and Company but that had not been recorded by the bank.

3. To check any service charges that had been made against the company account by the bank.

4. To see whether the balance on deposit as reported by the bank on the monthly statement agreed with the balance shown by the checkbook record kept by Fred.

This means of testing the accuracy of a bank statement is known as the *reconciliation of a checking account.* Although the sums of money used in the following examples are a great deal smaller than those that Fred encountered in his work, the principles for reconciling an account are the same.

To illustrate: On October 31, a depositor's bank statement showed a balance of $2,208.46. His checkbook balance was $1,560.06. Checks for $206.50 and $290.70 have been issued by the depositor but have not yet reached the bank. The depositor had forgot to record a late deposit of a check for $151.20. Reconcile the bank balance against the depositor's balance.

Explanation 1: Since he had forgot to record a deposit of $151.20, the depositor not only had $1,560.06, as his record showed, but also $151.20; hence, the total he had on deposit is the sum of $1,560.06 and $151.20, or $1,711.26. Although he had written checks for the amounts of $206.50 and $290.70, the bank had not received them. Therefore, as far as the bank was concerned, the total of these checks was still on deposit. Therefore, the bank would include the sum of these checks ($206.50 + $290.70, or $497.20) as part of its record. Hence, the depositor would have to add this amount to the balance that his record showed, to obtain the balance that the bank had recorded. Thus, $1,711.26 + $497.20 equals $2,208.46, which is the balance shown on the bank statement.

Solution:

Checkbook balance		$ 1,560.00	Bank balance	$ 2,208.46
Add:				
Deposit not recorded		151.20		
		$ 1,711.26		
Add:				
Outstanding checks	$ 206.50			
	290.70	497.20		
Bank balance		$ 2,208.46	Bank balance	$ 2,208.46

An alternative method is frequently used to reconcile a bank statement. The explanation of this method follows.

Explanation 2: The total on deposit as recorded by the depositor is found in the same way as in Explanation 1. However, since the depositor has, in reality, written two checks for $206.50 and $290.70, their total should be deducted from the balance shown by the bank, for these checks will eventually return to the bank. Hence, when their sum is subtracted from the bank balance of $2,208.46, the difference, $1,711.26 ($2,208.46 − $497.20), will be the same as that recorded by the depositor. This difference ($1,711.26) is called the *true* or *adjusted* bank balance

Solution:

Checkbook balance	$ 1560.06	Bank balance		$ 2,208.46
Add:		Deduct:		
Deposit not recorded	151.20	Outstanding checks	$ 206.50	
			290.70	497.20
Correct, or adjusted, checkbook balance	$ 1,711.26	True, or adjusted, bank balance		$ 1,711.26

LEARNING EXERCISES

Reconcile the bank and checkbook balances.

No.	Balance As Per Bank Statement	Balance As Per Checkbook	Outstanding Checks	Deposits Not Yet Recorded by Depositor
1	$ 2,176.40	$1,729.00	$197.40	$250.00
2	908.08	614.58	125.00	168.50
3	5,105.08	4,919.68	42.50 and 65.00	77.90
4	2,225.96	1,877.52	127.56 and 33.92	186.96
5	2,244.91	1,490.86	12.74, 3.58, and 46.39	691.34
6	10,229.73	7,525.94	427.32, 695.47, and 1,304.25	276.75

7. On September 3, Mr. Prentiss received his statement from the bank showing that his balance as of August 31 was $829.22. In going over the statement, he discovered that he had issued two checks of

$56.80 and $43.45 that had not yet been returned to his bank. In addition, the bank had made a service charge of $2.50 against his account. His checkbook balance as of August 31 is $731.47. Reconcile the bank statement.

8. When reconciling his monthly bank statement, Mr. Arben found that he had failed to record a deposit of $127.15 that he had made. A check for $124.50 that he had mailed late in the month in payment of a bill had not yet been deposited by the person receiving it. For issuing more checks than his deposit warranted, the bank had charged him $3 that month. His checkbook record showed a balance of $1,346.54; the bank's record was $1,595.19. Reconcile the bank statement.

9. The May bank statement of Mr. Stuart showed a balance of $1,189.18. In reconciling this statement against his own checkbook balance of $992.26, Mr. Stuart noticed that the bank had charged him $2.50 for issuing more checks than his monthly balance permitted. He also discovered that he had failed to record a check for $338.64 that he had written while at work. In addition, he had been negligent in not recording a deposit of $335.68 that he had made that month. A check for $202.38 that had been issued during the month had not as yet been returned to his bank. Reconcile the bank and checkbook balances.

UNIT 7   Making Change

One of the most important applications of subtraction is the simple process of returning change to a customer who has purchased an article. In fact, R. C. Bond and Company and most retail stores consider this matter so important that special training in "change making" is given to their sales help before they are placed behind a counter. Two points are stressed in all these training programs:

1. When handed a bill by the customer, keep the bill in full view while repeating the cost of the article and the size of the bill. Thus, say, "$3.79 out of $5."

2. In making change, use the largest bills and coins possible.

The process of making change depends on a method of subtraction known as the *additive method of subtraction*. Many of you may be familiar with this method, for this is the manner in which you were taught to subtract.

To illustrate: Subtract 5 from 7.

Explanation: The difference can be found by rephrasing the statement to read, "What number should be added to 5 so that the sum of 5 and this number will be 7?" Actually, this is what you have been doing each time you have checked a subtraction example. Since addition is used in finding the difference, this process is known as the *additive method of subtraction*.

Similarly, when Fred Wilson was taught to give change when a $5 bill was offered for the purchase of an article that cost $3.79, he was told to think to himself, "How much should I add to $3.79 so that the sum will be $5?" *Never*, at any time, was he to make change by actually subtracting $3.79 from $5 and giving the difference to the customer. Errors occur too frequently whenever this method is used.

Business Transaction 1: Fred Wilson received a $5 bill from a customer in payment of a $3.79 purchase. How should he make the change?

Solution: He added 1 penny to the $3.79, making a total of $3.80. To this he added 2 dimes, bringing the total to $4. Then he gave the customer a $1 bill for a final total of $5. Thus: $3.79 + 1¢ + 20¢ + $1 = $5.

Business Transaction 2: Using a form similar to the one shown here, show how you would give change for a $10 bill offered on a purchase of $2.43.

Amount of Purchase	Bill Given in Payment	Change Due								
		1¢	5¢	10¢	25¢	50¢	$1	$2	$5	$10
$2.43	$10.00	2	1			1		1	1	

Explanation: This form shows that first 2 pennies were given, making $2.45. Then 1 nickel for a total of $2.50; the 1 half dollar brought the sum to $3; and finally the $2 bill and the $5 bill completed the change by making the final total $10. $2.43 + 2 cents + 5 cents + 50 cents + $2 + $5 = $10

LEARNING EXERCISES

Draw a form similar to the one shown in Business Transaction 2 and show how you would give change in each of the following purchases.

No.	Amount of Purchase	Bill Given in Payment	No.	Amount of Purchase	Bill Given in Payment
1	$ 3.12	$ 5.00	11	$ 5.63	$10.00
2	2.85	5.00	12	7.14	20.00
3	11.64	20.00	13	9.75	10.00
4	8.73	10.00	14	18.11	20.00
5	4.98	10.00	15	1.87	2.00
6	3.76	5.00	16	3.38	5.00
7	5.82	10.00	17	4.96	10.00
8	2.27	10.00	18	5.88	20.00
9	12.58	20.00	19	13.76	20.00
10	14.96	20.00	20	8.81	10.00

UNIT 8 Measuring Your Skill in Subtraction

The following sections, like those in Unit 7 of Chapter 1, are designed to enable you to compare your speed and accuracy with those of the average student who is taking business arithmetic. The timed drills at the end of each chapter were planned with this in mind.

TIMED DRILL A   10 Minutes

Find the difference in each of these problems. (Do *not* copy these problems. Place a piece of paper below each problem, and write the differences on this paper.)

1	2	3	4	5	6	7	8
68	426	508	815	739	902	4,052	3,007
39	209	109	407	298	623	2,068	1,009

9	10	11	12
4,380	$94.01	$620.13	$598.32
2,836	53.26	264.34	368.59

	13	14	15
a	89 − 36 = xxx	258 − 138 = xxx	8,256 − 3,042 = xxx
b	94 − 57 = xxx	467 − 284 = xxx	7,456 − 3,278 = xxx
c	63 − 28 = xxx	867 − 289 = xxx	$308.46 − $139.78 = $xxx

TIMED DRILL B   10 Minutes

The increase in the per-capita personal income in dollars for 10 states over a 7-year period are given in the following table. Find the increase in income during this period. Copying time is not to be included in the 10 minutes.

State	Beginning of Period	End of Period	Increase
Alabama	$ 794	$1,091	$xxx
Arizona	1,149	1,582	xxx
Arkansas	719	979	xxx
California	1,678	2,162	xxx
Colorado	1,338	1,686	xxx
Connecticut	1,693	2,361	xxx
Delaware	1,634	2,372	xxx
Florida	1,143	1,610	xxx
Georgia	884	1,237	xxx
Idaho	1,251	1,433	xxx

TIMED DRILL C   15 Minutes

The total sales and the total cost for the current year of 8 departments of R. C. Bond and Company are shown in the following table. Copy and complete this form. Copying time is not to be included in the 15 minutes.

Department	Total Sales	Total Cost	Profit
Furniture	$68,821	$57,845	$xxx
Men's Shoes	29,158	23,864	xxx
Women's Shoes	48,014	40,932	xxx
Men's Ties	3,723	2,847	xxx
Optical	14,634	13,549	xxx
Kitchenware	20,672	18,396	xxx
Scouting Equipment	6,814	5,872	xxx
Stationery	11,158	9,980	xxx
Total	$ xxx	$ xxx	$xxx

TIMED DRILL D   5 Minutes

Draw a form similar to the following. Show the exact denominations of change that you would give a customer on each of the purchases if the bills given in payment are as shown. Copying time is not to be included in the 5 minutes.

No.	Amount of Purchase	Bill Given in Payment	Change Due								
			1¢	5¢	10¢	25¢	50¢	$1	$2	$5	$10
1	$ 3.75	$ 5.00									
2	2.15	5.00									
3	2.87	5.00									
4	.56	5.00									
5	8.45	10.00									
6	6.12	10.00									
7	2.39	10.00									
8	17.10	20.00									
9	14.66	20.00									
10	8.03	20.00									

3

Improving
Multiplication Skills

PREVIEW

At the close of each month, Fred Wilson and the other employees who worked in the stock room completed forms similar to the one shown on page 41.

The quantity of each article was found by counting the stock on the shelves on June 30. The men who had helped Fred knew little about why this form was compiled, to whom it was sent, and of what value it served the store. It was to help answer questions such as these that the training program at R. C. Bond and Company had been started. Officers of large concerns have great difficulty in making many important decisions unless it is possible for them to foresee the effects of these decisions on all areas of the company. Though this small inventory sheet held little significance to the

Inventory Sheet

Stock Room Supplies for *Children's Wear* Department

Compiled by *Fred Wilson*

Date *June 30, 19—*

ARTICLE	QUANTITY
Pants	375
Dresses	256
Socks	842
Ties	594
Undershirts	2,356
T shirts	405
Ski pants	258
Mufflers	1,485
Coats	524
Gloves	2,560
Sweaters	745

men in the stock room, it was from information contained on these sheets that the company would decide such matters as:
1. The type and quantity of stock to be purchased.
2. The selling price of various articles.
3. The number of salesclerks to be employed.
4. Even whether certain departments should be eliminated.

After leaving the stock room, the inventory sheet was sent to the Accounting Department. There, as Fred learned during his period of training, the information was rewritten on a larger sheet for the purpose of including additional figures that were related to these articles. A section of this sheet is shown here.

Article	Quantity	Cost per Unit		Amount
Pants	375	1	75	
Dresses	256	2	20	
Socks	842		32	
Ties	594		46	
		Total		

Needless to say, someone had to find the cost of the 375 pairs of pants. The same was true of the 256 dresses, the 842 pairs of socks, and the 594 ties. As 1 pair of pants cost $1.75, then, to find the cost of 375 pairs of pants, it was necessary to multiply 375 by $1.75. It would have been foolish for Fred to attempt to multiply decimals before spending at least a brief period reviewing the multiplication of whole numbers, devices for checking the answer, and short cuts that can be used to increase speed.

UNIT 1   **Multiplication of Whole Numbers**

You will learn many new terms during your study of business arithmetic. The best way to become familiar with these words is to use them as frequently as possible in situations where they are appropriate. For example, if it is necessary for you to call attention to the answer to a subtraction problem, do not call it the *answer*, but refer to it by its name, the *difference*. Similarly, the answer to an addition problem is called the *sum*. In the operation of multiplication that you are now reviewing, the answer is referred to as the *product*.

When you memorized the multiplication table, you also learned that multiplication is really a short way of doing addition. Thus, although you had memorized that $3 \times 7 = 21$, you knew that the number 21 was determined as the sum of $7 + 7 + 7$. Similarly, 3×684 means $684 + 684 + 684$. When this example is written vertically,

$$\begin{array}{r} 684 \\ \times 3 \\ \hline 2{,}052 \end{array}$$

The 684 is called the *multiplicand*.
The 3 is called the *multiplier*.
The 2,052 is called the *product*.
Thus, the multiplier indicates how many times the multiplicand would be added if the product were to be found by addition.

A great deal of time would be wasted if the operation of multiplication were to be performed each time by resorting to addition. On the other hand, it is impossible to perform multiplication otherwise unless the multiplication table has been thoroughly memorized.

The exercises that follow were designed to help you determine whether you need to spend more time practicing the multiplication process. If you find that you can determine the products *correctly* in the time designated at the beginning of each of the sections, then no further practice is necessary.

LEARNING EXERCISES

Find the product in each of the examples in the sections that follow.

A. You should be able to find the product in each of these 60 problems in 60 seconds. Multiply by *reading* the products.

	1	2	3	4	5	6	7	8	9	10	11	12	13	14	15
a.	1	2	3	1	2	3	1	2	3	3	9	8	1	7	6
	9	7	5	8	6	4	7	5	3	7	2	2	2	6	4
	?	?	?	?	?	?	?	?	?	?	?	?	?	?	?
b.	4	8	5	8	7	8	8	8	6	3	4	8	4	5	7
	4	4	5	9	7	6	8	7	9	1	9	5	1	4	4
	?	?	?	?	?	?	?	?	?	?	?	?	?	?	?
c.	1	2	1	2	3	6	3	1	2	9	6	5	5	9	7
	6	4	5	3	9	3	8	1	2	5	6	6	7	9	9
	?	?	?	?	?	?	?	?	?	?	?	?	?	?	?
d.	2	5	9	9	6	8	7	6	7	4	5	0	2	6	4
	9	8	3	8	7	0	5	2	8	6	2	9	8	5	8
	?	?	?	?	?	?	?	?	?	?	?	?	?	?	?

B. You should be able to do these 10 problems in 8 minutes.

1.	645	2.	728	3.	493	4.	571	5.	806
	×34		×25		×71		×58		×63

6.	934	7.	278	8.	393	9.	890	10.	589
	×82		×47		×94		×69		×87

C. You should be able to do these 8 problems in 10 minutes.

1.	5,346	2.	6,857	3.	4,605	4.	2,468
	×752		×328		×932		×135

5.	7,811	6.	1,357	7.	8,329	8.	3,579
	×684		×246		×584		×468

UNIT 2   **Checking the Product of Two Numbers by Interchanging Multiplier and Multiplicand**

As the accuracy of his work was always uppermost in his mind, Fred Wilson spent some time in investigating methods that would enable him to check the accuracy of multiplication both quickly and reliably. Eventually, he settled on the methods described in this unit and in Unit 3. Although he found the first of these methods the more reliable, he frequently used the second when he was pressed for time, as it is much the easier to apply.

The first of the devices for checking the product of two numbers depends on the principle that, if the multiplicand and the multiplier are interchanged, the product of the two numbers will not change. Thus, both 6 times 7 and 7 times 6 result in exactly the same product, 42. When this principle is applied to checking the product of two numbers, it simply means that should you find the product of, for example, 523 and 416, then it is possible to check your answer by multiplying 416 by 523. If your work is correct, both answers will be the same.

To illustrate:

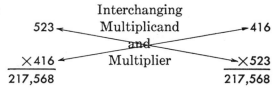

LEARNING EXERCISES

Copy the following problems, and find the product in each. Check each answer by interchanging the multiplicand and the multiplier and again finding the product.

1.	368	2.	259	3.	825	4.	936	5.	21,357
	×274		×364		×362		×648		×924

6. 92,745	7. 6,824	8. 8,462	9. 82,460	10. 24,357
×2,468	×357	×5,137	×5,793	×1,689

End mon 9/7

UNIT 3
Checking the Product of Two Numbers by Casting Out 9's

SECTION 1 How to Cast 9's Out of a Number

This check should be used with caution. It is possible to make errors in finding the product of two numbers, and yet this check might indicate that the answer is correct. The value of the check lies in the speed with which it can be applied, not in the fact that it is foolproof.

Casting out 9's from a number merely means that 9's are subtracted from that number until the final difference is a number that is less than 9. Thus, for the number 23, if 9 is subtracted, the difference is 14; since this number is greater than 9, then 9 is subtracted again, leaving a remainder of 5. It is this remainder that will be important to you.

If the number is large, such as 35,628, subtracting 9's until you arrive at a remainder that is less than 9 would be a very lengthy and tedious process. It is known, however, that the remainder can be found by adding the digits 3, 5, 6, 2, and 8 and then casting 9's out of the sum.

To illustrate: 35,628 $3 + 5 + 6 + 2 + 8 = 24$
If 9's are cast out of 24, the first difference will be 15 ($24 - 9$); the second difference, 6 ($15 - 9$); therefore, the remainder that you seek is 6. This remainder (6) is exactly the same remainder you would have obtained had you cast 9's out of 35,628. This can be verified by dividing 35,628 by 9 and noting that the remainder is 6.

Example 1: Find the remainder when 9's are cast out of 8,976.
  Solution: 8,976 $8 + 9 + 7 + 6 = 30$
        $30 - 9 = 21; 21 - 9 = 12; 12 - 9 = 3$
        Remainder $= 3$

Example 2: Find the remainder when 9's are cast out of 356,702.
  Solution: 356,702 $3 + 5 + 6 + 7 + 0 + 2 = 23$
        $23 - 9 = 14; 14 - 9 = 5$
        Remainder $= 5$

You may have noticed that a faster way of obtaining the remainder is to add the digits in the sum of the digits of the number. Thus, in Example 1 had you added the 3 and the 0, your sum would be 3, which is the remainder; in Example 2, had you added the 2 and the 3, your sum would have been 5, which is the remainder in that example.

ORAL EXERCISES

Find the remainder after casting out 9's from each of the following numbers.

1. 47	5. 467	9. 593	13. 99,929
2. 85	6. 872	10. 6,437	14. 954,276
3. 63	7. 507	11. 8,499	15. 810,354
4. 28	8. 400	12. 9,799	16. 73,004,736

17. Look carefully at your answers to Problems 12, 13, 14, and 15. Can you suggest a short method for finding the remainder by comparing the answers with the problems?

SECTION 2   Applying the Remainders to Checking the Product of Two Numbers

With your understanding of how to cast 9's out of a number, checking the operation of multiplication should be simple.

Example 1: Multiply 4,562 by 904 and check the product by casting out 9's.

> **Solution:**   4,562   Remainder   8
> X904   Remainder   X4
> 18248   32   Remainder ⑤
> 410580
> 4124048   Remainder ⑤

Explanation: After casting 9's out of the multiplicand, 4,562, the remainder will be 8. After doing the same with the multiplier, the remainder will be 4. The product of these two remainders is 32. Casting 9's out of this number will leave a remainder of 5. Now, when 9's are cast out of the product (4,124,048) the remainder will also be 5 if the answer is correct.

Example 2:
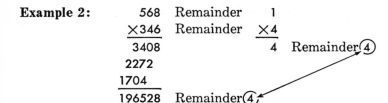

568	Remainder 1
×346	Remainder ×4
3408	4 Remainder④
2272	
1704	
196528	Remainder④

It should be pointed out that, had an error been made and the product found to be 197,428, the remainder would still be 4, thus giving the appearance that this were the correct answer. That is why you were cautioned to use this check with care.

Checking by casting out 9's can also be employed in the operations of addition and subtraction, but the method is more difficult to apply and less accurate than the methods that were shown.

LEARNING EXERCISES

Find the product in each of the following problems. Check each product by casting out 9's.

1. 583	4. 19,032	7. 9,543	10. 36,246
×642	×408	×6,838	×9,751
2. 897	5. 18,822	8. 6,623	11. 38,227
×769	×564	×5,595	×7,648
3. 4,501	6. 7,346	9. 75,628	12. 94,257
×329	×592	×1,308	×9,348

U N I T **4**   **Finding the Product of Two Decimals**

For the greater part, finding the product of two decimals is no different than finding the product of two whole numbers. The digits in the answer are obtained by ignoring the fact that the numbers contain decimal points. It is in the placing of the decimal point in the product that the product of two decimals differs from the product of two whole numbers. To help refresh your memory, the following examples are presented.

Example 1: Multiply 7.23 by .456.

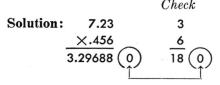

Check

Solution: 7.23   3
            ×.456   6
            3.29688 (0)   18 (0)

Explanation: In order to place the decimal point in the product, count the number of digits to the right of the decimal point in the multiplicand. There are 2 (the 2 and the 3). To that number, add the number of digits to the right of the decimal point in the multiplier. There are 3 (the 4, 5, and 6). The sum of these (2 + 3 = 5) will tell you how many digits there should be to the right of the decimal point in the product. Therefore, the digits 2, 9, 6, 8, and 8 will all have to be to the right of the decimal point in the answer.

Example 2: Multiply 5.063 by 2.0075.

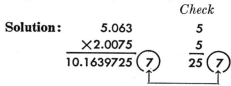

Check

Solution: 5.063   5
             ×2.0075   5
           10.1639725 (7)   25 (7)

Explanation: There are three digits to the right of the decimal point in the multiplicand (0, 6, 3) and 4 digits to the right of the decimal point in the multiplier (0, 0, 7, 5). Hence, there will be 7 digits to the right of the decimal point in the product (1, 6, 3, 9, 7, 2, 5). Note that, in applying the check, the decimal points are ignored.

LEARNING EXERCISES

Find the product in each of the problems below. Check your answers.

1. 4.72 × 83.4
2. 596 × 3.28
3. 108.2 × 35.6
4. 7.414 × 7.8
5. 6.005 × .0807

6. 8.038 × 2.765
7. 52.25 × .007875
8. 328.67 × .764
9. 27.875 × .0125
10. 9.375 × .4375

11. 4.748 × .9139375
12. 62.1733 × 33.875
13. 583.9833 × .4875
14. 2.6875 × .7041875
15. .482375 × 4.5625

UNIT **5**   **Short Cuts in Multiplication**

A great many so-called "short cuts" can be used in determining the product of two numbers. Most of these, as Fred Wilson learned, can be applied so infrequently in actual business practice that it hardly seems worth the effort to try to learn them. A few, however, find wide application in business transactions, particularly where rates, such as tax rate, insurance rate, per cent, and the like, are involved. Fred Wilson used these short cuts when he was computing the cost of merchandise to R. C. Bond and Company. The store purchased a great many articles in "lots" of 100 or 1,000, for Bond's received a sizable reduction in the cost of the articles by buying in large quantities. Knowing these short cuts in finding the product of two numbers where one number is 10, 100, or 1,000 was of great value to Fred. It will be for you, too; therefore, these short cuts will be presented in this section.

Multiplication by 10, 100, 1,000

When the multiplier is the number 1 followed by zeros, then, to find the product, simply move the decimal point in the multiplicand as many places to the right as there are zeros in the multiplier.

Example 1: 436.875 $\times$ 10 = ?
Solution: 436.875 $\times$ 10 = 4,36.8.75

Explanation: Since there is only one zero after the 1 in the multiplier, move the decimal point in 436.875 one place to the right.

Example 2: .00574 $\times$ 1,000 = ?
Solution: .00574 $\times$ 1,000 = .005.74 = 5.74

Explanation: Since the zeros before the 5 in the product are meaningless, they should not appear in the answer.

Example 3: 67 $\times$ 100 = ?
Solution: 67 $\times$ 100 = 6,7.00.

Explanation: If no decimal point appears in a number, then its position is at the right of the number. The number 67 can be written with a decimal following (67.). When this is done, then, in multiplying 67 by 100, the decimal point and two zeros must follow the 67 before the product can be found.

LEARNING EXERCISES

Copy each of the following examples. To the right of each write the product.

1. 62.75 × 10
2. 3.476 × 100
3. 6.295 × 1,000
4. 854.6 × 100
5. 67.24 × 1,000
6. 1.274 × 100

7. .0426 × 1,000
8. .0023 × 10
9. .04 × 100
10. .056 × 1,000
11. .048 × 10
12. 473 × 100

13. 52 × 10
14. 8 × 1,000
15. $62.56 × 100
16. $.04 × 1,000
17. $323 × 10
18. $56 × 1,000

UNIT 6   Horizontal Multiplication

While working as a salesman, Fred Wilson found that skill in performing horizontal multiplication was a great aid in preparing sales slips. Sales slips often resemble a form such as that shown here.

R. C. BOND AND COMPANY		
QUANTITY	ITEM	AMOUNT
6	Socks @ .89	5 34
3	Ties @ 1.75	5 25
	TOTAL	10 59

Name _Mrs. C. L. Kremitz_
Street _14 Oak-Tree Drive_
Town _Bay Ridge_   State _N. Y._

The symbol @, read "at," which appears after the words "Socks" and "Ties" means that each pair of socks was sold at 89 cents and each tie at $1.75. Therefore, to find the cost of 6 pairs of socks, it is necessary to multiply $.89 by 6. Similarly, $1.75 has to be multiplied by 3 to find the cost of the 3 ties. Frequently, these computations have to be performed quickly. Hence, to rewrite each multiplication example vertically, as

$.89
×6

would be a needless waste of time and effort. Consequently, salesmen, like Fred Wilson, learn to find these products horizontally without rewriting them. There are two points to be kept in mind whenever you do horizontal multiplication:

→1. Never use horizontal multiplication if the multiplicand and the multiplier each consists of more than one digit, such as 46 × $1.54.

→2. Although the product can be found by multiplying either the number on the right by the number on the left or in the reverse direction, you will usually find it easier to multiply the right number by the left one.

To illustrate: 7 shirts are purchased at $3.95 each. Find the total cost.

Solution: Since the total cost is to be written to the right, multiply $3.95 by 7. Your thinking should be as follows: 7 times 5 is 35; write down the 5 and "carry" 3; 7 times 9 is 63, plus 3 is 66; write down the 6 and "carry" 6; 7 times 3 is 21, plus 6 is 27. Thus, the product is $27.65.

LEARNING EXERCISES

1. Copy the following table, and place your answer in the column headed "Product." Do *not* rewrite the problem vertically. Find the product at sight.

No.	Example	Product	No.	Example	Product
a	4 × 75	xxx	i	8 × $.49	$xxx
b	2 × 156	xxx	j	3 × $2.89	xxx
c	7 × 89	xxx	k	5 × $6.07	xxx
d	5 × 347	xxx	l	4 × $45.32	xxx
e	68 × 3	xxx	m	6 × $17.98	xxx
f	235 × 4	xxx	n	493 × $.02	xxx
g	849 × 6	xxx	o	756 × $.08	xxx
h	3,476 × 9	xxx	p	2,576 × $.09	xxx

2. Copy and complete the following sales slip.

Date: *5/12* R. C. Bond and Company Dept. *47*		
Quantity	Item	Amount
4	*Shirts @ 2.95*	xxx xx
6	*Ties @ 1.50*	xxx xx
3	*Undershirts @ 1.25*	xxx xx
8	*Socks @ .79*	xxx xx
	Total	xxx xx

Name: *Samuel Trent*
Street: *West 14th Street*
Town: *Jamaica, Long Island, New York*

3. Fill out sales slips similar to the one in Problem 2 for each of the following purchases.

a. Mrs. Earl T. Stoddard:
   2 Boxes Christmas cards @ $1.79
   6 Boxes Christmas cards @ $.89
   4 Rolls gift wrapping @ $.99

b. Mrs. Thomas Riley:
   8 Bath towels @ $1.59
   8 Hand towels @ $.74
   6 Face cloths @ $.29
   4 Fingertip towels @ $.39
   3 Kitchen towels @ $1.29

U N I T **7**   **Application of Multiplication to Extensions**

Part 1

The process that you have been performing of completing a sales slip by placing the total price to the right of each item sold is called *finding the extensions*. In general, it involves finding the total cost when the number of items sold and the price per item are known. You first met this situation on the inventory sheet on page 41 of this chapter. Now you are able to complete forms such as this one, which is a portion of a complete form.

Article	Quantity	Cost per Unit	Amount
Pants	375	1 75	656 25
Dresses	256	2 20	563 20
		Total	1,219 45

The number $656.25 was found by multiplying 375 by $1.75; $563.20 is the product of 256 and $2.20. Since none of the numbers contain one digit only, the product had to be found by rewriting each of the examples vertically on a separate sheet of paper. The product found was then transferred to the Amount column.

There are forms other than the inventory sheet and the sales slip on which Fred found it necessary to compute extensions. The most common of these is called an *invoice*. This form consists of a statement listing the items purchased, the number of each purchased, the cost of each, and the total cost of all items. The word *bill*, with which you are probably familiar, is commonly interchanged with the word *invoice*. One form of invoice is the sales slip that you have already examined. Most invoices, however, resemble the statement shown here. This is a copy of an invoice that Fred received while working in the Accounting Department.

GENERAL SUPPLY COMPANY

Customer: R. C. Bond and Company

INVOICE   City: New York   Date: 6/8/--

		Items Requested		
Quantity	Catalogue No.	Description	Each	Amount
12	572	Desk lamps	14.75	177 00
9	386	Floor lamps	32.40	291 60
25	439	Floor lamps	29.50	737 50
50	884	Wall lamps	16.10	805 00
			Total	2,011 10

To determine the total cost of the 12 desk lamps at $14.75, the product of these two numbers was found. This cost, $177, was placed in the last column. The same was done for each of the other items.

LEARNING EXERCISES

Copy and complete each of the following business forms.

1

INVENTORY SHEET				
Stock Room Supplies for Sporting Goods Department				
Compiled by Fred Wilson				
Date July 17, 19--				
Article	Quantity	Cost per Unit	Amount	
Set of 8 irons	16	49 99	xxx	xx
Set of 3 irons	27	24 99	xxx	xx
Tennis racquet	85	9 99	xxx	xx
Spin reel	63	15 99	xxx	xx
Tennis balls (3)	157	1 49	xxx	xx
Basketball	96	4 78	xxx	xx
Rubber swimming fins	208	3 27	xxx	xx
Air mattress	174	4 89	xxx	xx
		Total	xxx	xx

2

PURCHASE ORDER			
R. C. Bond and Company			
Purchase Order to: Miner Candy Mfr. Durham, N. C.		Order No. 472 Date 10/6/--	
Quantity in Pounds	Description	Amount	
235	Frozen Milk Caramels @ 59¢	xxx	xx
350	Red & Black Pectin Berries @ 69¢	xxx	xx
475	Miniature Fruit Slices @ 73¢	xxx	xx
648	Toasted Coconut @ 64¢	xxx	xx
962	Licorice Berries @ 38¢	xxx	xx
176	Crystallized Jelly Frappe @ 91¢	xxx	xx
506	Chocolate—Miniature Cherries @ 85¢	xxx	xx
739	Chocolate—Large Cherries @ $1.07	xxx	xx
	Total	xxx	xx

Part 2

It is a common practice among most business firms to set up a checking system whereby one employee will check the computation performed by another employee. Frequently, the fastest way of checking another person's work is to ignore the answers he has obtained and to complete the computation by oneself. In this way, the checker is not led into the same errors that the person who performed the original operations made.

LEARNING EXERCISES

Errors were made in computing the extensions below. Check and correct each problem, indicating the correct extension to the right of the extension listed.

1

		Correct Extension
27 lbs. @ 48¢	12 96	xx xx
36 lbs. @ 56¢	21 06	xx xx
52 lbs. @ 38¢	19 76	xx xx
44 lbs. @ 65¢	82 06	xx xx
Total	135 84	xxx xx

2

93 bu. @ $1.25	116 25	xxx xx
35 bu. @ .66	23 10	xxx xx
58 bu. @ 1.35	87 30	xxx xx
46 bu. @ 1.08	49 68	xxx xx
Total	276 33	xxx xx

3

76 qts. @ 32¢	24 32	xx xx
58 qts. @ 54¢	32 31	xx xx
87 qts. @ 45¢	39 15	xx xx
64 qts. @ 26¢	16 64	xxx xx
Total	112 42	xxx xx

4

72 pcs. @ $1.30		93	60		xx	xx
58 pcs. @ .89		51	62		xx	xx
39 pcs. @ 1.56		60	84		xx	xx
65 pcs. @ .96		64	20		xx	xx
	Total	270	26		xxx	xx

U N I T 8   Measuring Your Skill in Multiplication

TIMED DRILL A   14 Minutes

Multiply and check.

1	2	3	4	5	6	7	8
83	108	317	248	574	468	3,074	5,139
27	64	58	106	253	187	208	426
xxx	xxx	xxx	xxx	xxx	xxx	xxx	xxx

TIMED DRILL B   10 Minutes

How much would each of the following lists of merchandise cost? Copying time is not to be included in the 10 minutes.

1	2	3
83 art. @ $3 = $xxx	2 lbs. @ 67¢ = $xxx	3 yds. @ $1.24 = $xxx
75 art. @ 8 = xxx	5 lbs. @ 82¢ = xxx	5 yds. @ 2.17 = xxx
26 art. @ 7 = xxx	6 lbs. @ 24¢ = xxx	4 yds. @ 1.86 = xxx
58 art. @ 6 = xxx	7 lbs. @ 38¢ = xxx	8 yds. @ 1.49 = xxx
94 art. @ 9 = xxx	9 lbs. @ 59¢ = xxx	6 yds. @ 1.98 = xxx
39 art. @ 5 = xxx	4 lbs. @ 93¢ = xxx	9 yds. @ 2.04 = xxx
Total = $xxx	Total = $xxx	Total = $xxx

TIMED DRILL C   15 Minutes

Copy and complete the following invoice. Copying time is not to be included in the 15 minutes.

INVOICE				
Hillsdale Auto Supply Company				
Terms: Net Cash			Date: 6/18/--	
No discount allowed		Customer R. C. Bond and Company		
Quantity	Description	Unit Price	Amount	
948	Side-view mirrors	1|85	xxx	xx
636	Black-wall tires	19|75	xxx	xx
756	White-wall tires	26|75	xxx	xx
408	Liquid cleaner	1|35	xxx	xx
240	Deluxe seat cushions	8|60	xxx	xx
564	Recapped snow tires	14|45	xxx	xx
Total			xxx	xx

4

Improving
Division Skills

PREVIEW

There are many details that must be considered when the price at which an article should be sold is to be set. Establishing prices is among the duties of department managers and their assistants, such as Fred Wilson. The first thing to be considered, of course, is the cost of the article to the store. But cost is only one factor. The price must also include a share of:

1. Local, state, and Federal taxes that have to be paid by the store.

2. Maintenance of the property by employees, such as janitorial staff, painters, carpenters, plumbers, electricians, and the like.

3. The constant remodernization of the plant in the form of new equipment, new lighting, new escalators, new showcases, and so on.

4. The heating and lighting costs.

5. The salaries of sales and supervisory employees.

Expenses such as these are referred to as the *overhead* of a business. To stop here would be to ignore completely the fact that the company can operate only if it does so profitably. This means that a profit, too, must be included in the price. Having thus arrived at a tentative basis for pricing the article, there are two other important questions that have to be considered:

→1. What are competitors charging for this same article?

→2. Will customers be willing to pay this price?

Only after all these things have been considered is it possible to place the price on the tag that is found attached to each article in a store. Though Fred Wilson knew that all these factors went into determining the price of every article, he knew, too, that to attempt to set the price for each article on the basis of these expenses would be almost impossible, and certainly impracticable. Using past experience, the Cost or Accounting department would notify Fred Wilson and others engaged in price fixing what rate of overhead they should include when considering the selling price of an article. The profit for the store is established in a similar manner.

To illustrate: A case of 24 cans of tuna fish was bought by R. C. Bond and Company for their Food Department at a cost of $6.24. After adding overhead and profit, it was found that each case would have to sell for $8.88. At what price would each can of tuna have to be sold?

Explanation: In order to find the selling price of each can, it is necessary to divide the total selling price of the entire case by the number of cans in the case, 24.

Solution: Selling price per can = $8.88 ÷ 24
= $ .37, or 37¢

UNIT 1 **Division of Whole Numbers**

It has probably been some time since you had to apply the operation of division. Before it is possible to speak intelligently about any process, it is important to learn the names of the quantities involved in that process. Each of the numbers, as well as the answer, in a division problem has its own individual name. You should review these names at this time.

Example: 240 ÷ 12 = 20.

1. The number being divided is called the *dividend*. In this example it is 240.

2. The number doing the dividing is called the *divisor*. Here it is 12.

3. The answer is called the *quotient*. Here it is 20.

This example can be written in three different ways:

$$\textbf{a. } 240 \div 12 = 20$$

$$\textbf{b. } 12\overline{)240}^{\,20}$$

$$\textbf{c. } \tfrac{240}{12} = 20$$

In each case, the 240 is the dividend; the 12, the divisor; and the 20, the quotient.

Fred Wilson seemed to find the operation of division the most difficult of all arithmetic operations to perform quickly. He felt that, since this operation depended on a knowledge of addition, subtraction, and multiplication, if he were slow in any one of these three processes, he would be slow in division, too. After trying to find little "tricks" that might increase his speed, he finally realized that there was no better way of improving his skill in division than constant practice.

The exercises that follow were designed to help you determine whether there is a need for you to devote time to practicing division. If you find that you can determine the quotients *correctly* in the time designated at the beginning of each section, then no further practice is necessary.

LEARNING EXERCISES

4 minute

A.   7 Minutes

1. 984 ÷ 3   *328*   6. 69,032 ÷ 8   *8629*
2. 996 ÷ 4   *249*   7. 57,213 ÷ 9   *6357*
3. 2,185 ÷ 5   *437*   8. 73,954 ÷ 6   *12325 R4*
4. 3,768 ÷ 6   *628*   9. 476,823 ÷ 5   *95364 R3*
5. 40,929 ÷ 7   *5847*   10. 765,947 ÷ 8   *95743 R3*

B.   12 Minutes

1. 83,008 ÷ 24   6. 58,310 ÷ 51
2. 18,612 ÷ 36   7. 32,875 ÷ 64
3. 6,902 ÷ 17   8. 34,195 ÷ 85
4. 14,628 ÷ 46   9. 75,893 ÷ 96
5. 24,089 ÷ 52   10. 84,874 ÷ 87

C.   20 Minutes

1. 32,754 ÷ 264   6. 255,270 ÷ 402
2. 75,832 ÷ 587   7. 134,596 ÷ 437
3. 96,438 ÷ 793   8. 567,483 ÷ 769
4. 64,879 ÷ 764   9. 658,937 ÷ 684
5. 204,564 ÷ 563   10. 964,581 ÷ 321

UNIT **2**   **The "Divisor Times Quotient Plus Remainder Equals Dividend" Check in Division**

As was the case in checking the product of two numbers, so in division, Fred Wilson found that he was using one of two methods for checking the quotient. Although the first of these methods used was the more reliable, he felt that the second was easier to apply. Hence, the check he applied depended on how much time he had.

The first method of checking the operation of division depends on information with which you are familiar. Thus, the quotient of 42 divided by 7 is 6; if you were asked to justify your answer (6), you would probably say, "Well, if 6 is multiplied by 7, the product is 42." What you have said is true because the operations of multiplication and division are *inverse* operations. This merely means that one can be checked by applying the other. The same relationship exists between the operations of addition and subtraction.

In order that you may better understand the check when larger numbers are involved, the example concerning 42, 7, and 6 is shown in the diagram below:

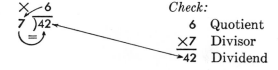

Check:

```
        6   Quotient
      ×7    Divisor
       42   Dividend
```

If the divisor does not happen to be an *exact* divisor of the dividend, then the check will involve one additional step:

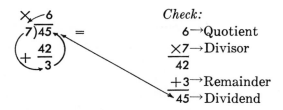

Not only must the 6 be multiplied by the 7 as before, but the remainder, 3, also must be added to the product, 42, to obtain the dividend, 45.

This principle can be expressed as follows:

→If the quotient is multiplied by the divisor and the remainder added to the product just obtained, the result should be the dividend.

To illustrate: Divide 38,675 by 564, and check.

Solution:

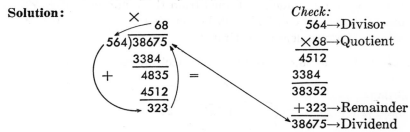

LEARNING EXERCISES

Copy the following problems, and find the quotient in each. Check each by the "divisor times quotient plus remainder equals dividend" check. Show the details of the work in arriving at the check, as in the illustration above.

1. $423\overline{)72,654}$ 4. $835\overline{)562,684}$ 7. $3,582\overline{)796,842}$

2. $574\overline{)87,891}$ 5. $467\overline{)341,965}$ 8. $4,276\overline{)635,897}$

3. $681\overline{)70,132}$ 6. $294\overline{)881,793}$ 9. $9,862\overline{)843,268}$

UNIT **3**   **The Casting-Out-9's Check in Division**

Checking division by casting out 9's can be applied faster than the check you have just learned. Unfortunately, it is open to the same criticism in division as in multiplication. Though the likelihood of its occurrence is somewhat slight, there always exists the possibility of obtaining an incorrect answer that is not detected by the use of this check. Although the check by casting out 9's is not foolproof, its simplicity of application warrants its use.

The principle learned in Unit 2 of this chapter applies equally well to the check by casting out 9's. Now, however, rather than dealing with the actual quotient, divisor, dividend, and remainder, the principle is applied to the remainders obtained from these numbers after 9's are cast out of each of them. This will be clarified through the use of the same illustrative problem as in Unit 2.

Example 1: Divide 38,675 by 564, and check by casting out 9's.

Solution:

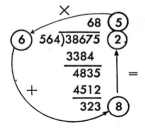

The 5, 6, 8, and 2 are the remainders found after the 9's were cast out of the quotient (68), the divisor (564), the remainder (323), and the dividend (38,675). Treating these remainders as you did the actual quotient, divisor, remainder, and dividend in the previous check, you will obtain:

$$
\begin{array}{l}
5 \rightarrow \text{ Quotient} \\
\underline{\times 6} \rightarrow \text{ Divisor} \\
30 \\
\underline{+8} \rightarrow \text{ Remainder} \\
38 \rightarrow 2 \text{ Dividend}
\end{array}
$$

If 9's are cast out of 38, the result will be the "dividend," 2.

Example 2: Divide 64,935 by 731, and check by casting out 9's.

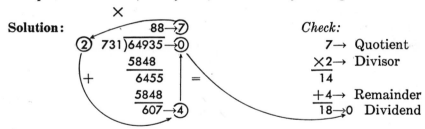

LEARNING EXERCISES

Copy the following problems, and find the quotient in each. Check each by the casting-out-9's check. Show the details of the work in arriving at the check, as in the illustrative examples above.

1. 87)9,458

2. 56)7,859

3. 63)8,643

4. 49)5,796

5. 75)6,974

6. 378)67,418

7. 436)86,387

8. 817)54,896

9. 542)27,675

UNIT 4 Division Where Decimals Are Involved

SECTION 1 Dividing a Decimal by a Whole Number

Having reviewed the process of division where only whole numbers were involved, Fred Wilson was now in a position to return to his task of finding the unit price of an article when he knew the price for which the entire case was to be sold. As an example, what should be set as the selling price of a can of tuna if the entire case of 24 cans was marked to sell at $7.09. It is evident that a problem such as this involves a knowledge of the method for dividing a decimal (7.09) by a whole number (24). The quotient is found in the same manner as in dividing a whole number by a whole number except for one additional step. At the outset, the decimal point is placed directly above its position in the dividend. After this has been done, the division is completed as though there were no decimal point in the problem. Using the situation above as an illustration—

Solution:

$$29\frac{13}{24}$$
$$24\overline{)7.09}$$
$$\underline{4\ 8}$$
$$2\ 29$$
$$\underline{2\ 16}$$
$$13$$

Explanation: After the decimal point was placed in the position it will occupy in the quotient, division took place as if the decimal point did not exist in the dividend, 7.09.

LEARNING EXERCISES

A. Find the cost to R. C. Bond and Company of each of the following items, if purchases were made as follows:

No.	No. of Cans in Case	Total Cost	Cost per Can	No.	No. of Cans in Case	Total Cost	Cost per Can
1	24	$ 4.96	$xxx	10	36	$13.32	$xxx
2	24	3.60	xxx	11	36	14.40	xxx
3	24	4.32	xxx	12	36	12.96	xxx
4	24	3.36	xxx	13	48	8.43	xxx
5	18	4.92	xxx	14	48	12.59	xxx
6	18	5.52	xxx	15	48	16.87	xxx
7	18	7.92	xxx	16	72	35.69	xxx
8	18	9.36	xxx	17	72	18.53	xxx
9	36	10.80	xxx	18	86	23.95	xxx

B. If yard goods were purchased by R. C. Bond as follows, what was the cost of each yard of material?

No.	No. of Yards	Total Cost	Cost per Yard	No.	No. of Yards	Total Cost	Cost per Yard
1	95	$ 82.73	$xxx	5	218	$ 367.24	$xxx
2	97	104.69	xxx	6	547	1,264.83	xxx
3	104	110.56	xxx	7	682	2,342.77	xxx
4	108	146.49	xxx	8	876	4,672.93	xxx

SECTION 2   **Dividing a Decimal by a Decimal**

Department stores, like many well-run businesses, operate each of their departments on a budget. When Fred Wilson's training was completed and he was considered competent to make important decisions, he was assigned the responsibility of deciding on the quantity and quality of merchandise that should be purchased. He was allotted a sum of money for the purchase of dresses for the Women's Dress Department. On the basis of what he believed would be the trend in women's clothing styles, he had to decide what types of dresses should be purchased now for the coming season. If his judgment was bad, the store would lose a good deal of money. To spread the risk of the likelihood of this occurring, he apportioned various sums to a large variety of styles. In this way he insured against disaster because of one bad selection.

To illustrate: If Fred allotted **$526.75** toward the purchase of a certain style dress in various sizes, and the cost of each dress was **$12.25**, how many dresses of this style could he buy?

Solution: Finding the answer involves dividing **$526.75** by **$12.25**. As both these numbers are decimals, it might be well to review the process of division where the divisor is a decimal. If the divisor (12.25) were a whole number, it would be possible to find the quotient in exactly the same manner as was done in Section 1 of this unit. To make 12.25 a whole number, the decimal point would have to be moved two places to the right, placing it after the **5**. If it is moved two places in the divisor, however, the decimal point in the dividend must also be moved, making the dividend 526.75. Now that the divisor and the dividend are whole numbers, division can proceed as before.

$$
\begin{array}{r}
43. \\
12.25. \overline{)526.75.} \\
490\ 0 \\
\hline
36\ 75 \\
36\ 75 \\
\hline
\end{array}
$$

Hence, 43 dresses can be purchased with the money allotted for the purchase of that style.

The principle of moving the decimal point can be stated as follows:
→If the divisor is a decimal, change it to a whole number by moving the decimal point to the right, after the last digit. If this is done, then the

decimal point in the dividend must be moved to the right exactly the same number of places as it was moved in the divisor. If the number of places that the decimal point can be moved in the dividend is less than the number of places it was moved in the divisor, then zeros will have to be inserted to the right of the last digit in the dividend.

To illustrate: If the decimal point has to be moved three places to the right in the number 526.4, then the number must be rewritten as 526.400 before the decimal point can be moved.

The reason why neither the problem nor the value of the quotient is affected by moving the decimal point in the manner shown will be explained thoroughly in Chapter 5. At that point the discussion will be more meaningful than here.

Example 1: Divide 51.084 by .0027.

Solution:

$$18920.$$
$$.0027.\overline{)51.0840.}$$

Explanation: The decimal point was moved four places in the divisor, to place it after the last digit (7). In order to move it four places in the dividend, one zero had to be written after the number 4. From this point, the division was completed in the same manner as if the numbers had been whole numbers.

Example 2: Divide 56 by 1.02.

Solution:

$$54.90\tfrac{20}{102}, \text{ or } 54.90\tfrac{10}{51}$$
$$1.02\overline{)56.00.00}$$
$$\underline{51\ 0}$$
$$5\ 00$$
$$\underline{4\ 08}$$
$$92\ 0$$
$$\underline{91\ 8}$$
$$20$$

Explanation: The decimal point in a whole number, such as 56, belongs at the right of the 6, although it is not always written there. Moving the decimal point two places further to the right necessitated adding two zeros before this could be done. If the division is not "exact," the quotient should either be "rounded off" to the nearest cent if money is involved or expressed in the form shown here if no money is involved.

LEARNING EXERCISES

Divide, leaving your quotient in the manner shown in Example 2 if the division is not exact.

1. 34.68 ÷ .06
2. 58 ÷ .08
3. .1 ÷ .4
4. 95 ÷ 2.3
5. 8.4 ÷ .26
6. .53 ÷ .058
7. 29.7 ÷ 3.94
8. .00919 ÷ 37

9. 48 ÷ 1.02
10. .0193 ÷ .287
11. .0025 ÷ .25
12. 807.6 ÷ .53
13. 745.46 ÷ .084
14. 9.0081 ÷ .0072
15. 32.76 ÷ 4.009
16. 3.388 ÷ 246.6

17. .004648 ÷ 5.6
18. .0003478 ÷ .37
19. .11502 ÷ 4.6
20. .025488 ÷ .72
21. .00804 ÷ 27.6
22. .167445 ÷ 5.49
23. .15344 ÷ 68.5
24. .05811 ÷ .975

UNIT 5   Short Cuts in Division

SECTION 1   Division by 10, 100, 1,000

Short cuts in dividing by 10, 100, and 1,000 are performed in very much the same way as in multipling by these numbers. This procedure must be understood because division by these numbers occurs frequently in business transactions. When the divisor is the number 1 followed by zeros, then, to find the quotient, simply move the decimal point in the dividend as many places to the left as there are zeros in the divisor.

Example 1: 472.34 ÷ 10 = ?
   Solution: 472.34 ÷ 10 = 47.2.34
Explanation: As there is only one zero after the 1 in the divisor, the decimal point in 472.34 is moved one place to the left.

Example 2: 576 ÷ 100 = ?
   Solution: 576 ÷ 100 = 5.76.
Explanation: If no decimal point appears in a number, then its position is at the right of the number. The number 576 can be written as 576.; therefore, to divide 576 by 100, move the decimal point between the 5 and the 7.

Example 3: 46.37 ÷ 1,000 = ?
   Solution: 46.37 ÷ 1,000 = .046.37

Explanation: As the decimal point had to be moved three places to the left, it was necessary to insert one zero to the left of the 4 before the decimal could be moved.

LEARNING EXERCISES

Copy each of the following problems. To the right of each of them, write the quotient.

1. 63.56 ÷ 10
2. 348.5 ÷ 100
3. 6,754.2 ÷ 1,000
4. 8.72 ÷ 100
5. 326.75 ÷ 10,000

6. .4 ÷ 10
7. .34 ÷ 100
8. 5,670 ÷ 1,000
9. 842 ÷ 100
10. 3 ÷ 10

11. 5 ÷ 10,000
12. $34.26 ÷ 100
13. $1.56 ÷ 100
14. $8,425 ÷ 1,000
15. $5,000 ÷ 100

SECTION 2   Purchases Made by the Hundred, Hundredweight, or Thousand

Having learned how to divide by 10, 100, and 1,000, Fred Wilson began to notice many occasions when division by these numbers occurred in the daily conduct of business at R. C. Bond and Company. Some of these were:

1. Meat was purchased for the store restaurant, the cafeteria, and the retail Meat Department by the hundredweight. *Hundredweight* means "by the hundred pounds." The lengthy phrase "by the hundredweight" is usually abbreviated to "per cwt."

2. The Bakery Department bought flour, sugar, and shortening by the hundredweight.

3. So many sales slips were needed that they were purchased at a certain price per 1,000 pads. The same was true for many other business forms that were used. Fred learned that the abbreviation for the phrase "per 1,000" was "per M."

4. Both wooden and wire hangers on which clothes were hung in the showcases and on the racks were also purchased by the 1,000 units.

5. Oil to heat the store was purchased in terms of a price per 1,000 gallons.

Example 1: Find the cost of 6,725 wire hangers at $10.25 per M.

Solution: The number of thousands in 6,725 is found by dividing this number by 1,000. The quotient (6.725) is then multiplied by the cost for each 1,000 ($10.25), making a total of $68.93125, or $68.93.

Outline: Number of Thousands = 6,725 ÷ 1,000

$$= 6.725$$

$$\text{Cost} = 6.725 \times \$10.25$$

$$= \$68.93125, \text{ or } \$68.93$$

Example 2: Find the cost of 875 pounds of sugar purchased at $6.77 per cwt.

Solution: The number of hundreds in 875 can be found by dividing 875 by 100. The quotient (8.75) is then multiplied by the cost of each 100 pounds ($6.77), giving a total of $59.2375, or $59.24.

Outline: Number of Hundreds = 875 ÷ 100

$$= 8.75$$

$$\text{Cost} = 8.75 \times \$6.77$$

$$= \$59.2375, \text{ or } \$59.24$$

LEARNING EXERCISES

1. Purchases of sugar were made under slightly varying prices during the month of September. Find the total cost of the sugar for the entire month.

Date	Quantity in Pounds	Cost per Cwt.	Amount
9/5	400	$6.69	$xxx
9/12	720	6.72	xxx
9/17	635	6.75	xxx
9/26	875	6.70	xxx
		Total	$xxx

2. Compute the selling price of the following bill for lumber sold.

Quantity in Board Feet	Kind	Price per M	Amount
8,640	*Flooring, No. 1*	$135	$xxx
6,860	*Siding*	95	xxx
12,600	*Floor timbers*	115	xxx
6,530	*Flooring, No. 2*	93	xxx
3,750	*Scantlings*	107	xxx
9,500	*Sheathing boards*	89	xxx
		Total	$xxx

3. Find the cost of the following invoice for business forms purchased by R. C. Bond and Company.

No. of Pads	Description	Cost per M	Amount
2,000	Form 523	$ 86.15	$xxx
4,200	Form 437	92.70	xxx
3,420	Form 685	104.85	xxx
9,750	Form 126	76.08	xxx
12,000	Form 75	53.92	xxx
10,500	Form 346	126.44	xxx
		Total	$xxx

UNIT 6   Computing the Average of a Set of Numbers

With the passing of time, it appeared to Fred Wilson that not only were the number of decisions that he was called on to make increasing, but also they seemed to be of greater importance and of more interest to him.

One that he found particularly interesting was an outgrowth of a conference held between him and the director of personnel. It concerned a choice that had to be made as to which of two salesmen would receive a promotion at that particular time. As there was only one vacancy, only one of the men could be promoted. The backgrounds of the two men were almost identical in all factors of usual importance, such as period of employment with the company, educational background, personality, personal appearance, absence record, and tardiness record. It was finally agreed that the one who had proved himself to be the better salesman would be selected. The one chosen as the "better salesmen" was to be the one whose "average" sales over the past 5 years were the greater. The sales of both men for the 5-year period were as follows:

	Salesman A	Salesman B
1st year	$20,450	$18,375
2d year	21,460	20,230
3d year	23,520	22,425
4th year	22,895	24,650
5th year	22,460	23,760

To determine average sales, the total amount sold by each salesman during the 5 years was first found. For salesman A, this was $110,785; for salesman B, $109,440. The average sales of each salesman was found by dividing each of these numbers by the number of years, which was 5. The average of the first salesman was $22,157; that of the second was $21,888. Though the difference was rather small, it was on this basis that salesman A received the promotion.

Averages have become very important to the world of business in recent years. The word "average" is usually interpreted to mean the sum of the numbers divided by the number of numbers.

LEARNING EXERCISES

1. Find the average yearly salary for the number of years listed for each of the following clerks:

Clark: $2,720, $2,910, $3,075, $3,240, $3,350
Hale: $2,675, $2,735, $2,872, $2,995, $3,126, $3,473
Rand: $2,467.50, $2,644.25, $2,892.34, $3,005.82, $3,143.58

2. During a Community Chest drive, the 2,374 employees of R. C. Bond and Company contributed $8,695.48. What was the average contribution of each employee?

3. Compare the average sales in the Toy Department for the period 1949–1953 with the period 1954–1958.

Year	Sales	Year	Sales
1949	$43,450	1954	$45,975
1950	$47,520	1955	$46,820
1951	$40,375	1956	$50,395
1952	$41,680	1957	$50,570
1953	$44,535	1958	$52,640

4. The total personal income in billions of dollars for everyone in the United States during the years 1945 to 1955 is given in the following table. Find the average for this period.

Year	Personal Income	Year	Personal Income
1945	171.2	1951	255.3
1946	178.0	1952	271.1
1947	190.5	1953	286.2
1948	208.7	1954	287.6
1949	206.8	1955	300.1
1950	227.1		

UNIT **7**   **Measuring Your Skill in Division**

TIMED DRILL A   8 Minutes

Divide:

1. 672 ÷ 3
2. 2,316 ÷ 4
3. 87,626 ÷ 7
4. 638,424 ÷ 9

5. 17,918 ÷ 34
6. 34,216 ÷ 52
7. 10,160 ÷ 16
8. 60,860 ÷ 85

9. 37,442 ÷ 97
10. 172,032 ÷ 256
11. 214,489 ÷ 527
12. 410,400 ÷ 608

TIMED DRILL B   9 Minutes

Divide, carrying your answer to the nearest cent.

1. $63.75 ÷ 84
2. $75.93 ÷ 67

3. $5.98 ÷ 1.06
4. $67.43 ÷ .74

5. $87.56 ÷ 1.02
6. $1,275.48 ÷ 1.56

TIMED DRILL C   5 Minutes

Find the cost of each of the following purchases.

1. 6,300 articles @ $4.27 per 100.
2. 8,000 articles @ $52.25 per M.
3. 4,800 pounds @ $61.90 per cwt.
4. $6,250 insurance @ 28¢ per $1,000.
5. $575 baggage insurance @ 55¢ per $100.

TIMED DRILL D   20 Minutes

1. In 14 years, a commission merchant reported annual sales as follows: $19,874.50, $32,645.97, $24,586.46, $26,800.95, $11,125.75, $18,645.64, $17,286.58, $23,891.43, $15,206.84, $21,076.40, $13,178.64, $31,801.96, $25,236.79, and $28,816.62. Find his average annual sales.

2. The contributions of 387 employees in District A toward an employees' mutual benefit fund were $46,892, and the contributions of

467 employees in District B toward the same fund were $68,790. Compare the average contribution of the two districts.

3. Frederick Herbert's monthly expenses during a recent year were: January, $312.40; February, $264.75; March, $257.80; April, $272.40; May, $302.60; June, $295.85; July, $317.85; August, $266.80; September, $315.75; October, $273.35; November, $264.80; and December, $345.85. Find the average monthly expenses during the year.

4. The 9 men on a league baseball team totaled the following runs during a recent season: 135, 187, 86, 57, 203, 153, 126, 144, 117.

    a. Find the total number of runs scored by the team for the season.

    b. Find the average number of runs scored by all the players.

5

Improving Skills in Using Fractions

PREVIEW

Many firms have established the policy of fining employees who report late to work. A common method is to reduce an employee's pay by $\frac{1}{6}$ of an hour's salary for each 10 minutes, or fraction thereof, that he is late to work. Thus, if an employee is late 1 to 10 minutes, he would lose $\frac{1}{6}$ of an hour's salary; if late 11 to 20 minutes, he would lose $\frac{2}{6}$, or $\frac{1}{3}$, of an hour's salary; if late 21 to 30 minutes, he would lose $\frac{3}{6}$, or $\frac{1}{2}$, of an hour's salary; and so on. At the close of each week, the payroll clerk determines the sum of the fractional periods that each employee has been late during the week and computes the salary accordingly. For example, if an employee were late $\frac{1}{3}$ of an hour on Monday, $\frac{1}{6}$ of an hour on Wednesday, and $\frac{1}{2}$ of an hour on Thursday, the payroll clerk would add these three fractions to determine the total number of hours working time lost by this employee. This is but one example of a case where a knowledge of the principles relating to fractions plays an important part in business.

The addition of fractions or any of the other operations with fractions are not difficult tasks to perform. The reason *why* these operations are performed in the manner in which they are is not always clear to students. They are curious about questions such as those listed below.

For Class Discussion

1. Why is it necessary to find a common denominator when fractions are added?

2. Why add only the numerators, and not the denominators, when fractions are added?

3. Why should the divisor be inverted when one fraction is divided by another? Also, why invert only the divisor? Why not the dividend, too?

4. In the illustration in the opening paragraph of the preview, why is $\frac{2}{6}$ of an hour the same as $\frac{1}{3}$ of an hour, or $\frac{3}{6}$ of an hour the same as $\frac{1}{2}$ of an hour?

The purpose of this chapter is to clarify these points and many more similar to these. It is not that you will be called on to answer questions of this variety in the course of a business day. It is well known, however, that greater efficiency will accompany the mechanical processes if the person has an understanding of *why* he is performing the operation in the manner required.

U N I T **1**   **Meaning of a Fraction**

S E C T I O N 1   A Fraction As an Indication of Division

There are several interpretations for a number that is written in fractional form. One of these was given in Chapter 4 on division. Thus, the fraction $\frac{56}{7}$ merely means that the "top" number (56) is to be divided by the "bottom" number (7). Although earlier in the book these numbers were called the *dividend* and the *divisor*, they have other names when the division is expressed in fractional form. Thus, in

$$\frac{56}{7} = 8$$

→The 56 is the *numerator* of the fraction.
→The 7 is the *denominator* of the fraction.
→The 8 is the *value* of the fraction.

It matters not whether the numerator is larger or smaller than the denominator. In either case, the fraction can still be interpreted as a problem indicating division. If the denominator is larger than the numerator, as in the fraction $\frac{3}{4}$, the value of this fraction can be found as before:

$$\frac{3}{4} = \overset{.75}{4\overline{)3.00}}$$

The number .75 is commonly called *the decimal value* of the fraction $\frac{3}{4}$ rather than simply *the value* of the fraction.

Should it so happen that the denominator is not an exact divisor of the numerator, as in the fraction $\frac{22}{3}$, then the value of the fraction will be a *mixed number*—in this example, $7\frac{1}{3}$. A mixed number is a number that consists of the sum of a whole number and a fraction. The number $7\frac{1}{3}$ represents the whole number 7 added to the fraction $\frac{1}{3}$.

No matter what the nature of the original fraction may be, it is important to remember the principle that:
→The decimal value, the whole-number value, or the mixed-number value of any fraction can always be found by dividing the numerator of the fraction by the denominator.

The mixed number $7\frac{1}{3}$ was obtained from the fraction $\frac{22}{3}$ as follows:

$$\frac{22}{3} = 3\overline{)22} \\ \quad\ \ \underline{21} \\ \quad\ \ \ \ 1$$

(with 7 above the division)

In Chapter 4 on division, you learned that, if the quotient (in this case 7) is multiplied by the divisor (3), and to the product (21) is added the remainder (1), the result will be the dividend (22). Hence, to change the mixed number $7\frac{1}{3}$ back to the fraction $\frac{22}{3}$, simply multiply the quotient (the whole number 7) by the divisor (the denominator 3) and to the product add the remainder (the numerator 1). Doing this will result in the numerator of the fraction (22).

Example: Change the mixed number $15\frac{1}{2}$ to a fraction.

Solution: If the whole number (15) is multiplied by the denominator (2) and to this product (30) is added the numerator (1), the numerator of the new fraction will be 31. Hence, the fraction that is equal to the mixed number $15\frac{1}{2}$ is $\frac{31}{2}$.

Outline: $15\frac{1}{2} = \frac{31}{2}$

15	Whole number
$\times 2$	Denominator
30	Product
$+1$	Numerator
31	Numerator of new fraction

Thus far, no distinction has been made between the varieties of fractions that exist. As an example, if the numerator of a fraction is smaller than the denominator, this is considered to be proper; therefore, such a fraction is called a *proper fraction*. On the other hand, fractions are considered to be improper if the numerator is equal to or larger than the denominator; these fractions are known as *improper fractions*. Numbers that have been referred to as *decimals* earlier in the text are also called *decimal fractions*. The term "decimal fractions," however, is disappearing from the language and is being replaced by the shorter and and more meaningful term, *decimals*.

Examples of these fractions are:

Proper fractions: $\frac{2}{3}$, $\frac{7}{15}$, $\frac{21}{100}$

Improper fractions: $\frac{5}{2}$, $\frac{23}{19}$, $\frac{126}{43}$, $\frac{6}{6}$, $\frac{73}{73}$

Decimal fractions, or decimals: .24, .05, 1.67

LEARNING EXERCISES

A. Find the whole-number or the mixed-number value of each of the following improper fractions.

1. $\frac{43}{4}$	5. $\frac{95}{5}$	9. $\frac{616}{25}$	13. $\frac{487}{25}$
2. $\frac{59}{3}$	6. $\frac{133}{6}$	10. $\frac{824}{16}$	14. $\frac{1170}{12}$
3. $\frac{67}{7}$	7. $\frac{259}{5}$	11. $\frac{911}{12}$	15. $\frac{717}{7}$
4. $\frac{88}{12}$	8. $\frac{468}{9}$	12. $\frac{336}{11}$	16. $\frac{1256}{50}$

B. Find the decimal value of each of the following proper fractions.

1. $\frac{1}{4}$	5. $\frac{3}{8}$	9. $\frac{7}{25}$	13. $\frac{2}{7}$
2. $\frac{2}{5}$	6. $\frac{7}{8}$	10. $\frac{19}{25}$	14. $\frac{5}{9}$
3. $\frac{3}{5}$	7. $\frac{3}{20}$	11. $\frac{1}{3}$	15. $\frac{4}{15}$
4. $\frac{7}{10}$	8. $\frac{11}{20}$	12. $\frac{5}{6}$	

C. Change each of the following mixed numbers to improper fractions.

1. $5\frac{2}{3}$	6. $18\frac{1}{2}$	11. $21\frac{4}{5}$	16. $64\frac{1}{4}$
2. $6\frac{4}{5}$	7. $28\frac{2}{3}$	12. $42\frac{2}{3}$	17. $72\frac{2}{3}$
3. $7\frac{3}{4}$	8. $58\frac{3}{4}$	13. $46\frac{1}{2}$	18. $84\frac{3}{5}$
4. $9\frac{1}{2}$	9. $79\frac{2}{5}$	14. $51\frac{3}{8}$	19. $67\frac{3}{4}$
5. $16\frac{2}{3}$	10. $31\frac{1}{6}$	15. $72\frac{2}{5}$	20. $58\frac{7}{8}$

SECTION 2   A Fraction As an Indication of a Part of a Whole Quantity

The second interpretation for a fraction is that it shows a part of a whole quantity. Thus, if the owner of a bakery cut a large cheese cake into 4 equal parts for the purpose of selling each section separately, then one of these parts is considered to be 1 fourth of the entire cake. Two of these parts is 2 fourths of the entire cake, and three parts is 3 fourths of the entire cake. Each of these parts can be written in the form $\frac{1}{4}$, $\frac{2}{4}$, and $\frac{3}{4}$. You will notice that the denominator of the fraction tells you the "kind" or "denomination" of the quantity with which you are dealing. In this case, they are fourths. In other fractions they may be fifths or eighths, depending on the number of equal pieces into which the original quantity was divided. The word *denominator* has the same meaning as the word *denomination*.

You are aware that there are different denominations of fruit—for example, apples, pears, bananas, grapes, and so on; or different denominations of trees—for example, oak, maple, pine, birch, and so on. So, too, there are different denominations of fractional parts; as, thirds, fourths, eighths, and so on. These denominations are identified by the denominators of the fractions. It is these denominators that will tell you, as stated before, the number of equal parts into which the whole quantity has been divided.

The numerator, on the other hand, will "enumerate"; that is, tell "how many" there are of that denomination. In the illustration used previously, the numerators showed that there was 1 fourth, 2 fourths, or 3 fourths. To illustrate further, in the fraction $\frac{5}{6}$, the denominator points out the *kind* of quantity to be considered—these are sixths—and the numerator indicates *how many* sixths there are—in this case, 5 of them. To summarize, the two major interpretations of a fraction are:

→1. As an indication of the operation of division.

→2. As an indication of a part of a whole quantity.

LEARNING EXERCISES

A. In terms of each of the following fractions, state:

1. The number of equal parts into which the whole quantity was divided.

2. How many of these equal parts are represented by each fraction.

a. $\frac{2}{3}$ **c.** $\frac{1}{4}$ **e.** $\frac{15}{16}$ **g.** $\frac{24}{24}$

b. $\frac{3}{5}$ **d.** $\frac{5}{6}$ **f.** $\frac{8}{8}$ **h.** 1

B. In terms of the second meaning of a fraction, interpret each of the following statements.

1. A line is $\frac{3}{8}$ of an inch long.

2. John's inheritance will be $\frac{4}{5}$ of his father's property.

3. The building is now half empty.

C. Classify each of the following fractions as to whether they are proper fractions, improper fractions, or decimals.

1. $\frac{5}{7}$ **4.** $\frac{16}{3}$ **7.** 4.67   **10.** .006

2. $\frac{1}{12}$ **5.** $\frac{15}{16}$ **8.** $\frac{7}{7}$ **11.** $\frac{1}{2}$

3. $\frac{23}{24}$ **6.** .23   **9.** $\frac{18}{9}$ **12.** $\frac{2}{1}$

UNIT **2**   **Changing Fractions to Equivalent Fractions**

SECTION 1   Reducing Fractions to Lowest Terms

It is very likely that you have been asked frequently to "reduce" a fraction, such as $\frac{9}{12}$, to lowest terms. Probably you immediately replied, "$\frac{9}{12} = \frac{3}{4}$." When asked how you obtained your answer, you may have said, "I divided 3 into the numerator and 3 into the denominator of the fraction $\frac{9}{12}$." Did you ever stop to consider the possibility of subtracting the same number from the numerator and the denominator of a fraction in order to reduce it to lowest terms? Has it occurred to you that the fraction $\frac{3}{4}$ may not be equal to the original fraction $\frac{9}{12}$? In fact, have you ever considered what the words "reducing a fraction to lowest terms" might mean?

The question of greatest importance is, can the fraction $\frac{9}{12}$ be shown to be equivalent to the fraction $\frac{3}{4}$? The simplest way of doing this is to find the decimal value of each fraction and show that the values are the same number. Thus:

$$\frac{9}{12} = 12\overline{)9.00}^{.75} \xleftrightarrow{\hspace{1cm}} \frac{3}{4} = 4\overline{)3.00}^{.75}$$

Since the decimal values of both are the same number (.75), then the fractions $\frac{9}{12}$ and $\frac{3}{4}$ are equal to each other.

Similarly, if both the numerator and the denominator of the fraction $\frac{12}{24}$ are divided by 6, the new fraction will be $\frac{2}{4}$. If the decimal value of each fraction is found:

$$\frac{12}{24} = 24\overline{)12.00}^{.50} \xleftrightarrow{\hspace{1cm}} \frac{2}{4} = 4\overline{)2.00}^{.50}$$

again it becomes apparent that the two fractions are equivalent. Hence, the principle can be stated that:

→If the numerator and the denominator of a fraction are both divided by the same number, a new fraction will be obtained, which will be equal in value to the original fraction.

Actually, whenever a fraction is reduced to lowest terms, this principle is being applied.

In answer to the question, "What do the words 'reducing a fraction to lowest terms' mean?" you will note that earlier the fraction $\frac{12}{24}$ was changed to the equivalent form $\frac{2}{4}$ by dividing the numerator and the denominator by 6. Your reply to the question, "Is $\frac{2}{4}$ reduced to lowest terms?" would very likely be, "No, the numerator and denominator have a common divisor of 2; that is, both can still be divided by 2." On the other hand, were you asked if the fraction $\frac{9}{10}$ is reduced to lowest terms, your answer would be that it is, since the two numbers 9 and 10 have no common divisor. Actually, you overlooked the fact that the number 1 is an exact divisor of these two numbers. Basically, however, you have given the essence of what is meant by the statement that a fraction is "reduced to lowest terms." It can be stated as a principle in the following manner:

→If there are no whole numbers, other than 1, that are exact divisors of the numerator and the denominator of a fraction, that fraction is said to be reduced to lowest terms.

Example: Reduce the fraction $\frac{18}{24}$ to lowest terms.

   Solution: $\frac{18}{24} = \frac{6}{8} = \frac{3}{4}$

Explanation: The numbers 18 and 24 have the exact divisor 3 in common; therefore, after dividing both by this number, the new fraction $\frac{6}{8}$ is obtained. Examination of the fraction $\frac{6}{8}$ leads to the discovery that 6 and 8 still have the exact divisor 2 in common. Dividing by this number, the fraction reduces to $\frac{3}{4}$; and there is no common exact divisor (other than 1) for the numbers 3 and 4. Hence, the fraction $\frac{18}{24}$ has been reduced to lowest terms when it is written in the form $\frac{3}{4}$. Had it been noticed at the outset that 6 was an exact divisor of both 18 and 24, then the answer $\frac{3}{4}$ could have been obtained immediately without the need of the additional fraction $\frac{6}{8}$. Therefore, to shorten your work, always try to find the *largest* whole number that is an exact divisor of the numerator and the denominator of a fraction if you are reducing the fraction to lowest terms.

LEARNING EXERCISES

Reduce each of the following fractions to lowest terms.

1. $\frac{10}{15}$	**7.** $\frac{12}{20}$	**13.** $\frac{14}{49}$	**19.** $\frac{16}{56}$
2. $\frac{12}{16}$	**8.** $\frac{12}{30}$	**14.** $\frac{18}{45}$	**20.** $\frac{40}{72}$
3. $\frac{5}{10}$	**9.** $\frac{10}{16}$	**15.** $\frac{20}{36}$	**21.** $\frac{35}{84}$
4. $\frac{12}{18}$	**10.** $\frac{12}{32}$	**16.** $\frac{24}{54}$	**22.** $\frac{60}{75}$
5. $\frac{6}{14}$	**11.** $\frac{30}{50}$	**17.** $\frac{36}{48}$	**23.** $\frac{42}{189}$
6. $\frac{14}{21}$	**12.** $\frac{16}{40}$	**18.** $\frac{24}{60}$	**24.** $\frac{75}{90}$

SECTION 2   Changing a Fraction to Higher Terms

In Section 1, you learned that dividing the numerator and the denominator of a fraction by the same number did not alter the value of the fraction. In this section you will learn how to change a fraction from a form such as $\frac{3}{4}$ to one where the denominator is a larger number, such as, perhaps, 8. Outlined, this problem would be:

$$\frac{3}{4} = \frac{?}{8}$$

To obtain the denominator of the second fraction, it is apparent that 4 must have been multiplied by the number 2 in order to obtain the number 8. Therefore, also multiplying the numerator 3 by 2 will make the new numerator 6. Now, if the value of $\frac{3}{4}$ is equal to the value of $\frac{6}{8}$, the process just completed can be considered correct.

$$.75 \longleftrightarrow .75$$
$$\frac{3}{4} = 4\overline{)3.00} \qquad \frac{6}{8} = 8\overline{)6.00}$$

Since both fractions have the value **.75**, they are equal to each other.

This example leads to the second principle:

→If the numerator and the denominator of a fraction are multiplied by the same number, a new fraction will be obtained that is equal in value to the original fraction.

It is this principle that you applied in Chapter 4 on division each time you divided by a decimal. Thus, in the example:

$$3.275\overline{)46.8429}$$

you will recall that the first thing you did was to move the decimal point three places to the right in the divisor and three places to the right in the dividend. If the example were written in fractional form, it would be:

$$\frac{46.8429}{3.275} = \frac{46.842.9}{3.275.}$$

Also, you know that moving the decimal three places to the right in a number means that the number has been multiplied by 1,000. Hence, in the preceding example, the numerator (46.8429) and the denominator (3.275) were merely multiplied by the same number (1,000), which will not alter the value of the fraction. It is true, in general, that each time the decimal point is moved in the divisor and in the dividend of a division problem, the result is the same as multiplying the denominator and the numerator of a fraction by the same number.

The process of multiplying the numerator and the denominator of a fraction by the same number is commonly called *changing a fraction to higher terms*. This name was selected because the numbers in the new fraction are larger than those in the original fraction. It is important to remember, however, that the values of the two fractions are the same.

Example: Change the fraction $\frac{7}{8}$ to an equivalent fraction having a denominator of 72.

Solution: This problem can be rewritten in the form

$$\frac{7}{8} = \frac{?}{72}$$

Now you need simply ask yourself, "By what number was 8 multiplied in order to obtain 72?" The easiest way of discovering the answer to this question is to divide 8 into 72. The quotient (9) will be the number that was multiplied by 8 to yield 72. Since the denominator was multiplied by 9, the numerator (7) will also have to be multiplied by 9. Hence, the new fraction is $\frac{63}{72}$.

Outline: $\frac{7}{8} = \frac{?}{72}$ $72 \div 8 = 9$

$\frac{7}{8} = \frac{7 \times 9}{8 \times 9} = \frac{63}{72}$

$\frac{7}{8} = \frac{63}{72}$

LEARNING EXERCISES

Change each of the following fractions to equivalent fractions by finding the numerator of the new fraction.

1. $\frac{3}{4} = \frac{?}{48}$

2. $\frac{1}{6} = \frac{?}{78}$

3. $\frac{5}{8} = \frac{?}{56}$

4. $\frac{4}{5} = \frac{?}{65}$

5. $\frac{11}{12} = \frac{?}{84}$

6. $\frac{9}{10} = \frac{?}{90}$

7. $\frac{5}{9} = \frac{?}{36}$

8. $\frac{7}{12} = \frac{?}{96}$

9. $\frac{6}{7} = \frac{?}{21}$

10. $\frac{2}{9} = \frac{?}{45}$

11. $\frac{7}{8} = \frac{?}{72}$

12. $\frac{7}{15} = \frac{?}{75}$

UNIT 3   Addition of Fractions

SECTION 1   Addition of Proper Fractions

Finding the sum of $\frac{2}{9}$ and $\frac{5}{9}$ is much the same as finding the sum of 2 apples and 5 apples. The "apples" indicate the kind of quantity to be added, and the 2 and 5 indicate how many there are of each quantity. So, too, the denominator (9) indicates the denomination of the quantities (ninths); and the numerators tell how many ninths there are in each fraction. Therefore, adding 2 ninths and 5 ninths will yield 7 ninths, or $\frac{7}{9}$, in the same manner as you would find the previous sum of 7 apples.

Difficulty arises when the denominations of the quantities are different. That is, it would not be possible to add 2 apples and 3 pears because they are different "kinds" of quantities. If, however, they were changed into the same "kind" of quantity, such as *fruit*, the sum could be expressed as 5 pieces of fruit. Similarly, fractions such as $\frac{2}{5}$ and $\frac{3}{4}$ cannot be added as they are written, for they represent two different "kinds" of quantities (fifths and fourths). If it were possible to change them into the same denomination, as with the fruit, the two fractions could be added. To accomplish this, the principle of multiplying the numerator and the denominator by the same number is applied. But, before this can be done, it is necessary to determine the smallest number for which both 5 and 4 are exact divisors. This is the number 20. The example can now be rewritten as:

$$\frac{2}{5} = \frac{?}{20}$$
$$+\frac{3}{4} = \frac{?}{20}$$

Thus, the addition of fractions depends on whether or not fractions of different denominations (in this case, fifths and fourths) can be changed to the same denomination (in this case, twentieths). You learned to do this at the time you changed fractions to higher terms. Hence, the example becomes:

$$\frac{2}{5} = \frac{8}{20}$$
$$+\frac{3}{4} = \frac{15}{20}$$
$$\frac{23}{20} = 1\frac{3}{20}$$

When the number of twentieths in each fraction (8 and 15) are added, the sum of 23 twentieths, or $\frac{23}{20}$ is obtained. In turn, this improper fraction can be changed to a mixed number by dividing 20 into 23, giving a quotient of $1\frac{3}{20}$.

The common denomination (twentieths) into which the fifths and fourths were converted is called the *common denominator*. It would have been possible to use fortieths as a common denominator, for both 5 and 4 are exact divisors of 40. Had this been done, however, the sum would have been $\frac{46}{40}$, which reduces to $\frac{23}{20}$, the answer found earlier. The smallest number of which each of the denominators is an exact divisor is called the *lowest common denominator;* in the preceding example, the lowest common denominator is 20.

Example: Find the sum of $\frac{2}{3}$, $\frac{3}{4}$, and $\frac{5}{8}$.

Solution: The smallest number for which 3, 4, and 8 are exact divisors is the number 24. Hence, the lowest common denominator is 24.

Outline:
$$\frac{2}{3} = \frac{16}{24}$$
$$\frac{3}{4} = \frac{18}{24}$$
$$+\frac{5}{8} = \frac{15}{24}$$
$$\frac{49}{24} = 2\frac{1}{24}$$

LEARNING EXERCISES

Add the following fractions.

1. $\frac{2}{5} + \frac{1}{5}$

2. $\frac{1}{8} + \frac{3}{8}$

3. $\frac{5}{12} + \frac{7}{12}$

4. $\frac{1}{8} + \frac{5}{8} + \frac{7}{8}$

5. $\frac{3}{10} + \frac{7}{10} + \frac{9}{10}$

6. $\frac{3}{16} + \frac{5}{16} + \frac{7}{16} + \frac{9}{16}$

7. $\frac{2}{3} + \frac{3}{4}$

8. $\frac{2}{5} + \frac{2}{3}$

9. $\frac{5}{9} + \frac{2}{3}$

10. $\frac{3}{8} + \frac{15}{16}$

11. $\frac{3}{4} + \frac{5}{6}$

12. $\frac{7}{8} + \frac{1}{6}$

13	14	15	16	17	18	19	20
$\frac{1}{2}$	$\frac{1}{2}$	$\frac{5}{6}$	$\frac{1}{6}$	$\frac{4}{5}$	$\frac{5}{6}$	$\frac{1}{2}$	$\frac{5}{9}$
$\frac{1}{3}$	$\frac{2}{3}$	$\frac{2}{3}$	$\frac{5}{8}$	$\frac{1}{4}$	$\frac{7}{8}$	$\frac{2}{7}$	$\frac{1}{3}$
$\frac{1}{4}$	$\frac{5}{6}$	$\frac{3}{4}$	$\frac{1}{3}$	$\frac{11}{12}$	$\frac{5}{12}$	$\frac{13}{14}$	$\frac{1}{6}$

21	22	23	24	25	26	27	28
$\frac{1}{4}$	$\frac{1}{2}$	$\frac{5}{8}$	$\frac{2}{3}$	$\frac{5}{6}$	$\frac{1}{7}$	$\frac{3}{5}$	$\frac{1}{9}$
$\frac{5}{6}$	$\frac{1}{3}$	$\frac{11}{16}$	$\frac{1}{2}$	$\frac{1}{3}$	$\frac{5}{8}$	$\frac{5}{12}$	$\frac{2}{3}$
$\frac{3}{8}$	$\frac{1}{4}$	$\frac{5}{6}$	$\frac{11}{12}$	$\frac{1}{8}$	$\frac{1}{2}$	$\frac{1}{4}$	$\frac{7}{8}$
$\frac{1}{2}$	$\frac{1}{6}$	$\frac{1}{2}$	$\frac{5}{8}$	$\frac{1}{4}$	$\frac{3}{4}$	$\frac{2}{15}$	$\frac{2}{3}$
				$\frac{11}{12}$	$\frac{2}{3}$	$\frac{5}{6}$	$\frac{7}{12}$

SECTION 2   Addition of Mixed Numbers

Addition of mixed numbers involves a combination of the addition of whole numbers and the addition of fractions. As was stated earlier, a mixed number consists of the sum of a whole number and a fraction. Hence, the problem of adding two mixed numbers is treated in sections. First the whole numbers are added; then the proper fractions are added; and, to complete the problem, the sum of these two answers is determined.

Example 1: Find the sum of $5\frac{3}{4}$ and $9\frac{7}{8}$.

Solution:

$$5\frac{3}{4} = 5\frac{6}{8}$$
$$+9\frac{7}{8} = 9\frac{7}{8}$$
$$14\frac{13}{8} = 14 + \frac{13}{8} = 14 + 1\frac{5}{8} = 15\frac{5}{8}$$

Explanation: The two proper fractions $\frac{3}{4}$ and $\frac{7}{8}$ were first changed to 8ths and then added, making a total of $\frac{13}{8}$. The sum of the whole numbers (5 and 9) is 14. But $14\frac{13}{8}$ represents $14 + \frac{13}{8}$. Since the value of the improper fraction $\frac{13}{8}$ is $1\frac{5}{8}$, when that number is added to 14, the sum will be $15\frac{5}{8}$.

Example 2: Find the sum of $17\frac{1}{2}$, $23\frac{2}{3}$, and $15\frac{5}{6}$.

Solution:

$$17\frac{1}{2} = 17\frac{3}{6}$$
$$23\frac{2}{3} = 23\frac{4}{6}$$
$$+15\frac{5}{6} = 15\frac{5}{6}$$
$$55\frac{12}{6} = 55 + \frac{12}{6} = 55 + 2 = 57$$

Explanation: Again, the whole numbers were added separately, giving a total of 55. The proper fractions were converted to sixths and combined, making a total of $\frac{12}{6}$. The value (2) of $\frac{12}{6}$ was found and added to 55, making a total of 57.

LEARNING EXERCISES

Add the following mixed numbers.

1. $5\frac{1}{4} + 4\frac{3}{4}$

2. $12\frac{2}{3} + 3\frac{4}{5}$

3. $27\frac{2}{3} + 14\frac{1}{2}$

4. $7\frac{2}{5} + 3\frac{4}{5}$

5. $14\frac{3}{4} + 12\frac{1}{2}$

6. $56\frac{3}{4} + 27\frac{5}{6}$

7. $3\frac{2}{3} + 5\frac{1}{2} + 7\frac{1}{6}$

8. $\frac{2}{3} + 12\frac{1}{2} + 7\frac{3}{4}$

9. $26\frac{5}{16} + 24\frac{7}{8} + 42\frac{3}{4}$

10. $6\frac{3}{4} + 7\frac{5}{8} + 2\frac{1}{2}$

11. $\frac{5}{6} + 6\frac{2}{3} + \frac{3}{4}$

12. $17\frac{5}{12} + 29\frac{3}{4} + 35\frac{2}{3}$

13	14	15	16
$72\frac{5}{6}$	$24\frac{1}{2}$	$46\frac{3}{4}$	$85\frac{2}{5}$
$76\frac{1}{2}$	$56\frac{2}{3}$	$27\frac{1}{2}$	$36\frac{2}{3}$
$35\frac{3}{4}$	$94\frac{1}{4}$	$54\frac{7}{8}$	$72\frac{5}{6}$
$29\frac{2}{3}$	$76\frac{11}{12}$	$68\frac{11}{12}$	$93\frac{9}{10}$

17. A yard-goods store ran a special on Orlon material. In one hour the following number of yards were purchased from 1 bolt of goods: $5\frac{1}{2}$, 8, $4\frac{1}{3}$, $7\frac{3}{4}$, $9\frac{1}{2}$, $10\frac{2}{3}$, and 6. How much material was sold from the bolt in 1 hour?

18. James Cox built a mica-top table $38\frac{1}{2}$ inches long and $17\frac{5}{8}$ inches wide. How much metal edging must he buy to go around the table?

19. Some of the showcases at a department store were decorated with paper each Christmas. How many feet of paper would be needed to decorate 5 of the showcases in the Children's Wear Department if the showcases were of the following lengths: $17\frac{1}{2}$ feet, $20\frac{1}{4}$ feet, 22 feet, $23\frac{1}{12}$ feet, $24\frac{5}{6}$ feet?

20. At the outset of each day, one of the butchers in the Meat Department of a large food store grinds a considerable supply of meat to be sold as chopped meat during the day. If the following numbers represent the number of pounds of chopped meat purchased between 10 and 11 A.M. one day, how much of the chopped-meat supply was sold during that hour? $\frac{3}{4}$, 3, $2\frac{1}{2}$, $1\frac{1}{4}$, $5\frac{1}{2}$, $2\frac{3}{16}$, $4\frac{9}{16}$, $1\frac{1}{2}$, 4.

U N I T 4 Subtraction of Fractions

In one basic principle, subtraction and addition of fractions are identical: when either operation is performed, it is necessary to

change the fractions into fractions having a common denomination
before either addition or subtraction can take place.

Example 1: Subtract $\frac{3}{5}$ from $\frac{2}{3}$.

> **Solution:** $\quad \frac{2}{3} = \frac{10}{15}$
> $$-\frac{3}{5} = \frac{9}{15}$$
> $$\overline{\phantom{-\frac{3}{5} = }\frac{1}{15}}$$

Explanation: The thirds and fifths were changed into the common
denomination fifteenths. Then, if 9 fifteenths are subtracted from 10
fifteenths, the difference will be 1 fifteenth, or $\frac{1}{15}$.

However, a number of special situations arise in the subtraction of
fractions that do not occur when fractions are added. Each of these
cases will be treated separately.

Example 2: Subtract $8\frac{5}{6}$ from 43.

> **Solution:** $\quad 43 = 42\frac{6}{6}$
> $$-8\frac{5}{6} = \ \ 8\frac{5}{6}$$
> $$\overline{\phantom{-8\frac{5}{6} = }34\frac{1}{6}}$$

Explanation: As in addition of mixed numbers, so, too, in subtraction
of mixed numbers, the whole number must be subtracted from the
whole number, and the fraction must be subtracted from the fraction.
Since 43 had no fractional part, 1 was "borrowed" from 43, making it
42; this 1 was then converted into a fraction. Although the number 1
can be changed to any number divided by itself, such as $\frac{5}{5}$, $\frac{7}{7}$, $\frac{56}{56}$, as each
of these fractions has a value of 1, in the example here it was changed to
6 sixths so that the denominator would be the same as that of the
subtrahend. From this point, the problem was completed in the same
manner as in Example 1.

Example 3: Subtract $\frac{2}{3}$ from 16.

> **Solution:** $16 \ \ = 15\frac{3}{3}$
> $$-\frac{2}{3} = \ \ \ \frac{2}{3}$$
> $$\overline{\phantom{-\frac{2}{3} = \ \ }15\frac{1}{3}}$$

Explanation: This example is very similar to Example 2. Before subtraction can take place, the whole number (16) must be changed to a
mixed number, so that the fraction $\frac{2}{3}$ can be subtracted from the fractional part of the mixed number. Borrowing 1 from 16 makes the whole
number 15. The 1 is changed to 3 thirds, so that it will be of the same
denomination as the 2 thirds. As nothing has to be subtracted from the
15, that number remains as 15. When 2 thirds are subtracted from 3
thirds, the difference is 1 third, or $\frac{1}{3}$.

Example 4: Subtract $15\frac{3}{4}$ from $22\frac{2}{3}$.

Solution:
$$22\frac{2}{3} = 22\frac{8}{12} = 21\frac{20}{12}$$
$$-15\frac{3}{4} = 15\frac{9}{12} = 15\frac{9}{12}$$
$$\overline{\phantom{-15\frac{3}{4} = 15\frac{9}{12} = }\;\; 6\frac{11}{12}}$$

Explanation: After the 2 thirds and the 3 fourths were changed to the common denomination twelfths, it was discovered that the problem cannot be completed as it stands, for 9 twelfths cannot be subtracted from 8 twelfths. Hence, 1 is borrowed from 22, making the whole number 21. The borrowed 1 is changed into 12 twelfths and added to 8 twelfths, making a sum of 20 twelfths, or $\frac{20}{12}$. The problem is then completed in the same manner as in Example 1.

LEARNING EXERCISES

Find the difference in each of the following examples.

1. $\frac{5}{7} - \frac{2}{7}$	13. $\frac{5}{8} - \frac{1}{3}$	25. $46\frac{15}{16} - 12\frac{3}{4}$
2. $\frac{9}{16} - \frac{5}{16}$	14. $\frac{1}{2} - \frac{5}{12}$	26. $51\frac{7}{8} - 50\frac{5}{6}$
3. $\frac{5}{8} - \frac{3}{8}$	15. $\frac{11}{12} - \frac{3}{8}$	27. $32\frac{1}{2} - 17\frac{2}{3}$
4. $\frac{3}{4} - \frac{1}{2}$	16. $16\frac{3}{4} - 9$	28. $46\frac{2}{3} - 23\frac{5}{6}$
5. $\frac{7}{8} - \frac{1}{4}$	17. $27\frac{5}{8} - 6$	29. $28\frac{1}{4} - 21\frac{3}{4}$
6. $\frac{9}{10} - \frac{3}{5}$	18. $18 - 5\frac{1}{2}$	30. $64\frac{5}{8} - 39\frac{5}{6}$
7. $\frac{5}{6} - \frac{5}{12}$	19. $25 - 18\frac{2}{3}$	31. $84\frac{4}{5} - 45\frac{9}{10}$
8. $\frac{2}{3} - \frac{1}{6}$	20. $21 - 15\frac{5}{6}$	32. $58\frac{3}{4} - 37\frac{2}{3}$
9. $\frac{5}{8} - \frac{3}{16}$	21. $17 - \frac{1}{3}$	33. $64\frac{5}{9} - 28\frac{5}{6}$
10. $\frac{2}{3} - \frac{1}{4}$	22. $29 - \frac{7}{8}$	34. $99\frac{1}{2} - 31\frac{3}{4}$
11. $\frac{3}{4} - \frac{2}{3}$	23. $15\frac{3}{4} - 7\frac{5}{8}$	35. $787\frac{3}{4} - 564\frac{7}{16}$
12. $\frac{5}{6} - \frac{3}{4}$	24. $32\frac{2}{3} - 19\frac{2}{5}$	36. $488\frac{3}{8} - 291\frac{5}{12}$

37. A piece of wood $26\frac{5}{16}$ inches long was cut from a board 36 inches long. How long was the piece of wood that remained?

38. While making a dress, a woman cut a piece of material $15\frac{3}{4}$ inches wide from a piece that was $42\frac{1}{2}$ inches wide. How wide was the piece of material that remained?

39. A woman purchased a $2\frac{1}{2}$-pound sirloin steak at a butcher store. On returning home, she cut out the bone and weighed it. If the weight of the bone was $\frac{9}{16}$ of a pound, how much actual meat did she purchase?

40. A carpenter had an 18-foot piece of lumber, from which he cut off two pieces. One of these pieces was $5\frac{3}{4}$ feet long; the other was $2\frac{5}{12}$ feet long. If the widths of the saw cuts are ignored, how long was the piece that remained?

41. To make a canvas awning, three pieces of material each $34\frac{3}{4}$ inches long are cut from a bolt of canvas on which 240 inches of material was originally rolled. How much canvas still remained on the bolt?

42. From a piece of broadloom carpeting 12 feet long and 9 feet wide, two strips of carpeting, each 12 feet long, were cut to be used as runners. If the strips were $2\frac{5}{16}$ feet and $3\frac{1}{4}$ feet wide, respectively, how wide was the piece of carpeting that remained?

U N I T 5   Multiplication of Fractions

SECTION 1   Multiplying a Whole Number by a Fraction

If a person bought 5 apples on each of 4 different occasions, in order to determine the total number of apples purchased, it would be necessary only to multiply the 4 by the 5, giving a product of 20 apples. The product of 4 by $\frac{5}{6}$ can be interpreted in the same manner. At the beginning of this chapter it was pointed out that the denominator of a fraction represented the "kind," or denomination, of the quantity that was being considered and that the numerator enumerated or told "how many" of these quantities there were. Hence, the fraction $\frac{5}{6}$ can be written, in terms of its meaning, as 5 sixths. Therefore, finding the product of 4 by 5 sixths is no different than finding the product of 4 by 5 apples. In one case the denomination is sixths, and in the other it is apples. Thus, 4×5 sixths equals 20 sixths. It is possible, however, to write the quantity 20 sixths as the fraction $\frac{20}{6}$. If you examine the original problem:

$$4 \times \tfrac{5}{6}$$

you will notice that the same answer ($\frac{20}{6}$) could have been obtained by multiplying the whole number (4) by the numerator (5) and then placing the product over the denominator (6). This problem can now be completed by changing the answer to the mixed number $3\frac{1}{3}$.

Outlining this example will help you discover how this product could have been found by a somewhat shorter method.

$$
\begin{array}{ccccc}
(a) & (b) & (c) & (d) & (e)
\end{array}
$$
$$
4 \times \tfrac{5}{6} = \frac{4 \times 5}{6} = \tfrac{20}{6} = \tfrac{10}{3} = 3\tfrac{1}{3}
$$

In fraction (*b*), the numerator and the denominator have a common exact divisor of 2. If this were divided into the numerator and the denominator of the fraction, the value of the fraction would not be changed. Thus:

$$\frac{\overset{2}{\cancel{4}} \times 5}{\underset{3}{\cancel{6}}} = \tfrac{1\,0}{3}$$

It is possible to arrive at the same fraction ($\tfrac{1\,0}{3}$) by dividing before multiplication takes place. This process of dividing the numerator and the denominator by the same number, as was done here, is sometimes called *cancellation*. It seems like a needless term, however, as the word that it replaces, "division," is much more meaningful.

Example 1: Multiply 15 by $\tfrac{3}{5}$.
   Solution:

$$15 \times \tfrac{3}{5} = \frac{\overset{3}{\cancel{15}} \times 3}{\underset{1}{\cancel{5}}} = \tfrac{9}{1} = 9$$

You have learned that the product of 7 × 6 is exactly the same as the product of 6 × 7. You learned this principle of interchanging the multiplicand and the multiplier when you studied one of the methods for checking the product of two numbers. This principle is now used to find the product of a fraction multiplied by a whole number. To illustrate, $\tfrac{3}{5}$ × 15 is exactly the same as 15 × $\tfrac{3}{5}$. The solution to the latter problem precedes this paragraph. The product of $\tfrac{3}{5}$ by 15 can be found in the same manner.

$$\tfrac{3}{5} \times 15 = \frac{3 \times \overset{3}{\cancel{15}}}{\underset{1}{\cancel{5}}} = \tfrac{9}{1} = 9$$

It is important to remember that the phrase "$\tfrac{3}{5}$ of 15 apples" has the same meaning as "$\tfrac{3}{5}$ × 15 apples." Should the 15 apples be separated into the 5 equal groups that are indicated by the denominator of the fraction (5), the grouping might be represented graphically as follows:

. . ./ . . ./ . . ./ . . ./ . . .

The numerator (3), in turn, indicates how many of the 5 equal groups are to be considered. Thus, the number of apples in these three groups is 9, which means that $\tfrac{3}{5}$ of 15 apples is 9 apples. This same number 9 could have been found by multiplying $\tfrac{3}{5}$ by 15. The knowledge that the word "of" indicates the operation of multiplication will be of great value to you in interpreting many of the problems that arise in business.

Example 2: Find $\frac{5}{12}$ of $18.

Solution:

$$\frac{5}{12} \times \$18 = \frac{5 \times \overset{3}{\cancel{18}}}{\underset{2}{\cancel{12}}} = \frac{15}{2} = 7\frac{1}{2}$$

LEARNING EXERCISES

Find the product in each of the following problems.

1. $18 \times \frac{2}{3}$ 6. $\frac{7}{8} \times 32$ 11. $\frac{5}{16} \times 28$ 16. $35 \times \frac{6}{7}$

2. $15 \times \frac{3}{5}$ 7. $\frac{7}{12} \times 20$ 12. $\frac{11}{12}$ of 54 17. $100 \times \frac{5}{6}$

3. $10 \times \frac{3}{4}$ 8. $20 \times \frac{2}{3}$ 13. $\frac{15}{16} \times 72$ 18. $\frac{9}{16}$ of 80

4. $14 \times \frac{5}{6}$ 9. $16 \times \frac{3}{5}$ 14. $56 \times \frac{3}{7}$ 19. $\frac{7}{8}$ of 100

5. $\frac{1}{4} \times 28$ 10. $\frac{1}{3}$ of 14 15. $86 \times \frac{3}{4}$ 20. $\frac{11}{12}$ of 100

SECTION 2   Multiplying a Whole Number by a Mixed Number

Part 1

As it is possible to change a mixed number into a fraction, to multiply a whole number by a mixed number involves no new process.

Example: Multiply 15 by $2\frac{1}{3}$.

Solution:

$$15 \times 2\frac{1}{3} = 15 \times \frac{7}{3} = \frac{\overset{5}{\cancel{15}} \times 7}{\underset{1}{\cancel{3}}} = \frac{35}{1} = 35$$

Explanation: After the mixed number $2\frac{1}{3}$ has been changed to the improper fraction $\frac{7}{3}$, the product is found in the same manner as in Section 1.

LEARNING EXERCISES

Find the product in each of the following problems.

1. $12 \times 5\frac{1}{2}$ 7. $7\frac{5}{8} \times 24$

2. $16 \times 2\frac{3}{4}$ 8. $9\frac{2}{3} \times 16$

3. $25 \times 7\frac{3}{5}$ 9. $8\frac{3}{4} \times 22$

4. $32 \times 8\frac{1}{4}$ 10. $12\frac{5}{6} \times 20$

5. $6\frac{1}{2} \times 18$ 11. $18 \times 10\frac{3}{4}$

6. $9\frac{2}{3} \times 24$ 12. $24 \times 5\frac{5}{16}$

13. Copy and complete the following sales slip.

THE BRADLEY STORE		
Quantity	Item	Amount
$4\frac{1}{2}$ yds.	Cotton @ $1.28	$xxx xx
$12\frac{1}{4}$ yds.	Cotton @ $.56	xxx xx
$5\frac{2}{3}$ yds.	Wool @ $3.75	xxx xx
$3\frac{3}{4}$ yds.	Wool @ $2.19	xxx xx
$6\frac{1}{3}$ yds.	Orlon @ $1.79	xxx xx
	Total	$xxx xx

Part 2

If a mixed number is somewhat large, it is not always advisable to change it to an improper fraction before multiplying it by a whole number. In that case, the mixed number is considered as a whole number plus a fraction, which it is; and each part is multiplied separately by the whole number. To complete the problem, the two parts are added together.

Example: Multiply 46 by $25\frac{3}{4}$.

Solution: The 46 is first multiplied by the $\frac{3}{4}$:

$$\tfrac{3}{4} \times 46 = \frac{3 \times 46}{4} = \tfrac{138}{4} = 34\tfrac{1}{2}$$

Then 46 is multiplied by the 25:

$$
\begin{array}{r}
46 \\
\times 25 \\
\hline
230 \\
92 \\
\hline
1{,}150
\end{array}
$$

The two products are then added to complete the problem:

$$
\begin{array}{r}
1{,}150 \\
+ \quad 34\tfrac{1}{2} \\
\hline
1{,}184\tfrac{1}{2}
\end{array}
$$

Instead of solving two separate problems, the usual manner of finding the product is to arrange the problem as follows:

$$
\begin{array}{r}
46 \\
\times 25\frac{3}{4} \\
\hline
4\,|\,138 \\
34\frac{1}{2} \quad \frac{3}{4}\times 46 \\
230 \quad 5\times 46 \\
92 \quad 2\times 46 \\
\hline
1{,}184\frac{1}{2}
\end{array}
$$

You will notice that 46 was multiplied by $\frac{3}{4}$ by first multiplying the 46 by 3, resulting in the number 138. This number was then divided by 4, giving a quotient of $34\frac{1}{2}$. The advantage of computing the product in this form is in the comparative compactness with which it can be written.

LEARNING EXERCISES

Find the product in each of the following problems by the method illustrated above.

1. $54 \times 16\frac{1}{3}$
2. $85 \times 19\frac{3}{5}$
3. $84 \times 26\frac{5}{6}$
4. $87 \times 32\frac{3}{4}$
5. $35\frac{2}{3} \times 76$

6. $64\frac{5}{9} \times 63$
7. $58\frac{3}{5} \times 85$
8. $160 \times 17\frac{3}{10}$
9. $186 \times 36\frac{5}{12}$
10. $228 \times 67\frac{1}{6}$

SECTION 3   Multiplying a Fraction by a Fraction

Business Transaction: George Tatum is one of four partners who own equal sections of a piece of property. In payment of a debt, Tatum gave $\frac{1}{2}$ of the $\frac{1}{4}$ that he owns to Arthur Barton. What fraction of the entire property did Arthur Barton receive?

The answer to this question can best be illustrated by the diagram below:

Section given to Mr. Barton

Mr. Tatum's Property

If each of the other three partners had divided his share of the property in half, then the picture would have been as shown below.

Section given to Mr. Barton

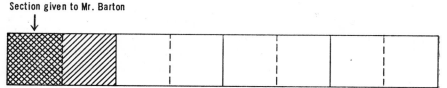

Mr. Tatum's Property

This diagram shows that the property is divided into **8** equal parts, only one of which is owned by Mr. Barton. Hence, Mr. Barton owns $\frac{1}{8}$ of the property.

The original problem could have been stated as: "Mr. Tatum gave $\frac{1}{2}$ of the $\frac{1}{4}$ to Mr. Barton. How large was this piece?" Earlier it was pointed out that the word "of" indicates the operation of multiplication; hence, $\frac{1}{2}$ of $\frac{1}{4}$ is the same as $\frac{1}{2} \times \frac{1}{4}$. As just shown, this product is $\frac{1}{8}$. Therefore,

$$\tfrac{1}{2} \times \tfrac{1}{4} = \tfrac{1}{8}$$

Examination of this equality should reveal that the product could have been found by multiplying the numerators together to obtain the numerator in the product ($1 \times 1 = 1$) and multiplying the denominators together to obtain the denominator of the product ($2 \times 4 = 8$). Therefore, the following principle can be stated:

→The product of two fractions is a fraction whose numerator is obtained by multiplying the numerators of the two fractions and whose denominator is obtained by multiplying the denominators of the two fractions.

Example 1: Multiply $\frac{2}{3}$ by $\frac{4}{5}$.
  Solution: $\dfrac{2}{3} \times \dfrac{4}{5} = \dfrac{2 \times 4}{3 \times 5} = \dfrac{8}{15}$

Example 2: Multiply $\frac{5}{6}$ by $\frac{8}{35}$.
  Solution:
$$\dfrac{5}{6} \times \dfrac{8}{35} = \dfrac{\overset{1}{\cancel{5}} \times \overset{4}{\cancel{8}}}{\underset{3}{\cancel{6}} \times \underset{7}{\cancel{35}}} = \dfrac{4}{21}$$

Explanation: In the fraction $\dfrac{5 \times 8}{6 \times 35}$, the numerator and the denominator were first divided by **2**, changing the 8 to 4 and the 6 to 3.

Then both the numerator and the denominator were divided by 5, changing the 5 to 1 and the 35 to 7. The common practice is to leave the two fractions $\frac{5}{6}$ and $\frac{8}{35}$ as two distinct fractions at the time the numerators and denominators are divided by the same number. Even then, however, they are considered to be a single fraction, so that the principle of dividing the numerator and the denominator by the same number can be applied. To illustrate, the problem could have been completed as follows:

$$\frac{\overset{1}{\cancel{5}}}{\underset{3}{\cancel{6}}} \times \frac{\overset{4}{\cancel{8}}}{\underset{7}{\cancel{35}}} = \frac{4}{21}$$

Example 3: Multiply $3\frac{1}{5}$ by $2\frac{5}{8}$.
 Solution:
$$3\frac{1}{5} \times 2\frac{5}{8} = \frac{\overset{2}{\cancel{16}}}{5} \times \frac{21}{\underset{1}{\cancel{8}}} = \frac{42}{5} = 8\frac{2}{5}$$

Explanation: Each of the mixed numbers was changed to an improper fraction, and the problem was completed by finding the product of two fractions as in Example 2.

LEARNING EXERCISES

Find the product in each of the following problems.

1. $\frac{2}{5} \times \frac{7}{9}$
2. $\frac{1}{2} \times \frac{5}{6}$
3. $\frac{3}{4} \times \frac{5}{9}$
4. $\frac{2}{3} \times \frac{7}{8}$
5. $\frac{5}{6} \times \frac{3}{4}$
6. $\frac{2}{5} \times \frac{5}{8}$
7. $\frac{1}{4}$ of $\frac{8}{9}$
8. $\frac{3}{7}$ of $\frac{14}{15}$
9. $\frac{24}{25}$ of $\frac{5}{8}$
10. $\frac{7}{16}$ of $\frac{4}{5}$

11. $1\frac{1}{2} \times 1\frac{1}{2}$
12. $2\frac{3}{4} \times 2\frac{1}{4}$
13. $2\frac{1}{2} \times 3\frac{1}{2}$
14. $1\frac{1}{4} \times 5\frac{1}{3}$
15. $4\frac{2}{3} \times 7\frac{1}{2}$
16. $6\frac{3}{4} \times 5\frac{1}{3}$
17. $10\frac{1}{2} \times 3\frac{1}{7}$
18. $5\frac{5}{6} \times 6\frac{3}{5}$
19. $1\frac{3}{8} \times 4\frac{2}{3}$
20. $3\frac{1}{16} \times 1\frac{1}{7}$

21. A woman purchased $5\frac{1}{2}$ pounds of chopped meat for a meat loaf. If the cost of the meat was 62 cents a pound, what was the total cost of the meat?

22. When James Tremont repaired his home, he bought $3\frac{3}{4}$ pounds of nails at $5\frac{1}{2}$ cents a pound. What was the total cost of the nails?

23. To complete an end table that he was making, Robert Gross bought a special piece of wood, 18 inches wide and 2 inches thick, for the top. If the cost of each foot was $1.26 and Robert needed $2\frac{1}{3}$ feet, how much did this piece of lumber cost him?

24. A tract of farm land was divided into $1\frac{3}{4}$-acre plots and sold separately to persons desiring to build their own homes. If there were 125 of these plots, how many acres were there in the original piece of farm land?

25. For the installation of an automatic clothes washer, John Higgins needed 2 pieces of $\frac{5}{8}$-inch copper tubing, each $8\frac{3}{4}$ feet long, in order to draw the hot and cold water to the washer. What was the total cost of the tubing if each foot cost $23\frac{1}{2}$ cents?

26. Mrs. Hall purchased $4\frac{1}{2}$ yards of material at 89 cents a yard and $2\frac{1}{3}$ yards of another material at $1.35 a yard to make a skirt and a blouse. What was the total cost of the material for this outfit?

27. While constructing an addition to his home, Ronald Kelly cut 5 $2\frac{1}{6}$-foot pieces of wood from a piece that was originally 24 feet long. If the widths of the cuts are ignored, how much of the original piece still remained?

28. When John Carton died, he left a will dividing his estate of $24,000 among his 3 children. If Robert received $\frac{1}{4}$ of the estate and Mary was willed $\frac{3}{8}$ of the estate, how much money was left for Betty, the third child?

29. William Cavlin owned a $\frac{2}{3}$ interest in a business valued at $75,000. If he sold $\frac{1}{6}$ of his holdings in the business, how much should he have received?

30. Daniel Lester earned $450 a month. During one month he spent $\frac{1}{4}$ of this amount for rent, $\frac{1}{5}$ for food, $\frac{1}{6}$ for clothing, $\frac{1}{8}$ for recreation, and saved the rest. How much money was allotted to each item that month?

SECTION 4   **(Optional) Multiplying a Mixed Number by a Mixed Number**

If somewhat large mixed numbers are to be multiplied, it is usually preferable to treat them as the sum of a whole number and a proper fraction rather than change them to improper fractions as was done in Section 3. The whole number and the fractional part of the multiplicand are each multiplied separately by the whole number and the fraction of the multiplier. To complete the problem, the separate products are added. This is merely an extension of the principle that you have been using whenever you have multiplied two numbers, such as **35** and **27**. Thus:

$$\begin{array}{r} 35 \\ \times 27 \\ \hline 245 \\ 70 \\ \hline 945 \end{array}$$

First, the **35** was multiplied by the **7**; then the **35** was multiplied by the **2**. To complete the problem, the two products were added.

If the numbers to be multiplied had been $35\frac{1}{2}$ and $27\frac{3}{4}$, it would have been necessary to continue the process, taking the fractions into consideration. Thus:

$$\begin{array}{r} 35\frac{1}{2} \\ \times 27\frac{3}{4} \\ \hline \end{array}$$

First, the $\frac{1}{2}$ is multiplied by the $\frac{3}{4}$, giving $\frac{3}{8}$.

Then, the **35** is multiplied by the $\frac{3}{4}$, giving $\frac{105}{4}$, or $26\frac{1}{4}$. Since the $35\frac{1}{2}$ has now been multiplied by the fraction in the multiplier, the next step is to multiply the $35\frac{1}{2}$ by the whole number in the multiplier.

The $\frac{1}{2}$ is first multiplied by the **27**, giving $13\frac{1}{2}$. Then, the **35** is multiplied by the **27**, giving **945**. To complete the problem, all four products are added:

$$\frac{3}{8} + 26\frac{1}{4} + 13\frac{1}{2} + 945$$

making a total of $985\frac{1}{8}$.

For convenience, the problem is usually condensed to the following form:

$$\begin{array}{rl} 35\frac{1}{2} & \\ \times 27\frac{3}{4} & \\ \hline \frac{3}{8} & \quad \frac{3}{4} \times \frac{1}{2} \\ 26\frac{1}{4} & \quad \frac{3}{4} \times 35 \\ 13\frac{1}{2} & \quad 27 \times \frac{1}{2} \\ +945 & \quad 27 \times 35 \\ \hline 985\frac{1}{8} & \end{array}$$

Note that the **35** and the $\frac{1}{2}$ are multiplied by the $\frac{3}{4}$. Then the **35** and the $\frac{1}{2}$ are multiplied by the **27**.

LEARNING EXERCISES

Find the product in each of the following problems.

1. $16\frac{1}{2} \times 12\frac{1}{4}$	**6.** $84\frac{3}{4} \times 42\frac{2}{3}$	**11.** $156\frac{2}{3} \times 126\frac{1}{2}$
2. $15\frac{2}{3} \times 24\frac{3}{5}$	**7.** $25\frac{2}{3} \times 24\frac{1}{2}$	**12.** $235\frac{3}{4} \times 164\frac{3}{5}$
3. $30\frac{2}{5} \times 25\frac{3}{10}$	**8.** $35\frac{3}{4} \times 21\frac{1}{3}$	**13.** $124\frac{1}{2} \times 253\frac{1}{5}$
4. $24\frac{3}{4} \times 48\frac{1}{3}$	**9.** $72\frac{2}{3} \times 57\frac{5}{6}$	**14.** $346\frac{1}{6} \times 184\frac{3}{4}$
5. $68\frac{5}{6} \times 54\frac{3}{4}$	**10.** $124\frac{5}{8} \times 240\frac{1}{4}$	**15.** $275\frac{3}{8} \times 175\frac{2}{3}$

16. What is the cost of $4\frac{1}{2}$ pounds of candy at $89\frac{1}{2}$ cents a pound?

17. Mrs. Kemp purchased $12\frac{3}{4}$ pounds of cookies at $64\frac{1}{2}$ cents a pound. What was the cost of the cookies?

18. In repairing the shingles on his home, Mr. Wells purchased $5\frac{1}{2}$ pounds of nails at $14\frac{1}{2}$ cents a pound. What was the cost of the nails?

19. If potatoes were selling for 39 cents for a 5-pound bag, how much would Mrs. Griffin have to pay for a bag that weighed $7\frac{1}{2}$ pounds?

20. What is the cost of $10\frac{3}{4}$ pounds of grapes that sell at 8 pounds for a dollar?

SECTION 5   Finding the Product of Three or More Fractions

In this course you will learn how to determine the interest on a debt when the money has been borrowed for a fraction of a year. You will also learn how to determine the discount on a purchase if the buyer is granted, not one, but two or more successive discounts. Both these problems involve an understanding of the method of finding the product of three or more fractions.

Just as the product of three or more whole numbers is found by multiplying the first by the second, and this answer by the third number, so, too, the product of three fractions is determined in the same manner. Thus, the product of $\frac{2}{3} \times \frac{9}{10} \times \frac{5}{6}$ can be found by multiplying the first fraction by the second and this answer by the third.

$$(a) \qquad \frac{\overset{1}{\cancel{2}}}{\underset{1}{\cancel{3}}} \times \frac{\overset{3}{\cancel{9}}}{\underset{5}{\cancel{10}}} = \tfrac{3}{5}$$

Then: $\qquad (b) \qquad \frac{\overset{1}{\cancel{3}}}{\underset{1}{\cancel{3}}} \times \frac{\overset{1}{\cancel{5}}}{\underset{2}{\cancel{6}}} = \tfrac{1}{2}$

Since the product ($\frac{3}{5}$) that was determined in Step (a) was not altered when it was rewritten in Step (b), there seems to be little need for rewriting it. Thus, the product of the three fractions could have been found as follows:

$$\frac{\overset{1}{\cancel{2}}}{\underset{1}{\cancel{3}}} \times \frac{\overset{\overset{1}{\cancel{3}}}{\cancel{9}}}{\underset{\underset{1}{\cancel{5}}}{\cancel{10}}} \times \frac{\overset{1}{\cancel{5}}}{\underset{2}{\cancel{6}}} = \tfrac{1}{2}$$

Notice that what was formerly Step (*a*)—the numbers that are enclosed within the box—has now been combined with Step (*b*). This procedure eliminates the need for treating this problem in two distinct steps.

As the product of three numbers is not altered by changing the order in which the numbers are multiplied—that is, 2 × 3 × 4 is the same as 2 × 4 × 3—it would have been possible to have multiplied $\frac{2}{3} \times \frac{9}{10} \times \frac{5}{6}$ in any order desired. This fact, in turn, implies that division of numerators and denominators by the same number can be done in any order desired.

To illustrate: Find the product of 72 by $\frac{8}{9}$ by $\frac{3}{4}$.

   Solution:

$$\overset{8}{\underset{1}{7\!\!\!/2}} \times \overset{2}{\underset{1}{\frac{8\!\!\!/}{9\!\!\!/}}} \times \frac{3}{4\!\!\!/} = 48$$

Explanation: There was no requirement that the 8 in the second fraction be divided by 4; the 8 over the 72 could have been selected just as well. Similarly, rather than divide 9 into 9 and 9 into 72, the same product could have been obtained if 3 had been divided into the numerator of the third fraction and 3 into the denominator of the second fraction. The choice for the order in which division takes place rests in the hands of the person doing the problem; no matter what order is selected, the product will always be the same.

LEARNING EXERCISES

Find the product in each of the following problems.

1. $\frac{2}{3} \times \frac{3}{4} \times \frac{5}{6}$
2. $\frac{1}{2} \times \frac{9}{10} \times \frac{2}{3}$
3. $\frac{1}{2} \times \frac{9}{16} \times \frac{8}{9}$
4. $\frac{3}{8} \times \frac{5}{6} \times \frac{4}{15}$
5. $18 \times \frac{2}{3} \times \frac{5}{6}$
6. $\frac{7}{8} \times \frac{1}{2} \times 48$
7. $\frac{3}{5} \times 45 \times \frac{2}{27}$

8. $\$54 \times \frac{5}{9} \times \frac{2}{3}$
9. $\$100 \times \frac{4}{5} \times \frac{3}{4}$
10. $\$350 \times \frac{6}{100} \times \frac{60}{360}$
11. $\frac{1}{6} \times \frac{2}{5} \times 100$
12. $\frac{3}{8} \times \frac{2}{3} \times 100$
13. $2\frac{1}{2} \times 3\frac{1}{4} \times 16$
14. $5\frac{1}{3} \times 24 \times 4\frac{3}{4}$

15. A man inherited $3,600. He invested $\frac{2}{3}$ of this amount. If $\frac{1}{2}$ of his investment was in stocks, how much money did he use for this stock purchase?

16. Mrs. Elliott purchased 5 dozen oranges. She kept $\frac{4}{5}$ of the oranges for herself. Of these, $\frac{1}{8}$ were bad and had to be thrown away. How many oranges did Mrs. Elliott throw away?

17. If 6 men worked 6 hours at 1.92\frac{1}{2}$ an hour, what were the total wages paid for the work?

18. Mr. Johnson purchased 250 tulip bulbs for his garden. He planted $\frac{2}{5}$ of this number at the rear of the house. He planted the remainder in his front flower beds. If $\frac{4}{25}$ of those planted in front of the house were distributed around the bird bath, how many were planted in this area?

19. Mr. Edwards purchased a house for $24,000. He paid $\frac{3}{8}$ of this amount in cash and took out a mortgage for the amount that he still owed. If his father had given him $\frac{3}{4}$ of the cash payment, how much money would Mr. Edwards have received from his father?

20. George Tyson borrowed $3,600 to purchase a car. If he had waited a year to pay off the debt, the charge for borrowing the money would have been $\frac{1}{20}$ of the amount borrowed. The debt, however, was paid off at the end of $\frac{3}{4}$ of the year. What charge did Tyson have to pay for borrowing the $3,600?

U N I T 6 Division of Fractions

If a number is divided by 1, the quotient will be the same as the original number. This implies that any number can be written as a fraction where 1 is the denominator of that fraction. Thus, the number 6 is the same as $\frac{6}{1}$; $15 = \frac{15}{1}$; $125 = \frac{125}{1}$. The same is true for any other number. This principle is employed in learning how one fraction can be divided by another.

The answer to the problem "5 divided by 6" can be written in the form of a fraction, $\frac{5}{6}$. The same answer could have been found if the 6 had been expressed as $\frac{6}{1}$ and the problem rewritten as:

$$5 \div 6 = 5 \div \tfrac{6}{1}$$

Now, if the positions of the 1 and the 6 are interchanged and the operation changed to multiplication, the result would be:

$$5 \times \tfrac{1}{6} = \tfrac{5}{6}$$

This answer $(\frac{5}{6})$ is the same as the one found before.

Similarly, the problem "$5 \div \frac{2}{3}$" can be written as

$$\frac{5}{\frac{2}{3}}$$

You have already learned that, if the numerator and the denominator of a fraction are multiplied by the same number, the value of the fraction is not altered. Applying this rule to the fraction

$$\frac{5}{\frac{2}{3}}$$

it is possible to multiply the numerator and the denominator by 3 in the following manner:

$$\frac{3 \times 5}{\overset{1}{\cancel{3}} \times \frac{2}{\cancel{3}}_{1}} = \frac{15}{2}$$

Hence, $5 \div \frac{2}{3} = \frac{15}{2}$. The same quotient, however, could have been found if the positions of the 2 and 3 had been interchanged and the operation changed to multiplication.

Thus: $5 \div \frac{2}{3} = 5 \times \frac{3}{2} = \frac{15}{2}$

On the basis of these two problems, the following principle can be stated:

→In the division of any number by a fraction, if the positions of the numerator and the denominator of the divisor (the fraction) are interchanged, the operation will change from division to multiplication and the problem can be completed by the methods learned in Unit 5 on the multiplication of fractions.

The process of interchanging the positions of the numerator and the denominator of a fraction is called *inverting the fraction.*

Example 1: Divide $\frac{3}{4}$ by $\frac{7}{8}$.
 Solution:
$$\frac{3}{4} \div \frac{7}{8} = \frac{3}{4} \times \frac{\overset{2}{\cancel{8}}}{7}_{1} = \frac{6}{7}$$

Explanation: The divisor ($\frac{7}{8}$) was inverted, changing it to $\frac{8}{7}$, and the operation was changed from division to multiplication. From this point, the problem was completed according to the methods learned in Unit 5.

Example 2: Divide $7\frac{1}{2}$ by 5.
 Solution:
$$7\frac{1}{2} \div 5 = \frac{15}{2} \div \frac{5}{1} = \frac{\overset{3}{\cancel{15}}}{2} \times \frac{1}{\cancel{5}}_{1} = \frac{3}{2} = 1\frac{1}{2}$$

Explanation: The mixed number $(7\frac{1}{2})$ was changed to the improper fraction $(\frac{15}{2})$, and the whole number (5) was written in the form of a fraction $(\frac{5}{1})$. The problem was completed in the same manner as in Example 1.

Example 3: Divide $26\frac{2}{3}$ by $3\frac{1}{3}$.
  Solution:
$$26\tfrac{2}{3} \div 3\tfrac{1}{3} = \tfrac{80}{3} \div \tfrac{10}{3} = \tfrac{\cancel{80}^{8}}{\cancel{3}_{1}} \times \tfrac{\cancel{3}^{1}}{\cancel{10}_{1}} = \tfrac{8}{1} = 8$$

Explanation: Each of the mixed numbers was changed to a fraction, making the problem similar to Example 1.

LEARNING EXERCISES

Find the quotient in each of the following problems.

1. $\frac{5}{6} \div \frac{2}{3}$	15. $30 \div \frac{3}{10}$	28. $3\frac{1}{2} \div 14$
2. $\frac{7}{8} \div \frac{3}{16}$	16. $28 \div \frac{7}{8}$	29. $5\frac{1}{4} \div 3$
3. $\frac{1}{2} \div \frac{1}{4}$	17. $15 \div \frac{1}{2}$	30. $15\frac{3}{4} \div 9$
4. $\frac{2}{3} \div \frac{1}{9}$	18. $32 \div \frac{6}{7}$	31. $24\frac{2}{3} \div 5$
5. $\frac{5}{6} \div \frac{5}{12}$	19. $100 \div \frac{4}{5}$	32. $2\frac{1}{2} \div \frac{5}{6}$
6. $\frac{3}{16} \div \frac{5}{8}$	20. $120 \div \frac{5}{6}$	33. $3\frac{1}{5} \div \frac{2}{5}$
7. $\frac{4}{5} \div \frac{3}{10}$	21. $\frac{3}{4} \div 4$	34. $6\frac{2}{3} \div \frac{2}{3}$
8. $\frac{3}{8} \div \frac{5}{16}$	22. $\frac{5}{6} \div 8$	35. $10\frac{4}{5} \div \frac{8}{9}$
9. $\frac{3}{4} \div \frac{1}{2}$	23. $\frac{7}{8} \div 14$	36. $15\frac{1}{3} \div \frac{4}{5}$
10. $\frac{9}{16} \div \frac{3}{8}$	24. $\frac{2}{3} \div 6$	37. $8\frac{2}{3} \div 6\frac{1}{2}$
11. $\frac{3}{5} \div \frac{3}{5}$	25. $\frac{15}{16} \div 3$	38. $12\frac{3}{4} \div 7\frac{1}{2}$
12. $\frac{7}{12} \div \frac{3}{4}$	26. $\frac{5}{12} \div 2$	39. $24\frac{2}{3} \div 16\frac{3}{4}$
13. $14 \div \frac{2}{7}$	27. $\frac{1}{2} \div 5$	40. $64\frac{7}{8} \div 32\frac{2}{3}$
14. $24 \div \frac{2}{3}$		

41. A carpenter cut a piece of lumber 24 feet long into sections, each $2\frac{2}{3}$ feet in length. If the widths of the saw cuts are ignored, into how many sections was the entire piece of lumber cut?

42. A clothing-store merchant purchased wire hangers on which to hang his merchandise. How many hangers could he buy for $5 if each hanger cost $2\frac{1}{2}$ cents?

43. A tract of land containing 240 acres was divided into plots of ground $\frac{3}{4}$ of an acre in size, in order to develop the land for a housing project. If the land needed for roads that are to run through the development are ignored, how many plots will there be in this project?

44. The Truddy Sweet Shoppe advertised a special on summer candy. A 2½-pound box of candy was reduced to $1.95. At this rate, what would be the cost of 1 pound of this candy?

45. William was sent to the store to buy as many pounds of a certain type of nail as he could for 50 cents. At the store he learned that 1 pound of these nails cost 9½ cents. How many pounds could he buy for the 50 cents?

✓**46.** A 7¾-ounce can of salmon was bought in the Grocery Department of a market for 53 cents. At this rate, what was the cost per ounce?

✓ **47.** Two different, but comparable, brands of canned tuna fish were sold in a food store. If the price of a 7½-ounce can of one brand was 37 cents and an 8¼-ounce can of the other brand sold for 42 cents, which was the better buy?

48. One of the items packaged and frozen by the Freeze-Wel Corporation was cultivated blueberries. The corporation purchased the blueberries in wooden pint containers, washed and processed them, and then repackaged them in plastic containers holding ⅔ pint of blueberries each.

a. If there was no waste, how many plastic containers would be filled by 4,000 pints of berries?

b. If the normal loss through spoilage was ⅛ of the quantity purchased, then how many plastic containers would be filled by a purchase of 4,000 pints of berries?

49. Joseph Nunes is an employee of the radio-clock division of the Triden Radio Corporation. The operation he performs on each instrument takes ¾ of an hour. How many instruments can he process in a work week of 5 days if each workday is 7½ hours long?

50. A manufacturer of children's dresses purchased 15 bolts of the same print of cotton material, each bolt containing 35 yards. From these he planned to make children's dresses of the same style. If, including waste, he found that he needed 2⅓ yards of material for each dress, how many dresses would he be able to cut from the 15 bolts?

UNIT **7**   **Aliquot Parts of $1**

SECTION 1   **Computing Aliquot Parts of $1**

Businessmen frequently use a convenient and simple device for finding quickly the cost of merchandise that they are selling in large quantities. As an illustration, consider the invoice shown on page 105.

INVOICE				
Springdale Automotive Supplies				
Terms: Net Cash			Date: 5/17/--	
		Customer: K. L. Clinton		
Quantity	Description	Unit Price	Amount	
84	Arm-rest covers	50¢	$ 42	00
240	Taillight bulbs	25¢	60	00
		Total	$ 102	00

You recall that, in order to find the numbers in the Amount column, it is necessary to multiply the number of items purchased by the cost of each item. Hence, to find the cost of the 84 arm-rest covers, 84 must be multiplied by 50 cents. Instead of multiplying as you have been taught, the businessman will think of 50 cents as being $\frac{1}{2}$ of a dollar and then multiply 84 by $\$\frac{1}{2}$. The advantage of this can be seen below:

$$84 \times \$\tfrac{1}{2} = \frac{\$84}{2} = \$42$$

As multiplying 84 by 1 does not change the value of 84, the problem becomes one of simply dividing 84 by 2, giving a quotient of 42. As it is much easier to divide a number by 2 than to multiply it by 50, most people in such situations prefer to consider 50 cents as $\frac{1}{2}$ of a dollar.

In the same manner, to find the cost of the 240 taillight bulbs, the 25 cents is considered as $\frac{1}{4}$ of a dollar. This, in turn, will mean that 240 must be multiplied by $\$\frac{1}{4}$. Multiplying 240 by $\frac{1}{4}$, however, is the same as dividing the number by 4.

$$240 \times \$\tfrac{1}{4} = \frac{\$240}{4} = \$60$$

Hence, the $60 in the Amount column was found by dividing $240 by 4.

These two special situations that you have just examined would apply equally well to certain unit prices other than 25 cents and 50 cents. The simplicity with which the Amount in the illustration can be found depends on the fact that both 25 cents and 50 cents are exact divisors of 100 cents, which is merely another way of writing $1. Whenever one number divides into another, giving a whole number as a quotient, the first number is called an *aliquot part* of the second number. The second number is called the *base* with reference to the first number.

To illustrate: 3 is an aliquot part of 15, since 3 will divide into 15, giving a whole number as the quotient. In this situation, 15 would be known as the *base*.

In the same manner, 8 is an aliquot part of 56, since it is an exact divisor of 56. Here, 56 is the base. The mere fact that one number is an aliquot part of another number does little in simplifying the computation of the cost of merchandise. This method is a very valuable tool, however, if the number happens to be an aliquot part of $1 (100 cents). When this occurs, the total cost of the merchandise can readily be found, as in the invoice shown at the beginning of this section. Only aliquot parts of the base $1 will be studied in the work that follows.

It is not only important to know that a number is an aliquot part of $1—that is, an exact divisor of 100 cents—but also it is necessary to know *what* aliquot part of $1 the number happens to be. The phrase "what aliquot part of $1" means "what fractional part of $1 is the number." Is it $\frac{1}{5}$ of a dollar or $\frac{1}{8}$, $\frac{1}{10}$, $\frac{1}{15}$? For the illustration, 25 cents and 50 cents were selected because we daily think of these amounts as being $\frac{1}{4}$ of a dollar and $\frac{1}{2}$ of a dollar. But how were these fractions determined? The method used to obtain these fractions is shown below:

$$(1) \qquad (2) \qquad\qquad (3) \qquad\qquad (4)$$

$$25¢ = \frac{25¢}{100¢} \times 100¢ = \tfrac{1}{4} \times 100¢ = \tfrac{1}{4} \text{ of } \$1, \text{ or } \$\tfrac{1}{4}$$

Explanation: Step 1 is equal to Step 2 because multiplying 25 cents by 100 cents and then dividing it by 100 cents will not change its value. Step 3 was obtained by reducing the fraction $\frac{25}{100}$ to lowest terms. In Step 4, the 100 cents was changed to $1, and the multiplication sign was replaced by the word "of." (You learned on page 91 of this chapter that the word "of" indicates the operation of multiplication.)

To change 50 cents to $\frac{1}{2}$ of $1, the same procedure is used:

$$50¢ = \frac{50¢}{100¢} \times 100¢ = \tfrac{1}{2} \times 100¢ = \tfrac{1}{2} \text{ of } \$1, \text{ or } \$\tfrac{1}{2}$$

Unlike 25 cents and 50 cents, some aliquot parts of $1 are not whole numbers. To find *what* aliquot part of $1 they are involves an additional step.

Example: $16\frac{2}{3}$ cents is what aliquot part of $1?
Solution:

$$16\tfrac{2}{3}¢ = \frac{16\tfrac{2}{3}¢}{100¢} \times 100¢ = \tfrac{1}{6} \times 100¢ = \tfrac{1}{6} \text{ of } \$1, \text{ or } \$\tfrac{1}{6}$$

Explanation: In order to reduce the fraction $\dfrac{16\frac{2}{3}\cancel{c}}{100\cancel{c}}$ to $\frac{1}{6}$, it was necessary to remember that a fraction is an indication of division. Hence, the fraction $\dfrac{16\frac{2}{3}\cancel{c}}{100\cancel{c}}$ can be written as:

$$16\tfrac{2}{3}\cancel{c} \div 100\cancel{c} = \dfrac{\overset{1}{\cancel{50}}}{3} \times \dfrac{1}{\underset{2}{\cancel{100}}} = \tfrac{1}{6}$$

The mixed number $16\frac{2}{3}$ was changed to the improper fraction $\frac{50}{3}$, and the divisor 100 was inverted in accordance with the method taught for the division of fractions.

LEARNING EXERCISES

Find what aliquot part of $1 each of the following amounts represents. Show the details of your work in arriving at each result.

1. 2¢	6. $7\frac{1}{7}$¢	11. $6\frac{2}{3}$¢
2. 5¢	7. $12\frac{1}{2}$¢	12. $3\frac{1}{3}$¢
3. 10¢	8. $8\frac{1}{3}$¢	13. $2\frac{1}{2}$¢
4. 20¢	9. $6\frac{1}{4}$¢	14. $2\frac{2}{9}$¢
5. 4¢	10. $11\frac{1}{9}$¢	15. $1\frac{2}{3}$¢

SECTION 2   Application of Aliquot Parts to Business Transactions

In Section 1 of this unit, an invoice was completed by the use of the fact that 50 cents and 25 cents are aliquot parts of $1. There are many numbers that are aliquot parts of $1. Only a few, however, are of value as an aid in computation. As an example, $2\frac{2}{9}$ cents is an aliquot part of $1, since it is an exact divisor of 100 cents. As the cost of an article would probably never be $2\frac{2}{9}$ cents, it seems hardly worth the effort to memorize that $2\frac{2}{9}$ is $\frac{1}{45}$ of $1. The few that do occur frequently in business are given in the table below. These numbers should be committed to memory.

IMPORTANT ALIQUOT PARTS OF $1

Amount	$6\frac{1}{4}$¢	$8\frac{1}{3}$¢	10¢	$12\frac{1}{2}$¢	$16\frac{2}{3}$¢	20¢	25¢	$33\frac{1}{3}$¢	50¢
Part of $1	$\$\frac{1}{16}$	$\$\frac{1}{12}$	$\$\frac{1}{10}$	$\$\frac{1}{8}$	$\$\frac{1}{6}$	$\$\frac{1}{5}$	$\$\frac{1}{4}$	$\$\frac{1}{3}$	$\$\frac{1}{2}$

Example: Find the cost of 232 pounds of waste fat at $12\frac{1}{2}$ cents a pound.

Solution: Cost $= 232 \times 12\frac{1}{2}$¢
$= 232 \times \$\frac{1}{8}$
$= \$29$

LEARNING EXERCISES

Oral: At sight, give the cost of each of the following purchases.

1. 20 lbs. @ 25¢	7. 42 pcs. @ $16\frac{2}{3}$¢	13. 64 yds. @ $6\frac{1}{4}$¢
2. 60 lbs. @ 50¢	8. 48 pcs. @ $8\frac{1}{3}$¢	14. 120 yds. @ $8\frac{1}{3}$¢
3. 40 lbs. @ 20¢	9. 86 pcs. @ 50¢	15. 540 yds. @ $16\frac{2}{3}$¢
4. 24 lbs. @ $12\frac{1}{2}$¢	10. 36 pcs. @ 25¢	16. 240 yds. @ 25¢
5. 16 lbs. @ $6\frac{1}{4}$¢	11. 27 pcs. @ $33\frac{1}{3}$¢	17. 210 yds. @ $33\frac{1}{3}$¢
6. 35 lbs. @ 20¢	12. 160 pcs. @ $12\frac{1}{2}$¢	18. 620 yds. @ 50¢

Written: Find the total cost of each of the following groups of purchases. Show in parentheses after each price what aliquot part of $1 that price is.

1	2	3
236 lbs. @ 25¢	372 pcs. @ $8\frac{1}{3}$¢	2,670 yds. @ 10¢
574 lbs. @ 50¢	576 pcs. @ $33\frac{1}{3}$¢	3,652 yds. @ 50¢
145 lbs. @ 20¢	272 pcs. @ $6\frac{1}{4}$¢	6,475 yds. @ 20¢
470 lbs. @ 10¢	184 pcs. @ $12\frac{1}{2}$¢	1,671 yds. @ $33\frac{1}{3}$¢

4	5	6
3,648 art. @ $12\frac{1}{2}$¢	378 qts. @ 25¢	✓170 qts. @ $8\frac{1}{3}$¢
2,754 art. @ $16\frac{2}{3}$¢	271 qts. @ 50¢	235 qts. @ $6\frac{1}{4}$¢
4,768 art. @ 25¢	468 qts. @ 20¢	578 qts. @ $33\frac{1}{3}$¢
4,635 art. @ 20¢	472 qts. @ 10¢	439 qts. @ $16\frac{2}{3}$¢
5,232 art. @ $6\frac{1}{4}$¢	292 qts. @ $12\frac{1}{2}$¢	843 qts. @ 25¢

SECTION 3   Computing Multiples of Aliquot Parts of $1

The value of using aliquot parts as a short cut in computation can be extended to numbers that are multiples of aliquot parts of $1. A number is said to be a *multiple* of a second number if the first number can be obtained by multiplying the second number by a whole number. Thus, the numbers 8, 16, 24, and 32 are all multiples of 8, since each of them can be obtained by multiplying 8 by a whole number. Similarly, $\frac{5}{12}$ is a multiple of $\frac{1}{12}$, since it can be obtained by multiplying $\frac{1}{12}$ by the whole number 5. The tendency in business is to call aliquot parts of $1 and numbers that are multiples of aliquot parts of $1 by the same name. Both are known as *aliquot parts of $1*. Although $37\frac{1}{2}$ cents does not divide into 100 cents an exact number of times, it is still referred to as an aliquot part of $1 because it is a multiple of an aliquot part of

$1. $37\frac{1}{2}$ cents is 3 times $12\frac{1}{2}$ cents. Since $12\frac{1}{2}$ cents is an aliquot part of $1, then $37\frac{1}{2}$ cents is also considered to be an aliquot part of $1. In keeping with this trend, the term *aliquot parts* as used in this book will mean both aliquot parts and multiples of aliquot parts.

The method used to find *what* aliquot part of $1 a number is equal to is exactly the same as that shown in Section 1 of this unit.

Example 1: 40 cents is what aliquot part of $1?
   Solution:

$$40¢ = \frac{40¢}{100¢} \times 100¢ = \tfrac{2}{5} \times 100¢ = \tfrac{2}{5} \text{ of } \$1, \text{ or } \$\tfrac{2}{5}$$

Example 2: $87\frac{1}{2}$ cents is what aliquot part of $1?
   Solution:

$$87\tfrac{1}{2}¢ = \frac{87\tfrac{1}{2}¢}{100¢} \times 100¢ = \tfrac{7}{8} \times 100¢ = \$\tfrac{7}{8}$$

The fraction $\dfrac{87\tfrac{1}{2}¢}{100¢}$ was simplified as follows:

$$\frac{87\tfrac{1}{2}¢}{100¢} = 87\tfrac{1}{2}¢ \div 100¢ = \frac{\overset{7}{\cancel{175}}}{2} \times \frac{1}{\underset{4}{\cancel{100}}} = \tfrac{7}{8}$$

LEARNING EXERCISES

Find what aliquot part of $1 each of the following amounts represents. Show the details of your work in arriving at each result.

1. 30¢	9. $41\frac{2}{3}$¢	17. $81\frac{1}{4}$¢
2. 60¢	10. $58\frac{1}{3}$¢	18. $93\frac{3}{4}$¢
3. 80¢	11. $83\frac{1}{3}$¢	19. $7\frac{1}{2}$¢
4. 75¢	12. $91\frac{2}{3}$¢	20. $68\frac{3}{4}$¢
5. 90¢	13. $18\frac{3}{4}$¢	21. $8\frac{1}{3}$¢
6. 70¢	14. $31\frac{1}{4}$¢	22. $62\frac{1}{2}$¢
7. $66\frac{2}{3}$¢	15. $43\frac{3}{4}$¢	23. $13\frac{1}{3}$¢
8. $37\frac{1}{2}$¢	16. $56\frac{1}{4}$¢	24. $28\frac{4}{7}$¢

SECTION 4   Application of Multiples of Aliquot Parts of $1

As with the aliquot parts of $1, not all multiples of aliquot parts of $1 are important to remember. Because many occur infrequently in business transactions, only comparatively few need be committed to memory. Those that you should memorize are listed in the accompanying table.

IMPORTANT ALIQUOT PARTS OF $1
(Including Multiples of Aliquot Parts)

Halves Amount	50¢														
Part of $1	$\frac{1}{2}$														
Thirds Amount	33$\frac{1}{3}$¢	66$\frac{2}{3}$¢													
Part of $1	$\frac{1}{3}$	$\frac{2}{3}$													
Fourths Amount	25¢	50¢	75¢												
Part of $1	$\frac{1}{4}$	$\frac{2}{4}$ ($\frac{1}{2}$)	$\frac{3}{4}$												
Fifths Amount	20¢	40¢	60¢	80¢											
Part of $1	$\frac{1}{5}$	$\frac{2}{5}$	$\frac{3}{5}$	$\frac{4}{5}$											
Sixths Amount	16$\frac{2}{3}$¢	33$\frac{1}{3}$¢	50¢	66$\frac{2}{3}$¢	83$\frac{1}{3}$¢										
Part of $1	$\frac{1}{6}$	$\frac{2}{6}$ ($\frac{1}{3}$)	$\frac{3}{6}$ ($\frac{1}{2}$)	$\frac{4}{6}$ ($\frac{2}{3}$)	$\frac{5}{6}$										
Eighths Amount	12$\frac{1}{2}$¢	25¢	37$\frac{1}{2}$¢	50¢	62$\frac{1}{2}$¢	75¢	87$\frac{1}{2}$¢								
Part of $1	$\frac{1}{8}$	$\frac{2}{8}$ ($\frac{1}{4}$)	$\frac{3}{8}$	$\frac{4}{8}$ ($\frac{1}{2}$)	$\frac{5}{8}$	$\frac{6}{8}$ ($\frac{3}{4}$)	$\frac{7}{8}$								
Tenths Amount	10¢	20¢	30¢	40¢	50¢	60¢	70¢	80¢	90¢						
Part of $1	$\frac{1}{10}$	$\frac{2}{10}$ ($\frac{1}{5}$)	$\frac{3}{10}$	$\frac{4}{10}$ ($\frac{2}{5}$)	$\frac{5}{10}$ ($\frac{1}{2}$)	$\frac{6}{10}$ ($\frac{3}{5}$)	$\frac{7}{10}$	$\frac{8}{10}$ ($\frac{4}{5}$)	$\frac{9}{10}$						
Twelfths Amount	8$\frac{1}{3}$¢	16$\frac{2}{3}$¢	25¢	33$\frac{1}{3}$¢	41$\frac{2}{3}$¢	50¢	58$\frac{1}{3}$¢	66$\frac{2}{3}$¢	75¢	83$\frac{1}{3}$¢	91$\frac{2}{3}$¢				
Part of $1	$\frac{1}{12}$	$\frac{2}{12}$ ($\frac{1}{6}$)	$\frac{3}{12}$ ($\frac{1}{4}$)	$\frac{4}{12}$ ($\frac{1}{3}$)	$\frac{5}{12}$	$\frac{6}{12}$ ($\frac{1}{2}$)	$\frac{7}{12}$	$\frac{8}{12}$ ($\frac{2}{3}$)	$\frac{9}{12}$ ($\frac{3}{4}$)	$\frac{10}{12}$ ($\frac{5}{6}$)	$\frac{11}{12}$				
Sixteenths Amount	6$\frac{1}{4}$¢	12$\frac{1}{2}$¢	18$\frac{3}{4}$¢	25¢	31$\frac{1}{4}$¢	37$\frac{1}{2}$¢	43$\frac{3}{4}$¢	50¢	56$\frac{1}{4}$¢	62$\frac{1}{2}$¢	68$\frac{3}{4}$¢	75¢	81$\frac{1}{4}$¢	87$\frac{1}{2}$¢	93$\frac{3}{4}$¢
Part of $1	$\frac{1}{16}$	$\frac{2}{16}$ ($\frac{1}{8}$)	$\frac{3}{16}$	$\frac{4}{16}$ ($\frac{1}{4}$)	$\frac{5}{16}$	$\frac{6}{16}$ ($\frac{3}{8}$)	$\frac{7}{16}$	$\frac{8}{16}$ ($\frac{1}{2}$)	$\frac{9}{16}$	$\frac{10}{16}$ ($\frac{5}{8}$)	$\frac{11}{16}$	$\frac{12}{16}$ ($\frac{3}{4}$)	$\frac{13}{16}$	$\frac{14}{16}$ ($\frac{7}{8}$)	$\frac{15}{16}$

You will notice that certain aliquot parts are repeated in the table. One of these is 50 cents. It is represented as $\$\frac{1}{2}$, $\$\frac{2}{4}$, $\$\frac{3}{6}$, $\$\frac{4}{8}$, $\$\frac{5}{10}$, $\$\frac{6}{12}$, and $\$\frac{8}{16}$. Whenever a repetition like this occurs, it is advisable to memorize only the fraction that is reduced to lowest terms. The other fractions are included in the table for completeness.

Business Transaction 1: A merchant purchased for resale 48 gallons of cider at $62\frac{1}{2}$ cents a gallon. What is the total cost of the cider?

Solution: Cost = $48 \times 62\frac{1}{2}¢$ $(62\frac{1}{2}¢ = \frac{5}{8}$ of \$1$)$

$$= \overset{6}{\cancel{48}} \times \$\frac{5}{\underset{1}{\cancel{8}}} = \frac{\$30}{1}$$

$$= \$30$$

Business Transaction 2: A merchant purchased 2 bolts of yard goods containing the following amounts of material:

608 yards at $87\frac{1}{2}$ cents

864 yards at $83\frac{1}{3}$ cents

Find the total cost of the merchandise.

Solution:

608 yds. @ $87\frac{1}{2}¢$ ($\$\frac{7}{8}$) = \$532 $(\overset{76}{\cancel{608}} \times \frac{7}{\underset{1}{\cancel{8}}} = \$532)$

864 yds. @ $83\frac{1}{3}¢$ ($\$\frac{5}{6}$) =   720 $(\overset{144}{\cancel{864}} \times \frac{5}{\underset{1}{\cancel{6}}} = \$720)$

Total Cost = \$1,252

LEARNING EXERCISES

Oral: At sight, give the cost of each of the following purchases.

1. 24 qts. @ $66\frac{2}{3}¢$	7. 16 lbs. @ 75¢	13. 45 doz. @ 80¢
2. 30 qts. @ 30¢	8. 94 lbs. @ 50¢	14. 90 doz. @ $16\frac{2}{3}¢$
3. 35 qts. @ 40¢	9. 48 lbs. @ $37\frac{1}{2}¢$	15. 32 doz. @ 75¢
4. 40 qts. @ $62\frac{1}{2}¢$	10. 45 lbs. @ 60¢	16. 36 doz. @ $66\frac{2}{3}¢$
5. 24 qts. @ $83\frac{1}{3}¢$	11. 75 lbs. @ $33\frac{1}{3}¢$	17. 90 doz. @ 70¢
6. 96 qts. @ $12\frac{1}{2}¢$	12. 42 lbs. @ $83\frac{1}{3}¢$	18. 56 doz. @ $62\frac{1}{2}¢$

Written: Find the total cost of each of the following groups of purchases. Show in parentheses after each price what aliquot part of \$1 that price is.

1	2	3
232 lbs. @ 25¢	125 yds. @ 80¢	264 qts. @ $8\frac{1}{3}¢$
428 lbs. @ 75¢	230 yds. @ 90¢	750 qts. @ $16\frac{2}{3}¢$
542 lbs. @ 50¢	140 yds. @ 70¢	594 qts. @ $33\frac{1}{3}¢$
375 lbs. @ 40¢	296 yds. @ 75¢	325 qts. @ 60¢
195 lbs. @ 20¢	730 yds. @ 40¢	328 qts. @ $12\frac{1}{2}¢$

4

750 art. @ 66⅔¢
102 art. @ 83⅓¢
264 art. @ 33⅓¢
246 art. @ 16⅔¢
848 art. @ 50¢

5

390 bu. @ 60¢
550 bu. @ 80¢
236 bu. @ 75¢
380 bu. @ 30¢
396 bu. @ 25¢

6

132 doz. @ 8⅓¢
372 doz. @ 33⅓¢
630 doz. @ 16⅔¢
576 doz. @ 12½¢
375 doz. @ 40¢

7

240 hrs. @ 6¼¢
184 hrs. @ 37½¢
256 hrs. @ 62½¢
424 hrs. @ 87½¢
396 hrs. @ 50¢

8

312 gals. @ 83⅓¢
297 gals. @ 66⅔¢
288 gals. @ 87½¢
416 gals. @ 62½¢
636 gals. @ 75¢

9

368 pts. @ 37½¢
252 pts. @ 8⅓¢
582 pts. @ 16⅔¢
675 pts. @ 60¢
438 pts. @ 83⅓¢

10

427 pcs. @ 50¢
368 pcs. @ 40¢
287 pcs. @ 75¢
469 pcs. @ 25¢

11

325 qts. @ 66⅔¢
350 qts. @ 37½¢
358 qts. @ 33⅓¢
274 qts. @ 80¢

12

425 yds. @ 12½¢
450 yds. @ 62½¢
386 yds. @ 83⅓¢
324 yds. @ 87½¢

UNIT **8**   **Measuring Your Skill in Using Fractions**

TIMED DRILL A   10 Minutes

Find the sum in each of the following problems.

1. $\frac{1}{4} + \frac{1}{6}$

2. $\frac{2}{3} + \frac{4}{5}$

3. $\frac{5}{6} + \frac{7}{8}$

4. $\frac{7}{15} + \frac{2}{3} + \frac{4}{5}$

5. $\frac{5}{8} + \frac{3}{4} + \frac{1}{2} + \frac{11}{16}$

6. $\frac{3}{4} + \frac{1}{3} + \frac{5}{6} + \frac{1}{2}$

7. $4\frac{7}{9} + 5\frac{4}{9}$

8. $9\frac{5}{8} + 7\frac{3}{4}$

9. $17\frac{2}{3} + 46\frac{8}{9}$

10. $24\frac{3}{4} + 39\frac{5}{6}$

11. $26\frac{5}{6} + 31\frac{3}{8}$

12. $7\frac{3}{4} + 5\frac{7}{8} + 9\frac{2}{3}$

TIMED DRILL B   8 Minutes

Find the difference in each of the following problems.

1. $\frac{11}{12} - \frac{5}{12}$

2. $\frac{5}{8} - \frac{3}{8}$

3. $\frac{1}{4} - \frac{1}{8}$

4. $\frac{4}{5} - \frac{1}{3}$

5. $\frac{5}{6} - \frac{5}{9}$

6. $9\frac{8}{9} - 8\frac{4}{9}$

7. $5\frac{5}{6} - 2\frac{2}{3}$

8. $8\frac{1}{3} - 7\frac{1}{4}$

9. $16\frac{1}{2} - 14\frac{1}{4}$

10. $47\frac{7}{8} - 29\frac{3}{4}$

11. $36 - 7\frac{1}{6}$

12. $54 - 43\frac{2}{3}$

13. $35 - 12\frac{3}{8}$

14. $78\frac{1}{2} - 16\frac{2}{3}$

15. $80\frac{1}{4} - 19\frac{5}{6}$

16. $56\frac{1}{2} - 41\frac{4}{5}$

TIMED DRILL C   10 Minutes

Find the product in each of the following problems.

1. $\frac{7}{8} \times \frac{5}{6}$

2. $\frac{5}{12} \times \frac{7}{15}$

3. $\frac{3}{8} \times \frac{4}{9}$

4. $\frac{1}{5} \times 20$

5. $\frac{3}{4} \times 8$

6. $\frac{5}{6} \times 14$

7. $35 \times \frac{4}{5}$

8. $\frac{3}{8} \times 2\frac{2}{3}$

9. $\frac{7}{12} \times 15\frac{3}{4}$

10. $18\frac{2}{3} \times \frac{3}{4}$

11. $36\frac{5}{6} \times \frac{5}{9}$

12. $36 \times 2\frac{1}{2}$

13. $27 \times 8\frac{5}{6}$

14. $7\frac{1}{4} \times 6$

15. $3\frac{3}{5} \times 5\frac{5}{6}$

16. $12\frac{3}{4} \times 16\frac{2}{3}$

TIMED DRILL D   12 Minutes

Find the quotient in each of the following problems.

1. $\frac{1}{2} \div \frac{1}{2}$

2. $\frac{3}{4} \div \frac{1}{4}$

3. $\frac{8}{9} \div \frac{2}{3}$

4. $\frac{6}{7} \div \frac{5}{8}$

5. $12 \div \frac{3}{4}$

6. $32 \div \frac{6}{7}$

7. $\frac{3}{4} \div 12$

8. $\frac{8}{9} \div 18$

9. $\frac{5}{6} \div 8\frac{1}{3}$

10. $\frac{7}{8} \div 6\frac{1}{4}$

11. $5\frac{5}{12} \div \frac{5}{6}$

12. $46\frac{3}{8} \div \frac{7}{9}$

13. $36 \div 4\frac{1}{2}$

14. $42 \div 2\frac{2}{5}$

15. $59 \div 8\frac{3}{4}$

16. $15\frac{3}{4} \div 9$

17. $81\frac{2}{3} \div 24$

18. $8\frac{1}{3} \div 6\frac{1}{4}$

19. $24\frac{3}{5} \div 10\frac{1}{8}$

20. $17\frac{5}{6} \div 13\frac{6}{7}$

TIMED DRILL E   15 Minutes

Find the total cost of each of the following groups of purchases. The time spent in copying the problems is not to be included in the 15 minutes.

1	2	3
42 yds. @ 50¢	35 lbs. @ 40¢	48 bu. @ 33$\frac{1}{3}$¢
24 yds. @ 25¢	32 lbs. @ 6$\frac{1}{4}$¢	39 bu. @ 66$\frac{2}{3}$¢
32 yds. @ 12$\frac{1}{2}$¢	36 lbs. @ 8$\frac{1}{3}$¢	75 bu. @ 60¢
30 yds. @ 16$\frac{2}{3}$¢	45 lbs. @ 20¢	36 bu. @ 75¢

4	5	6
40 qts. @ 37$\frac{1}{2}$¢	120 qts. @ 87$\frac{1}{2}$¢	35 pts. @ 50¢
32 qts. @ 62$\frac{1}{2}$¢	240 qts. @ 83$\frac{1}{3}$¢	56 pts. @ 30¢
54 qts. @ 16$\frac{2}{3}$¢	135 qts. @ 66$\frac{2}{3}$¢	41 pts. @ 25¢
25 qts. @ 80¢	184 qts. @ 75¢	44 pts. @ 37$\frac{1}{2}$¢

TIMED DRILL F   40 Minutes

Problems to Be Solved

1. A merchant sold an electric calculator for $852, making a profit equal to $\frac{1}{6}$ of the selling price. What was the amount of his profit?

2. An estate was divided into 150 plots for a housing development. If each plot was 1$\frac{3}{4}$ acres in size, what was the total number of acres in the estate? (Ignore the areas needed for roadways.)

3. From a piece of material 25$\frac{1}{2}$ yards long, 12$\frac{2}{3}$ yards was cut off. How long was the material that remained?

4. Salaries were so scaled in a certain office that a stenographer received $\frac{4}{5}$ of the salary of a bookkeeper. If the weekly salary of a bookkeeper was $97.75, what was the yearly salary of the stenographer?

5. A man earned $6,900 a year. He spent $\frac{1}{4}$ for taxes, $\frac{1}{5}$ for food, $\frac{1}{3}$ for shelter, $\frac{1}{20}$ for clothes, and $\frac{1}{10}$ for recreation. How much money remained?

6. A vegetable dealer purchased 240 quarts of strawberries at 37$\frac{1}{2}$ cents a quart. What is the total cost of this purchase?

7. Of a man's earnings of $6,200 a year, $\frac{1}{5}$ was used to pay off a

mortgage. If $\frac{1}{20}$ of the mortgage money was for the charge on the debt, how much money did the man pay each year on this charge?

8. During a 5-day week, a man worked the following number of hours each day: $7\frac{1}{2}$, $6\frac{3}{4}$, $8\frac{1}{4}$, $7\frac{1}{3}$, $7\frac{2}{3}$. How many hours did he work during that week?

9. A plot of land containing $487\frac{1}{2}$ acres was broken up into smaller plots, each $3\frac{1}{4}$ acres in size. How many of these smaller plots were formed?

10. Of the 450 freshmen entering a certain high school, only $\frac{2}{3}$ will graduate 4 years later. Of those that graduate, $\frac{1}{6}$ will receive at least one A mark at some time during these 4 years. How many of the graduating seniors will receive an A mark?

CAR OWNERSHIP
percent of families

61%
Own One Car

Own No Car
30%

9%

Own Two or More Cars

Graphic Syndicate

6

Improving Skills in Using Percentage

PREVIEW

To the surprise and delight of his family, Anthony Finn drove into his driveway one spring day with a shiny, new convertible roadster. Although this purchase had reduced his savings by $3,450, Mr. Finn felt that he would be amply repaid by the pleasure that he and his family would derive from the use of the car. His spirits, however, were somewhat dampened the following day when he showed the car to a neighbor.

Quite innocently, the neighbor had remarked that the value of the car was 20% less that day than it had been the previous day. In fact, Mr. Finn was even more surprised to learn that the moment he drove the car away from the automobile agency it was no longer worth the $3,450 he had paid for it. His neighbor also pointed out that the value of the car would continue to fall each year by a certain per cent until at the end of 7 or 8 years it would simply have a "junk value" of about $50. Anthony Finn's curiosity was now thoroughly aroused. He usually kept a car three years before "trading it in" for a new model. Because of the per cent by which the value of the car decreased each year, would he gain financially if he should purchase a new car every two years rather than every three?

For Class Discussion

1. Why should the new car be worth 20% less at the moment Mr. Finn took possession of it?

2. What is the name for the process whereby property decreases in value each succeeding year?

3. What is meant by the "junk value" of a piece of property?

4. If Mr. Finn should drive his car less than 5,000 miles during the next 8 years, would it then be worth only the junk value, just like cars that might be driven many more miles? Justify your answer.

5. How would you interpret the statement that the car decreased 20% in value?

6. Can you name three places where you have seen the term *per cent* used?

Terms You Should Know

Probably the most frequently used and least understood term in business is the word *per cent*. The word *per cent*, like the word *century*, comes directly from the Latin word *centum*, meaning "a hundred," from which they are both derived. Both imply the number 100. The word *century*, as you know, means "100 years"; the word *per cent* means *per* 100 or *parts of 100*. To illustrate, 20 per cent is interpreted as 20 parts out of 100 parts.

As used here, the term carries with it the same meaning that you learned for a fraction. In reality, it is a fraction; 20 per cent can be and frequently is written in its fractional form, $\frac{20}{100}$. From your study of the preceding chapter on fractions, you should recall that the denominator 100 indicates the denomination of the quantity—in this case, hundredths—and that the numerator indicates how many hundredths there are. In this case, there are 20. Hence, 20 per cent and $\frac{20}{100}$ are merely two different ways of writing *exactly* the same thing—20 parts out of 100 equal parts.

A per cent value is also interpreted as a *rate*, just as you interpret a speed of 40 miles an hour as a rate. That phrase means that 40 miles of distance were traveled in every hour of time. So, too, 40 per cent represents 40 units out of every 100 units. In one situation the term "40 per cent" may mean that 40 pupils out of each 100 pupils in a certain school are boys. In a second situation, "40 per cent" may mean that $40 out of every $100 in the cost of building a house is spent on material.

The base 100 that is used for comparison is selected simply because it is more convenient to use than any other number. In computing batting averages or team standings in baseball, the base 1,000 was found to be the most convenient number to use. These batting averages are not per cent values, as such values are commonly called, for they express a rate per 1,000 rather than per 100. (*Per cent* implies a base of 100.) Thus, a batting average of 285 means that, out of every 1,000 times the player came to bat, he would manage to get to base 285 times. Batting averages, the speed of an automobile, and the cost of electricity and gas are but a few of the many things that are expressed as rate values. The most frequently used rate, however, is the rate that is based on 100 units and that you have come to know as *per cent*.

There is yet a third way of writing "20 per cent," and that is with the familiar symbol %. Thus, 20 per cent can be abbreviated into the form 20%. Doubtless this symbol was once written as the number 100, for the symbol % itself contains the number 1 with the two zeros. With the passing of years, people became more and more careless of the manner in which the per cent sign was written until now there seems to be little connection between the number 100 and the sign %. In summary, 20 per cent, 20%, and $\frac{20}{100}$ all bear the same meaning.

Concerning This Chapter

It would be impossible in any one chapter or any one book to teach all the various business transactions in which per cent is applied. In this chapter you will study a few of the more general applications of this term; in later chapters, you will find many, many more situations where the word *per cent* is used.

There would be little value in trying to present applications of per cent in the field of business unless you were thoroughly familiar with the variety of forms in which it is possible to express a per cent value. Hence, the early units of this chapter will be devoted to acquainting you with the methods of changing a number written in per cent form to its fractional equivalent or its decimal equivalent. In turn, methods for changing fractions and decimals to per cent values will also be explained. Before leaving these early units, you will be asked to commit to memory a few common per cent values with their fractional equivalents because of their frequent use in business.

UNIT 1

Representing a Per Cent Value in Equivalent Forms

SECTION 1   Representing a Per Cent Value As a Fraction

To say that a merchant's profit was 50% of the cost of his merchandise would give very little information. It would simply suggest that, for each $100 that an article cost him, he was able to gain a profit of $50. But, unless the actual cost of his merchandise was known, it would be impossible to determine whether his profit was $5, $5,000, or $50,000. As an illustration, if the cost of the merchandise was $60,000, then, since his profit was $50 on every $100 of the cost, his gain would be $\frac{1}{2}$ of the $60,000, or a profit of $30,000.

Far too much time would be wasted if a merchant had to interpret a profit of 50% in the manner that was just shown. That is, a 50% profit means $50 out of every $100 of the cost; this in turn means $1 out of every $2 of the cost; and, finally, this merely means that, after the article is sold, the merchant's profit will be one-half the amount he paid for it. Unless he realizes that 50% of the cost is the same as $\frac{1}{2}$ of the cost, it would be unlikely that he would be able to determine the actual profit. Hence, it is important to know the relation between a per cent value and a fractional value. Therefore, before you are shown how to analyze business transactions involving a knowledge of per cent, it is advisable to learn how a per cent value can be changed to its equivalent fractional form (a fraction having a value equal to the per cent value).

Example 1: Find a fraction equivalent to 40%.

   Solution: $40\% = \frac{40}{100} = \frac{2}{5}$

   Explanation: Since 40% means 40 parts of 100 parts, or the fraction $\frac{40}{100}$, the per cent value was written in the fractional form. This fraction ($\frac{40}{100}$) was then reduced to lowest terms by dividing the numerator and denominator by 20.

Example 2: Change $7\frac{1}{2}\%$ to a fraction.

   Solution:

$$7\frac{1}{2}\% = \frac{7\frac{1}{2}}{100} = 7\frac{1}{2} \div 100 = \frac{\overset{3}{\cancel{15}}}{2} \times \frac{1}{\underset{20}{\cancel{100}}} = \frac{3}{40}$$

   Explanation: Since $7\frac{1}{2}\%$ means $7\frac{1}{2}$ parts of 100 parts, $7\frac{1}{2}\%$ was written as $\frac{7\frac{1}{2}}{100}$. This fraction, however, indicates the operation of division. Therefore, it was rewritten as $7\frac{1}{2} \div 100$. The example was completed by the methods that were taught in Chapter 5 on the division of fractions.

Example 3: Express 225% as a fraction.

   Solution: $225\% = \frac{225}{100} = \frac{9}{4}$

   Explanation: Again, from its meaning, 225% was written as $\frac{225}{100}$. The fraction was reduced to lowest terms by dividing the numerator and the denominator by 25. You will find that, in dealing with per cent equivalents, it is frequently better to leave an improper fraction in that form rather than change it to a mixed number.

   Per cent values that are greater than 100%, such as the per cent value in Example 3, are interpreted in a manner similar to that presented in the following illustration.

Illustration: The enrollment at Eagleston College last year was 225% of what it was in 1948.

   Explanation: This means that, for each 100 students enrolled in the college in 1948, last year there were 225 students.

LEARNING EXERCISES

A. Change each of the following per cent values to a fraction. Show all your work, as in the examples above.

1. 30%	11. 325%	21. 37$\frac{1}{2}$%
2. 70%	12. 175%	22. 66$\frac{2}{3}$%
3. 60%	13. 12$\frac{1}{2}$%	23. 62$\frac{1}{2}$%
4. 80%	14. 6$\frac{1}{4}$%	24. 83$\frac{1}{3}$%
5. 35%	15. 8$\frac{1}{3}$%	25. 41$\frac{2}{3}$%
6. 45%	16. 16$\frac{2}{3}$%	26. 58$\frac{1}{3}$%
7. 25%	17. 33$\frac{1}{3}$%	27. 91$\frac{2}{3}$%
8. 75%	18. 2$\frac{1}{2}$%	28. 81$\frac{1}{4}$%
9. 200%	19. 3$\frac{1}{3}$%	29. 68$\frac{3}{4}$%
10. 150%	20. 7$\frac{1}{7}$%	30. 93$\frac{3}{4}$%

B. Interpret each of the following statements without using the term *per cent.*

1. *5%* of the employees of the Great Lakes Manufacturing Company are tardy for work each day.

2. On the day of a blizzard, *75%* of the students of the Alexander School were absent.

3. The Friendly Notion Company makes a profit of 40% of the cost of its merchandise.

4. The Quality Furniture Mart makes a profit of 30% of the selling price of its merchandise.

5. During a recent year, 64% of the money spent by the United States Government went toward defense.

6. 26% of the men over 65 who are still working are employed as farmers.

7. In 1900 only 1% of all students were in college; whereas, in a recent year, 7% of those attending school were in college.

8. During a recent year the earnings of production workers in the petroleum-refining industry were 142% of what they had been 8 years before.

9. During a recent year the United States exported to Africa 162% of what it exported in 1950.

10. In one of our states student "dropouts" from high schools are about 28%.

SECTION 2   Representing a Per Cent Value As a Decimal

Part 1

Frequently, there is greater advantage in expressing a per cent value as a decimal rather than as a fraction. This is particularly true with values such as 47% or 62.3%. If these values were changed to fractions, they would be cumbersome to use in business computations. Therefore, a knowledge of how to change per cent values to equivalent decimal values is important to you.

Example 1: Change 62.3% to a decimal.

Solution: $62.3\% = \frac{62.3}{100} = .623$

Explanation: In terms of the meaning of *per cent*, 62.3% was written as the fraction $\frac{62.3}{100}$. On page 68 in Chapter 4 you learned that the quickest way of dividing a number by 100 was to move the decimal point two places to the left. Hence, the decimal point was moved from the left of the 3 to the left of the 6.

Example 2: Change $17\frac{1}{2}\%$ to a decimal.

Solution: $17\frac{1}{2}\% = 17.5\% = \frac{17.5}{100} = .175$

Explanation: By the method learned in Chapter 5, the decimal value of $\frac{1}{2}$ was found to be .5; then, $17\frac{1}{2}\%$ was rewritten as 17.5%; and the example was completed in the same manner as in Examples 1 and 2.

In business, the mixed numbers that are most frequently used as per cent values are those where the fractional part of the mixed number is either $\frac{1}{4}$, $\frac{1}{3}$, $\frac{1}{2}$, $\frac{2}{3}$, or $\frac{3}{4}$; for example, $6\frac{1}{4}\%$, $33\frac{1}{3}\%$, $12\frac{1}{2}\%$, $66\frac{2}{3}\%$, and $4\frac{3}{4}\%$. If the fractional part of the mixed number is either $\frac{1}{4}$, $\frac{1}{2}$, or $\frac{3}{4}$, it is advisable to convert these fractions immediately to their decimal values. Thus, the per cent value $5\frac{1}{4}\%$ should be rewritten at once as 5.25%; similarly, $4\frac{3}{4}\%$ should be expressed as 4.75% before it is changed to a decimal.

LEARNING EXERCISES

Change each of the following per cents to decimals. Show all your work, as in the examples above.

1. 57%	6. 350%	11. 4%	16. $3\frac{1}{4}\%$
2. 83%	7. 56.4%	12. 3.2%	17. .5%
3. 14%	8. 42.3%	13. 2.5%	18. $\frac{3}{4}\%$
4. 127%	9. 123.5%	14. $23\frac{1}{2}\%$	19. .01%
5. 200%	10. 8%	15. $14\frac{3}{4}\%$	20. 100%

Part 2

If the per cent values in the two examples in Part 1 of this section and their decimal equivalents were arranged beneath one another, a definite relationship between the per cent and decimal values would become apparent. Thus,

Per Cent Value		Decimal Value
62.3%	$= \frac{62.3}{100} =$	.623
47.%	$= \frac{47.}{100} =$	.47
17.5%	$= \frac{17.5}{100} =$	.175
4.75%	$= \frac{4.75}{100} =$	.0475

Note that the digits in the decimal value are exactly the same as those in the corresponding per cent value. The only change that has taken place is in the position of the decimal point. In each case, the decimal point has been moved two places to the left as the number changed from the per cent value to its decimal value. This change, however, should have been apparent at the very outset, for, by definition, a per cent value is merely a fraction whose denominator is 100. Since a fraction is one means of representing division, then every per cent value is an indication that division by 100 should take place. And, as noted earlier, the fastest way of dividing by 100 is to move the decimal point two places to the left in the dividend. Hence, the following principle can be formulated:

→To change a per cent value to a decimal, move the decimal point two places to the left and drop the % sign.

Example 1: Change 14% to a decimal.
  Solution: 14% = .14.

Explanation: The decimal point was moved from its position at the right of the 4 to its new position at the left of the 1.

Example 2: Change $3\frac{1}{4}$% to a decimal.
  Solution: $3\frac{1}{4}$% = 3.25% = .0325
Explanation: The fraction $\frac{1}{4}$ was changed to its decimal value .25, and the $3\frac{1}{4}$% was rewritten as 3.25%. Before moving the decimal point two places to the left of its present position, a zero had to be written to the left of the 3.

LEARNING EXERCISES

Change each of the following per cent values to decimals. Show all your work, as in the examples above.

1. 48%	**11.** 6%	**21.** .3%	**31.** 825%
2. 67%	**12.** 2%	**22.** .7%	**32.** .032%
3. 19%	**13.** 1%	**23.** .04%	**33.** $12\frac{1}{2}\%$
4. 135%	**14.** 10%	**24.** $\frac{1}{2}\%$	**34.** $6\frac{1}{4}\%$
5. 300%	**15.** 4.3%	**25.** $\frac{3}{4}\%$	**35.** $5\frac{3}{4}\%$
6. 250%	**16.** 5.7%	**26.** $\frac{1}{4}\%$	**36.** 142%
7. 42.7%	**17.** $16\frac{1}{2}\%$	**27.** 100%	**37.** 3.9%
8. 39.4%	**18.** $17\frac{1}{4}\%$	**28.** .15%	**38.** .02%
9. 156.8%	**19.** $26\frac{3}{4}\%$	**29.** 15%	**39.** 6%
10. 32.67%	**20.** $4\frac{1}{2}\%$	**30.** 8.2%	**40.** 2,000%

UNIT **2** **Representing Decimals and Fractions As Per Cent Values**

In examining his books at the end of the year, Roy Norton, the owner of an electrical-appliance store, found that he had sold $225,471.36 worth of merchandise during the year. Of this amount, after paying all his bills, he had $29,374.14 left as profit. In order to determine the trend of his business, he compared these figures with corresponding figures for the prior year. During the preceding year he had sold $204,362.83 worth of merchandise, making a profit of $28,965.54. It was apparent to Mr. Norton that the amount of his sales had increased. He was uncertain, however, as to whether the profits had increased in proportion to the increased sales.

Comparisons such as these are made every day in the world of business. Before Roy Norton or any other businessman can interpret such figures, they must be simplified. Thus, the information in the preceding paragraph may be expressed as follows:

Last Year's Rate of Profit: $29,374.14 out of $225,471.36

Previous Year's Rate of Profit: $28,965.54 out of $204,362.83

As the numbers now stand, a comparison is impossible, since the rate of profit is based on two different quantities: $225,471.36 and $204,362.83. Needless to say, the numbers are extremely awkward to use. If both profit rates were expressed as so many dollars per $100 of the sales—for example, $13.50 per $100 and $14.10 per $100—then a mere examination of the two numbers $13.50 and $14.10 would immediately indicate in which year the rate of profit was the greater. Secondly, the amount $100 is easier to understand and to interpret than are the eight-figure numbers that were used before. Also, if the base is $100, then these values can be written as per cent values, for that is exactly the meaning you have learned for a per cent value—so many units per 100 units. It can thus be seen that, unless businessmen are able to convert information such as that just noted into per cent form, it would be difficult for them to make any comparisons.

SECTION 1   Representing a Decimal As a Per Cent Value

Part 1

Example 1: What per cent value is equivalent to the decimal .36?
   Solution: $.36 = \frac{.36}{1} = \frac{36}{100} = 36\%$
   Explanation: On page 101 of Chapter 5 you learned that any number can be written as a fraction by using 1 as the denominator of that fraction. Hence, .36 was expressed as $\frac{.36}{1}$. Since *per cent* means so many parts per 100 parts—*not* per 1 part—it is necessary to change the denominator from 1 to 100. Again, in Chapter 5 the principle was stated that, if the numerator and the denominator of a fraction are multiplied by the same number, the value of the fraction will not be altered. Therefore, the denominator (1) was changed to 100 by multiplying it (1) by 100. In turn, .36 was also multiplied by 100, making it 36. (The fastest way to multiply a number by 100 is to move the decimal point two places to the right.) But the fraction $\frac{36}{100}$ means 36 parts of 100, which can be written as 36%.

Example 2: Change $1\frac{3}{4}$ to a per cent value.
   Solution: $1\frac{3}{4} = 1.75 = \frac{1.75}{1} = \frac{175}{100} = 175\%$
   Explanation: The fraction $\frac{3}{4}$ was changed to its decimal value .75; therefore, the number $1\frac{3}{4}$ could be written as 1.75. From this point, the problem was completed as was the previous example.

LEARNING EXERCISES

Change each of the following numbers to its equivalent per cent form. Show all your work, as in the examples on page 125.

1. .43	6. .07	11. .005	16. $2\frac{1}{2}$
2. .96	7. .02	12. .045	17. $3\frac{1}{4}$
3. .17	8. .325	13. .0275	18. $5\frac{3}{4}$
4. 1.34	9. .304	14. 2.5	19. 1
5. 2.08	10. .056	15. 3	20. .01

Part 2

If the decimal values and the per cent values in the examples in Part 1 of this section were arranged beneath one another, the relationship between a decimal and its per cent value would become apparent. Thus:

Decimal Value					Per Cent Value
.36	$=$	$\frac{36}{100}$	$=$		36%
.06	$=$	$\frac{6}{100}$	$=$		6%
1.75	$=$	$\frac{175}{100}$	$=$		175%

Note that the digits in the decimal and the digits in the corresponding per cent value are exactly the same. The numbers differ only in the position of the decimal point. In each of the per cent values the decimal point is really two places farther to the right than it had been in its decimal value. This is as it should be, for, in order to place each of the decimals over 100, each decimal had to be multiplied by 100 so as not to change its value. Multiplying a number by 100 implies moving the decimal point two places to the right. Therefore, the following principle can be stated:

→To change a decimal value to a per cent value, move the decimal point two places to the right and insert a per cent sign.

Example 1: Change .09 to a per cent value.

   Solution: .09 $=$ 9%

Explanation: The decimal point was actually moved two places to the right and the per cent sign was added.

Example 2: Change $2\frac{3}{4}$ to a per cent value.

   Solution: $2\frac{3}{4} = 2.75 = 275\%$

Explanation: The fraction $\frac{3}{4}$ was changed to the decimal .75, and the number $2\frac{3}{4}$ was rewritten as **2.75**. To change this decimal to a per cent, the decimal point was moved two places to the right.

LEARNING EXERCISES

Change each of the following numbers to its per cent value.

1. .46	9. .0354	17. 2	25. 1.06
2. .62	10. .05	18. 1	26. .03
3. .14	11. .03	19. $2\frac{1}{2}$	27. .0275
4. 1.67	12. .01	20. $3\frac{1}{4}$	28. $.02\frac{1}{2}$
5. 3.50	13. .1	21. $1\frac{3}{4}$	29. $.05\frac{3}{4}$
6. .436	14. .062	22. $\frac{3}{4}$	30. $.18\frac{1}{4}$
7. .374	15. .059	23. $\frac{1}{2}$	31. $1.04\frac{1}{2}$
8. 1.784	16. 3	24. .0062	32. 15

SECTION 2 **Representing a Fraction As a Per Cent Value**

Since the decimal value of any fraction can readily be determined, changing a fraction to a per cent is no different from changing a decimal to a per cent. After finding the decimal value of the fraction by dividing the denominator into the numerator, simply move the decimal point two places to the right as you learned to do in Section 1 of this unit.

Example 1: Change $\frac{7}{8}$ to a per cent value.
  Solution:

$$\frac{7}{8} = .87\frac{1}{2} = 87\frac{1}{2}\% \qquad 8\overline{)7.00} \rightarrow .87\frac{1}{2}$$

Explanation: The decimal value of $\frac{7}{8}$ was found to be a $.87\frac{1}{2}$. The example was then completed in the manner taught in Section 1 of this unit.

Example 2: Change $1\frac{2}{3}$ to a per cent value.

Solution: $1\frac{2}{3} = \frac{5}{3} = 1.66\frac{2}{3} = 166\frac{2}{3}\% \qquad 3\overline{)5.00} \rightarrow 1.66\frac{2}{3}$

Explanation: The mixed number $1\frac{2}{3}$ was first changed to the fraction $\frac{5}{3}$. Then the work was completed as in Example 1. Note in Examples 1 and 2 the division was "carried out" to only two digits after the decimal point. This was done in this way because, in changing a decimal to a per cent, the decimal point is moved only two places to the right. Hence, no further division is needed.

LEARNING EXERCISES

Change each of the following fractions and mixed numbers to per cent values.

1. $\frac{1}{6}$	11. $\frac{3}{8}$	21. $\frac{19}{100}$	31. $2\frac{7}{8}$
2. $\frac{5}{8}$	12. $\frac{5}{6}$	22. $\frac{23}{100}$	32. $1\frac{3}{16}$
3. $\frac{5}{12}$	13. $\frac{1}{4}$	23. $\frac{17}{50}$	33. $4\frac{1}{2}$
4. $\frac{7}{16}$	14. $\frac{9}{16}$	24. $\frac{49}{50}$	34. $3\frac{2}{7}$
5. $\frac{3}{5}$	15. $\frac{1}{12}$	25. $\frac{3}{25}$	35. $1\frac{9}{45}$
6. $\frac{2}{3}$	16. $\frac{5}{16}$	26. $\frac{18}{25}$	36. $\frac{17}{53}$
7. $\frac{3}{4}$	17. $\frac{3}{7}$	27. $\frac{31}{25}$	37. $\frac{85}{248}$
8. $\frac{4}{5}$	18. $\frac{7}{8}$	28. $2\frac{2}{3}$	38. 128/1354
9. $\frac{11}{12}$	19. $\frac{1}{3}$	29. $3\frac{3}{5}$	39. $2.50/$12
10. $\frac{3}{16}$	20. $\frac{11}{16}$	30. $1\frac{5}{6}$	40. $3.75/$17.34

UNIT **3**   **Application of the Percentage Formula**

A news commentator announced that 60% of the employees of a plant employing 15,000 men had walked off the job. As a natural reaction, many of his listeners probably wondered just how many men this was. 60% of the men implies that 60 out of every 100 left the plant. The per cent value does not tell you the actual number of men that left; it merely indicates the rate that left.

This situation can be analyzed as follows. 60% of the men can be expressed in the fractional form as $\frac{3}{5}$ of the men. The total number of men was 15,000; hence, $\frac{3}{5}$ of the 15,000 men walked off the job. The word *of*, as you learned some time ago, indicates the operation of multiplication; therefore,

$$\frac{3}{5} \text{ of } 15,000 \text{ means } \frac{3}{5} \times 15,000.$$

Multiplying the fraction $\frac{3}{5}$ by the whole number 15,000 yields the product of 9,000. This represents the number of men who left the plant. The 60% could have been represented in its decimal form as .60 rather than as the fraction $\frac{3}{5}$. Were this done, multiplying .60 by 15,000 would still give the same product as before (9,000). In either event, it was imperative that 60% be changed to either its fractional or decimal equivalent before the number of men who left the plant could be found.

Each of the numbers in the situation you have just examined has a special name.

→60% is called the *rate*.

→15,000 is called the *base*.

→9,000 is called the *percentage*.

The 60% is called the rate because it indicates just that. As you know, a per cent value will never give the actual number of quantities there are but simply how many per 100 are involved; hence, it signifies a rate. The number 15,000 is referred to as the base since it is the basic quantity involved in the situation. It (15,000) represents the quantity on which the rate is based. While the rate only indicates how many quantities per 100 are to be considered, the percentage, on the other hand, tells you exactly how many of these quantities there are. In this example, the rate pointed out that 60 out of each 100 men left work. The percentage, how-ever, stated that exactly 9,000 men left work. The terms *per cent* and *percentage* should *not* be used interchangeably. *Per cent* is a rate, and *percentage* is the actual number of quantities.

SECTION 1   Finding the Percentage

In the example cited in the introduction to this unit, the percentage (9,000) was found by multiplying 15,000 (the base) by 60% (the rate). From the method applied here for finding the percentage, the following principle can be formulated:

→The percentage is equal to the base times the rate. Using P to repre-sent the word percentage, B for base, and R for rate, this principle is usually written as the formula:

$$P = B \times R$$

Example 1: Find 25% of $2,400.

Solution: In this example the base is $2,400, and the rate is 25%. Since you are really being asked to find the percentage, the problem can be outlined as follows:

Outline: → Known: Base = $2,400

Rate = 25%

→ To Find: Percentage

→ Method: P = B × R

= $2,400 × 25%

= $2,400 × $\frac{1}{4}$

= $600

Example 2

20% of Robert Green's yearly income of $5,240 is spent for rent. How much money does Mr. Green spend on rent each year?

Solution: In this example the 20% is based on the yearly income; hence, $5,240 is the base, and 20% is the rate. The yearly rent that you are asked to find represents the percentage.

Outline: → Known: Base = $5,240
                    Rate = 20%
           → To Find: Percentage
           → Method: P = B × R
                    = $5,240 × 20%
                    = $5,240 × $\frac{1}{5}$
                    = $1,048   Rent

Example 3

Floyd Rogers, a painting contractor, has discovered that 56% of the amount that he charges his customers is needed to pay his employees. To how much did the wages paid his painters amount on a job for which he charged $2,375?

Solution: The 56% is based on the charge of $2,375; hence, the base is $2,375, and the rate is 56%. You are required to find the percentage.

Outline: → Known: Base = $2,375
                    Rate = 56%
           → To Find: Percentage
           → Method: P = B × R
                    = $2,375 × 56%
                    = $2,375 × .56
                    = $1,330   Salary

You may have noticed that in the first two examples the per cent values were changed to fractions, but that in the third example the per cent value was changed to a decimal. This was done in the third example because the fractional equivalent of 56% would have been awkward to use. There are certain fractional equivalents for per cent values that occur so frequently in business that you should memorize them. These fractions are similar to the aliquot parts of $1 listed on page 110.

LEARNING EXERCISES

A. *Oral:* At sight, find the percentage in each of the following problems.

odd number

check Clased Kirkley

1. 50% of 24
2. 66⅔% of 18
3. 30% of 50
4. 40% of 25
5. 62½% of 32
6. 12½% of 72

7. 75% of 28
8. 50% of 98
9. 37½% of 56
10. 60% of 55
11. 33⅓% of 90
12. 83⅓% of 54

13. 80% of 45
14. 16⅔% of 84
15. 75% of 36
16. 66⅔% of 60
17. 70% of 80
18. 62½% of 64

B. *Written:* Find the percentage in each of the following problems. Whenever possible, use the fractional equivalents from the table on page 110.

1. 25% of $1,764
2. 12½% of $2,272
3. 36% of $843
4. 16⅔% of 3,543 students
5. 52% of 1,879 acres
6. 96% of 2,083 bushels
7. 37½% of 5,768 trees
8. 33⅓% of 7,347 tires
9. 62½% of 4,360 dresses
10. 86% of 3,264 apples
11. 46% of 14,000 desks
12. 4½% of $425

13. 2¾% of $1,375
14. 3¼% of $4,350
15. 115% of $37.60
16. 225% of $152.50
17. 200% of $56.84
18. 300% of $235.25
19. 4.2% of $385
20. 16.4% of $4,590
21. 3.05% of $37,000
22. 3⅓% of $420
23. 4⅔% of $690
24. ½% of $100,000

C. *Problems to Be Solved*

1. Find 100% of each of the following amounts:

   $56 $35.75 $124.56

   a. What relationship exists between 100% of a number and the number itself? Why should this be so?

   b. Write out a principle stating what you have discovered through this problem.

2. In a certain city, 48.2% of the population were males. If the total population was 62,473 people, how many males were there? Interpret your answer.

3. If 18.2% of the sophomore class of 342 students in Wallington High School failed at least one subject, how many sophomores did not fail any subject?

4. During a recent frost, 33⅓% of a peach crop valued at $3,456,000 was destroyed. How great a loss was this to the peach growers?

5. A recent poll showed that 82% of the high school students questioned enjoyed the singing of a certain popular male vocalist. The re-

maining students did not even know who he was. If 43,000 students were polled, how many were unaware of the existence of this singer?

6. The manufacturer of a crab-grass killer guaranteed that after two applications of his product 85% of the crab grass in the area treated would be dead. Mr. Drake bought a can of this liquid and applied it twice in accordance with directions. If the plot that he sprayed covered 2,800 square feet, how many square feet of crab grass would still remain to be killed after the second application?

7. A department store employs 1,842 people. If 87% are sales help, 5% office help, and the remaining employees supervisory employees, how many people are employed in each of these groups?

8. An estimate furnished by a contractor for the construction of a new building was $48,000. Of this amount, 19% was for plumbing, 34% for building materials and supplies, and 36% for labor. His profits were equal to the remainder. Find the amount of each item.

9. Out of an income of $4,260, a man spent $12\frac{1}{2}\%$ for rent, 22% for food, 12% for clothing, $16\frac{2}{3}\%$ for other items, and the rest he saved.

> **a.** How much did he spend for each of the items given in the problem?
>
> **b.** How much money did he save?

10. A man invested $12\frac{1}{2}\%$ of his money in real estate, $37\frac{1}{2}\%$ in bank stocks, $16\frac{2}{3}\%$ in government bonds, and deposited the rest in the bank. Find the total of each investment if his original net worth was $42,000.

SECTION 2   Finding the Rate

Part 1

If the product of two numbers is equal to a third number, then either number divided into the third number will give the other number.

To illustrate: 6 times 7 equals 42. If 6 is divided into 42, the quotient will be 7; and if 7 is divided into 42, the quotient will be 6. These three different relationships can be expressed in the form of three different equalities:

$$
\begin{array}{cccc}
& (3) & (2) & (1) \\
(a) & 42 & = 6 & \times 7
\end{array}
$$

$$
\begin{array}{cccc}
& (3) & (2) & (1) \\
(b) & 42 & \div 6 & = 7
\end{array}
$$

$$
\begin{array}{cccc}
& (3) & (1) & (2) \\
(c) & 42 & \div 7 & = 6
\end{array}
$$

These three equations should help you understand the principle stated at the outset of this section. In equation (a), the product of two numbers, labeled (2) and (1), is shown equal to the third number, labeled (3). Equation (b) shows that, if the product labeled (3) is divided by the number labeled (2), the result will be the number labeled (1). In equation (c) you can see that, if the product labeled (3) is divided by the number labeled (1), the result will be the number labeled (2).

This principle is a very valuable aid in helping you understand other variations of the formula: $P = B \times R$. As with the numbers **42, 6,** and **7** in the illustration, the number P is the product of the numbers B and R. Hence, it is possible to find three equations relating P, B, and R similar to the three established for **42, 6,** and **7.** These should be:

$$\text{(3)}\quad\text{(2)}\quad\text{(1)}\qquad\qquad\text{(3)}\quad\text{(2)}\quad\text{(1)}$$
$$(a)\ \ P\ =\ B\ \times\ R\qquad\qquad 42\ =\ 6\ \times\ 7$$

$$\text{(3)}\quad\text{(2)}\quad\text{(1)}\qquad\qquad\text{(3)}\quad\text{(2)}\quad\text{(1)}$$
$$(b)\ \ P\ \div\ B\ =\ R\qquad\qquad 42\ \div\ 6\ =\ 7$$

$$\text{(3)}\quad\text{(1)}\quad\text{(2)}\qquad\qquad\text{(3)}\quad\text{(1)}\quad\text{(2)}$$
$$(c)\ \ P\ \div\ R\ =\ B\qquad\qquad 42\ \div\ 7\ =\ 6$$

The two sets of equations were arranged beside one another so that the similarity between the two can be seen.

The interpretations for equations (b) and (c) are as follows:

(b) If the percentage is divided by the base, the quotient will be the rate.

(c) If the percentage is divided by the rate, the quotient will be the base.

The formulas (b) and (c) are usually written in the reverse of the way they appear here. It would be advisable for you to learn them in the following manner:

$$(b)\ \ R\ =\ P\ \div\ B\qquad\quad (c)\ \ B\ =\ P\ \div\ R$$

The formula for the rate (b) is the one with which this section will be concerned.

Example 1

A boy who earned \$24 spent \$8 for ice skates. What per cent of his earnings did he spend for the skates?

Solution: As you are asked to find a per cent value—that is, a rate value—it is necessary to use the "rate" formula. In order to apply this formula, some means must be found from the wording of the problem to determine which number is the base and which is the percentage. If you examine the simple illustration:

$$\text{\$10 is 25 per cent of \$40}$$

you will note that the $40, which is the base, follows the words "per cent of." What is noted here will *always* be true:

The number that is written *after* the words "per cent of" will *always* be the base.

In the same illustration, the number $10, which precedes the verb *is*, represents the percentage. This, too, will always be true:

The number that is written *before* the words "is what per cent of" will *always* be the percentage.

If the question in Example 1 were reworded as follows, the percentage and base would immediately become evident:

The amount ($8) he spent on his ice skates is what per cent of his earnings ($24)?

The number following the words *per cent of* is $24; therefore, this number is the base. The number $8, which precedes the words *is what per cent of*, is the percentage.

Outline: → Known: Base = $24
$$\qquad\qquad\qquad\text{Percentage} = \$8$$
→ To Find: Rate
→ Method: R = P ÷ B
$$= \$8 \div \$24$$
$$= .33\tfrac{1}{3}, \text{ or } 33\tfrac{1}{3}\%$$

It is important to realize that before this method can be applied, it is necessary to reword the question in a manner similar to the following:

This number (percentage) is what per cent of that number (base)? Only then will the numbers representing the base and percentage be easy to determine.

Example 2

The student enrollment at Hillsdale High School in 1957 was 1,256 pupils. In 1958, there were 314 additional students. What per cent of the 1957 enrollment was the increase?

Solution: The question can be reworded as follows: The increase (314) is what per cent of the 1957 enrollment (1,256)?

Outline: → Known: Base = 1,256
Percentage = 314
→ To Find: Rate
→ Method: R = P ÷ B
= 314 ÷ 1,256
= .25, or 25%

Note: If the per cent value is a number like .636, it is best to "round off" your answer at the second digit after the decimal point. Thus, .636 should be expressed as .64 or 64%.

Example 3

A merchant purchased a dinette set for $84.25 and sold it for $139.95. What per cent of the cost is the selling price?

Solution: Rewording: The selling price ($139.95) is what per cent of the cost ($84.25)?

Outline: → Known: Base = $84.25
Percentage = $139.95
→ To Find: Rate
→ Method: R = P ÷ B
= $139.95 ÷ $84.25
= 1.661
= 166.1%, or 166%

Note that, when the percentage is larger than the base, the rate will be greater than 100%.

LEARNING EXERCISES

A. Find the rate in each of the following examples.

1. $15 is what per cent of $60?
2. $75 is what per cent of $375?
3. $41 is what per cent of $328?
4. $19 is what per cent of $114?
5. $13 is what per cent of $156?
6. $495 is what per cent of $660?
7. $61 is what per cent of $427?
8. $51 is what per cent of $255?
9. $93 is what per cent of $248?

10. $146 is what per cent of $219?

11. $140 is what per cent of $490?

12. What per cent of $.60 is $.30?

13. What per cent of $.75 is $.50?

14. What per cent of $.50 is $.02?

15. What per cent of $50 is $75?

16. What per cent of $125 is $250?

17. What per cent of $38 is $46?

18. What per cent of $1.09 is $.17?

19. What per cent of $1.35 is $.28?

20. What per cent of $1.98 is $.43?

21. What per cent of $104.50 is $26.75?

22. What per cent of $112.75 is $169.95?

B. *Problems to Be Solved*

1. A merchant sold a tennis racket for $17.85, making a profit of $5.95. The profit was what per cent of the selling price?

2. A chemical plant employs 527 people this year. Last year it employed 346 people. The number of employees this year is what per cent of the number of employees last year?

3. During the past 5 years, the football team of Morrison High School played 47 games and won 39 of them. What per cent of the games did the team win?

4. In a basket of 165 peaches, 34 were found to be damaged. What per cent of the total number of peaches was damaged?

5. The 1950 census of a town showed the population to be 5,474 people. In 1956 an aircraft plant was built on the outskirts of the town, and the population jumped to 18,756 people. What per cent of the 1950 population was the 1956 population?

6. Fred Egan earns $572 a month. Of this amount, he spends $125 each month for rent. What per cent of his monthly earnings is needed to pay the rent?

7. At the Glen View High School, approximately 35 students are late every day. If the enrollment is 1,624 students, what is the average per cent of students who are tardy each day?

8. The average weekly earnings of production workers in the electrical machinery industry 10 years ago were $54.27. At present they are $89.56. The present average is what per cent of the average weekly earnings of these men 10 years ago?

9. One month after finding his first job, William Blakely bought a new car on the installment plan. If his monthly payments were $54.17 and

his monthly salary was $207.42, what per cent of his salary was needed to meet these payments?

Part 2

Situations frequently arise where it is necessary to determine the percentage before the rate can be found. The method for solving these problems can best be illustrated by the following examples.

Example 1

A merchant purchased a hat for $4.25 and sold it for $6.95. What per cent of the cost was his gain?

Solution: Rewording: The gain is what per cent of the cost of the hat? When the question is written in this form, it is immediately apparent that the gain represents the percentage and the cost is the base. Hence, before the rate of gain can be found, the gain itself must be known. This can be determined by subtracting $4.25 from $6.95.

Outline:→ Known: Cost = $4.25 (Base)
　　　　　　　　　Selling Price = $6.95
　　　　→ To Find: Rate of Gain
　　　　→ Method: Gain = $6.95 − $4.25
　　　　　　　　　　　　 = $2.70 (Percentage)
　　　　　　　　R = P ÷ B
　　　　　　　　　 = $2.70 ÷ $4.25
　　　　　　　　　 = .635
　　　　　　　　　 = 63.5%, or 64% (Per Cent of Gain)

Example 2

After Clarence Martin was graduated from college, his earnings on his first job were $3,750 a year. At present his yearly salary is $5,465. What per cent of increase has he received?

Solution: Rewording: The increase in salary is what per cent of the original salary? Again it can be seen that the increase is the percentage. The increase can be found by subtracting the original salary from the present salary. This example calls attention to another important point. Per cent of increase or per cent of decrease is *always* based on the original quantity. To illustrate, the salary that Clarence Martin received on his first job is the original quantity and, hence, is the base.

Outline: → Known: Original Salary = $3,750 (Base)

Present Salary = $5,465

→ To Find: Rate of Increase

→ Method: Increase = $5,465 − $3,750

= $1,715 (Percentage)

R = P ÷ B

= $1,715 ÷ $3,750

= .457

= 45.7%, or 46% (Per Cent of In-crease)

LEARNING EXERCISES

Problems to Be Solved

1. An article that originally sold for $8 now sells for $10. What is the per cent of increase?

2. Two months ago Elizabeth Foster's typing speed was 32 words a minute. At present she can type at the rate of 47 words a minute. What per cent of increase has she achieved in the past two months?

3. In an English class of 27 students, 4 failed the subject. What per cent of the class passed?

4. After Mary Walker was graduated from high school, she went to work as a clerk-typist for an insurance firm at $47.50 a week. After 2 years, her earnings were $71.50 a week. What was the per cent of increase in her salary over the 2-year period?

5. In a school of 1,458 students, 57 were absent one day. What per cent of the students were in attendance that day?

6. The number of people employed in leather production 10 years ago was 362,000. Now only 342,000 people are employed in this industry. What is the per cent of decrease?

7. In 1949, 57.8 million dollars were spent on television advertisements. Only 5 years later, 803.6 million dollars were spent on this means of advertising. What was the per cent of increase during these 5 years?

8. Before retiring, Bernard Sanborn earned a monthly salary of $526.55. After retirement, both he and his wife received $152.40 in monthly Social Security payments. What per cent of decrease in his monthly income was this?

9. Several years ago, the yearly income per person in the state of Nevada was $2,414; in Kansas it was $1,689. What per cent greater was the per person income in Nevada over that in Kansas?

10. In one of the states, the average beginning salary for an engineer was $4,150 a year. At that time, the average starting salary for a school teacher in the same state was $3,200 a year. At what per cent smaller income did a teacher begin his career in that state than did an engineer?

11. A man whose house was valued at $28,000 insured it for only $20,000 against loss by fire. What per cent of the value of the property remained uninsured against this type of loss?

12. Factory employees in a certain company number 1,209 women and 551 men.

    a. What per cent of the employees are women?

    b. What per cent of the employees are men?

13. The total attendance at a motion-picture show was 2,664. Of this total, 666 were children, 888 were women, and the remainder men. Find the per cent of total attendance represented by each group.

14. Three men started a business by contributing $10,000, $14,000, and $25,000, respectively. What per cent of the total did each contribute?

15. In a high school that had 1,258 students enrolled, 426 were freshmen, 351 were sophomores, 283 were juniors, and the rest were seniors. What per cent of the school enrollment was each of the classes?

SECTION 3   Finding the Base

On page 133 of this chapter, three forms of the percentage formula were presented.

$$(a) \quad P = B \times R$$
$$(b) \quad R = P \div B$$
$$(c) \quad B = P \div R$$

The first two formulas have already been studied. In this section, applications of the third form will be studied.

Problems that require the use of the formula

$$B = P \div R$$

are those in which you are told the percentage and the rate and are asked to find the base. These problems occur in situations such as those illustrated in the following examples.

Example 1

Mr. Richards spent $85 each month for rent. This was 18% of his monthly salary. How much did he earn each month?

Solution: If the problem were reworded in a manner similar to the rewording of the problems you examined in Section 2, it would read:

The monthly rent ($85) is 18% of his monthly salary.

In this form, it is clear that the $85 that precedes the word "is" is the percentage and that the monthly salary that follows the words "per cent of" is the base. Hence, it is the base that you are asked to determine in this situation.

Method: → Known: Rent = $85 (Percentage)
　　　　　　　　　　Rate = 18%
　　　　　→ To Find: Monthly Salary (Base)
　　　　　→ Method: B = P ÷ R
　　　　　　　　　　= $85 ÷ 18%
　　　　　　　　　　= $85 ÷ .18
　　　　　　　　　　= $472.22 (Monthly Salary)

Example 2

As a result of a dust storm, 12 acres of corn were destroyed. If this is 25% of the entire crop, how many acres of corn had been planted?

Solution: Rewording: The 12 acres destroyed are 25% of the number of acres planted.

Method: → Known: Acres Destroyed = 12 (Percentage)
　　　　　　　　　　Rate = 25%
　　　　　→ To Find: Total Number of Acres Planted (Base)
　　　　　→ Method: B = P ÷ R
　　　　　　　　　　= 12 ÷ 25%
　　　　　　　　　　= 12 ÷ $\frac{1}{4}$
　　　　　　　　　　= 48 (Acres Planted)

LEARNING EXERCISES

A. Find the base in each of the following examples.

1. $12 is 20% of what amount?
2. $15 is 6% of what amount?
3. $70 is 12$\frac{1}{2}$% of what amount?
4. $90 is 33$\frac{1}{3}$% of what amount?
5. $63 is 7% of what amount?
6. $81 is 37$\frac{1}{2}$% of what amount?
7. $95 is 62$\frac{1}{2}$% of what amount?
8. $72 is 75% of what amount?
9. $84 is 28% of what amount?
10. $18 is 4$\frac{1}{2}$% of what amount?
11. 3$\frac{3}{4}$% of what amount is $45?
12. 2$\frac{1}{4}$% of what amount is $54?
13. 16% of what amount is $4.50?
14. 5% of what amount is $23.95?
15. 72% of what amount is $54.50?
16. 85% of what amount is $108.75?
17. 120% of what amount is $18?
18. 300% of what amount is $46?
19. $72 is 100% of what amount?
20. $52 is 4.2% of what amount?

B. *Problems to Be Solved*

1. A merchant sold an article at a profit of $6. If this was 40% of what he paid for the article, how much did the article cost him?

2. Five students failed the first-year bookkeeping course. This was

10% of the students taking the course. How many students were taking the bookkeeping course?

3. In a commercial-arithmetic examination given in a high school, 27 pupils passed. This number was equal to 75% of the total number who took the examination. Find the total number who were examined.

4. The selling expenses of a musical-instrument concern last year were 23% of the total sales. If the expenses were $4,991, how much were the total sales? *21700*

5. In one year, a young man saved $1,095. If this represented 23% of his total income, what was his annual income? *4761*

6. When Jane Norton purchased her spinet, the salesman asked for a deposit of 20% of the cost of the instrument. If she gave him $175, what was the total cost of the spinet?

7. As a result of wage negotiations, carpenters on a housing project received an increase in salary of 16 cents an hour. If this was a raise of 5% of the wages they had been receiving, how much was their previous hourly wage?

8. The average salary of production workers in all manufacturing industries rose 44% during a 6-year period. This rise amounted to $23.50 a week.

   a. What was the average weekly salary at the beginning of the 6-year period?

   b. What was the average weekly salary at the end of the 6-year period?

9. Employees of the Durable Plastic Company who work on Saturdays receive an hourly rate of 150% of their normal hourly rate. Fred Urban's hourly salary on Saturday is $3.32. What is his normal hourly wage?

10. $2\frac{1}{2}$% of the employees of the Tarkington Toy Company are absent from work each day either because of illness or other personal reasons. If the daily absence is 35 employees, how many people work for the company?

UNIT **4**   **Trading on Commission**

SECTION 1   Computing Net Proceeds on Commission Sales

Several important applications of the use of per cent will be discussed in the remaining units of this chapter. The first of these applications concerns the sale of goods on a "commission" basis. Manufacturers and producers of goods do not always find it possible to sell their own goods either to merchants or directly to the consumer. This is particularly true of farmers who do not have the time or the means of marketing their fruits and vegetables. They, therefore, arrange with men called *commission merchants*, or *agents*, or *factors*, to sell their goods for them. Department stores and large produce markets sometimes find it impossible to obtain certain articles locally. They, too, will arrange with these same agents to buy merchandise for them. For example, a chain of grocery stores selling fruits and vegetables wishes 1,000 crates of grapefruit. Having no means of buying them from the growers in either Florida or California, the chain will contact a commission merchant, who will do the buying for them.

In return for their services, commission merchants charge a fee called a *commission;* thus the name *commission merchant*. This charge is in one of two forms; either it is a definite amount for each article bought or sold, or a certain per cent of the cost or selling price of the goods.

To Illustrate: A commission merchant sold $1,575 worth of vegetables for a farmer. If the agent's commission was $4\frac{1}{2}\%$ of the sales, how much money did he turn over to the farmer?

Solution: The fee that the commission merchant charges is found by multiplying $1,575 by $4\frac{1}{2}\%$. This fee (commission) is then deducted from the $1,575 and the difference sent to the farmer.

Outline: → Known: Selling Price = $1,575
Commission Rate = $4\frac{1}{2}\%$

→ To Find: Farmer's Return

→ Method: Commission = Selling Price × Commission Rate
= $ 1,575 × $4\frac{1}{2}\%$
= $ 1,575 × .045
= $70.875, or $70.88 Fee (Commission)

Farmer's Return = Selling Price − Commission
= $1,575 − $70.88
= $1,504.12 (Amount Farmer Received)

Had the commission merchant made no charge for his services, then he would have given the entire amount of money collected to the farmer. This amount is called the *gross proceeds*. The amount that he actually turns over to the person for whom he is selling the merchandise is called the *net proceeds*. In the illustration above:

→$1,575 is the *gross proceeds*.

→$1,504.12 is the *net proceeds*.

There are other charges besides his fee that a commission merchant often deducts from the gross proceeds before he forwards the difference to the *principal*—the person for whom the merchandise is sold. The charges that occur most frequently are:

1. Freight charges—cost of shipping the merchandise from one city to another by freight train.

2. Truckage or cartage—cost of transporting the merchandise from the freight yard to the purchaser.

3. Storage—the charge for storing the merchandise in the event that it is not sold immediately.

4. Insurance—to protect himself against loss incurred by damage to the merchandise, the agent will insure the merchandise.

After selling the merchandise, the agent will submit a written report to the principal, giving an accounting of the money he received from the sale and what he spent on each of the charges. This report is called an *account sales;* its name comes from the purpose it serves—an accounting of the sales. A sample report is shown below.

ACCOUNT SALES

Newark, N. J., ... *May 5,* 19–

SMITH BROTHERS AND PIERCE

Commission Merchants

Sold for Account of:

.... *Warren Classens* .....

.... *Freehold, N. J.* ....

19–						
May	2	410 crates Strawberries @ $4.20	1,722 00			
	4	160 crates Raspberries @ 3.95	632 00			
	5	650 bags Potatoes @ 2.15	1,397 50			
		Gross Proceeds		3,751 50		
		Charges:				
		Freight and cartage	72 75			
		Commission, 3½% of $3,751.50	131 30			
		Insurance, 1% of $3,751.50	37 52	241 57		
		Net Proceeds		3,509 93		

Explanation: The $1,722 was found by multiplying 410 by $4.20. The same method was used to find the total selling price of the raspberries and the potatoes. The Gross Proceeds is the sum of the total selling prices of the strawberries, raspberries, and potatoes. Each of the charges was listed separately, and their total ($241.57) was written in the right-hand column under the gross proceeds ($3,751.50). The Net Proceeds were found by subtracting the total charges ($241.57) from the gross proceeds ($3,751.50).

Business Transaction: A commission merchant sold 720 bags of potatoes at $2.85 a bag. If his commission rate was 4%, insurance 1½%, and freight $32.25, what were the net proceeds to the farmer?

Solution: Gross Proceeds = 720 × $2.85
= $2,052

Commission = 4% of $2,052
= .04 × $2,052
= $82.08

Insurance = 1½% of $2,052
= .015 × $2,052
= $30.78

Net Proceeds = Gross Proceeds − Charges
= $2,052 − ($82.08 + $30.78 + $32.25)
= $2,052 − $145.11
= $1,906.89 (Farmer's Return)

LEARNING EXERCISES

A. Find the net proceeds in each of the following commission sales.

No.	Gross Proceeds	Commission Rate	Net Proceeds
1	$ 275.00	2%	$xxx 269.50
2	454.50	3%	xxx
3	642.25	5%	xxx
4	725.00	2½%	xxx
5	4,375.00	4¾%	xxx

B. Find the net proceeds in each of the following commission sales.

No.	Gross Proceeds	Commission Rate	Insurance Rate	Transportation	Net Proceeds
1	$ 360	3%	1%	$ 13.25	$xxx
2	820	4%	1%	27.50	xxx
3	925	5%	2%	30.54	xxx
4	600	$4\frac{1}{2}$%	1%	21.25	xxx
5	752	3%	$1\frac{3}{4}$%	23.95	xxx
6	2,300	$2\frac{1}{2}$%	$1\frac{1}{2}$%	67.25	xxx
7	4,250	$3\frac{3}{4}$%	$\frac{1}{2}$%	126.50	xxx

C. *Problems to Be Solved*

1. A real estate agent sold a house for Robert Thompson for $22,000. If the agent's fee amounted to 5% of the selling price, how much did Mr. Thompson actually receive from the sale?

2. For his commission on the sale of life insurance, an agent receives 45% of the first year's premium. On a $5,000 life insurance policy, R. C. Bates paid a premium of $132.50 the first year. How much money did his agent receive from the insurance company for this sale?

Prepare an account sales similar to the one on page 143 for each of the following problems.

3. Robert Miner, a commission merchant, sold 5,400 pounds of butter at 53 cents a pound for the United Dairy Farmers. Mr. Miner's commission was $2\frac{1}{4}$%; the freight charges were $63.20; insurance 1%; and storage $75.30. What were the net proceeds returned to the United Dairy Farmers? Use the current date.

4. T. Fenner, a fruit grower, shipped 430 barrels of apples and 725 baskets of peaches to Smith Brothers and Pierce, commission merchants, to be sold on a commission of $3\frac{1}{2}$%. The apples were sold at $5.40 a barrel and the peaches were sold at $1.95 a basket. Insurance was $1\frac{1}{2}$%; cartage, $63.75; freight, $107.30. Find the net proceeds.

5. Tanner and Benson, commission merchants, sold 920 sacks of potatoes for C. Roberts, an Idaho potato grower. 410 sacks were sold at $3.05 a sack; 235 sacks at $3.15; 150 sacks at $3.20; and the remaining 125 sacks at $3.30. If the commission was 5%; insurance, $1\frac{3}{4}$%; freight, $67.95, what were the net proceeds?

6. An account sales of merchandise, sold for the account of Alfred Fleming by Kelton Brothers, commission merchants, showed the following sales: October 12, 840 bushels of wheat at **$2.35** a bushel; October 18, 380 bushels at **$2.40** a bushel; and October 27, 780 bushels at **$2.25** a bushel. Charges: commission, $3\frac{1}{2}\%$; insurance, $1\frac{1}{2}\%$; freight and cartage, **$263**; and storage, **$96.75**. Find the net proceeds sent to the principal by the commission merchant.

SECTION 2   Computing Gross Cost on Commission Purchases

As was noted in the preceding section, commission merchants not only sell merchandise but also purchase goods for persons who cannot do so themselves. If these agents did not charge a fee for their services and if there were no charges for other expenses, then the only cost to the buyer would be the cost of the merchandise. The cost of the merchandise alone is called the *prime cost,* meaning the first cost. In addition, all the other charges that were pointed out in Section 1 of this unit are made by the commission merchant. The total of the prime cost and the charges is called the *gross cost.* It is this amount that the principal—the person who ordered the purchase to be made—must pay.

To illustrate: Martin Brothers, commission merchants, purchased **750** dozen eggs at **47** cents a dozen for Wellington Markets, Inc. The commission was $3\frac{1}{2}\%$; cartage, **$27.25**; insurance, 1%. What was the gross cost of the eggs to the Wellington Markets?

Solution:

$$
\begin{aligned}
\text{Prime Cost} \;&=\; 47\cancel{c} \times 750 \\
&=\; \$352.50 \\
\text{Commission} \;&=\; 3\tfrac{1}{2}\% \text{ of } \$352.50 \\
&=\; \$12.34 \\
\text{Insurance} \;&=\; 1\% \text{ of } \$352.50 \\
&=\; \$3.53 \\
\text{Gross Cost} \;&=\; \text{Prime Cost} + \text{Charges} \\
&=\; \$352.50 \qquad + (\$12.34 + \$3.53 + \$27.25) \\
&=\; \$352.50 \qquad + \$43.12 \\
&=\; \$395.62 \text{ (Cost to Wellington Markets, Inc.)}
\end{aligned}
$$

Notice that the *prime cost* (**$352.50**) included only the cost of the eggs and that the *gross cost* (**$395.62**) included the cost of the eggs plus the other charges.

When the purchase is completed, the commission merchant submits a report to the principal, showing the cost of each of the items purchased, the charges made, and the gross cost. This report, accounting for the purchases made by the agent, is called an *account purchase*. In reality, it is simply a bill. An illustration of an account purchase is shown here.

		ACCOUNT PURCHASE				
		Chicago, Illinois____*August 8,*____ 19–				
		LEONARD & MAIN				
		Commission Merchants				
Bought for the Account of:						
		Silas Perkins				
		Cairo, Illinois				
19— *Aug.*	8	450 pounds Coffee @ 74¢		333 00		
		270 pounds Tea @ 62¢		167 40		
		Prime Cost			500 40	
		Charges:				
		Cartage and storage		13 80		
		Commission, 4½% of $500.40		22 52		
		Insurance, ½% of $500.40		2 50	38 82	
		Gross Cost			539 22	

LEARNING EXERCISES

A. Find the gross cost in each of the following commission purchases.

No.	Prime Cost	Commission Rate	Gross Cost
1	$ 375.00	2%	$xxx
2	635.70	3%	xxx
3	783.29	5%	xxx
4	450.00	3½%	xxx
5	2,745.00	2¾%	xxx

B. Find the gross cost in each of the following commission purchases.

No.	Prime Cost	Commission Rate	Insurance Rate	Transportation	Gross Cost
1	$ 250.00	3%	1%	$11.75	$xxx
2	640.00	5%	1%	18.50	xxx
3	875.00	4%	2%	19.23	xxx
4	500.00	$3\frac{1}{2}$%	1%	14.86	xxx
5	830.00	5%	$1\frac{1}{4}$%	17.83	xxx
6	1,200.00	$4\frac{1}{2}$%	$1\frac{1}{2}$%	29.75	xxx
7	467.54	$4\frac{1}{4}$%	$\frac{1}{2}$%	13.05	xxx

C. *Problems to Be Solved*

Prepare an account purchase similar to the one on page 147 for each of the following problems. Use the current date.

1. A commission merchant purchased for a customer 6,200 bushels of wheat at $2.42 a bushel. The freight and cartage charges were $968 and the commission charges, $3\frac{1}{2}$%. Find the gross cost of the wheat.

2. A commission merchant was requested to purchase 90 barrels of sugar, 250 pounds to the barrel, at 5.75 cents a pound. The commission charges were $3\frac{1}{2}$%; the other charges, $96.85. Find the gross cost of the sugar.

3. A principal requested his agent to buy for him 600 bales of cotton. The agent was able to make the purchase at $32\frac{1}{2}$ cents a pound. Each bale of cotton weighed 500 pounds. Charges for the purchase were as follows: commission, 4%; insurance, $1\frac{1}{2}$%; freight, $44.90. Find the gross cost of the cotton.

4. A principal received an account purchase from his agent showing the following purchases for his account: 135 crates of eggs, 30 dozen to a crate, at 43 cents a dozen; and 640 bushels of potatoes, 60 pounds to a bushel, at 1.9 cents a pound. The charges were: cartage, $97.25; commission, $3\frac{1}{4}$%; other charges, $71.60. Find the total amount charged to the principal's account.

U N I T 5   Computing Depreciation Charges

Doubtless at sometime in your experience you have tried to either buy or sell a secondhand article. This may have been anything from an old bugle for which you no longer had any need to a bicycle that you had long since outgrown. If you were selling the article, you soon found out that no one was willing to give you the same price you had paid for the article. On the other hand, if you were buying "used" merchandise, you yourself were unwilling to pay the price that the article had sold for when new. The probability is that during the bargaining session the following two points kept running through your mind:

1. This article has been used for a number of years; hence some of the parts are probably worn out and should be replaced.

2. The new models of this article have new attachments and other advantages that this one lacks.

In view of this, you had good cause for refusing to pay the original value of the article.

The businessman or the manufacturer is faced with exactly the same problem—but on a much larger scale. He knows that his machines, his buildings, his showcases, his tools, and everything else will decline in value with the passing of time. Their values will decrease for reasons identical with those listed earlier. To provide for the day when he will have to replace these articles, he usually sets aside each year an amount of money that is equal to the loss in value of that article during the year. There are very few objects that are completely worthless at the time they are discarded. Even an automobile that has been completely destroyed in an accident can be sold to a junk dealer at some price. Or a manufacturing plant that is being torn down because it is so "out of date" that it can no longer be used efficiently, may have bricks that can be cleaned and re-used.

A machine, a tool, or a building, such as the ones just cited, is said to be *obsolete* if it can be replaced with newer and more efficient equipment. The value of this property at the time it is finally discarded is called the *scrap* or *junk value* of the article. If the scrap value of the equipment or its value at the time it is resold is subtracted from the original value, then the difference is known as the *depreciation*. The depreciation of an article is simply its decrease in value. There are three methods commonly used by businessmen, of charging the depreciation losses against the profits of their business.

1. The straight-line method
2. The fixed-rate method
3. The decreasing-rate method

In each of these methods, money is set aside to provide for the replacement of obsolete or worn-out equipment.

SECTION 1   The Straight-Line Method

By the straight-line method, the depreciation is divided by the number of years the equipment will be used. The quotient is considered to be the yearly loss in value of the equipment and is called the *annual depreciation*.

To illustrate: A machine that cost $800 has an estimated scrap value of $200. The company expects to use the machine for only 5 years. Find the amount that should be charged as a loss against this machine each year.

Solution: If the scrap value ($200) is subtracted from the original value ($800), the difference ($600) is the depreciation. Dividing the $600 by 5, the number of years the machine will be used, gives $120. This is the amount that the machine decreases in value each year.

Outline: Depreciation = $800 − 200
= $600
Annual Depreciation = $600 ÷ 5
= $120

A company sometimes wishes to report its depreciation charges not only as the actual number of dollars lost each year but also as a per cent value. Thus, in the preceding illustration, the management would be interested in knowing not only the actual annual depreciation of $120 but also the *annual rate of depreciation* based on the *original value* of the machine. Placed in the form of a question, this would be:

$120 is what per cent of $800?

This is a direct application of that form of the percentage formula where it is necessary to find the rate. Hence,

Outline: → Known: Annual Depreciation = $120 (Percentage)
Original Value = $800 (Base)
→ To Find: Rate
→ Method: R = P ÷ B
= $120 ÷ $800
= .15
= 15% (Annual Rate of Depreciation)

Business Transaction: A metal lathe that cost $12,300 when new had a resale or trade-in value of $800 after 15 years.
a. What was the annual depreciation?
b. What was the annual rate of depreciation?

Solution: Depreciation = Original Value − Resale Value
= $12,300 − $800
= $11,500
Annual Depreciation = Depreciation ÷ Number of Years
= $11,500 ÷ 15
= $766.67
(Percentage)   (Base)
Annual Rate = Annual Depreciation ÷ Original Cost
= $766.67 ÷ $12,300
= .062
= 6.2%

LEARNING EXERCISES

A. Find: (a) the annual depreciation; (b) the annual rate of depreciation.

No.	Property	Cost	Scrap Value	Time Held Yrs.	Annual Depreci- ation	An- nual Rate
1	*Wood lathe*	$ 850.00	$ 70	12	$xxx	xx%
2	*Metal lathe*	7,400.00	600	10	xxx	xx%
3	*Elec. motor*	625.00	75	8	xxx	xx%
4	*Outboard motor*	329.00	150	3	xxx	xx%.
5	*Typewriter*	176.75	35	7	xxx	xx%
6	*Metal desk*	109.95	15	15	xxx	xx%
7	*Gas furnace*	627.50	0	18	xxx	xx%
8	*Refrigerator*	399.98	25	16	xxx	xx%
9	*Power mower*	117.25	55	4	xxx	xx%
10	*Factory building*	124,000.00	2,000	25	xxx	xx%

B. *Problems to Be Solved*

1. Billie Green's father bought him a 22-inch bicycle for $32.95 when
Billie was 6 years old. After using it for 3 years, he outgrew the bicycle
and it was sold for $10.

    a. What was the annual depreciation?

    b. What was the annual rate of depreciation?

2. Raymond Langley purchased a motion-picture camera for $93.50.
After keeping it for 2 years, he sold it for $46 in order to buy a more
expensive model. What was the annual rate of depreciation?

3. A man purchased a motorboat for $3,750. At the end of a year he sold it for $2,600 because he found that the upkeep was beyond his means. What was the annual rate of loss?

4. The New Products Chemical Corporation purchased $350,000 worth of equipment for their new plant. If, at the end of 8 years, the equipment will be completely worthless because it will be obsolete, at what annual rate is it depreciating?

5. Twenty-four new typewriters costing $159.75 each were purchased for the typing room of Edison High School. Assuming that the estimated life of the typewriters is 4 years, after which they have a trade-in value of $25:

    a. What is the annual depreciation on the 24 typewriters?

    b. What is the annual rate of depreciation?

6. An auto-renting agency purchased 12 cars for $1,975 each. If the agency expects to keep the cars for only 2 years, after which they plan to trade them in at $1,135 each:

    a. What is the annual depreciation on these 12 cars?

    b. What is the annual rate of depreciation?

SECTION 2   The Fixed-Rate Method

By the fixed-rate method of determining depreciation, the value of the property decreases at a fixed rate of its changing value.

To illustrate: By the fixed-rate method, if the value of a $10 article depreciates 20% each year, then:

During the first year it will depreciate $2 (20% × $10). Therefore, its value at the end of the first year will be $8 ($10 − $2).

During the second year it will depreciate $1.60 (20% × $8). Therefore, its value at the end of the second year will be $6.40 ($8 − $1.60).

During the third year it will depreciate $1.28 (20% × $6.40). Therefore, its value at the end of the third year will be $5.12 ($6.40 − $1.28).

This will continue annually for as long as the property is kept by the owner.

You should note that, although the rate of depreciation remains the same (20%), the actual annual depreciation grows smaller with each succeeding year. This is true because the rate is based on an ever-decreasing value. In the preceding illustration, the first year's depreciation was 20% of *$10;* the second year, however, it was 20% of only *$8;* while the third year, 20% of *$6.40,* and so on. By this method, the value of the property can never depreciate to nothing.

Each succeeding year's value of the article is called the *book value* of the article. It is so named because it is the value that the company will record in its books and report to the owners whenever it becomes necessary to determine the total value of the company's property. Using the same illustration, the book value of the article is:

At the end of the first year, $8.
At the end of the second year, $6.40.
At the end of the third year, $5.12.

LEARNING EXERCISES

A. Based on the fixed-rate method, find the yearly depreciation and the book value for the first three years of the life of each of the following pieces of property.

No.	Property	Cost	Fixed Depreciation Rate
1	Planer	$ 3,600	20%
2	Factory	200,000	5%
3	Power drill	850	15%
4	Showcases	14,000	8%
5	Air-conditioning equipment	25,000	6%
6	Shingled roof	975	7%
7	Cutting machine	3,745	10%
8	Electric baggage cart	850	$4\frac{1}{2}\%$

B. *Problems to Be Solved*

1. The depreciation rate on an elevator costing $12,800 was 8% on the decreasing value. Find the annual depreciation and the carrying, or book, value each year for the first 5 years.

2. The depreciation charge on a machine costing $640 was figured at 12% on the decreasing annual value. Find the amount at which the machine was carried on the books at the end of the fourth year.

3. Machinery and equipment costing $23,800 was installed in the new plant of a manufacturing concern. In order to provide for the eventual replacement of this equipment, $12\frac{1}{2}\%$ of its decreasing value was set aside each year. Find the book value of the property at the end of the third year.

4. In order to provide for the purchase of new sanitation-department trucks, a town has set up a fund by putting aside each year $8\frac{1}{3}\%$ of the decreasing value of its present trucks. If the value of each of these trucks when new was $7,200, how much did the town put aside for each truck during the first 3 years after the trucks were purchased?

5. Provision for the replacement of calculators worth $720 is made each year by the Guaranteed Life Insurance Company. How much should be set aside during each of the first three years that the machines were used if a fixed-rate depreciation plan of $16\frac{2}{3}\%$ based on the decreasing value of the machines is used?

SECTION 3   The Decreasing-Rate Method

There are a number of articles that drop drastically in value during the first few years of their life. After that, their value levels off and remains more or less the same until the time they are scrapped. As a case in point, the value of an automobile drops as much as 35% during the first year after it is manufactured. In succeeding years, its per cent of depreciation grows smaller and smaller so that, during its fifth year, it may depreciate only 5% of its original value.

In the decreasing-rate method of determining depreciation, though the rate constantly changes, the amount on which the rate is based always remains the same. This base is the total depreciation that the company expects to lose during the time the article is under its ownership. Thus, if a machine cost $600 and after 5 years it is traded in at $100, then the base on which the depreciation rates depend is always $500 ($600 − $100).

The decreasing-rate and the fixed-rate methods differ from each other on two points:

1. In the decreasing-rate method, the base remains the same (fixed), but the annual depreciation rate decreases.

2. In the fixed-rate method, the annual depreciation rate remains the same (fixed), but the base decreases.

Business Transaction: It is the policy of a certain firm to trade in its delivery trucks every 4 years. The cost of each truck is $3,150 and the trade-in allowance is $650. Show the annual depreciation charge and the value at which each truck is carried during each year of its use if the following rates of depreciation are used.

First year	40%	*Third year*	20%
Second year	30%	*Fourth year*	10%

Solution: Depreciation = Original Value − Resale Value

$$= \quad \$3{,}150 \quad - \quad \$650$$

$$= \quad \$2{,}500 \text{ (Total Depreciation)}$$

Year	Yearly Depreciation	Book or Carrying Value
1	40% of $2,500, or $1,000	$2,150 ($3,150 − $1,000)
2	30% of $2,500, or 750	$1,400 ($2,150 − $750)
3	20% of $2,500, or 500	$900 ($1,400 − $500)
4	10% of $2,500, or 250	$650 ($900 − $250)
Total Depreciation	$2,500	

Note that the total depreciation shown by this sum must check with the total depreciation found above.

LEARNING EXERCISES

A. Other automobiles owned by the firm in the preceding business transaction depreciate in value in accordance with the per cents listed there. Find the book value of the following cars at the end of each of the first two years.

No.	Cost	Trade-in Value after 4 Years	No.	Cost	Trade-in Value after 4 Years
1	$2,000	$400	4	$2,709.00	$ 809.00
2	2,400	750	5	3,256.23	926.23
3	2,250	625	6	3,472.56	1,000.00

B. *Problems to Be Solved*

1. The total value of a firm's property, on which depreciation was computed, was $82,800. The rates used, based on this valuation, were:

First year	15%	Fourth year	10%
Second year	12%	Fifth year	8%
Third year	10%	Sixth year and succeeding years	5%

Find the book value of the property at the end of each of the first 8 years.

2. If among the property of the firm in Problem 1 there was a desk valued at $150, what would be the book value of this desk at the end of the fourth year?

3. Using the depreciation rates in Problem 1, what is the book value of an adding machine at the end of 5 years if its original value was $227.50 and its trade-in value is $25?

4. Using the depreciation rates in Problem 1, what is the book value of a tape recorder at the end of 10 years if its original cost was $159.95 and its trade-in value is $15?

UNIT 6   Measuring Your Skill in Using Percentage

Handin 5th period class

SECTION 1   Understanding Terms

Can you match the term in the column at the left with the proper definition in the column at the right?

Term	*Definition*
1. Per cent	**a.** The amount paid an agent for conducting business for another person.
2. Percentage	
3. Commission merchant	**b.** A form on which are itemized all the charges in a purchase made by a commission merchant.
4. Commission	
5. Net proceeds	
6. Gross proceeds	**c.** Total amount collected by a commission merchant at the close of a sale.
7. Prime cost	
8. Gross cost	**d.** The number of units determined by multiplying the base by the rate.
9. Account purchase	
10. Account sales	**e.** Total bill submitted by a commission merchant to a principal.
11. Scrap value	
12. Depreciation	**f.** Value of equipment at the time it is discarded.
13. Book value	
	g. Someone who buys or sells merchandise at a fee for another person.
	h. A rate where 100 is used as the base.
	i. Amount given by the commission merchant to the principal after the merchandise has been sold.
	j. Reduction in price given by a merchant to a consumer.
	k. A form on which is listed the selling price and all the charges in a sale made by a commission merchant.
	l. Decrease in the value of property.
	m. Cost of the merchandise to the buyer before

the various fees charged by the commission merchant are added.

n. Value of property during any year as recorded in the books of the company.

SECTION 2   Review Problems

If you are unable to solve the following problems, review the pages indicated within the parentheses.

1. Change each of the following fractions or decimals to per cent values. (Pages 124–128)

a. .56   d. $\frac{6}{25}$ g. $\frac{3}{7}$ j. 2.67

b. .04   e. .7   h. 3   k. $1\frac{1}{2}$

c. $\frac{17}{100}$ f. .0346   i. $\frac{19}{32}$ l. $.03\frac{1}{2}$

2. Change each of the following per cent values to decimals. (Pages 122–124)

a. 53%   c. 125%   e. $5\frac{1}{2}$%   g. .14%

b. 4%   d. 6.2%   f. 200%   h. $2\frac{3}{4}$%

3. Change each of the following per cent values to fractions. (Pages 119–121)

a. 40%   c. 300%   e. $3\frac{1}{3}$%

b. 55%   d. 6%   f. $22\frac{2}{9}$%

4. Find the percentage, the base, or the rate, as needed, in each of the following problems. (Pages 128–141)

a. 25% of $3,516 is what amount?

b. 17% of $2,375 is what amount?

c. $4\frac{1}{2}$% of $2,620 is what amount?

d. $16 is what per cent of $64?

e. $47 is what per cent of $92?

f. $1.98 is what per cent of $1.29?

g. $15 is 25% of what amount?

h. $75 is $33\frac{1}{3}$% of what amount?

i. $53 is 14% of what amount?

j. What amount is 20% of 127 pounds?

k. 18% of how many bushels is 44 bushels?

l. What per cent of 75 gallons is 40 gallons?

m. $2,500 is what per cent of $1,600?

n. $12\frac{1}{2}$% of 2,576 pints is how many pints?

o. $3.75 is 6% of what amount?

p. How many yards is $16\frac{2}{3}$% of 876 yards?

5. $15 is what per cent more than $10? (Page 137)

6. $62 is what per cent less than $76? (Page 137)

7. A leather-goods dealer purchased a brief case for $7.50 and sold it for $12.98. What per cent of the cost was his gain? (Page 137)

8. In order to clear out dinner jackets that were no longer in style, the owner of a men's wear shop sold them for $6.95, although he himself had paid $20.85 for each jacket. What per cent of loss based on his cost was the owner taking? (Page 137)

9. The cheering squad of Orville High School was decreased from 15 members to 12 members. What was the per cent of decrease? (Page 137)

10. 23% of Arthur North's income is spent on food. If he earns $6,342 a year, how much does he spend for food? (Page 129)

11. Hurricanes damaged 20% of the property in the business district of a Southern town. If the damage was estimated at half a million dollars, what was the total value of the property in the district? (Pages 139–140)

12. A woman's dress was bought for $16.50 and sold at a profit of $10.45. What per cent of the cost of the dress was the profit? (Page 132)

13. Hillsbrook High School found that about $2\frac{1}{2}$% of its students had to leave school each year in order to help support their families. If the enrollment at Hillsbrook was 1,296 students last year, approximately how many left school for this reason? (Page 129)

14. At a recent poll, 42.7% of the people interviewed said they would vote for a certain candidate at the next election. If 8,500 people were interviewed, how many would not commit themselves or would vote against that candidate? (Page 129)

15. The population of a Midwestern town is now 23,756 persons. If this is 140% of what it was during the 1950 census, what was the population of the town at that time? (Page 139)

16. Easter sales at Allison's Department Store were 18% better this year than they were last year. If last year's sales amounted to $575,256.82, what were this year's sales? (Page 129)

17. Prepare an account sales similar to the one on page 143 to include the following information: The Western Growers Association shipped 525 barrels of apples and 955 crates of oranges to Kemper Brothers, commission merchants, to be sold at a commission of $4\frac{1}{2}$%. The apples were sold at $4.75 a barrel, and the oranges were sold at $6.25 a crate. Insurance was 1%; freight, $276.45. Find the net proceeds. (Page 143)

18. Prepare an account purchase similar to the one on page 147 to include the following information: The Manner Coffee Company requested its agent, Benson and Benson, to purchase 18,000 pounds of coffee. The purchase was made at 72 cents a pound. The commission rate was 5%; insurance, $1\frac{1}{2}$%; shipping, $172.50; storage, $23.40. What was the gross cost of the coffee? (Page 147)

19. Thomas Kent purchased a sailboat for $1,257. He sold the boat 3 years later for $725 in order to buy a larger boat. Using the straight-line method of depreciation:

    a. Find the annual depreciation.

    b. Find the annual rate of depreciation. (Page 150)

20. The Belmont Candle Manufacturing Company recently purchased a $9,500 piece of equipment for molding candles. If the company depreciates its equipment at an annual rate of 8% of its decreasing value, what will be the book value of this purchase at the end of 2 years? (Page 152)

SECTION 3   Testing Your Understanding—50 Minutes

1. Express each of the following per cent values as a decimal.

    a. 27%   **b.** 5%   **c.** 134%   **d.** $4\frac{1}{2}$%

2. Express each of the following numbers as a per cent.

    a. .73   **c.** .054   **e.** 4

    b. $\frac{7}{25}$ **d.** $\frac{5}{12}$ **f.** $5\frac{3}{4}$

3. Express each of the following per cent values as a fraction.

    a. 23%   **b.** 75%   **c.** $6\frac{2}{3}$%

4. 18% of $425 is what amount of money?

5. 40 gallons of oil is what per cent of 120 gallons of oil?

6. $2.95 is 15% of what amount?

7. In the final stage of testing certain light switches, $1\frac{1}{2}$% are found to be defective and have to be discarded. Of the 8,800 tested in one week, how many had to be discarded?

8. Walter Trump's first salary check that included his new raise amounted to $78.55. If formerly he earned $74.35, what per cent of increase did he receive?

9. Fire destroyed 6,882 bales of cotton, which was 37% of the cotton stored in a warehouse. How many bales had been in the warehouse?

10. Out of an enrollment of 1,600 students in a school, 480 took an active part in athletics. At the end of the first year, 120 pupils received their letters.

    a. What per cent of the enrollment took part in athletics?

    b. What per cent of those engaged in athletics received their letters?

11. Office equipment costing $540 when new has a scrap value of $210. If its probable life is 6 years,

    a. What would the annual depreciation be by the straight-line method?

    b. What would be the rate of depreciation?

12. Find the book value at the end of 2 years of an automobile that cost $2,400 if the depreciation was computed at the rate of $12\frac{1}{2}\%$ on the decreasing value.

Simplex Time Recorder Co.

7

Preparation of Payrolls

PREVIEW

During the summer after his junior year in high school George Clark found his first job. He was proud of the fact that he had been able to qualify for a position that paid $1.25 an hour, although the Federal Minimum Wage Law did not require that he be paid that much. As any young man would be under the same circumstances, he looked forward to his first pay check with great eagerness. Knowing that he would work a 40-hour week, he had on numerous occasions during that first week multiplied 40 by $1.25, both mentally and on paper, only to learn over and over again that he would soon have earned his first $50—and in but one short week!

You can imagine his surprise and disappointment when he learned, on receiving his check, that, instead of the amount being

161

$50 as he had anticipated, it was only $38.80! Attached to his check was a slip of paper with letters thereon that seemed to be written in a foreign language. The one word he did recognize was written in large type—"DEDUCTIONS." Below this were the following abbreviations: "With.," "F.I.C.A.," "Bonds," "Hosp.," "Union." Under these abbreviations, numbers, such as 9.10, 1.00, —, .60, .50, were written. This was a mystery that George expected to get to the bottom of—and very soon, too—for, in some strange way $11.20 of his salary had vanished—$11.20 that he had already planned to spend on other things!

For Class Discussion

1. How many of the above abbreviations can you identify?
2. Why should the company wish to deduct for the item listed as "Bonds"?
3. What is meant by the Federal Minimum Wage Law?
4. What businesses are affected by the Federal Minimum Wage Law? Why does the Federal law on wages not affect all persons who are working?
5. Would it be possible for George to pay his taxes direct to the Federal Government without having them deducted from his salary by his employer?
6. What is meant by the phrase "a 40-hour week"?
7. If George had worked 42 hours that week, would his salary be found by multiplying 42 by $1.25? Justify your answer.

Concerning This Chapter

There are between 60 and 70 million people in the United States who are employed in one type of occupation or another. Most of them are working for someone else—a person or a company. For their services, they receive a salary that is determined in one of two ways:

1. The time payment, or hourly, wage system.
2. The straight piecework wage system.

Of the two wage systems, the first is the most widely used. The greater part of this chapter will, therefore, be devoted to explaining and illustrating how wages are determined on this basis. In addition, several examples will explain the manner in which the second wage system operates. Since, by Federal law, an employer is required to make certain deductions from an employee's salary, several sections are included to explain what these deductions are. Tables will then be presented showing how these deductions are computed. Because other sums are frequently taken from an employee's salary, in addition to those required by law, these, too, will be discussed. In conclusion, you will learn how the paymaster determines how many $20 bills, $10 bills, $5 bills, and so on, he will have to get from the bank in order to meet the weekly payroll in those companies that still pay their employees by cash.

UNIT 1 **The Time Payment, or Hourly, Wage System**

SECTION 1 Computing Regular and Overtime Pay

Most concerns use some method of determining whether an employee has reported to work each day and the number of hours he has spent at work. The most common way of obtaining this information is to have the employee punch a time clock each morning as he enters the building and repeat the process each evening as he leaves. In punching a time clock, the employee merely moves a knob attached to a clock, thus recording on a card his time of arrival or departure. These cards serve two purposes. They not only indicate whether the employee has reported for work, but, equally important, they also show how many hours the employee worked each day. The worker's weekly salary is determined on the basis of the number of hours recorded on these "time" cards.

To illustrate: Raymond Baker worked the following number of hours during one week:

Monday	Tuesday	Wednesday	Thursday	Friday
8	8	7	$7\frac{1}{2}$	8

If his hourly salary was $1.68, what should his salary be for that week?

Solution: During the entire week, Raymond worked a total of $38\frac{1}{2}$ hours. Since he received $1.68 for each hour of work, his salary can be found by multiplying $1.68 by $38\frac{1}{2}$.

Outline: Number of Hours $= 8 + 8 + 7 + 7\frac{1}{2} + 8$
$= 38\frac{1}{2}$
Weekly Salary $\quad = 38\frac{1}{2} \times \$1.68$
$= \$64.68$

In accordance with Federal law, employees must be paid "time and a half" for all hours that they work beyond 40 hours each week. Other firms that are not covered by this law usually abide by this regulation also. The phrase "time and a half" means that the hourly overtime salary will be $1\frac{1}{2}$ times the regular hourly salary. Thus, if the regular salary is $1.28 an hour, the overtime rate will be,

$$1\frac{1}{2} \times \$1.28 = \tfrac{3}{2} \times \$1.28 = \$1.92$$

Example 1

During the week of June 7, Robert Marsh worked $42\frac{1}{2}$ hours. If his regular hourly pay was $1.28, how much salary did he receive that week?

Solution: Regular Time Salary $= 40 \times \$1.28$
$$= \$51.20$$
Overtime Hourly Rate $= 1\frac{1}{2} \times \$1.28$
$$= \$1.92$$
Overtime Salary $= 2\frac{1}{2} \times \$1.92$
$$\quad .96$$
$$= \tfrac{5}{2} \times \$1.92$$
$$\quad 1$$
$$= \$4.80$$
Total Salary $=$ Regular Salary $+$ Overtime Salary
$$= \qquad \$51.20 \qquad + \qquad \$4.80$$
$$= \qquad \$56.00$$

The salaries of all the employees of a company are recorded on a form called a *payroll register*. This register contains all the information that a payroll clerk must have before he can compute a worker's wages. Part of this form is given in the example below; a complete form will be presented later in the chapter.

Example 2

Complete the following payroll register.

Employee	M T W T F S	Reg. Hrs.	Reg. Rate	Amount	Over. Hrs.	Over. Rate	Amount	Total
		(1)		(2)	(3)	(4)	(5)	(6)
Brennan, T.	8 7 8 8 6 0	xxx	1.65	$xxx	xxx	xxx	$xxx	$xxx
		(7)		(8)	(9)	(10)	(11)	(12)
Carter, R.	8 9 8 10 6 $3\frac{1}{2}$	xxx	1.72	xxx	xxx	xxx	xxx	xxx

Solution: The numbered steps that follow refer to the numbers in the parentheses in the register shown.

(1) Brennan worked less than 40 hours that week; the total number of hours he did work (37) would be recorded in this space.

(2) This represents his weekly "regular-time" salary and is found by multiplying $1.65 by 37. The product is $61.05.

Gail, Ann, Jane, Sheila, Linda

(3), (4), (5) Since there is no overtime work, dashes would be marked in these columns.

(6) The regular "Amount" $61.05 (see 2) added to the overtime "Amount" of zero will still give $61.05.

(7), (9) Carter worked 44½ hours that week; 40 of these are recorded under "Regular Hours" and 4½ under "Overtime Hours."

(8) The regular-time salary is found by multiplying $1.72 by 40, giving $68.80.

(10) The overtime rate is found by multiplying $1.72 by 1½; this will be $2.58.

(11) This "Amount" represents the overtime pay and is determined by multiplying $2.58 by 4½. This product is $11.61.

(12) Adding the regular "Amount" ($68.80) to the overtime "Amount" ($11.61) will give the total salary, $80.41.

Hence, the completed payroll register is:

Employee	M T W T F S	Reg. Hrs.	Reg. Rate	Amount	Over. Hrs.	Over. Rate	Amount	Total
Brennan, T.	8 7 8 8 6 0	37	$1.65	$61.05	—	—	—	$61.05
Carter, R.	8 9 8 10 6 3½	40	1.72	68.80	4½	2.58	11.61	80.41

LEARNING EXERCISES

1. Complete the following partial payroll register. None of the employees worked overtime during this week.

Employee	M	T	W	T	F	Reg. Hrs.	Reg. Rate	Total Earnings
B. Armond	8	8	8	8	8	xxx	$1.25	$xxx
S. Black	8	7	6	8	8	xxx	1.53	xxx
R. Camp	7	7	8	9	6	xxx	1.67	xxx
A. Dillon	7	7	7½	7	7	xxx	1.46	xxx
C. Ferris	7½	8	8	8	8	xxx	1.58	xxx
H. Hansen	8	—	6¼	8	8	xxx	1.96	xxx
W. James	8	6½	8	7¼	8	xxx	2.16	xxx
C. Leonard	8	6½	6½	8	5¼	xxx	2.84	xxx
							Total	$xxx

Payroll Register
Kean Manufacturing Company
Payroll for the Week Ending July 1, 19—

2. Complete the following partial payroll register. Consider all hours worked each week beyond 40 as overtime.

Employee's Number	M	T	W	T	F	S	Reg. Hrs.	Reg. Rate	Amt.	Over. Hrs.	Over. Rate	Amt.	Total
						Payroll Register **Laurel Mills** **Payroll for the Week Ending May 27, 19—**							
76	8	8	8	8	8	8	xxx	1.40	$xxx	xxx	$xxx	$xxx	$xxx
77	8	8	7	8	8	4	xxx	1.86	xxx	xxx	xxx	xxx	xxx
78	8	8	8	8	8	8	xxx	1.64	xxx	xxx	xxx	xxx	xxx
79	8	$7\frac{1}{2}$	8	8	8	$3\frac{1}{2}$	xxx	1.34	xxx	xxx	xxx	xxx	xxx
80	8	8	—	8	8	$4\frac{1}{4}$	xxx	2.32	xxx	xxx	xxx	xxx	xxx
81	8	$8\frac{3}{4}$	9	8	$7\frac{1}{2}$	8	xxx	1.96	xxx	xxx	xxx	xxx	xxx
82	8	8	10	9	8	3	xxx	2.54	xxx	xxx	xxx	xxx	xxx
83	10	8	8	8	8	4	xxx	2.82	xxx	xxx	xxx	xxx	xxx
Totals									$xxx			$xxx	$xxx

SECTION 2   Computing Social Security and Income Taxes

The Total column in each of the preceding payroll registers should in reality be called the *Gross Pay* or *Gross Salary*. This is the salary the employee would have received had there been no deductions. The Federal Government requires, however, that each employer withhold from his employee's salary money for two different taxes:

1. Income tax.

2. Federal Insurance Contributions Act taxes. This tax is commonly known either as the *Social Security tax* (Soc. Sec.) or as the *Federal Old Age Benefit tax* (F.O.A.B.)

It is not the purpose now to explain the need or the benefits of either of these taxes. This will be done in later chapters. At this time it is important that you learn how the paymaster computes both these taxes before they are deducted from the gross salary.

Part 1—Social Security Taxes

Until 1960, an employer is required to withhold $2\frac{1}{4}\%$ of the earnings under $4,200 a year of each of his employees. This amount is added to an equal amount contributed by the employer, and the sum is then forwarded to the Federal Government to be used, eventually, for the benefit of these employees when they retire.

To illustrate: A man earns $62 each week. How much will be deducted from his salary for Social Security tax?

> **Solution:** Social Security Tax $= 2\frac{1}{4}\% \times \$62$
> $= .0225 \times \$62$
> $= \$1.40$ Amount Taken from His Salary

Should an employee earn more than $4,200 in any one year, then, as soon as he has earned $4,200, his employer stops making deductions from his salary for the Social Security tax. Thus, if a man earns $200 a week, then at the end of 21 weeks (4,200 ÷ 200) he will have earned $4,200. For the first 21 weeks of the year, $2\frac{1}{4}\%$ deductions are taken from his salary. For the remainder of the year, nothing is taken from his salary for Social Security.

Although only $2\frac{1}{4}\%$ is deducted for Social Security until 1960, the rate will be larger after that year. The following table shows the increased rates that are scheduled.

Year	Employee Rate
1955–1959	$2\frac{1}{4}\%$
1960–1964	$2\frac{3}{4}\%$
1965–1969	$3\frac{1}{4}\%$
1970–1974	$3\frac{3}{4}\%$
1975 and after	$4\frac{1}{4}\%$

LEARNING EXERCISES

A. Find the amount of the Social Security tax on each of the following salaries. Assume that the employee has not as yet earned $4,200 during the year.

1. $46.00	5. $86.74	9. $126.34
2. $47.50	6. $93.95	10. $135.57
3. $56.74	7. $97.63	11. $146.75
4. $60.29	8. $104.50	12. $236.18

B. During what week of the year will Social Security taxes cease to be deducted from each of the following weekly salaries?

1. $100	5. $168	9. $104.50
2. $84	6. $175	10. $123.48
3. $120	7. $210	11. $156.74
4. $150	8. $93	12. $219.18

F.I.C.A. EMPLOYEE TAX TABLE

TABLE OF 2¼ PER CENT EMPLOYEE TAX DEDUCTIONS

(1) Wages			(2) Wages			(3) Wages			(4) Wages		
At least	But less than	F.I.C.A. tax to be withheld	At least	But less than	F.I.C.A. tax to be withheld	At least	But less than	F.I.C.A. tax to be withheld	At least	But less than	F.I.C.A. tax to be withheld
$25.56	$26.00	$0.58	$51.34	$51.78	$1.16	$77.12	$77.56	$1.74	$102.00	$102.45	$2.30
26.00	26.45	.59	51.78	52.23	1.17	77.56	78.00	1.75	102.45	102.89	2.31
26.45	26.89	.60	52.23	52.67	1.18	78.00	78.45	1.76	102.89	103.34	2.32
26.89	27.34	.61	52.67	53.12	1.19	78.45	78.89	1.77	103.34	103.78	2.33
27.34	27.78	.62	53.12	53.56	1.20	78.89	79.34	1.78	103.78	104.23	2.34
27.78	28.23	.63	53.56	54.00	1.21	79.34	79.78	1.79	104.23	104.67	2.35
28.23	28.67	.64	54.00	54.45	1.22	79.78	80.23	1.80	104.67	105.12	2.36
28.67	29.12	.65	54.45	54.89	1.23	80.23	80.67	1.81	105.12	105.56	2.37
29.12	29.56	.66	54.89	55.34	1.24	80.67	81.12	1.82	105.56	106.00	2.38
29.56	30.00	.67	55.34	55.78	1.25	81.12	81.56	1.83	106.00	106.45	2.39
30.00	30.45	.68	55.78	56.23	1.26	81.56	82.00	1.84	106.45	106.89	2.40
30.45	30.89	.69	56.23	56.67	1.27	82.00	82.45	1.85	106.89	107.34	2.41
30.89	31.34	.70	56.67	57.12	1.28	82.45	82.89	1.86	107.34	107.78	2.42
31.34	31.78	.71	57.12	57.56	1.29	82.89	83.34	1.87	107.78	108.23	2.43
31.78	32.23	.72	57.56	58.00	1.30	83.34	83.78	1.88	108.23	108.67	2.44
32.23	32.67	.73	58.00	58.45	1.31	83.78	84.23	1.89	108.67	109.12	2.45
32.67	33.12	.74	58.45	58.89	1.32	84.23	84.67	1.90	109.12	109.56	2.46
33.12	33.56	.75	58.89	59.34	1.33	84.67	85.12	1.91	109.56	110.00	2.47
33.56	34.00	.76	59.34	59.78	1.34	85.12	85.56	1.92	110.00	110.45	2.48
34.00	34.45	.77	59.78	60.23	1.35	85.56	86.00	1.93	110.45	110.89	2.49
34.45	34.89	.78	60.23	60.67	1.36	86.00	86.45	1.94	110.89	111.34	2.50
34.89	35.34	.79	60.67	61.12	1.37	86.45	86.89	1.95	111.34	111.78	2.51
35.34	35.78	.80	61.12	61.56	1.38	86.89	87.34	1.96	111.78	112.23	2.52
35.78	36.23	.81	61.56	62.00	1.39	87.34	87.78	1.97	112.23	112.67	2.53
36.23	36.67	.82	62.00	62.45	1.40	87.78	88.23	1.98	112.67	113.12	2.54

At least	Less than	Tax	At least	Less than	Tax	At least	Less than	Tax	At least	Less than	Tax
36.67	37.12	.83	62.45	62.89	1.41	88.23	88.67	1.99	113.12	113.56	2.55
37.12	37.56	.84	62.89	63.34	1.42	88.67	89.12	2.00	113.56	114.00	2.56
37.56	38.00	.85	63.34	63.78	1.43	89.12	89.56	2.01	114.00	114.45	2.57
38.00	38.45	.86	63.78	64.23	1.44	89.56	90.00	2.02	114.45	114.89	2.58
38.45	38.89	.87	64.23	64.67	1.45	90.00	90.45	2.03	114.89	115.34	2.59
38.89	39.34	.88	64.67	65.12	1.46	90.45	90.89	2.04	115.34	115.78	2.60
39.34	39.78	.89	65.12	65.56	1.47	90.89	91.34	2.05	115.78	116.23	2.61
39.78	40.23	.90	65.56	66.00	1.48	91.34	91.78	2.06	116.23	116.67	2.62
40.23	40.67	.91	66.00	66.45	1.49	91.78	92.23	2.07	116.67	117.12	2.63
40.67	41.12	.92	66.45	66.89	1.50	92.23	92.67	2.08	117.12	117.56	2.64
41.12	41.56	.93	66.89	67.34	1.51	92.67	93.12	2.09	117.56	118.00	2.65
41.56	42.00	.94	67.34	67.78	1.52	93.12	93.56	2.10	118.00	118.45	2.66
42.00	42.45	.95	67.78	68.23	1.53	93.56	94.00	2.11	118.45	118.89	2.67
42.45	42.89	.96	68.23	68.67	1.54	94.00	94.45	2.12	118.89	119.34	2.68
42.89	43.34	.97	68.67	69.12	1.55	94.45	94.89	2.13	119.34	119.78	2.69
43.34	43.78	.98	69.12	69.56	1.56	94.89	95.34	2.14	119.78	120.23	2.70
43.78	44.23	.99	69.56	70.00	1.57	95.34	95.78	2.15	120.23	120.67	2.71
44.23	44.67	1.00	70.00	70.45	1.58	95.78	96.23	2.16	120.67	121.12	2.72
44.67	45.12	1.01	70.45	70.89	1.59	96.23	96.67	2.17	121.12	121.56	2.73
45.12	45.56	1.02	70.89	71.34	1.60	96.67	97.12	2.18	121.56	122.00	2.74
45.56	46.00	1.03	71.34	71.78	1.61	97.12	97.56	2.19	122.00	122.45	2.75
46.00	46.45	1.04	71.78	72.23	1.62	97.56	98.00	2.20	122.45	122.89	2.76
46.45	46.89	1.05	72.23	72.67	1.63	98.00	98.45	2.21	122.89	123.34	2.77
46.89	47.34	1.06	72.67	73.12	1.64	98.45	98.89	2.22	123.34	123.78	2.78
47.34	47.78	1.07	73.12	73.56	1.65	98.89	99.34	2.23	123.78	124.23	2.79
47.78	48.23	1.08	73.56	74.00	1.66	99.34	99.78	2.24	124.23	124.67	2.80
48.23	48.67	1.09	74.00	74.45	1.67	99.78	100.23	2.25	124.67	125.12	2.81
48.67	49.12	1.10	74.45	74.89	1.68	100.23	100.67	2.26	125.12	125.56	2.82
49.12	49.56	1.11	74.89	75.34	1.69	100.67	101.12	2.27	125.56	126.00	2.83
49.56	50.00	1.12	75.34	75.78	1.70	101.12	101.56	2.28	126.00	126.45	2.84
50.00	50.45	1.13	75.78	76.23	1.71	101.56	102.00	2.29	126.45	126.89	2.85
50.45	50.89	1.14	76.23	76.67	1.72						
50.89	51.34	1.15	76.67	77.12	1.73						

Note.—Applies only to the first $4,200 of wages paid by the employer to the employee in a calendar year.

169

Part 2—Computing Social Security Taxes Through Use of a Table

The Federal Government supplies employers with tables for determining the F.I.C.A. (Soc. Sec.) tax that is to be withheld. In companies that employ thousands of men, using these tables rather than computing the tax as described in Part 1 saves many hours of labor. Part of this table is shown on pages 168–169.

Notice that there are four columns headed "Wages." The lowest salary for which this table is designed is $25.56; the highest is $126.89. The wages in each succeeding Wage column begin where the preceding one ended. Thus, the last wages in column (1) range between $50.89 and $51.34; column (2) starts with salaries between $51.34 and $51.78.

Example 1

Using the tax table, find the Social Security tax for a person who earns $45.37 a week.

Solution: Follow down the Wage column headed by the words "At least" until you come to two successive numbers, one slightly less than $45.37 and one slightly more than $45.37. They will be the numbers:

$$45.12$$
$$45.56$$

Look across the row containing the smaller number (45.12) and you will notice that the number 45.56 is again written in this row. This means that the wages ($45.37) that you are trying to locate are "at least" $45.12 "but less than" $45.56. The Social Security tax will appear in the next column to the right of these two numbers. It is $1.02.

Example 2

Using the Social Security tax table, find the tax on a weekly salary of $112.57.

Solution: In order to locate the salary of $112.57, it is necessary to go to the 4th Wages column. In the "At least" column, $112.57 will be found between $112.23 and $112.67. Look across the row containing $112.23 to the "F.I.C.A. tax" column, and there you will find the tax of $2.53.

LEARNING EXERCISES

Using the Social Security tax table, determine the tax that should be withheld from each of the following weekly salaries.

1. $26.35	7. $93.00	13. $62.25	19. $106.75
2. $32.93	8. $106.47	14. $64.75	20. $49.24
3. $46.50	9. $53.75	15. $93.75	21. $49.25
4. $53.04	10. $58.90	16. $104.25	22. $117.30
5. $64.29	11. $121.32	17. $120.53	23. $99.72
6. $82.25	12. $95.68	18. $106.74	24. $74.76

Part 3—Computing Income Taxes Through the Use of a Table

In computing the Social Security tax, the paymaster has a choice of using the tax table on pages 168–169 or multiplying the salaries of each of the employees by $2\frac{1}{4}\%$. In computing the income tax that is to be withheld, the paymaster has no choice. The only way he can determine how much money should be withheld from an employee's salary is by using a table provided for this purpose by the Federal Government. As the salaries of employees cover different periods of time, such as weekly, biweekly, semimonthly, or monthly, the Government has prepared tables to fit each of these methods of payment. All the tables are similar in nature. The weekly one, the one most frequently used, is presented in this section.

When the income tax law was enacted, Congress realized that, although two persons may be earning the same salary, they should not necessarily be taxed the same amount. Thus, it was felt that a bachelor who lived alone and supported no one but himself should pay more tax than a man who was supporting a wife and two children, even though both were earning the same salary. To adjust for these circumstances, each taxpayer is allowed a reduction in taxes for each person who is dependent on him. Each dependent is called an *exemption*. Thus, the bachelor can claim *one* exemption—himself. The husband can claim *four* exemptions—his wife, two children, and himself. Knowing the meaning of the word *exemption*, you are prepared to interpret the table on pages 172–173.

Example 1

How much income tax is deducted from Carl Walker's weekly salary of $46.75 if he lives alone and claims only one exemption, himself?

Solution: The table on pages 172–173 is read much like the Social Security table. Follow down the column headed by the words "At least" until you find two numbers, one slightly less than $46.75 and one slightly more. These will be 46 and 47. Run your pointer across the row

INCOME TAX

If the payroll period with respect to an employee is **weekly:**

At least	But less than	0	1	2	3	4	5	6	7	8	9	10 or more
						And the number of withholding exemptions claimed is—						
					The amount of income tax to be withheld shall be—							
$0	$13	18% of wages	$0	$0	$0	$0	$0	$0	$0	$0	$0	$0
13	14	$2.40	.10	0	0	0	0	0	0	0	0	0
14	15	2.60	.30	0	0	0	0	0	0	0	0	0
15	16	2.80	.50	0	0	0	0	0	0	0	0	0
16	17	3.00	.70	0	0	0	0	0	0	0	0	0
17	18	3.20	.80	0	0	0	0	0	0	0	0	0
18	19	3.30	1.00	0	0	0	0	0	0	0	0	0
19	20	3.50	1.20	0	0	0	0	0	0	0	0	0
20	21	3.70	1.40	0	0	0	0	0	0	0	0	0
21	22	3.90	1.60	0	0	0	0	0	0	0	0	0
22	23	4.10	1.70	0	0	0	0	0	0	0	0	0
23	24	4.20	1.90	0	0	0	0	0	0	0	0	0
24	25	4.40	2.10	0	0	0	0	0	0	0	0	0
25	26	4.60	2.30	0	0	0	0	0	0	0	0	0
26	27	4.80	2.50	.20	0	0	0	0	0	0	0	0
27	28	5.00	2.60	.30	0	0	0	0	0	0	0	0
28	29	5.10	2.80	.50	0	0	0	0	0	0	0	0
29	30	5.30	3.00	.70	0	0	0	0	0	0	0	0
30	31	5.50	3.20	.90	0	0	0	0	0	0	0	0
31	32	5.70	3.40	1.10	0	0	0	0	0	0	0	0
32	33	5.90	3.50	1.20	0	0	0	0	0	0	0	0
33	34	6.00	3.70	1.40	0	0	0	0	0	0	0	0
34	35	6.20	3.90	1.60	0	0	0	0	0	0	0	0
35	36	6.40	4.10	1.80	0	0	0	0	0	0	0	0
36	37	6.60	4.30	2.00	0	0	0	0	0	0	0	0
37	38	6.80	4.40	2.10	0	0	0	0	0	0	0	0
38	39	6.90	4.60	2.30	0	0	0	0	0	0	0	0
39	40	7.10	4.80	2.50	.20	0	0	0	0	0	0	0
40	41	7.30	5.00	2.70	.40	0	0	0	0	0	0	0
41	42	7.50	5.20	2.90	.50	0	0	0	0	0	0	0
42	43	7.70	5.30	3.00	.70	0	0	0	0	0	0	0
43	44	7.80	5.50	3.20	.90	0	0	0	0	0	0	0
44	45	8.00	5.70	3.40	1.10	0	0	0	0	0	0	0
45	46	8.20	5.90	3.60	1.30	0	0	0	0	0	0	0
46	47	8.40	6.10	3.80	1.40	0	0	0	0	0	0	0
47	48	8.60	6.20	3.90	1.60	0	0	0	0	0	0	0
48	49	8.70	6.40	4.10	1.80	0	0	0	0	0	0	0
49	50	8.90	6.60	4.30	2.00	0	0	0	0	0	0	0
50	51	9.10	6.80	4.50	2.20	0	0	0	0	0	0	0
51	52	9.30	7.00	4.70	2.30	0	0	0	0	0	0	0
52	53	9.50	7.10	4.80	2.50	.20	0	0	0	0	0	0
53	54	9.60	7.30	5.00	2.70	.40	0	0	0	0	0	0
54	55	9.80	7.50	5.20	2.90	.60	0	0	0	0	0	0

WITHHOLDING TABLE

weekly: payroll period—Continued

And the wages are—		And the number of withholding exemptions claimed is—										
At least	But less than	0	1	2	3	4	5	6	7	8	9	10 or more
		The amount of income tax to be withheld shall be—										
55	56	10.00	7.70	5.40	3.10	.80	0	0	0	0	0	0
56	57	10.20	7.90	5.60	3.20	.90	0	0	0	0	0	0
57	58	10.40	8.00	5.70	3.40	1.10	0	0	0	0	0	0
58	59	10.50	8.20	5.90	3.60	1.30	0	0	0	0	0	0
59	60	10.70	8.40	6.10	3.80	1.50	0	0	0	0	0	0
60	62	11.00	8.70	6.40	4.10	1.70	0	0	0	0	0	0
62	64	11.30	9.00	6.70	4.40	2.10	0	0	0	0	0	0
64	66	11.70	9.40	7.10	4.80	2.50	.20	0	0	0	0	0
66	68	12.10	9.80	7.40	5.10	2.80	.50	0	0	0	0	0
68	70	12.40	10.10	7.80	5.50	3.20	.90	0	0	0	0	0
70	72	12.80	10.50	8.20	5.90	3.50	1.20	0	0	0	0	0
72	74	13.10	10.80	8.50	6.20	3.90	1.60	0	0	0	0	0
74	76	13.50	11.20	8.90	6.60	4.30	2.00	0	0	0	0	0
76	78	13.90	11.60	9.20	6.90	4.60	2.30	0	0	0	0	0
78	80	14.20	11.90	9.60	7.30	5.00	2.70	.40	0	0	0	0
80	82	14.60	12.30	10.00	7.70	5.30	3.00	.70	0	0	0	0
82	84	14.90	12.60	10.30	8.00	5.70	3.40	1.10	0	0	0	0
84	86	15.30	13.00	10.70	8.40	6.10	3.80	1.50	0	0	0	0
86	88	15.70	13.40	11.00	8.70	6.40	4.10	1.80	0	0	0	0
88	90	16.00	13.70	11.40	9.10	6.80	4.50	2.20	0	0	0	0
90	92	16.40	14.10	11.80	9.50	7.10	4.80	2.50	.20	0	0	0
92	94	16.70	14.40	12.10	9.80	7.50	5.20	2.90	.60	0	0	0
94	96	17.10	14.80	12.50	10.20	7.90	5.60	3.30	.90	0	0	0
96	98	17.50	15.20	12.80	10.50	8.20	5.90	3.60	1.30	0	0	0
98	100	17.80	15.50	13.20	10.90	8.60	6.30	4.00	1.70	0	0	0
100	105	18.50	16.10	13.80	11.50	9.20	6.90	4.60	2.30	0	0	0
105	110	19.40	17.00	14.70	12.40	10.10	7.80	5.50	3.20	.90	0	0
110	115	20.30	17.90	15.60	13.30	11.00	8.70	6.40	4.10	1.80	0	0
115	120	21.20	18.80	16.50	14.20	11.90	9.60	7.30	5.00	2.70	.40	0
120	125	22.10	19.70	17.40	15.10	12.80	10.50	8.20	5.90	3.60	1.30	0
125	130	23.00	20.60	18.30	16.00	13.70	11.40	9.10	6.80	4.50	2.20	0
130	135	23.90	21.50	19.20	16.90	14.60	12.30	10.00	7.70	5.40	3.10	.80
135	140	24.80	22.40	20.10	17.80	15.50	13.20	10.90	8.60	6.30	4.00	1.70
140	145	25.70	23.30	21.00	18.70	16.40	14.10	11.80	9.50	7.20	4.90	2.60
145	150	26.60	24.20	21.90	19.60	17.30	15.00	12.70	10.40	8.10	5.80	3.50
150	160	27.90	25.60	23.30	21.00	18.70	16.40	14.10	11.70	9.40	7.10	4.80
160	170	29.70	27.40	25.10	22.80	20.50	18.20	15.90	13.50	11.20	8.90	6.60
170	180	31.50	29.20	26.90	24.60	22.30	20.00	17.70	15.30	13.00	10.70	8.40
180	190	33.30	31.00	28.70	26.40	24.10	21.80	19.50	17.10	14.80	12.50	10.20
190	200	35.10	32.80	30.50	28.20	25.90	23.60	21.30	18.90	16.60	14.30	12.00
		18 percent of the excess over $200 plus—										
$200 and over		36.00	33.70	31.40	29.10	26.80	24.50	22.20	19.80	17.50	15.20	12.90

containing the number 46 until you reach the column headed by the number 1. Your pointer should come to rest on the number $6.10. The number 1 that headed the column where your pointer stopped represents the number of exemptions claimed by Carl Walker. The $6.10 is the income tax he will have to pay each week.

Example 2

Mr. Berkely earns $127.42 weekly. When he received his position, he filled out a form notifying his employer that he was entitled to five exemptions—himself, his wife, and three children. How much income tax should be withheld from his salary each week by the payroll clerk?

Solution: As in Example 1, follow down the column headed "At least" until the salary $127.42 is isolated between two numbers—one slightly smaller, the other slightly larger. These will be 125 and 130. Move your pointer across the row containing the number 125 until you reach the column headed by the number 5. Your pointer should come to rest on $11.40. This is Mr. Berkely's weekly tax.

LEARNING EXERCISES

A. Gary Meeker worked during the summer, earning $47.50 a week. As he was already claimed as an exemption by his father, Gary listed no exemption for himself with his employer. How much income tax was withheld from Gary's salary each week?

B. In each of the following problems, find the income tax withheld. The amounts listed are weekly salaries.

No.	Salary	Exemptions	Income Tax	No.	Salary	Exemptions	Income Tax
1	$39.50	1	$xxx	11	$103.27	5	$xxx
2	43.75	2	xxx	12	75.42	6	xxx
3	56.87	3	xxx	13	54.27	5	xxx
4	59.70	4	xxx	14	127.30	5	xxx
5	96.25	3	xxx	15	149.73	3	xxx
6	75.56	2	xxx	16	156.27	6	xxx
7	44.00	5	xxx	17	188.34	11	xxx
8	62.00	1	xxx	18	99.72	0	xxx
9	83.00	3	xxx	19	14.25	0	xxx
10	41.27	0	xxx	20	196.82	3	xxx

C. Charles Armond earns $227.42 each week. If he claims three exemptions, how much will be withheld from his salary each week for income tax?

SECTION 3   Computing Net Salary

You are now prepared to consider the complete payroll register, or, what is more important to you, how your weekly salary will be computed in any position you may hold. Earlier you learned that the total salary you would receive if no money was withheld from you is called the *gross salary*. The amount that remains after the deductions have been subtracted is called the *net salary*, or *net pay*.

Example 1

Explain how the following payroll register was completed.

Payroll Register										
Em-ployee	Exemp-tions	M T W T F S	Reg. Hrs.	Reg. Rate	Gross Salary	Soc. Sec.	Income Tax	Total Deduc.	Net Salary
#357	3	8 8 7 8 8 —	39	$1.75	$68.25	$1.54	$5.50	$7.04	$61.21

Solution: All the numbers up to and including the gross salary were found in the same manner as was described in Section 1 of this unit. The Social Security tax and the income tax were found by referring to the tables in Section 2. The Total Deductions are simply the sum of the two taxes ($1.54 + $5.50). The Net Salary is the amount that is left after the Total Deductions were subtracted from the Gross Salary ($68.25 − $7.04).

Deductions required by the Federal Government for Social Security and income tax are not the only amounts that are withheld from an employee's salary. He may have money taken from his pay for each of the following items:

1. Savings Bonds. Many large companies, as a service to the Federal Government, have arranged to deduct a fixed amount from an employee's salary toward the purchase of Government savings bonds.

2. Hospitalization, etc. To insure against the loss of savings brought about by the necessity of paying hospital and medical bills, employees will protect themselves through weekly deductions from their salaries.

3. Union Dues. Many unions have made arrangements with the management of companies to have union dues deducted from the union member's salary.

4. Pension Fund. Within recent years, concerns have included pension funds among the many advantages of being employed by these companies. Usually, payments to these funds are made by both the company and the employee.

Because of these possible deductions and the requirements of overtime salary, a complete payroll register would resemble the accompanying form.

Example 2

PAYROLL REGISTER

Employee	Exemp-tions	M	T	W	T	F	S	Reg. Hrs.	Reg. Rate	Amount	Over-time Hrs.
1 Camp, T.	3	8	8	6	8	7	0	37	$1.68	$62.16	—
2 Port, S.	4	8	8	8½	8	8	8	40	2.06	82.40	8½

PAYROLL REGISTER (Continued)

	Over-time Rate	Amount	Gross Salary	Deductions				Net Salary
				Soc. Sec.	Income Tax	Other Deduc.	Total Deduc.	
1	—	—	$62.16	$1.40	$4.40	$1.87	$7.67	$54.49
2	$3.09	$26.27	108.67	2.45	10.10	2.04	14.59	94.08

Explanation: T. Camp, having worked less than 40 hours, received no overtime pay. Hence, dashes were entered in these places. The Social Security ($1.40) and income tax ($4.40) were found in their respective tables. All other deductions were grouped under the heading Other Deductions. The amount in the column Total Deductions is the sum of the three deductions listed ($1.40 + $4.40 + $1.87). The Net Salary is the difference between the Gross Salary and the Total Deductions ($62.16 − $7.67 = $54.49).

S. Port, who worked 48½ hours that week, received 40 hours' pay based on the regular rate and 8½ hours' pay based on the overtime rate. The Overtime Rate was found by multiplying the Regular Rate ($2.06) by 1½ to obtain $3.09. The rest of the register was completed as was done for T. Camp.

LEARNING EXERCISES

1. None of the men in the following table worked overtime during the week shown. Prepare a payroll register similar to the one shown in Example 1 on page 175 and complete it, using the information in the Social Security and Income Tax tables.

Employee	Exemp-tions	M	T	W	T	F	S	Regular Rate
Barr, S.	1	8	8	—	8	8	8	$1.32
Curtin, E.	0	8	7	8	8	—	6	1.56
Fern, L.	5	10	4	—	8	8	8	1.89
Lucas, G.	4	$7\frac{1}{2}$	8	8	—	8	8	2.64
Parlin, E.	4	$6\frac{3}{4}$	—	8	8	7	6	2.08
Sutton, M.	3	—	$7\frac{1}{2}$	8	$7\frac{1}{4}$	8	8	1.88

44.51

2. Prepare a payroll register similar to that used in Example 2 on page 176 and complete it, using the following information.

Payroll Register
Eric Joel Plastic Arts Company
Payroll for Week Ending November 10, 19—

Employee	Exemp-tions	M	T	W	T	F	Regular Rate	Other Deduc-tions
Archer, M.	5	8	8	8	8	8	$2.24	$1.08
Derk, T.	2	8	8	8	8	8	1.86	2.57
Fuller, G.	4	8	10	8	9	9	2.08	3.75
Grigg, P.	3	$8\frac{1}{2}$	8	4	8	8	1.44	.87
Mellen, S.	7	10	10	10	8	8	2.56	4.42
Noll, J.	0	8	$7\frac{1}{2}$	$6\frac{1}{2}$	8	8	1.18	.58
Rice, F.	1	$5\frac{1}{4}$	8	8	7	8	1.26	.69
Wagner, B.	3	8	$8\frac{3}{4}$	8	8	8	1.96	2.43
Warren, C.	2	9	8	$8\frac{1}{2}$	10	8	2.39	3.21
York, S.	5	8	7	$5\frac{3}{4}$	8	8	2.51	3.76

UNIT 2   The Straight Piecework Wage System

The straight piecework wage system, which is described in this unit, is used infrequently today as a method of paying wages to employees. At one time it was believed that the use of this method of payment would act as an incentive to workers to produce more goods. Now, however, both management and labor agree that, to a large extent, it has failed to fulfill this purpose.

In the straight piecework system, an employee's salary depends on the number of articles he is able to complete each week.

To illustrate: Howard Davis, a checker in a radio factory, was able to check 162 radios during the week of June 5, 19—. If he received 54 cents for each radio that he checked, what was his gross salary that week?

Solution: Since he received 54 cents for each of the 162 radios, to find his gross salary, 162 is multiplied by $.54, giving a product of $87.48.

Outline: Gross Salary = Number of Units × Salary per Unit
$$= \quad 162 \quad \times \quad 54¢$$
$$= \$87.48$$

From this salary, both the Social Security tax and the income tax have yet to be deducted. Hence, to find the net salary (assuming 2 exemptions):

Net Salary = Gross Salary − (Income Tax + Social Security)
$$= \$87.48 \quad − (\quad \$11.00 \quad + \quad \$1.97)$$
$$= \$87.48 \quad − \quad \$12.97$$
$$= \$74.51$$

The Social Security tax and the income tax were found in the tables, as in the problems in Unit 1.

Example

Complete the following payroll register.

Payroll Register												
Employee	Exemp-tions	Number of Articles					Total Articles	Rate	Gross Sal.	Deductions			Net Sal.
		M	T	W	T	F				Soc. Sec.	Inc. Tax	Total Deduc.	
Waldron, P.	3	19	16	23	24	20	xxx	63½¢	$xxx	$xxx	$xxx	$xxx	$xxx

Solution: The Total Articles is found by adding the number of articles produced each day during the week (19 + 16 + 23 + 24 + 20). This sum is 102. At 63½ cents an article, the Gross Salary will be 102 × 63½ cents, or $64.77. Social Security tax and Income Tax are found in the tables, and the Net Salary is found by subtracting the Total Deductions from the Gross Salary ($64.77 − $6.26 = $58.51).

PAYROLL REGISTER (Completed)												
Employee	Exemp-tions	Number of Articles					Total Articles	Rate	Gross Salary	Deductions			Net Salary
		M	T	W	T	F				Soc. Sec.	Inc. Tax	Total Deduc.	
Waldron, P.	3	19	16	23	24	20	102	63½¢	$64.77	$1.46	$4.80	$6.26	$58.51

LEARNING EXERCISES

1. Find the gross salary of each of the following employees by copying and completing the accompanying partial payroll register.

Payroll Register Carlson Thread Company Payroll for Week Ending May 27, 19—								
Employee	No. of Articles					Total Articles	Rate	Gross Salary
	M	T	W	T	F			
J. Adams	17	21	18	20	22	xxx	$.67	$xxx
W. Cook	24	23	20	22	19	xxx	.72½	xxx
H. Walsh	18	21	22	19	18	xxx	.65	xxx
S. Moran	19	22	24	25	21	xxx	.67½	xxx
W. Martin	26	23	20	22	24	xxx	.77½	xxx
H. Shaw	24	21	19	22	20	xxx	.78	xxx
H. Owens	27	24	23	28	24	xxx	.78½	xxx
C. Grant	20	18	16	19	21	xxx	.76	xxx

2. Prepare a payroll register similar to the one used in the illustrative example on page 179 and complete it, using the following information.

		No. of Articles						
Employee	Exemptions	M	T	W	T	F	S	Rate
B. Maxwell	2	23	26	29	22	15	25	$.57
R. Brubeck	1	18	21	23	19	20	14	.62
N. Langfield	3	21	20	22	25	23	12	.60
G. Meadows	0	24	22	25	23	26	13	.58
J. Carpenter	4	23	24	27	25	21	17	.57$\frac{1}{2}$
C. Burns	2	25	26	29	24	27	16	.55$\frac{1}{2}$

MARCIA ELIZABETH EDUCATIONAL TOYS, INC.

Payroll for the Week Ending April 17, 19—

UNIT 3   Preparation of a Currency Memorandum

Although many firms pay their employees by check, the majority still pay by cash. Most employees prefer this method of payment because it relieves them of the problem of having to cash their checks. Banks are not always open at times convenient to workers. Hence, many employees whose salaries are paid by check must resort to check-cashing agencies, which charge a fee for their services. On the other hand, companies that pay by cash run the risk of theft because large sums of money must be on hand to meet their payrolls. In addition, paying by cash requires extra hours of work for the paymaster. He must determine the exact currency that is needed for each employee. For example, four employees of the art department of an advertising firm earn weekly $92.50, $93.25, $108.90, and $105.35, respectively. The weekly payroll for these men totals $400. Should the payroll messenger return from the bank with 4 $100 bills, it would be impossible to pay any of these employees the exact amount of his salary because of the lack of the proper denominations of currency.

To prevent such situations from arising, forms called *currency break-*

ups or *currency breakdowns* or simply *change sheets* are prepared. When completed, these tabulations show the exact currency that is needed to meet the salary of every employee.

Thus, the following currency breakdown shows how the exact denominations of currency needed to pay the salaries of the four employees in the art department are determined.

Currency Breakdown											
Name	Net Salary	Bills					Coins				
		$20	$10	$5	$2	$1	50¢	25¢	10¢	5¢	1¢
Deering, F.	$ 92.50	4	1		1		1				
Gruen, J.	93.25	4	1		1	1		1			
Hunter, L.	108.90	5		1	1	1	1	1	1	1	
Walker, M.	105.35	5		1				1	1		
Total	$400.00	18	2	2	3	2	2	3	2	1	

Explanation: F. Deering's salary of $92.50 consisted of 4 $20 bills, 1 $10 bill, 1 $2 bill, and 1 50-cent piece. The bills and coins for each of the other men were found in the same way. The amounts in the Total row were found by adding the numbers in each of the columns. The numbers in this Total row show the total number of bills and coins of each denomination that are needed to make up the payroll.

In order to keep the payroll envelope from becoming too bulky, bills and coins of the largest possible denominations are used. Because merchants dislike receiving payment for merchandise with bills that are greater than $20, the largest denomination that usually appears in a currency breakdown is $20. The currency-breakdown form is somewhat cumbersome and contains much material that is of no value to the bank. Hence, the information contained thereon is summarized on another form called a *change memorandum*. It is this form that the bank clerk uses when counting the bills and coins needed to meet the payroll of a firm.

The information on the currency breakdown illustrated is summarized in the change memorandum shown on page 182.

Explanation: Each of the numbers in the column headed Number was taken from the Total row in the currency-breakdown form. The numbers in the Amount column were determined by multiplying each number in the Number column by its corresponding number in the Bills column. Thus, $360 was found by multiplying $20 by 18. Finding the total of $400 serves two purposes. Not only does it show the bank teller the total amount of money that is needed, but also it acts as a check on the total net salary that appears on the currency-breakdown form.

	Change Memorandum			
	Week Ending August 8, 19--			
BILLS	**NUMBER**	**AMOUNT**		
$20	18	$360	00	
10	2	20	00	
5	2	10	00	
2	3	6	00	
1	2	2	00	
COINS				
50¢	2	1	00	
25¢	3		75	
10¢	2		20	
5¢	1		05	
1¢	–		--	
	Total	$400	00	

LEARNING EXERCISES

1. Complete the following currency breakdown, and prepare a change memorandum similar to the one in the illustration above.

		Currency Breakdown									
		Bills					Coins				
Name	Net Salary	$20	$10	$5	$2	$1	50¢	25¢	10¢	5¢	1¢
Kane, M.	$67.25	xxx	xxx	xxx	xxx	xxx	xxx	xxx	xxx	xxx	xxx
Rich, T.	84.05	xxx	xxx	xxx	xxx	xxx	xxx	xxx	xxx	xxx	xxx
Traynor, H.	76.23	xxx	xxx	xxx	xxx	xxx	xxx	xxx	xxx	xxx	xxx
Waldo, H.	95.42	xxx	xxx	xxx	xxx	xxx	xxx	xxx	xxx	xxx	xxx
Total	$xxx	xxx	xxx	xxx	xxx	xxx	xxx	xxx	xxx	xxx	xxx

2. Copy and complete the following payroll register. After finding the net salary, prepare a currency breakdown and a change memorandum.

Payroll Register
Frederick Construction Company

Payroll for Week Ending August 8, 19—

Employee	Exemptions	M	T	W	T	F	Hrs.	Rate	Gross Salary	Deductions				Net Salary
										Soc. Sec.	Inc. Tax	Other Deduc.	Total Deduc.	
Becker, C.	3	8	8	8	8	8	xxx	$1.76	$xxx	$xxx	$xxx	$2.50	$xxx	$xxx
Cranse, T.	4	8	7	8	8	8	xxx	1.84	xxx	xxx	xxx	2.60	xxx	xxx
Fries, R.	2	6	6	8	8	8	xxx	2.06	xxx	xxx	xxx	3.25	xxx	xxx
Hunt, T.	5	8	8	8	8	8	xxx	2.58	xxx	xxx	xxx	3.56	xxx	xxx
Lee, S.	1	8	$7\frac{1}{2}$	8	8	8	xxx	3.08	xxx	xxx	xxx	4.25	xxx	xxx
Parr, K.	0	8	8	4	8	8	xxx	2.24	xxx	xxx	xxx	3.02	xxx	xxx

3. Prepare a currency breakdown and a change memorandum for the following payroll.

Name	Salary	Name	Salary
S. Barr	$ 72.50	*F. Kohler*	$ 97.28
A. Curry	106.65	*A. Noble*	62.04
E. Grimm	83.76	*R. Talbot*	174.26

UNIT **4**   **What Have You Learned?**

SECTION 1   **Understanding Terms**

Match the term in the column on the left with the proper definition in the column on the right.

Term

1. Time and a half
2. Payroll register
3. Gross salary
4. Net salary
5. Income tax exemptions
6. Straight piecework wage system
7. Currency breakdown
8. Change memorandum

Definition

a. An employee's salary before deductions are made.

b. A form showing the exact currency needed for *all* employees.

c. A method of paying employees that is dependent on the number of articles completed by the employee.

d. Overtime salary rate that is $1\frac{1}{2}$ times as large as the regular salary.

e. Amount received by an employee after deductions are made.

f. A form containing all the information pertaining to employees' salaries.

g. Tax taken from an employee's income to help pay for Federal Government expenditures.

h. Persons dependent on a taxpayer for their support.

i. A form showing the exact currency needed for *each* employee.

SECTION 2   Review Problems

If you are unable to solve the following problems, review the pages indicated in parentheses.

1. Robert Hunter worked 38½ hours during one week. If he receives $1.67½ an hour, what was his gross salary that week? (Page 163.)

2. During one week, Paul Moore worked 46½ hours. His regular hourly rate is $1.76. For work over 40 hours a week, he receives 1½ times the regular rate. Find his gross salary for the week. (Pages 163–165.)

3. Thomas Russell's gross salary for the week of June 9, 19—, was $86.42. For income tax purposes, he claimed his wife and two children as exemptions, in addition to himself. During this week,

    a. What was his income tax deduction? (Pages 171–174.)

    b. What was his Social Security deduction? (Pages 166–167.)

4. Find the amount that will be deducted from each of the following weekly salaries for the Social Security tax. Assume that the employee has not as yet earned $4,200 during the year. (Pages 166–167.)

    a. $48   **b.** $53.40   **c.** $87.75   **d.** $106.30

5. Find the income tax withheld from each of the following weekly salaries. (Pages 171–174.)

No.	Salary	Exemptions	No.	Salary	Exemptions
a	$42.75	1	c	$ 96.27	3
b	53.42	0	d	147.52	5

6. George Telfer was paid $2.26 an hour plus time and a half for all work over 40 hours a week. During the week of May 3, 19—, he worked 46¼ hours. What was his net salary that week after deductions for income tax, Social Security, and other items amounting to $2.50 were made from his salary? He claimed 3 exemptions. (Page 175.)

7. Elaine Tillson worked as a door-to-door saleswoman for the Elite Hosiery Company. She received 35 cents for each pair of stockings that she sold. During the week of May 17, 19—, she sold 182 pairs of stockings. Find her net salary after income tax and Social Security deductions. She claimed only 1 exemption. (Page 178.)

8. Prepare a currency breakdown and a change memorandum for the following employees of the Tobacco Sales Company. (Pages 180–182.)

Name	Net Salary	Name	Net Salary
W. Hoffman	$74.25	C. Reynolds	$ 96.82
J. Mason	83.56	P. Taft	54.07
E. Morton	69.45	A. Voorhies	127.58

9. Copy and complete the following payroll register, using a form similar to the one on page 176. Compute time and a half for all work over the 40-hour week. Prepare a currency breakdown and a change memorandum. (Pages 180–182.)

	Talktown Baking Company Payroll for the Week Ending June 5, 19—								
Employee	Exemp-tions	M	T	W	T	F	S	Reg. Rate	Other Deduc-tions
Harding, C.	2	8	8	8	8	8	—	$1.64	$2.57
Kohl, R.	4	8	8	—	8	10	8	2.16	3.04
McAdam, T.	3	9	8	$6\frac{1}{2}$	8	8	4	1.96	1.87
Renner, K.	1	8	8	$7\frac{1}{4}$	8	8	8	1.60	1.04
Sears, A.	0	$6\frac{1}{2}$	8	8	$7\frac{1}{2}$	—	8	1.14	.86
Swan, G.	5	8	8	8	8	8	8	3.28	4.73

SECTION 3   Testing Your Understanding

Part 1—40 Minutes

1. George Talbot received $1.48 an hour. What was his salary during a week in which he worked $38\frac{1}{4}$ hours?

2. Find the amount due an employee for a $48\frac{1}{2}$-hour week at $2.62 an hour if he receives time and a half for all work over 40 hours.

3. How much should be deducted from each of the following weekly salaries for Social Security tax? Assume that the salaries earned thus far during the year are less than $4,200.

    a. $56   **b.** $63.60   **c.** $67.75   **d.** $114.20

4. How much should be deducted from each of the following weekly salaries for income tax?

No.	Salary	Exemptions	No.	Salary	Exemptions
a	$45.65	0	c	$ 91.34	2
b	59.25	1	d	154.26	5

Payroll Register

Employee	Exemption	M	T	W	T	F	S	Reg. Hrs.	Reg. Rate	Amt.	Over-time Hrs.	Over-time Rate	Amt.	Gross Salary	Soc. Sec.	Income Tax	Other Deduc.	Total Deduc.	Net Salary
Dane, T.	2	8	8	8	8	8	—	xxx	$1.88	$xxx	xxx	$xxx	$xxx	$xxx	$xxx	$xxx	$1.56	$xxx	$xxx
Haas, P.	1	8	8	6	7	8	8	xxx	2.06	xxx	xxx	xxx	xxx	xxx	xxx	xxx	1.63	xxx	xxx
Park, R.	4	8	9½	8	8	6	8	xxx	3.24	xxx	xxx	xxx	xxx	xxx	xxx	xxx	2.27	xxx	xxx
Sarle, K.	0	8	8	8	8	8	5¼	xxx	2.96	xxx	xxx	xxx	xxx	xxx	xxx	xxx	1.18	xxx	xxx
Treat, A.	3	8	8	8	9	8	—	xxx	3.20	xxx	xxx	xxx	xxx	xxx	xxx	xxx	3.82	xxx	xxx
Wirt, W.	2	8	9	8	9	9	4	xxx	2.84	xxx	xxx	xxx	xxx	xxx	xxx	xxx	2.75	xxx	xxx
Young, C.	1	8	7	9	9	7	5	xxx	3.10	xxx	xxx	xxx	xxx	xxx	xxx	xxx	3.54	xxx	xxx

5. William Reid worked as a draftsman at $2.58 an hour plus time and a half for any time he was asked to work over a 40-hour week. In order to meet a work schedule during the week of September 15, 19—, he worked $58\frac{3}{4}$ hours. What was his net salary that week after income tax and Social Security payments were deducted from his gross salary? For income tax purposes he claimed 2 exemptions.

6. Copy and complete the following currency breakdown. On the basis of this breakdown, prepare a change memorandum that is to be taken to the bank.

		Bills					Coins				
Name	Net Salary	$20	$10	$5	$2	$1	50¢	25¢	10¢	5¢	1¢
Bayer, R.	$ 83.25	xxx	xxx	xxx	xxx	xxx	xxx	xxx	xxx	xxx	xxx
Ernst, A.	72.85	xxx	xxx	xxx	xxx	xxx	xxx	xxx	xxx	xxx	xxx
Hummel, G.	45.28	xxx	xxx	xxx	xxx	xxx	xxx	xxx	xxx	xxx	xxx
Mayo, L.	63.92	xxx	xxx	xxx	xxx	xxx	xxx	xxx	xxx	xxx	xxx
Ritter, S.	104.34	xxx	xxx	xxx	xxx	xxx	xxx	xxx	xxx	xxx	xxx
Total	$ xxx	xxx	xxx	xxx	xxx	xxx	xxx	xxx	xxx	xxx	xxx

Currency Breakdown
Robert's Auto Maintenance

Part 2—40 Minutes

Copy and complete the payroll register on page 187.

UNIT 5 General Review

SECTION 1 To Improve Your Speed and Accuracy

1. Addition:

a. 642
    87
  6,958
   516

b. $375.24
   87.02
    4.59
     .36

c. $73\frac{1}{3}$
  $24\frac{5}{8}$
  $56\frac{3}{4}$

d. $58 + $637 + $42.87 + $1.65

e. $15\frac{3}{4} + 8\frac{2}{3} + 16\frac{1}{2}$

2. Subtraction:

a. 385	**b.** $507.59	$24\frac{3}{4}$
296	372.68	$17\frac{2}{3}$

d. $67.25 − $.89   **e.** $37 − 14\frac{4}{5}$

3. Multiplication:

a. 538×67 **b.** 48.02×83 **c.** 69.14×83

d. $8\frac{2}{3} \times 15$ **e.** $5\frac{1}{3} \times 4\frac{2}{3}$ **f.** $65\frac{2}{3} \times 24\frac{1}{2}$

4. Division:

a. $5,336 \div 58$ **b.** $753 \div .03$ **c.** $4,685.37 \div 1.07$

d. $15 \div \frac{2}{3}$ **e.** $16\frac{1}{2} \div \frac{3}{8}$ **f.** $3\frac{1}{2} \div 1\frac{3}{4}$

SECTION 2   Do You Remember These?

1. Change to per cent values:

a. .42   **b.** .06   **c.** $\frac{17}{50}$

d. .3   **e.** 4   **f.** $2\frac{3}{4}$

2. Change to decimal values:

a. 47%   **b.** 2%   **c.** 5.3%   **d.** 127%

3. Change to a fraction:

a. 20%   **b.** 400%   **c.** 45%   **d.** $2\frac{1}{2}$%

4. 15% of $4,500 is how much money?

5. 50 cents is what % of $2.50?

6. $1.98 is 20% of how much money?

7. A box of candy weighing 12 ounces cost $1.08.

    a. What is the cost of 1 ounce of this candy?

    b. What is the cost of 1 pound of this candy?

8. The weekly salaries of the 6 men employed in a clothing store are: $85.72, $79.64, $93.25, $88.40, $102.56, $157.30. What is the average weekly salary of these 6 men?

9. William Collins insured his baggage and personal effects for $900 at the time he took a trip. If the rate was 95 cents for each $100 worth of insurance, what was the total cost of the insurance?

10. A woman bought $3\frac{3}{4}$ yards of material for a skirt at $1.79 a yard. What was the total cost of the material?

8

Trade and Cash Discounts

PREVIEW

In order to clear his storeroom of merchandise, a furniture manufacturer offers for 5 days only a discount rate of 5% on his entire stock in addition to his usual trade-discount rate of 20%. Ralph Marshall, as the owner of a retail furniture store, would like to take advantage of this reduction. Unfortunately, he does not have the cash to pay for the merchandise he would like to buy. Mr. Marshall must, therefore, either decline this offer or borrow the money from the bank at the rate of 6% a year. At the end of 2 months, however, he will be able to pay back the debt to the bank by using the profits from the sale of this furniture. Should Mr. Marshall borrow the money or decline the offer?

For Class Discussion

1. What is meant by the words *trade discount?*
2. Why do manufacturers offer discounts on their merchandise?
3. What type of a store is a *retail store?*
4. Why was the bank's discount rate quoted as *6% a year,* while the manufacturer's rate was simply quoted as *5%,* with no period of time noted?
5. Will the discounts of 20% and 5% be computed on the same amount of money?
6. If Mr. Marshall could not pay off the debt for an entire year, would it be to his advantage to borrow the money for the purchase of the furniture at the reduced rates?

Terms You Should Know

Making the choice in the situation described in the Preview problem is not merely a matter of tossing a coin into the air. The businessman who resorts to such tactics will soon find that he has no business. In order to make a wise decision, however, you must be familiar with the terms used in the problem. Even more important to you is the need for some understanding of how you might determine the cost of each alternative. Only then would you know whether going into debt is the better thing to do. What you learn in this chapter should help you to understand how to reach your decision.

Of the words in the Preview that may be unfamiliar to you, the most important is the term *trade discount.* This word owes its name to the fact that people in a particular business are spoken of by others in that business as being "in the trade." Thus, one shoe-store owner would refer to another shoestore owner as being "in the trade." Hence, a *trade discount* is a reduction in price that the manufacturer or the wholesaler grants to a merchant in the trade. The original price of the article is called either the *list price* or the *catalogue price,* since the prices of all the manufacturer's goods are *listed* in a book called a *catalogue.* It is the price at which he holds himself ready to sell to all customers. The actual cost to the merchant is the *net price.*

As an example, if a bicycle manufacturer lists a bicycle at $40 but charges the stores only $30, then:

→$40 is the *list,* or *catalogue,* price.

→$10 is the *trade discount.*

→$30 is the *net* price.

There are several reasons why the man who makes or distributes the article is willing to sell it to the store owner at a trade discount.

1. Most important is the fact that the price at which the article is eventually sold to the consumer is usually the catalogue, or list, price of the article. Hence, if the merchant received no trade discount from this price, he would not make a profit when he sells the article.

2. The cost of the article may change several times during the year. Rather than reprint a new and expensive catalogue, the manufacturer merely issues a discount sheet listing the number of the article and the new trade discount.

3. Frequently, the size of the trade discount is determined by the quantity purchased by the merchant; the larger the purchase, the greater the discount.

4. Under certain conditions, the manufacturer grants a merchant a special discount. This often occurs when a competing firm is trying to undercut the market—sell merchandise at cost or below.

In the world of business, the terms *discount* and *discount rate* are frequently used interchangeably. You should find it simple to keep them distinct. As you have just learned, *discount* is the actual number of *dollars* and *cents* by which an article is reduced in price. *Discount rate* is merely a *per cent* value, like 10% or 25%. As it is a per cent, it will not tell you by how many dollars the cost of the article was lowered but merely by what *rate*. Thus, a 10% discount rate means a $10 reduction for every $100 in the cost.

Example

An armchair was listed at $200, less 25%. This reduction of 25% of the list price amounted to $50 for the storekeeper.

→$200 is the *list price.*

→$50 is the *trade discount.*

→25% is the *discount rate.*

Concerning This Chapter

No merchant could stay in business very long if he was not able to determine the trade discount that was granted him by the manufacturer or wholesaler. Not only would he not know the cost of the goods purchased, but also he would find it impossible to decide at what price to sell the goods. Hence, in this chapter you will learn how to determine the trade discount and the net purchase price.

There are times when the manufacturer prefers to give several discount rates, such as 10% and 5%. You will probably be surprised to learn that such a rate is not the same as a 15% rate. Part of your work in this chapter will be to learn to what single rate of discount two or three successive rates are equivalent (the same as). You will also learn how to find the list price when the net price and the discount rate are given.

UNIT 1   Finding the Trade Discount and the Net Price

A METHOD FOR FINDING THE NET PRICE

Business Transaction: The Weber Piano Manufacturing Company listed its spinets at $850, less a trade discount of 35%. What did the dealer have to pay for these instruments?

Solution: Since the dealer is allowed a reduction of 35% of the list price, this discount is found by multiplying .35 by the list price of $850. The discount, $297.50, is then deducted from the catalogue price, $850, leaving a net price to the dealer of $552.50.

Outline: → Known: List Price $850
　　　　　　　　Discount Rate 35%
　　　　→ To Find: Net Price
　　　　→ Method: Discount = List Price × Discount Rate
　　　　　　　　　　　= $850 × 35%
　　　　　　　　　　　= $297.50
　　　　　　　Net Price = List Price − Discount
　　　　　　　　　　　= $850 − $297.50
　　　　　　　　　　　= $552.50

LEARNING EXERCISES

Find the discount and the net price in each of the following purchases.

No.	List Price	Trade Discount Rate	Trade Discount	Net Price
1	$ 60.00	20%	$xxx	$xxx
2	135.00	18%	xxx	xxx
3	240.00	12$\frac{1}{2}$%	xxx	xxx
4	475.25	27%	xxx	xxx
5	69.98	16$\frac{2}{3}$%	xxx	xxx
6	299.95	34.7%	xxx	xxx
7	798.50	25%	xxx	xxx
8	2,376.75	33$\frac{1}{3}$%	xxx	xxx
9	3,584.16	37$\frac{1}{2}$%	xxx	xxx
10	45,850.25	26.8%	xxx	xxx

A SECOND METHOD FOR FINDING THE NET PRICE

Business Transaction: The Better Built Furniture Company sold its sofas to department stores at $320, less 40%. What was the net price to the dealer?

Solution: As the dealer was allowed a reduction of 40% of the list, he had to pay only 60% of the list. 60% of $320 is $192. This is the net price.

Outline: $\rightarrow$ Known: List Price $320
Discount Rate 40%
$\rightarrow$ To Find: Net Price
$\rightarrow$ Method: Net Price Rate = 100% − Discount Rate
= 100% −   40%
= 60%
Net Price = List Price × Net Price Rate
= $320   ×   60%
= $192

A THIRD METHOD FOR FINDING THE NET PRICE

Business Transaction: The Better Built Furniture Company offered a discount of 37$\frac{1}{2}$% on its armchairs. What would be the net price of a chair catalogued at $160?

Solution: Frequently, it is better to change a per cent value to its common-fraction equivalent than to its decimal equivalent. As you learned in Chapter 6, $37\frac{1}{2}\% = \frac{3}{8}$. Hence, if the dealer is allowed a discount of $\frac{3}{8}$ of the list, he will have to pay only $\frac{5}{8}$ of the $160, or $100. The net price, therefore, is $100.

Outline: → Known: List Price $160

Discount Rate $37\frac{1}{2}\% = \frac{3}{8}$

→ To Find: Net Price

→ Method: Net Price Rate = 1 − Discount Rate

$$= 1 - \qquad \frac{3}{8}$$

$$= \frac{5}{8}$$

Net Price = List Price × Net Price Rate

$$= \qquad \$160 \quad \times \quad \frac{5}{8}$$

$$= \qquad \$100$$

LEARNING EXERCISES

A. Using the more appropriate of the preceding methods, find the net price in each of the following examples.

No.	List Price	Trade Discount Rate	Net Price
1	$600.00	30%	$xxx
2	425.00	24%	xxx
3	320.00	$12\frac{1}{2}\%$	xxx
4	184.25	18%	xxx
5	256.80	$33\frac{1}{3}\%$	xxx
6	499.95	2%	xxx

B. *Problems to Be Solved*

1. The Star Lighting Company purchased 7 floor lamps from its distributor at $18.75 each. This purchase was subject to a trade discount of 35%. What was the total net price?

2. Collier and Company, manufacturers of men's sport clothes, sold to one of its dealers 1 dozen sport jackets at $39.50 each and 3 dozen slacks at $12.50 each. The entire purchase carried with it a trade discount rate of $37\frac{1}{2}\%$. Find the total net cost to the dealer.

U N I T **2**   **Using a Series of Discounts**

Because of increased production, decrease in production costs, or perhaps to meet the price of a competitor, a manufacturer may desire during the year to grant a trade discount in addition to the one already noted in his catalogue. Thus, he might state that henceforth all articles listed in his catalogue are not only subject to the usual trade discount rate of 25% but also to an added rate of 10%. You may wonder why the manufacturer did not simply say that he was offering the merchandise at 35% off. The reason for this was that he did not wish to offer the high rate of 35%. 25% and 10% is less than a single discount rate of 35%. A *discount series* of 25% and 10% implies that a reduction of 25% is to be taken on the original amount, and that the 10% is to be found on the balance that remains after the first discount has been subtracted.

Business Transaction: Find the cost of merchandise listed at $840, less 20% and 10%.

Solution—Method 1: The first discount rate of 20% is computed on the original $840. 20% of $840 = $168. This leaves a balance of $672. The second discount rate of 10% is computed on the balance of $672. 10% of $672 = $67.20. The net price, or the cost of the article, therefore, is $672 less $67.20, or $604.80.

Outline: → Known: List Price $840
            Discount Series   20% and 10%
      → To Find: Net Cost
      → Method: First Balance = List Price − First Discount
                        = $840   − ($840 × 20%)
                        = $840   − $168
                        = $672
            Net Cost = First Balance − Second Discount
                        = $672   − ($672 × 10%)
                        = $672   − $67.20
                        = $604.80

Method 2: If you are allowed a discount rate of 20% *of* the list, it means that you must pay 80% *of* the $840. This amounts to $672. In addition, you are granted a reduction of 10% of this new price of $672, meaning that you are required to pay 90% *of* the $672. Therefore, the net cost will be $604.80.

Outline: → Known: List Price $840

Discount Series   20% and 10%

→ To Find: Net Cost

→ Method: First Balance = List Price × (100% − First
    Discount Rate)
    = $840   × (100% − 20%)
    = $840   × 80%
    = $672

Net Cost = First Balance × (100% − Second
    Discount Rate)
    = $672   × (100% − 10%)
    = $672   × 90%
    = $604.80

Method 3: As you have already learned, in some situations it may be more desirable to convert the per cents to common fractions than to decimals. Instead of expressing the discount rates as 20% and 10%, you could write them as $\frac{1}{5}$ and $\frac{1}{10}$. If this is done, the first balance will be $\frac{4}{5}$ of the $840, or $672. The net price will be $\frac{9}{10}$ of the $672, or $604.80. This last sentence could have been written $\frac{9}{10}$ of the ($\frac{4}{5}$ of $840), since $672 was found to be $\frac{4}{5}$ of $840. Thus, the problem can be expressed as $\frac{9}{10} \times \frac{4}{5} \times$ $840, or $840 $\times \frac{9}{10} \times \frac{4}{5}$, which is $604.80.

Outline: → Known: List Price $840

Discount Series   20% and 10%, or $\frac{1}{5}$ and $\frac{1}{10}$

→ To Find: Net Cost

→ Method:

Net Cost = List Price × (1 − First Discount Rate)
    × (1 − Second Discount Rate)
    = $840 × (1 − $\frac{1}{5}$) × (1 − $\frac{1}{10}$)
    = $\overset{84}{\$840} \times \frac{4}{5} \times \frac{9}{\underset{1}{10}}$
    = $\dfrac{\$3,024}{5}$
    = $604.80

LEARNING EXERCISES

A. Using Method 1, find the net cost in each of the following problems.

No.	List Price	Discount Series	Cost Price
1	$1,500	20% and 10%	$xxx
2	2,400	25% and 5%	xxx
3	8,750	20% and 20%	xxx
4	1,420	10% and 5%	xxx

B. Using Method 2, find the net price in each of the following problems.

No.	List Price	Discount Series	Cost Price
1	$3,250	20% and 10%	$xxx
2	1,800	20% and 15%	xxx
3	4,600	30% and 20%	xxx
4	6,200	30%, 10%, and 10%	xxx

C. Using Method 3, find the net price in each of the following problems.

No.	List Price	Discount Series	Cost Price
1	$1,620	25% and 20%	$xxx
2	840	$16\frac{2}{3}$% and 5%	xxx
3	800	20%, 10%, and 5%	xxx
4	2,496	$33\frac{1}{3}$%, $12\frac{1}{2}$%, and 10%	xxx

D. *Problems to Be Solved*

1. The list price of a rug is $36. If this price is subject to discounts of $16\frac{2}{3}$% and 10%, what is the net price?

2. A dealer received from a wholesaler an electric refrigerator that was to cost the dealer $210, less discounts of $12\frac{1}{2}$% and 20%. Find the net price of the refrigerator.

3. Find the amount due on goods invoiced at $1,268, subject to discounts of 40%, 20%, and 5%.

4. On men's neckties, listed at $24 a dozen, discounts of $12\frac{1}{2}\%$ and 10% are allowed. Find the net cost of each tie.

5. A furniture dealer bought 12 bookcases listed at $16.20 each, subject to discount rates of 20% and 10%. If the freight cost was $22.50, how much did the bookcases cost?

E. *Bonus Problems*

1. How much was paid for 16 lamps at $5.85 each, less discounts of $33\frac{1}{3}\%$, 10%, and 10%?

2. Which is better, and how much better, on a bill of goods amounting to $360—discount rates of 25%, 20%, and 15%, or a discount series of 50% and 10%?

3. A retail merchant purchased a quantity of merchandise for $240, less discounts of $16\frac{2}{3}\%$ and $12\frac{1}{2}\%$. He sold the goods at the same list price, less discounts of 20% and 5%. Find his profit or loss.

4. A wholesale hardware dealer gives discount rates of 15% and 10% on hammers and rates of 10% and 5% on crosscut saws. He sells 36 dozen hammers at $9.60 a dozen and 15 dozen crosscut saws at $20 a dozen. Find the total net selling price of the articles.

UNIT 3 Finding the Single Discount Rate Equivalent to a Series of Discount Rates

A salesman for one firm offered to sell his product to a retailer at list, less 20% and 10%; a rival firm was willing to sell the same product at list, less 25% and 5%. In terms of services, neither firm held any advantage over the other; hence, the retailer's only concern was to determine which firm's net selling price was the smaller. His first thought was that both offered the same rate, for the sum of the discount rates in each case was 30%. He soon realized, however, as you learned in the preceding unit, that only the first rate was based on the list price and the second was computed on the balance. He was left with no alternative but to find the net price in each case. It would have been possible for him, had he known, to change each discount series into a single discount rate and then merely compare the two rates to see which was the larger. You will now learn how to do this.

Part 1

Business Transaction: The Lite-Well Lamp factory offered retailers a discount of 20% and 10% from the list price on all its lamps. To what single rate are these two rates equivalent?

Solution—Per Cent Method: If the retailer was offered only the 20% rate, he would pay 80% of the list price. But he is allowed another discount rate of 10% of the 80%. This amounts to an 8% rate that is yet to be taken from the 80%, leaving a balance of 72% of the list price. Since he paid only 72% of the 100%, he must have received a total discount of 28%. This 28% is the single rate that is equivalent to the two successive rates of 20% and 10%.

Outline: → Known: Discount Series 20% and 10%

→ To Find: Single Equivalent Discount Rate

→ Method: First Balance Rate = 100% − First Discount Rate

= 100% −   20%

= 80%

Net   Price   Rate = 80% − (Second   Discount Rate × 80%)

= 80% − (10% × 80%)

= 80% − 8%

= 72%

Single Discount Rate = 100% − Net Price Rate

= 100% −   72%

= 28%

Fraction Method: The examples earlier in this chapter (see page 197, Method 3) showed that changing per cents to fractions rather than to decimals is an advantage in many examples. This is illustrated again in the following business transaction.

Business Transaction: Find the single discount rate that is equivalent to the series 10%, $16\frac{2}{3}$%, and $14\frac{2}{7}$%.

Solution: The rates can be written as $\frac{1}{10}$, $\frac{1}{6}$, and $\frac{1}{7}$. Since $\frac{1}{10}$ of the list price rate is to be deducted, then the retailer will pay only $\frac{9}{10}$ of the list rate of 100%. This can be written as $\frac{9}{10}$ × 100%. The second discount rate of $\frac{1}{6}$ means that $\frac{5}{6}$ of the balance of $\frac{9}{10}$ × 100% is to be paid. This is expressed as $\frac{5}{6}$ × ($\frac{9}{10}$ × 100%). A similar procedure is followed with the third rate. This results in the net price rate of $\frac{6}{7}$ × $\frac{5}{6}$ × $\frac{9}{10}$ × 100%, or $64\frac{2}{7}$%. If the retailer paid $64\frac{2}{7}$% of the list, he must have received a discount rate of $35\frac{5}{7}$% (100% − $64\frac{2}{7}$%). The $35\frac{5}{7}$% is the single rate equivalent to the discount series of 10%, $16\frac{2}{3}$%, and $14\frac{2}{7}$%.

Outline: → Known: Discount Series 10%, $16\frac{2}{3}\%$, and $14\frac{2}{7}\%$

→ To Find: Single Equivalent Discount Rate

→ Method:

Net Price Rate $= 100\% \times (1 - \text{First Rate}) \times (1 - \text{Second Rate})$
$\times (1 - \text{Third Rate})$

$= 100\% \times (1 - \tfrac{1}{10}) \times (1 - \tfrac{1}{6}) \times (1 - \tfrac{1}{7})$

$= 100\% \times \dfrac{9}{10} \times \dfrac{5}{6} \times \dfrac{6}{7}$

$= \dfrac{450\%}{7}$

$= 64\frac{2}{7}\%$

Single Discount Rate $= 100\% - \text{Net Price Rate}$
$= 100\% - 64\frac{2}{7}\%$
$= 35\frac{5}{7}\%$

LEARNING EXERCISES

1. Using the per cent method shown on page 200, find a single rate of discount equal to each of the following discount series.

    a. 20% and 10% **d.** 25%, 20%, and 10%

    b. 25% and 20% **e.** 10%, 10%, and 5%

    c. 25% and 10% **f.** 20%, 10%, and 5%

2. Using the fraction method shown on pages 200–201, find the single rate of discount equal to each of the following discount series.

    a. 20% and $12\frac{1}{2}\%$ **d.** 20%, $12\frac{1}{2}\%$, and 10%

    b. $16\frac{2}{3}\%$ and 10% **e.** $33\frac{1}{3}\%$, $16\frac{2}{3}\%$, and 10%

    c. $33\frac{1}{3}\%$ and 20% **f.** 25%, 10%, and 5%

Bonus Problems

Find the single discount rate to which each of the following series is equivalent. After examining the six answers, state a conclusion that appears to be true.

    1. $12\frac{1}{2}\%$, 20%, and 10% **4.** 25%, $12\frac{1}{2}\%$, and 20%

    2. 20%, $12\frac{1}{2}\%$, and 10% **5.** 20%, 25%, and $12\frac{1}{2}\%$

    3. 10%, 20%, and $12\frac{1}{2}\%$ **6.** $12\frac{1}{2}\%$, 25%, and 20%

Part 2 (*Optional*) Use of Discount Tables

The bookkeeper in a firm may find that he is very often granting the same discount series to many retailers. Rather than continually repeating the computation for the net cost with these same rates, he will probably prepare a table of the discount series that he uses most frequently. This table will enable him to find the net cost quickly and accurately without the endless repetition of computations needed to find a single-discount rate. Such a table is shown here.

DISCOUNT TABLE

Showing Net of $1 After Discounts, Shown at Top and Side, Are Taken Off

Rate per cent	5	7½	10	15	20	25	30	33⅓	40	50
2	.931	.9065	.882	.833	.784	.735	.686	.6533	.588	.49
2½	.9263	.9019	.8775	.8288	.78	.7313	.6825	.65	.585	.4875
5	.9025	.8788	.855	.8075	.76	.7125	.665	.6333	.57	.475
5–2½	.8799	.8568	.8336	.7873	.741	.6947	.6484	.6175	.5558	.4631
7½	.8788	.8556	.8325	.7863	.74	.6938	.6475	.6166	.555	.4625
7½–5	.8348	.8128	.7909	.7469	.703	.6591	.6151	.5858	.5273	.4394
10	.855	.8325	.81	.765	.72	.675	.63	.60	.54	.45
→10–2½	.8336	.8117	.7898	.7459	.702	.6581	.6143	.585	.5265	.4388
10–5	.8123	.7909	.7695	.7268	.684	.6413	.5985	.57	.513	.4275
10–5–2½	.7919	.7711	.7503	.7086	.6669	.6252	.5835	.5558	.5002	.4168
10–10	.7695	.7493	.729	.6885	.648	.6075	.567	.54	.486	.405
10–10–5	.7310	.7118	.6926	.6541	.6156	.5771	.5387	.513	.4617	.3848
20–5	.722	.703	.684	.646	.608	.57	.532	.5067	.456	.38
20–10	.684	.666	.648	.612	.576	.54	.504	.48	.432	.36
25	.7125	.6938	.675	.6375	.60	.5625	.5250	.50	.45	.375
25–5	.6769	.6591	.6413	.6056	.57	.5344	.4988	.475	.4275	.3563
25–10	.6413	.6244	.6075	.5738	.54	.5063	.4725	.45	.405	.3375
25–10–5	.6092	.5932	.5771	.5451	.513	.4809	.4489	.4275	.3748	.3206

Business Transaction: The Globe Pen Company billed one of its retailers for $560, subject to the discount rates of 20%, 10%, and 2½%. Find the net price of the merchandise.

Solution: The first step is to follow the Per Cent column down until the first two rates are found. Then, follow this row across to the 2½% column. Since there is no 2½% column, we start with the second and third rates of 10% and 2½% and find them in the Per Cent column. Follow this row to the right as far as the 20% column. The number there is .702. This number represents the fact that $.702 must be paid on each dollar of the list price of $560. Therefore, the cost can be found by multiplying $560 by .702, yielding $393.12. This is the net price.

Outline: → Known: List Price $560

Discount Series 20%, 10%, and 2½%

→ To Find: Net Price

→ Method: Net Price = List Price × Value in Table

= $560 × .702

= $393.12

LEARNING EXERCISES

Using the discount table, find the net price of each of the following invoices of merchandise.

No.	Invoice	Discount Series	Net Price
1	$728.00	20% and 10%	$xxx
2	384.00	10%, 5%, and $2\frac{1}{2}$%	xxx
3	176.00	30%, 10%, and 10%	xxx
4	280.00	25%, 20%, and 5%	xxx
5	86.75	15%, 10%, and $2\frac{1}{2}$%	xxx
6	263.70	25%, 10%, and $2\frac{1}{2}$%	xxx
7	411.90	50%, 25%, and 5%	xxx
8	393.40	40%, 25%, and 10%	xxx

UNIT 4 **Finding the Cash Discount and the Net Cash Price**

To encourage the prompt payment of bills, business firms offer bonus discounts to those customers who pay their bills within a specified period of time. This bonus is called a *cash discount*. The discount rate and the required period are shown on the invoice as follows: Terms: 3/10, n/30. This means that 3% of the *net price* may be deducted if the invoice is paid within 10 days of the date on the invoice. If not paid within that period, the entire net price must be paid in not more than 30 days after the date of the invoice.

Sometimes the terms are somewhat more involved; as, Terms: 2/10, 1/30, n/60. This means that 2% of the net price may be deducted if the invoice is paid within 10 days after the date of the invoice and that 1% may be deducted if the invoice is paid between the 11th day and the 30th day after the date of the invoice. The net price must be paid, however, if the invoice is paid between the 31st day and the 60th day after the date of the invoice. It is interesting to note that some concerns charge interest if the debt is not paid before the 60th day.

FINDING THE NET CASH PRICE

If the retailer takes advantage of the cash discount and *no* other discount is offered, then the net price can be found in the same way that the net cost was found in Unit 1 of this chapter, page 193.

Business Transaction: A bill dated December 18 and amounting to $780 was paid on December 22. The terms were 3/10, 2/30, n/60. Find the amount remitted.

Solution: Since the bill was paid within 10 days after December 18, the merchant is entitled to the 3% cash discount rate.

Outline: → Known: List Price $780

Cash Discount Rate 3%

→ To Find: Net Cash Price

→ Method: Cash Discount = List Price × Cash Discount Rate

$$= \quad \$780 \quad \times \quad 3\%$$
$$= \$23.40$$

Net Cash Price = List Price − Cash Discount

$$= \quad \$780 \quad - \quad \$23.40$$
$$= \$756.60$$

If other discounts are offered, then the amount due can be found in the same way that the net cost was found in the problems dealing with discount series in Unit 2, pages 196 and 199.

Business Transaction: How much must be paid on an invoice of merchandise amounting to $24.80, less 25% and 10%, terms 3/10, 1/30, n/60, if the invoice is dated March 3 and paid March 25.

Solution: Since the bill was paid 22 days after the date on the invoice, the retailer is entitled to a 1% cash discount rate.

Outline: → Known: List Price $24.80

Discount Series 25% and 10% and a Cash Discount Rate of 1%

→ To Find: Net Cash Price

→ Method: Net Cash Price $= \$24.80 \times \frac{3}{4} \times \frac{9}{10} \times \frac{99}{100}$

$$= \frac{1657.26}{100}$$
$$= \$16.57$$

LEARNING EXERCISES

A. Study the following invoice, and answer the questions that follow.

```
                              Invoice

                         Newark, N. J., May 4, 19--

            The Better Built Furniture Company

                            To:  Atlas Department Store
                                 Paterson, N. J.

  Terms: 3/10, n/30
─────────────────────────────────────────────────────────────
  3  │  Sofas #467              │ 120│00 │  xxx  │  │  xxx │
```

1. What is the total cost of the three sofas?
2. What are the terms of the invoice?
3. What is meant by these terms?
4. By what date must the Atlas Department Store pay this invoice in order to take advantage of the 3% cash discount rate?
5. What is the last date on which the invoice must be paid?
6. List three different things that the Better Built Furniture Company might do if the bill is not paid by the last day allowed?
7. If a trade discount of 10% was granted and the invoice was paid on May 10, what was the amount of the remittance?

B. Find the cash discount received and the net amount paid in each of the following invoices:

No.	List Price	Terms	Date of Invoice	Date Paid	Cash Dis.	Net Price
1	$2,400.00	5/10, n/30	Oct. 2	Oct. 9	$xxx	$xxx
2	1,680.00	2/10, n/30	Jan. 28	Feb. 4	xxx	xxx
3	3,650.00	5/30, n/60	Aug. 21	Sept. 10	xxx	xxx
4	1,008.00	4/10, n/30	Dec. 5	Dec. 15	xxx	xxx
5	3,175.00	3/10, 1/30, n/60	July 15	Aug. 3	xxx	xxx
6	29.95	5/10, 2/30, n/60	Oct. 21	Nov. 1	xxx	xxx

C. *Problems to Be Solved*

1. On October 20, the Clark Knitting Mills purchased raw materials invoiced at $7,863, terms 8/10, 4/30, n/3 mo. The bill was paid on November 1. Find the amount of the payment.

2. The Pioneer Garden Tool Company received an invoice dated May 4 for goods listed at $620, less a trade discount of 20%. Terms of the invoice were 3/10, n/30. If the bill was paid on May 10, what was the amount of the payment?

3. On July 17, Alfred's Motor Repair Company paid an invoice on automobile parts amounting to $280, less a discount series of 25% and 10%. If the invoice was dated July 10 and the terms were 2/10, n/60, what was the amount of the payment?

4. Find the amount of the check sent in full payment of the following bill of goods bought of the Use-Well Crockery Company, terms 8/10, 4/30, n/90, if the goods were purchased August 30 and the invoice was paid September 10.

24 Breakfast sets @ $ 5.50
32 Luncheon sets @   6.80
22 Dinner sets   @ 31.40

D. *Bonus Problems*

1. The Lester Construction Company purchased equipment invoiced at $7,853.75 from the Sebrook Equipment Company on May 27, terms 10/10, 6/30, 2/60, n/90. If payment was made June 7,

    a. What discount was received?

    b. What was the amount of the payment?

2. The Industrial Hardware Corporation on March 15 billed Moran's Hardware Store for $325, less $33\frac{1}{3}$%, 5%, and 2%. Terms of the bill were 2/10, 1/30, n/60. If the bill was paid April 10, what was the amount of the payment?

3. A farmer desires to purchase a tractor for cash. One farm-equipment corporation offers tractors for $885, less 20%, terms 5/10, n/90. Another firm offers the same tractor for $937.50, less 20%, terms 10/10, n/30. Which is the better offer for the farmer, and how much better?

4. Find the amount paid for the following invoice of merchandise bought of the Grand Furniture Company, terms 5/10, 3/30, n/90, if purchased on February 20 and paid March 1. All merchandise was subject to a discount series of 20% and 5%.

3 doz. Armchairs   @ $91.00
$1\frac{1}{2}$ doz. Kitchen Chairs @   8.60
$2\frac{1}{2}$ doz. Mirrors   @   9.75

153

153.0

UNIT 5   What Have You Learned?

SECTION 1   Understanding Terms

Can you match the term in the column on the left with the proper definition in the column on the right?

Term	*Definition*
1. Trade discount	**a.** Rate of list price paid by merchant
2. Catalogue price	**b.** Cost of article after deducting discount
3. Discount rate	**c.** Deduction given a buyer when stated in terms of a per cent
4. Net price	
5. Discount series	**d.** Increase in the cost of the article
6. Net price rate	**e.** Reduction in price granted a merchant
	f. Two or more discount rates granted a merchant on a single purchase
	g. Suggested selling price of article as listed by the manufacturer

SECTION 2   You As a Businessman

How wise a merchant would you be? Can you make the correct selection in each of the following situations and justify your answer? If you cannot do so, review the pages indicated at the end of the question.

1. You have the opportunity of either buying an article that lists at $75, less 38%, or buying the same article at $75, less 25% and 15%. Which offer would you select? (Pages 193, 196–197.)

2. You are approached by two salesmen, both offering to sell the same article at the same list price. The first salesman offers a trade discount series of 15% and 5%; the second offers a discount series of 5% and 15%. From which salesman should you purchase the article? (Pages 199 and 201.)

3. A few days ago you placed a 10% deposit on an article that the distributor said listed at $180, less 15%. Before receiving delivery, you discover that the article actually lists at $200, less discounts of 20% and 12½%. From the point of view of savings only, should you cancel the order, lose your 10% deposit, and buy the article elsewhere, or take delivery as is? (Pages 193, 196, and 197.)

SECTION 3   Review Problems

1. A desk that lists at $150 can be bought at a 35% discount rate. What is the net price? (Page 193.)

2. The catalogue price on a 9-by-12 rug is $180. It can be purchased, however, at trade discounts of $16\frac{2}{3}$% and 20%. What is the net cost of the rug? (Pages 196–197.)

3. Merchants were granted trade discount rates of 5% and 20% on all articles listed in a catalogue. If a single discount rate had been used rather than the series, what would that rate have been? (Pages 199–200.)

4. The Cutlery Supply Company mailed a bill dated March 4, 19—, for goods amounting to $156.50. The terms of the bill were 8/10, 5/30, n/90. If the bill was paid on March 28, 19—, how much did the Cutlery Supply Company receive? (Pages 203–204.)

5. The Leonard Supply Company, of Schenectady, New York, offered discounts of $16\frac{2}{3}$% and 10% from the list price on all merchandise sold by them. Their usual terms of sale were 6/10, 2/30, n/60. They sold $1,360 worth of merchandise on February 19 to the College Stationery Company. To how much should the check, which they received on March 1 in payment of this bill, have amounted? (Page 204.)

6. Find the amount due on goods invoiced at $390, subject to discounts of 40%, 20%, and 10%, terms 5/10, n/30, if the goods were purchased on February 27 and paid for on March 6. (Page 204.)

7. A local wholesaler buys and sells merchandise for cash only. If goods listed at $1,860 were bought at a trade discount series of 20% and 20%, terms 10/10, 4/30, n/60, and sold for $1,500 subject to trade discount rates of 10% and 5% and a cash discount rate of 5%, what was the profit on the transaction? (Page 204.)

SECTION 4   Testing Your Understanding—40 minutes

1. The catalogue price of a bookcase was $78.50, less 42%. What was the net price?

2. At what net price were machines that were listed at $132, less 25% and 5%, sold?

3. Merchandise was bought for $36. If the terms were 6/10, n/30, and the invoice was paid in 10 days, what was the net price?

4. A discount series of 20% and 10% is equivalent to what single discount rate?

5. The cash discount received on $72 worth of goods bought January 5 and paid for on February 1 was how large if the terms were 7/10, 2/30, n/60?

6. Find the amount due on goods invoiced at $375, subject to discounts of 40% and 20%, terms 5/10, n/30, if the goods were purchased on March 12 and paid for on March 21.

7. Do *not* copy the following invoice. Find the net cost to the purchaser.

	INVOICE	
	Trenton, N. J., May 12, 19--	

Use-Well Crockery Company

To: Dorothy's Gift Shop
Belleville, N. J.

Terms: 3/10, n/30

4	Luncheon sets @ 6.20	$xxx xx
20	Coffee sets @ 3.60	xxx xx
	Total	$xxx xx
	Less 25% trade discount rate	xxx xx
	Balance	$xxx xx
	Less 3% if paid within 10 days	xxx xx
	Net Cost	$xxx xx

UNIT 6 General Review

SECTION 1 To Improve Your Speed and Accuracy

1. Addition:

a. 874	**b.** $ 35.63	**c.** $2\frac{3}{4}$
9,356	95.00	$3\frac{1}{12}$
39	346.72	$14\frac{2}{3}$
593	.84	

d. $42 + $68.70 + $2.56 + $.37

e. $16\frac{2}{3} + 4\frac{1}{2} + 12\frac{1}{4}$

2. Subtraction:

    a. 2,940   **b.** $457.63   **c.** $15\frac{2}{3}$

       1,673   273.07 $6\frac{1}{2}$

    d. $576 − $3.84   **e.** $26\frac{1}{2} − 17\frac{5}{6}$

3. Multiplication:

    a. 576 × 38   **b.** $82.35 × 56   **c.** $67.23 × 1.04

    d. $5\frac{1}{2} × 6\frac{2}{3}$ **e.** 5% of $425.50

4. Division:

    a. 2,538 ÷ 47   **b.** 5,224.74 ÷ 62   **c.** 5,364 ÷ .06

    d. $\frac{3}{4} ÷ \frac{4}{9}$ **e.** $5\frac{2}{8} ÷ 9$

SECTION 2   Do You Remember These?

1. Base = 25, Rate = 7%, Percentage = ?

2. Base = 150, Percentage = 25, Rate = ?

3. Percentage = 75, Rate = 5%, Base = ?

4. $15\frac{3}{4}$ yards of goods at 80 cents a yard will cost how much?

5. The wages for a $7\frac{1}{2}$-hour day at $1.62 an hour will be how much?

6. Furniture that cost $8,347.56 was sold for $15,223.80. What was the profit?

7. A machine cost $10,000 when new. If it depreciates at the rate of $1,250 a year, what is its probable life?

8. Four baskets of peaches were sold at $1.90 a basket. What change should the customer receive from a $10 bill?

9. A man who earned $9,200 a year saved 12% of his income. To how much did this amount?

10. A dealer purchased the following quantities of shoes:

        $7\frac{1}{2}$ doz. pairs Oxfords

        $6\frac{3}{4}$ doz. pairs Pumps

       $10\frac{2}{3}$ doz. pairs Tennis shoes

How many pairs of shoes did he buy?

COST OF A $50 MAN'S SUIT

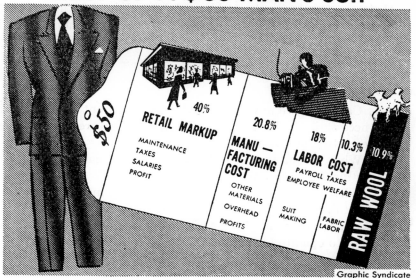

$50

RETAIL MARKUP 40%

MAINTENANCE
TAXES
SALARIES
PROFIT

MANU — FACTURING COST 20.8%

OTHER MATERIALS
OVERHEAD
PROFITS

LABOR COST 18%

PAYROLL TAXES
EMPLOYEE WELFARE

SUIT MAKING

FABRIC LABOR

10.3%

RAW WOOL 10.9%

Graphic Syndicate

9

Selling at Retail

PREVIEW

After trying to sell men's shirts at $5 and up, a merchant finds that his customers are either unwilling or unable to pay more than $3.95 for their shirts. At the same time, in order to cover employees' salaries, taxes, monthly rent, and many other expenses, the merchant has found that he must price his merchandise at least 28% above what he himself pays for the goods. Also, he knows that it would be impossible for him to remain in business if he was unable to make a profit. He has, therefore, fixed his return at 20%

211

of the cost, which he considers a fair return on his investment. He is now faced with the problem of determining how much he can possibly pay a shirt manufacturer for the merchandise and (1) sell the shirts for the price that the customers are willing to pay, and (2) make a fair profit in doing so.

For Class Discussion

1. Can you give any reasons why the merchant's problem will not necessarily be solved by finding a manufacturer who will sell moderately priced shirts?

2. What would you consider to be a reasonable per cent of return for the merchant?

3. What suggestions would you offer this merchant if he is unable to find the quality shirt for the price he is willing to pay?

4. What is the name for the expenses that a merchant must pay in order to operate his business?

5. Can you give at least two names by which the $3.95 mentioned is called?

Terms You Should Know

There are occasions in the study of business arithmetic when you will encounter words that are either identical in meaning or so closely related that distinguishing them from one another is very difficult. In fact, you may sometimes wonder whether these words were purposely used to confuse you! Take, for example, these terms: *list price, catalogue price, marked price,* and *retail price.* The price at which the manufacturer believes the article should be sold to the customer is called the *list,* or *catalogue, price.* If the retail merchant thinks that he can sell the article at that price, he places a tag on the article with this price marked thereon. This amount is now called the *marked,* or *retail, price.* Thus, in this case, all four words have exactly the same meaning.

Frequently, a merchant finds it necessary to reduce the price of his merchandise. This reduction is called a *discount* or *consumer discount,* to distinguish it from the trade discount studied in the preceding chapter. This same reduction is sometimes referred to as a *markdown.* Hence, the words *markdown* and *consumer discount* again express the same meaning. The term *consumer discount,* however, should not be confused with the term *consumer discount rate. Consumer discount* represents the actual number of dollars and cents by which the price was reduced; *consumer discount rate* is usually merely a per cent value. As such, it simply shows the number of dollars in each $100 by which the price was reduced.

Other terms used interchangeably in business are *profit, profit margin,* and *margin.* Each term refers to the same thing—the difference between the cost and the retail.

To illustrate: A sofa had been marked at $400 but was sold at $320. This was a reduction of 20% of the marked price.

→$400 is the *marked price.*

→$80 is the *consumer discount,* or *markdown.*

→20% is the *consumer discount rate,* or *markdown rate* (based on the marked price).

→$320 is the *selling price,* or *retail.*

Concerning This Chapter

"I have just paid $500 for this piano. The salary of each of my employees is $80 a week. Rent for this store amounts to $600 each month. Taxes, insurance, repairs, and the like, amount to a substantial sum. At what price should I mark this piano in order to clear a reasonable profit?"

This is the type of problem that confronts the merchant daily. This is the problem that he must somehow learn to solve or go out of business. You will find the answer to some of his questions in this chapter. Others will be answered in later chapters. Though you may learn to tell him at what price he should sell his merchandise, you will probably not be able to tell him where to find the customers. In this chapter you will examine methods of finding the *discount rate;* the *profit margin,* or *markup;* and the *per cent of profit margin,* or *markup.*

UNIT 1   **Computing Consumer Discount**

Business Transaction: During the month of September, Joan's Apparel Store offered all summer apparel at 20% off the marked price. What is the selling price, or retail, of a bathing suit that had originally been marked at $16.95?

Solution: The methods for finding the retail of this article are identical with those used for finding the net price. (See Chapter 8.) These methods were explained in detail on pages 193–195. The three methods for finding the selling price, or retail, in this business transaction are:

Outline: → Known: Marked Price $16.95

Discount Rate 20%, or $\frac{1}{5}$

→ To Find: Selling Price

→ *Method* 1: Discount = Marked Price × Discount Rate

= $16.95 × 20%

= $3.39

Selling Price = Marked Price − Discount

= $16.95 − $3.39

= $13.56

→ *Method* 2: Selling Price Rate = 100% − Discount Rate

= 100% − 20%

= 80%

Selling Price = Marked Price × Selling Price Rate

= $16.95 × 80%

= $13.56

→ *Method* 3: Selling Price Rate = 1 − Discount Rate

= 1 − $\frac{1}{5}$

= $\frac{4}{5}$

Selling Price = Marked Price × Selling Price Rate

= $16.95 × $\frac{4}{5}$

= $13.56

LEARNING EXERCISES

A. Using Method 1, find the discount and the selling price in each of the following purchases.

No.	Marked Price	Consumer Discount Rate	Discount	Selling Price
1	$ 80.00	20%	$xxx	$xxx
2	127.00	$16\frac{2}{3}\%$	xxx	xxx
3	59.95	$33\frac{1}{3}\%$	xxx	xxx
4	84.80	$12\frac{1}{2}\%$	xxx	xxx

B. Using Method 2, find the discount and the selling price, or retail, in each of the following purchases.

No.	Marked Price	Consumer Discount Rate	Selling Price
1	$ 225.00	25%	$xxx
2	85.50	37%	xxx
3	1,250.00	$7\frac{1}{2}\%$	xxx
4	129.95	$5\frac{1}{4}\%$	xxx
5	316.68	$8\frac{3}{4}\%$	xxx

C. Using Method 3, find the discount and the retail in each of the following purchases.

No.	Marked Price	Consumer Discount Rate	Retail
1	$ 42.75	$33\frac{1}{3}\%$	$xxx
2	156.50	$16\frac{2}{3}\%$	xxx
3	875.25	$8\frac{1}{3}\%$	xxx
4	3,499.95	$12\frac{1}{2}\%$	xxx
5	108.80	$6\frac{1}{4}\%$	xxx

D. *Problems to Be Solved*

1. After the Christmas holidays, ties that had been marked at $2.25 were reduced by 20%. How much would a customer save by buying a tie at the reduced price?

2. In order to clear its floor space for summer wear, C. Kolt and Company marked down its overcoats by $33\frac{1}{3}\%$.

    a. How much would a person save if he bought a coat that had originally been marked $79.95?

    b. What would this coat cost the buyer?

3. Walter's Men's Wear marked down by 40% the handkerchiefs that were usually retailed at 75 cents. To take advantage of this special offer, a customer purchased 2 dozen. How much did the customer pay for these handkerchiefs?

UNIT 2   **Computing the Discount Rate**

There is a tendency on the part of many merchants to advertise their sales by giving the discount *rates* rather than stating the *actual discount* that is offered. Thus, they apparently prefer to say that an article has been reduced by 30% rather than give the actual reduction in dollars and cents. Perhaps this is done because 30% might seem to the customer to be a larger reduction than the actual saving in money. Whatever their reasons, this practice requires that these merchants know what discount rate they can afford to allow the customer. To illustrate, the merchant who buys an article for $4 (usually retailing it at $6) knows that, if he were to put it on sale at a reduced price, he cannot sell it for less than $4 without losing money. If he fixes the special price sale at $4.50, he is then faced with the problem of determining what discount rate he has allowed the buyer. He is interested in this because he wants the advertisement to read, "20% Off," "30% Off," or whatever the actual rate may be, rather than "$1.50 Off."

To find the discount rate, it is important to remember two points:

→1. The discount rate is *always* based on the retail or marked price of the article, *not on the cost* of the article.

→2. The discount rate can be found only if the actual discount is known.

Business Transaction: A merchant purchased men's shirts at $4 and retailed them at $6. At a clearance sale, he sold the shirts at $4.50. What discount rate did he allow the purchaser?

Solution: As the cost is not considered in finding the discount rate, the $4 should be completely ignored. Before it is possible to find the discount rate, it is necessary to find the actual reduction allowed, which in this case is $1.50($6.00 − $4.50). $1.50 is $\frac{1}{4}$, or 25%, of $6. 1.50 ÷ 6.00 = .25, or 25%. Hence, the discount rate is 25%.

Outline: → Known: Cost $4.00

Retail Price $6.00

Clearance Price $4.50

→ To Find: Discount Rate

→ Method: Discount = Retail Price − Clearance Price

= $6.00 − $4.50

= $1.50

Discount Rate = Discount ÷ Retail Price

= $1.50 ÷ $6.00

= .25

= 25%

LEARNING EXERCISES

A. Find the discount and discount rate in each of the following purchases.

Yido kind m able

No.	Retail Price	Clearance Price	Discount	Discount Rate
1	$ 50.00	$ 46.00	$xxx	xxx%
2	85.00	78.00	xxx	xxx%
3	5.50	4.50	xxx	xxx%
4	69.95	63.95	xxx	xxx%
5	124.98	105.50	xxx	xxx%
6	1,456.50	1,025.00	xxx	xxx%
7	2,472.40	2,025.50	xxx	xxx%

B. *Problems to Be Solved*

1. During its January white sale, S. Williams and Sons offered its $3.75 sheets at $3. What discount rate was the purchaser receiving?

2. Shirts that regularly sell for $4.50 could be purchased for $3.15 during the R. C. Bond and Company store-wide sale. What was the rate of markdown on these purchases?

3. To increase business in the slip-cover department, slip covers that ordinarily sold for $98.60 were marked down to $73.95. Find the dis-count rate.

C. *Bonus Problems*

1. At R. C. Bond's store-wide sale, cotton pinafores that normally sold at $3.45 each were being sold at 2 for $4.60. What discount rate did a purchaser receive?

2. A $2\frac{1}{2}$-pound can of cookies that retails at 88 cents a pound was offered at $1.76 during the R. C. Bond sale. What was the per cent of discount?

3. At this same sale, men's washable tropical slacks that regularly sold at $9.95 to $11.94 were selling at $7.96.

    a. If a purchaser selected slacks that had formerly sold at the lowest price, what discount rate would he receive?

    b. If he selected slacks that had sold at the highest price, what discount rate would he receive?

    c. How great is the difference between the highest discount rate and the lowest?

UNIT **3** **Computing the Markup and the Per Cent of Markup**

The amount by which a merchant increases the price of an article above what he himself paid for the article is called the *gross markup*, or, quite frequently, simply the *markup*.

To illustrate: A clothing merchant purchased a topcoat for \$35. He later sold the coat for \$50.

→\$35 is the *cost* of the article.

→\$50 is the *selling price*, or the *retail*, of the article.

→\$15 is the *gross markup*, or *markup* (\$50 − \$35).

Through experience, a merchant learns at what fraction of the cost (or perhaps retail) he must mark up his merchandise in order to clear a reasonable profit. This fraction is usually expressed as a per cent value and is called the *per cent of markup*, or *rate of markup*. Unlike the discount rate, which is always based on the retail, the per cent of markup may be based on either the retail or the cost of the article. Which one is chosen depends entirely on the desire of the merchant. In business today, the per cent of markup is usually computed on the retail. By so doing, the actual markup is made to appear smaller than it would if the rate were computed on the cost to the merchant.

Business Transaction: A lamp that cost a dealer \$37.50 was sold for \$50. Find the per cent of markup.

Solution 1—When Per Cent of Markup Is Based on the Cost: Per cent of markup cannot be found unless the actual markup is first determined. Hence, if \$37.50 is subtracted from \$50, the difference is \$12.50, which is the markup. As the per cent of markup is based on the cost, the retail of \$50 is no longer used in the solution.

Outline: → Known:　Cost \$37.50

　　　　　　　　　　Retail \$50

　　　　→ To Find: Per Cent of Markup

　　　　→ Method: Markup = Retail − Cost

　　　　　　　　　　　　　=　\$50　− \$37.50

　　　　　　　　　　　　　= \$12.50

Per Cent of Markup = Markup ÷ Cost

　　　　　　　　　　= \$12.50　÷ \$37.50

　　　　　　　　　　= $.33\frac{1}{3}$

　　　　　　　　　　= $33\frac{1}{3}\%$

Solution 2—When Per Cent of Markup Is Based on the Retail: Exactly the same explanation applies here as was used in Solution 1, except that the rate is determined by dividing the markup of \$12.50 by the retail of \$50.

　　　　→ Method: Markup = Retail − Cost

　　　　　　　　　　　　　=　\$50　− \$37.50

　　　　　　　　　　　　　= \$12.50

$$\text{Per Cent of Markup} = \text{Markup} \div \text{Retail}$$
$$= \$12.50 \div \$50$$
$$= .25$$
$$= 25\%$$

LEARNING EXERCISES

1. Find the markup and the per cent of markup based on the cost in each of the following purchases.

No.	Cost	Retail	Markup	Per Cent of Markup
a	$ 50.00	$ 60.00	$xxx	xxx
b	64.00	80.00	xxx	xxx
c	18.50	24.05	xxx	xxx
d	137.20	224.98	xxx	xxx
e	188.50	399.99	xxx	xxx

2. Find the markup and the per cent of markup based on the retail in each of the following purchases.

No.	Cost	Retail	Markup	Per Cent of Markup
a	$ 54.00	$ 57.60	$xxx	xxx
b	48.60	51.84	xxx	xxx
c	129.50	148.00	xxx	xxx
d	45.00	58.50	xxx	xxx
e	67.40	80.88	xxx	xxx

UNIT 4 **Computing the Retail of an Article When the Per Cent of Markup Is Based on the Cost**

From experience, merchants know that, in order to meet their expenses, in addition to earning a reasonable profit for themselves, it is advisable to mark their merchandise at a fixed rate above the cost to them. In department stores, this rate varies from department to department, depending on how rapid the "turnover" of a particular article is. Thus, pianos, which do not sell very rapidly, may have a per cent of markup of 100%, based on the cost. On the other hand, the per cent of markup based on the cost of women's stockings may be very low, for large quantities of these articles are sold. Knowing this, the merchant is faced with the problem of fixing the selling price of an article in terms of what he has paid for it, plus a per cent of markup that he must charge in order to operate profitably.

Business Transaction: At what price should a man's hat be marked for sale so that the merchant can show a 30% rate of markup based on the cost of $6.50?

Solution: As the markup is 30% of the cost ($6.50), it is merely a matter of multiplying $6.50 by .30. The product ($1.95) is the markup. Adding $1.95 to the cost of $6.50 equals $8.45, retail.

Outline: → Known: Cost $6.50

Per Cent of Markup Based on Cost 30%

→ To Find: Retail

→ Method: Markup = Cost × Per Cent of Markup

= $6.50 ×   30%

= $1.95

Retail = Cost + Markup

= $6.50 + $1.95

= $8.45

LEARNING EXERCISES

Find the retail in each of the following sales.

No.	Cost	Per Cent of Markup Based on the Cost	Markup	Retail
1	$ 60.00	15	$xxx	$xxx
2	48.00	$33\frac{1}{3}$	xxx	xxx
3	175.00	45	xxx	xxx
4	63.50	28	xxx	xxx
5	99.75	25	xxx	xxx
6	128.48	$37\frac{1}{2}$	xxx	xxx
7	425.00	100	xxx	xxx
8	567.50	120	xxx	xxx

UNIT **5** **Computing the Retail of an Article When the Per Cent of Markup Is Based on the Retail**

In Unit 4 you learned how to determine the retail when the per cent of markup is based on the cost. Many merchants, however, prefer to base the markup rates on the retail of the article rather than on the cost. This complicates the picture somewhat, for the merchant knows only the cost of the article to himself, and not what he desires to sell it for.

Business Transaction: At what price should a man's hat be marked for sale so that the merchant can show a 30% rate of markup based on the retail, if the cost of the hat was $6.30?

Solution—Method 1: A markup of 30% of the retail means that the cost to the merchant must have been 30% below the retail. Hence, the cost of $6.30 is 70% of the retail. Therefore, 1% of the retail is $\frac{1}{70}$ of the $6.30, which is equal to $.09 ($6.30 ÷ 70). If 1% of the retail is $.09, then 100% of the retail must be 100 × .09, or $9. Therefore, $9 is the retail, or selling price, of the hat.

Outline: → Known: Cost $6.30

Per Cent of Markup Based on Retail 30%

→ To Find: Retail

→ Method: Cost = Retail − Markup

= 100% of the Retail − 30% of the Retail

= 70% of the Retail

Since 70% of Retail = Cost, or $6.30

1% of Retail = $.09   ($6.30 ÷ 70)

100% of Retail = $9.00   (100 × .09)

Therefore, Retail = $9.00

Method 2: Since 100% of the retail is the retail itself, then 30% below 100% is 70%. Hence, the cost ($6.30) is 70% of the retail. In the chapter on percentage, you learned that in a situation of this kind the $6.30 is the percentage, the 70% is the rate, and the retail to be found is the base. The method for finding the base is:

Base = Percentage ÷ Rate

Thus, when the percentage ($6.30) is divided by the rate (70%), the quotient will be $9 (base). The result obtained ($9) represents the base, or retail.

Outline: → Cost = Retail — Markup
= 100% of the Retail — 30% of the Retail
= 70% of the Retail
Base = Percentage ÷ Rate
Retail = Cost ÷ Rate
= $6.30 ÷ 70%
= $9.00

LEARNING EXERCISES

In the solution of the following problems, use either Method 1 or Method 2, as directed by your teacher.

A. Find the retail in each of the following sales.

No.	Cost	Per Cent of Markup Based on the Retail	Retail	Markup
1	$ 40.00	20%	$xxx	$xxx
2	54.00	25%	xxx	xxx
3	33.60	30%	xxx	xxx
4	72.98	50%	xxx	xxx
5	125.60	28%	xxx	xxx
6	156.98	34%	xxx	xxx
7	180.00	$33\frac{1}{3}\%$	xxx	xxx
8	175.50	$16\frac{2}{3}\%$	xxx	xxx
9	210.35	$12\frac{1}{2}\%$	xxx	xxx

B. *Problems to Be Solved*

1. At what price should a merchant sell typewriters that he bought at $76.20 if his markup is 40% based on the retail? /27

2. What are the markup and the retail on fountain pens that cost $4.60 if the rate of markup is 35% based on the retail?

3. A merchant purchased a bookcase for $72.50, less a trade discount of 20%. At what price should he sell it in order to realize a profit of 50%, based on the cost?

4. Silver candlesticks were purchased by a gift-shop operator at

$7.96, less 25%. If he desires to retail the candlesticks at a markup of 35% of the cost, what should the selling price be?

5. The Wilson Clothing Company purchased men's suits at $40.50, less a trade discount of $33\frac{1}{3}\%$. If their markup rate is $16\frac{2}{3}\%$ of the cost, at what price should these suits be sold? 31.50

6. The Fisher Shoe Store purchased shoes at $8.50, less 16%. At what price should the shoes be sold if the 30% markup rate is based on the retail? 10.20

7. 9-by-12 rugs were purchased at $175, less 40%. At what price 233.33 should the rugs be sold if the markup rate of 55% is based on the retail?

C. *Bonus Problems*

1. Find the markup and the retail of goods purchased for $123.75, less $33\frac{1}{3}\%$ and 10%, and sold at a markup of $16\frac{2}{3}\%$ of the retail. 89.10

2. A merchant bought merchandise for $380, less 20% and 5%. Freight, insurance, and handling costs amounted to $10.90. He sold the goods at a markup of 10% of the total cost. Find the markup and the retail. 32.14 329.67

3. An article purchased by a dealer for $32.80, less 25% and 20%, was sold by him at a markup of 20% of the retail. Find the retail. 24.60

4. A textbook costing $3.15 is sold by a publishing firm for $4.80, less a teacher's discount of 25%. Find the markup and the per cent of markup on the retail.

5. The catalogue of a mail-order house lists garden utensils at $3.20 each, less discounts of 20% and $6\frac{1}{4}\%$. The company purchased these utensils at $3.20 and received discounts of $33\frac{1}{3}\%$ and 25%. Find the net markup and the per cent of markup on the cost. $80¢$ diff. 50% markup

---

UNIT 6   Computing the Cost of an Article When the Per Cent of Markup Is Based on the Retail

Through experience, merchants know that their customers have either an upper limit or a lower limit for the amount they are willing to pay for certain articles. For most persons, it is the upper limit that is important to them. Thus, in certain areas, a shoe-store proprietor would be unwise to stock shoes to be sold for more than $12.95 when those who shop in the area do not buy the more expensive shoes. On the other hand, in some exclusive women's footwear "shoppes" customers would frown on merchandise that was marked under $25. The first case, which occurs more frequently in business, is the one that you will examine. Here the merchant is faced with the task of trying to find a manufacturer from whom he can buy shoes at a price low enough so that he, the merchant, can sell them at $12.95 and still clear a reasonable profit.

Business Transaction: Bart's Shoe Outlet handles men's canvas shoes, for which his customers will pay no more than $3.95. In order to meet expenses, in addition to realizing a return for himself, Bart must price the shoes at a markup, or gross profit, of 30% of the retail. What is the maximum (largest) amount that he can pay for these canvas shoes and still realize the per cent of gross profit he desires?

Solution: Since the markup is 30% of the retail of $3.95, the markup is $1.19 ($3.95 × .30). If the retail is $3.95 and the markup is $1.19, then the difference, or $2.76, represents the highest price that the merchant may pay for the shoes.

Outline: → Known: Retail $3.95
Per Cent of Markup Based on Retail 30%
→ To Find: Cost
→ Method: Markup = Retail × Per Cent of Markup
= $3.95 × 30%
= $1.19
Cost = Retail − Markup
= $3.95 − $1.19
= $2.76

LEARNING EXERCISES

Find the cost to the merchant in each of the following transactions.

No.	Retail	Per Cent of Markup Based on the Retail	Markup	Cost
1	$ 80.00	25%	$xxx	$xxx
2	42.50	40%	xxx	xxx
3	56.99	24%	xxx	xxx
4	287.98	36%	xxx	xxx
5	497.34	$16\frac{2}{3}$%	xxx	xxx
6	2,348.96	$12\frac{1}{2}$%	xxx	xxx
7	5,675.25	$33\frac{1}{3}$%	xxx	xxx

UNIT 7   What Have You Learned?

SECTION 1   Understanding Terms

Match each term in the column at the left with the term having the identical meaning in the column at the right.

Term
1. List price
2. Retail price
3. Markup
4. Markdown
5. Net profit
6. Operating expenses
7. Discount rate
8. Net markup rate

Synonym
a. Gross profit
b. Overhead
c. Marked price
d. Discount series
e. Net profit rate
f. Selling price
g. Net markup
h. Markdown rate
i. Catalogue price
j. Consumer discount

SECTION 2   You As a Businessman

How wise a merchant would you be? Can you make the correct selection and justify your answer in each of the following situations? If you cannot do so, review the pages indicated at the end of each problem.

1. Your store is an exclusive outlet for a name-brand product. In order to meet competition, you have priced a popular model 11-cubic-foot freezer at $340, less a 35% discount. The cost to you was $310, less a trade discount of 10% and 10%. Can you afford to continue indefinitely to sell the freezer at this price? (Pages 196, 213–214.)

2. In the area in which your clothing store is located your customers will pay no more than $35 for a man's suit. Your business can operate profitably only if your gross markup is at least 30% of the cost of the merchandise. You are approached by a clothing-factory salesman who is willing to sell you a good-quality suit at $25.50. Should you consider doing business with him or try to find a cheaper suit? (Pages 219–220.)

3. The price to you of a 10-cubic-foot Cold-Aire Refrigerator is $220, less trade discounts of 20% and 5%. Your competitor is selling these

refrigerators at $208.95. In order to meet operating expenses without making any profit for yourself, your markup must be 20% of the selling price. Considering only the profit or loss to yourself, should you meet your competitor's price? (Pages 213, 214, and 221.)

4. As the manager of the shirt department of a large department store, you find that your $3.95 shirt sells at the rate of approximately 225 a month. By lowering the price to $3.25, you find that you can increase the sales to about 500 a month. The cost of these shirts to the company is $3.50, less trade discounts of 30% and 5%. Is it advisable to drop the price? (Page 196.)

SECTION 3   You As a Consumer

How wise a consumer would you be? Can you make the correct purchase and justify your answer in each of the following situations? If you cannot do so, review the pages indicated at the end of each problem.

1. After doing some comparison shopping, you find that in one store you can purchase a certain model of the Well-Vue Television set for $275, less a discount of 35%, and in another store for $200, less a discount of only 10%. At which store should you make the purchase? (Pages 213–214.)

2. You have just heard of a close-out sale at which a gas range that normally sells for $285, less 20% discount, can be bought for $209.95. You had planned to buy this range sometime, but you do not have the money to pay for it at present. Should you buy the range now with money borrowed for a period of 6 months, for which you will have to pay a charge of $6.30, or would it be advisable to wait the 6 months and then buy it at the regular price? (Pages 213–214.)

3. Several days ago you ordered aluminum louvered windows and paid a deposit of 10% on the $704.50 purchase price. Today, you learned that the windows can be bought for $695.75, less a discount of 12%. Should you cancel your order, thereby losing your deposit, and reorder at the second shop, or let the original order stand? (Pages 213–214.)

4. You have an opportunity of purchasing a new, but slightly damaged, famous-make 3-speed portable phonograph for $39.95. The set lists at $69.95, less 15%. The cost of repairing the phonograph before it can be used will be $12.75. Should you buy the damaged instrument or pay the price of a new one? (Pages 213–214.)

SECTION 4 Review Problems

1. Martha's Millinery Shoppe reduced all its summer hats by 25% during the month of August. What was the price of a hat that originally sold for $12.95? (Pages 213–214.)

2. Christmas candy that originally sold at $3.75 for a 5-pound box was marked down $33\frac{1}{3}\%$ after the holidays. How much did the buyer save by buying a box of the candy at the sales price? (Pages 213–214.)

3. During its June store-wide sale, B. Alton's reduced its cotton sport shirts from $2.99 to $2.59 each. What discount rate were they offering the purchaser? (Page 216.)

4. Boy's T shirts that regularly sell at $1.99 each were placed on sale at 3 for $5. What discount rate did the purchaser gain by buying the shirts at this time? (Page 216.)

5. The Consumer Mart purchased lawn mowers at $18.50 and sold them at $26.75.

    a. What was the per cent of markup based on the cost? (Page 218.)

    b. What was the per cent of markup based on the retail? (Pages 218–219.)

6. As a result of smoke damage caused by a fire, Kalt's Furniture Store reduced its dining-room suites to $109.95, although it had paid $134.95 for these suites.

    a. What rate of loss based on the cost was the store willing to take? (Page 218.)

    b. What rate of loss based on the retail was the store willing to take? (Pages 218–219.)

7. The shoe department of R. Baxter and Company operates on a gross markup of 45% of the cost. At what price should shoes that were purchased at $10.75 a pair be marked? (Page 220.)

8. A merchant purchased fans at $27.50 and sold them at a markup of 35% of the retail. What was the price that the consumer paid for these fans? (Page 221.)

9. In order to attract customers, Carl's Men's Shop finds that the maximum price at which it can sell a certain brand of canvas shoes is $4.95 a pair. What is the highest price Carl's can afford to pay for these shoes if its gross profit must be at least 23% of the retail? (Pages 223–224.)

SECTION 5   **Testing Your Understanding**

40 Minutes

1. The Sussex Lumber Company, before closing out its Unpainted furniture department, lowered the price of this furniture by **35%**. How much is saved on the purchase of a bookcase that originally sold for $39.80?

2. Modern upholstered armchairs that regularly sold at **$49.95** each went on sale at a reduction of $33\frac{1}{3}\%$. What was the sale price of these chairs?

3. An innerspring chair pad was reduced from $19.99 to $14.99. What discount rate was being offered the customer?

4. An imported caned armchair cost the T. C. Clark Furniture Store **$2.85**. At what price would the store have to sell the armchair if it operated on a **75%** gross markup based on the cost?

5. R. C. Bond and Company purchased a set of imported Sheffield steak knives at **$4.50** and sold them at **$8.98**. At what per cent of markup based on the retail was Bond operating?

6. Parker's of Patterson purchased a wrought-iron telephone table at **$2.78** and sold it at a markup of **60%** of the retail price. What was the retail of this table?

7. Because of excessive handling by customers, a shopworn jacket had to be sold at **$7.95**, although the merchant himself had paid $10.50 for the jacket. What per cent of loss based on the cost did the merchant incur?

U N I T **8**   **General Review**

SECTION 1   **To Improve Your Speed and Accuracy**

1. Addition:

a. 17,863	b. $ 4.82	c. $28\frac{2}{3}$
2,914	456.31	$35\frac{1}{2}$
896	82.07	$52\frac{3}{4}$
4,038	544.58	$78\frac{5}{6}$
36,549	98.79	
765	45.61	

d. $375.46 + $47.35 + $2.09 + $85 + $.96

e. $84\frac{7}{8} + 56\frac{1}{6} + 39\frac{1}{2}$

2. Subtraction:

a. 3,765	**b.** $4,275.00	**c.** 85
958	37.54	$16\frac{2}{3}$

    d. $526.04 − $375.25   **e.** $75\frac{3}{4} - 42\frac{1}{2}$

3. Multiplication:

    a. 435 × 673   **b.** 50.95 × .86   **c.** $40.07 × 2.08

    d. $12 \times 3\frac{2}{3}$ **e.** $125.40 × $2\frac{1}{2}\%$

4. Division:

    a. 365,512 ÷ 856   **b.** $732 ÷ 1.04   **c.** $42.56 ÷ 65%

    d. $12 \div 4\frac{1}{2}$ **e.** $42\frac{1}{2} \div 2\frac{1}{2}$

5. Change the following per cent values to equivalent fractions.

    a. 20%   **b.** 25%   **c.** 50%   **d.** $33\frac{1}{3}\%$ **e.** $16\frac{2}{3}\%$

    f. $8\frac{1}{3}\%$ **g.** 40%

SECTION 2   Do You Remember These?

1. Base = $36.50, Rate = 15%, Percentage = ?

2. Base = $84.98, Percentage = $5.00, Rate = ?

3. Percentage = $37.25, Rate = 75%, Base = ?

4. Catalogue Price = $120, Trade Discount Rate = 25%, Trade Discount = ?

5. List Price = $250, Discount Series = 15% and 10%, Net Price = ?

6. How much will a man earn in an 8-hour day if his salary is $2.56 an hour?

7. The discount series of 20% and 10% is equivalent to what single discount rate?

8. A man who earned $420 a month spent $85 on rent for his apartment. What per cent of his salary was needed for rent?

9. What is the cost of $6\frac{1}{2}$ gallons of pure turpentine at 84 cents a gallon?

10. In a certain high school only 62% of the 420 entering freshmen are expected to graduate 4 years later. How many of these students will probably receive their diplomas on graduation day?

Earn **4%** per annum at Wisconsin's Largest Federal Savings Association

- Current rate: 4% per annum up to 1% bonus for monthly savings.
- Every account insured by the F.S.L.I.C. United State
- Conserva... serves... men...

EARN More With INSURED Safety

4%

Each Savings & Loan account insured to $10,000 by Federal Savings & Loan a U. S. Government

FREE BROCHURE

& Co.

THE MANHATTAN SAVINGS BANK

"Serving the Thrifty Since 1850"

Resources Exceed $300,

Total Dividend 3 %

Compounded Semiannu...

385 MADISON
NEW YORK 17,

MOHAWK SAVINGS Increases Dividends!

$3\frac{1}{4}\%$ per annum

FOR THIS QUARTER

FROM JAN

costs you only 4% to finance your new car

Founded June 30 QUAR...

10

Computing Interest

PREVIEW

The peak season each year for the Berkely Painting and Contracting firm is September through December. During this period the firm finds it necessary to hire additional painters. In order to pay the salaries of these temporary helpers, the firm usually borrows money from the bank.

To obtain the paint and other supplies he needs, Mr. Berkely has arranged with the paint-store merchant to buy on account everything he needs during these 4 months. Payment for this merchandise will not fall due until January, when Berkely will begin to receive money for the work just completed.

In the meantime, the paint-store merchant, having emptied his shelves by selling his merchandise on credit to Mr. Berkely and other customers, must either withdraw money from his own savings account or else borrow money from the bank in order to replenish his stock. As doing either of these things will cost the merchant money, he is faced with the problem of whether or not to charge the Berkely firm for this additional cost. If he decides in favor of the charge, how large should the charge be?

For Class Discussion

1. Why should withdrawing money from his savings account cost the paint-store merchant money?

2. What is the name of the charge for the money borrowed from the bank?

3. Can you give two reasons why the paint-store merchant would not wish to charge Mr. Berkely for granting him credit?

4. How many other businesses can you name that have peak seasons at various times during the year?

5. What reasons would a merchant or a contractor have for not being able to set aside money during the year in order to carry him through these peak seasons?

6. In order to avoid borrowing money from the bank, why does Mr. Berkely not tell his employees that he will pay them in January after he has received his payments?

Terms You Should Know

You have probably had some type of savings account since you were in the third or fourth grade. Each year, or perhaps twice a year, you looked forward to seeing your savings increased by the small amount that the bank added to your account for having kept your money there. During those early days you gave little thought as to how the bank was able to pay you and all the other depositors for leaving money with it. Now you will study one of the means by which banks earn money. If the money that you save were merely kept in storage in the bank vaults, there would be no way by which the bank employees could be paid salaries or for you to receive a return on your savings.

One of the major sources of income of a bank is derived from lending money to men such as Mr. Berkely or the paint-store dealer. In return for lending them this money, the bank charges them a fee, the size of which depends on the length of time and the amount that is borrowed. This fee is called an *interest charge,* or, more briefly, *interest.* The actual amount that the person borrows is referred to as the *principal of the debt,* or, simply, *principal.*

Banks are not the only sources from which a person may borrow money. There are other concerns and also private individuals who are both willing and eager to lend money. The source, bank or otherwise, that lends the money is called the *lender;* the person borrowing the money is known as the *borrower.*

The interest charge is computed on the basis of an *interest rate.* Like most other rates, it is expressed as a per cent value, such as 5%. This means that the borrower must pay $5 for each $100 that he borrows. After a moment of reflection, you will realize that some information is still lacking. Should the person who borrows $100 for 6 months pay $5 for this service, the same amount that the person who borrows $100 for 1 month or 1 year pays? Business practice has established the principle that, unless it is otherwise noted, the interest rate will always be quoted for a period of 1 *year.* Thus, the term "with interest at 2%" means that, if the borrower should hold the money for an entire year, the charge would be $2 for each $100 borrowed.

To illustrate: Mr. Berkely borrowed $400 from Mr. Hall for a period of 1 year at an interest rate of 6%. At the end of the year, Mr. Berkely returned the $400 plus an additional $24 that Mr. Hall charged for lending the money.

→Mr. Berkely is the *borrower.*
→Mr. Hall is the *lender.*
→$400 is the *principal.*
→$24 is the *interest.*
→6% is the *interest rate.*

Concerning This Chapter

A number of different types of agencies are in business for the purpose of lending money to people who need it. The agencies are willing to lend this money because they, in turn, receive a fee for this service. In this chapter you will examine how the size of this fee, or interest, is found. You will find that the method for determining the interest is very much the same whether the time for which the money is lent is for days, months, or years.

In addition to using short cuts for finding the interest in special situations, you will learn how to find this charge through the use of tables—exactly as a bank-loan clerk would do.

UNIT 1   **Computing the Interest for Monthly or Daily Periods**

For many years, banks and other commercial enterprises have been using the 360-day year whenever it was necessary to determine the interest on a debt. This practice is legally accepted. Although the 360-day year probably originated when there were few calculating machines and few interest tables to simplify arithmetical calculations, this practice is still widely used today. The 360-day year is called by different names, the most commonly used being *bank* or *banker's year, commercial year, business year, ordinary year.*

Business Transaction: $720 was borrowed at 6% for 90 days. What was the interest on this loan?

Solution: As was pointed out in the Preview to this chapter, the interest rate is quoted in periods of one year. Hence, it is necessary to find what fraction of a year the 90 days represents. As 360 is used as the number of days in a year, the 90 days would be $\frac{90}{360}$ of a year, or $\frac{1}{4}$ of a year.

Outline: → Known: Principal $720
                   Rate   6%
                   Time   90 days
         → To Find: Interest
         → Method: Interest = Principal × Rate × Time
              or: I = P × R × T
                  = $720 × 6% × 90 Days

$$= \$720 \times \frac{6}{100} \times \frac{90}{360} = \frac{\$54}{5}$$

Interest = $10.80

Business Transaction: $540 was borrowed at $3\frac{3}{4}$% for 3 months. Find the interest.

Solution: In this transaction it is necessary to change the 3 months to a fraction of a year. With 12 months in a year, the 3 months would be $\frac{3}{12}$, or $\frac{1}{4}$ of a year.

Outline: →Known: Principal $540
    Rate $3\frac{3}{4}\%$
    Time 3 Months
→To Find: Interest
→Method: I = P × R × T
    = $540 × $3\frac{3}{4}\%$ × 3 Months
    $$= \$\overset{27}{\cancel{540}} \times \underset{20}{\cancel{\tfrac{15}{100}}} \times \underset{4}{\overset{1}{\cancel{\tfrac{3}{12}}}} = \frac{\$405}{80}$$

Interest = $5.06

There are two important points to remember when interest is to be found:

→1. If the time is given in months, divide the number of months by 12 to determine for what fraction of a year the money has been borrowed.

→2. If the time is given in days, divide the number of days by 360 to determine for what fraction of a year the money has been borrowed. (Note: This is true only when a banker's year is used.)

LEARNING EXERCISES

1. Find the interest on each of the following loans.

    a. $600 @ 5% for 60 days
    b. $800 @ 4% for 90 days
    c. $900 @ 7% for 120 days
    d. $450 @ 6% for 30 days

    e. $760 @ $4\frac{1}{2}\%$ for 180 days
    f. $520 @ $5\frac{1}{4}\%$ for 40 days
    g. $1,200 @ $3\frac{3}{4}\%$ for 60 days
    h. $1,600 @ $5\frac{1}{2}\%$ for 270 days

2. Find the interest on each of the following loans.

    a. $428 @ 6% for 54 days
    b. $584 @ 5% for 76 days
    c. $724 @ 4% for 82 days
    d. $468 @ 6% for 46 days
    e. $236 @ 7% for 94 days

    f. $860 @ 3% for 68 days
    g. $662 @ 8% for 75 days
    h. $196 @ 9% for 42 days
    i. $388 @ 2% for 82 days
    j. $326 @ $4\frac{1}{2}\%$ for 45 days

3. Find the interest on each of the following loans.

    a. $500 @ 4% for 4 months
    b. $450 @ 5% for 7 months
    c. $625 @ 6% for 8 months
    d. $875 @ 3% for 9 months

    e. $420 @ $4\frac{1}{2}\%$ for 3 months
    f. $840 @ $3\frac{1}{4}\%$ for 6 months
    g. $285 @ 4% for 2 months
    h. $795 @ 5% for 10 months

4. What charge is made on a loan of $5,420 for 12 days at an interest rate of $2\frac{1}{4}\%$?

5. How much will it cost a merchant to borrow $4,575 for 1 month at an interest rate of 5%?

6. In order to take advantage of an excellent business opportunity, Mr. Blake needed $1,275 for 15 days. If he borrowed this money at an interest rate of $5\frac{1}{2}$%, to how much would the interest amount?

UNIT **2**   **Finding Exact Interest**

Although the 360-day year is used in almost all commercial transactions that involve interest, the United States Government, in all interest computations, *always* uses 365 as the number of days in a year. Therefore, the 365-day year is called a *government year*. The 365-day year is also referred to as an *exact year*, since it contains the actual number of days in the year. Finding interest when the exact year is involved differs little from the method used for the ordinary, or banker's, year. The number 365 replaces the number 360 in determining what fractional part of a year a fixed number of days are. When interest is found by this method, it is called *exact*, or *accurate, interest*.

Business Transaction: John Gibbins borrowed $640 at 6% for 85 days. Find the exact interest on this loan.

Outline: → Known: Principal $640
              Rate   6%
              Time   85 Days
        → To Find: Interest
        → Method: I = P × R × T
                 = $640 × 6% × 85 Days
                 $$= \$\overset{32}{\underset{5}{640}} \times \frac{6}{100} \times \frac{\overset{17}{85}}{\underset{73}{365}} = \frac{\$3,264}{365}$$

        Interest = $8.94

LEARNING EXERCISES

1. Find the exact interest on the following loans.

   a. $600 @ 5% for 80 days   **d.** $800 @ $4\frac{1}{2}$% for 100 days
   b. $400 @ 4% for 65 days   **e.** $375 @ 6% for 75 days
   c. $550 @ 6% for 200 days   **f.** $720 @ 3% for 84 days

g. $950 @ 6% for 54 days   **j.** $180 @ 6% for 112 days
h. $946 @ 4% for 125 days   **k.** $425 @ $4\frac{1}{2}$% for 146 days
i. $520 @ 5% for 210 days   **l.** $585 @ 7% for 312 days

2. $5,000 was borrowed for 90 days at a 6% interest rate.

   a. Find the exact interest on this loan.

   b. Find the interest on this loan using the ordinary, or banker's, year.

   c. If you had your choice, under which condition would you borrow money?

   d. In this loan, how much would be saved by borrowing under one rate rather than under the other?

   e. Explain, from an arithmetical point of view, why the interest in one case should be smaller than in the other.

UNIT **3**   **The Banker's 60-Day Interest Method**

SECTION 1   Computing the Interest for a 60-Day Period

As the 360-day year is used so much more frequently in the lending of money than the 365-day year, a *year*, unless otherwise stated, should be considered to mean a *banker's 360-day year*. In addition, as the interest rate of 6% is used most frequently by lending agencies, there are several short cuts with which you should become familiar.

Business Transaction: What is the interest on a $575 loan at 6% for 60 days?

Outline: → Known: Principal $575
               Rate   6%
               Time   60 Days
      → To Find: Interest
      → Method: I = P × R × T
$$= \$575 \times 6\% \times 60 \text{ Days}$$
$$= \$575 \times \frac{\overset{1}{\cancel{6}}}{100} \times \frac{\overset{1}{\cancel{60}}}{\underset{\underset{1}{\cancel{6}}}{\cancel{360}}} = \frac{\$575}{100}$$

        Interest = **$5.75**

It is important to observe that, if the rate is 6% and the time 60 days, the last two fractions will always be $\frac{6}{100}$ and $\frac{60}{360}$. The product of these

end for Tuesday

two fractions, as shown in the preceding business transaction, must be $\frac{1}{100}$. Therefore, no matter what the principal of the debt may be, it has to be multiplied by $\frac{1}{100}$. This is merely another way of saying that the principal has to be divided by 100. As you have learned earlier, the quickest way to do this is to move the decimal point in the principal two places to the left. In this problem, the principal was $575; the interest, as shown in the outline, was $5.75. This interest ($5.75) can be obtained by moving the decimal point in the principal ($575), two places to the left.

What you have just learned can be stated briefly as follows:

→To find the interest on any amount for 60 days at 6% interest rate, move the decimal point in the principal two places to the left.

This principle is commonly called the *6% for 60-day method*, or the *banker's 6% 60-day method*, of finding interest.

Business Transaction: Find the interest on a debt of $475.80 for 60 days at 6%.

Solution: Moving the decimal point in the principal two places to the left, the interest is found to be $4.7580, or $4.76.

LEARNING EXERCISES

Find the interest on each of the following loans that were made for 60 days at an interest rate of 6%.

1. $325	5. $3,750	9. $407.62
2. $476	6. $4,752	10. $3,425.50
3. $590	7. $854.30	11. $12,575
4. $4,000	8. $765.84	12. $14,700.20

13. If each of the preceding loans had been made for 120 days rather than for 60 days, how would the interest be found?

14. If these loans had been made for 30 days, what would you do to find the interest?

SECTION 2   Time Combinations Used in Computing Interest by the Banker's 60-Day Interest Method

The banker's 60-day interest method can be used to find the interest for periods of time other than 60 days. To find the interest for 120 days, simply multiply the interest for 60 days by 2; for 30 days, multiply the interest for 60 days by $\frac{1}{2}$. If the time was 180 days, multiply the interest for 60 days by 3. The numbers 2, $\frac{1}{2}$, and 3 were found by comparing 120 days, 30 days, and 180 days with 60 days. This is done by dividing each of these numbers by 60.

Those periods of time that can be used to best advantage in extending the 6% for 60-day method of finding interest are:

30 days: $\frac{30}{60}$, or $\frac{1}{2}$, the interest for 60 days

20 days: $\frac{20}{60}$, or $\frac{1}{3}$, the interest for 60 days

15 days: $\frac{15}{60}$, or $\frac{1}{4}$, the interest for 60 days

12 days: $\frac{12}{60}$, or $\frac{1}{5}$, the interest for 60 days

10 days: $\frac{10}{60}$, or $\frac{1}{6}$, the interest for 60 days

6 days: $\frac{6}{60}$, or $\frac{1}{10}$, the interest for 60 days

5 days: $\frac{5}{60}$, or $\frac{1}{12}$, the interest for 60 days

4 days: $\frac{4}{60}$, or $\frac{1}{15}$, the interest for 60 days

3 days: $\frac{3}{60}$, or $\frac{1}{20}$, the interest for 60 days

2 days: $\frac{2}{60}$, or $\frac{1}{30}$, the interest for 60 days

1 day: $\frac{1}{60}$ the interest for 60 days

As division by 10 is performed by moving the decimal point one place to the left in the dividend, it would be wise in finding the interest for 3 days to find it first for 30 days and then move the decimal one place to the left, thus obtaining the interest for 3 days.

Interest on periods of time that are combinations of the above numbers are also easily determined.

Example 1: To determine the interest for 56 days, find the following fractional parts of 60 days; then add:

60 days

30 days = $\frac{1}{2}$ of 60 days   60 days

20 days = $\frac{1}{3}$ of 60 days   or: -4 days = $\frac{1}{15}$ of 60 days

6 days = $\frac{1}{10}$ of 60 days   56 days

56 days

Example 2: To find the interest for 100 days, proceed as follows:

60 days

30 days = $\frac{1}{2}$ of 60 days

10 days = $\frac{1}{6}$ of 60 days

100 days

Example 3: To find the interest for 24 days, proceed as follows:

60 days

30 days = $\frac{1}{2}$ of 60 days

-6 days = $\frac{1}{10}$ of 60 days

24 days

Example 4: To find the interest for 37 days, proceed as follows:

$$\underline{\begin{array}{l} 60 \text{ days} \\ 30 \text{ days} = \frac{1}{2} \text{ of } 60 \text{ days} \\ +10 \text{ days} = \frac{1}{6} \text{ of } 60 \text{ days} \end{array}}$$
$$\begin{array}{l} 40 \text{ days} \\ \underline{-3 \text{ days}} = \frac{1}{20} \text{ of } 60 \text{ days} \\ 37 \text{ days} \end{array}$$

or

$$\underline{\begin{array}{l} 60 \text{ days} \\ 30 \text{ days} = \frac{1}{2} \text{ of } 60 \text{ days} \\ 6 \text{ days} = \frac{1}{10} \text{ of } 60 \text{ days} \\ 1 \text{ day} = \frac{1}{60} \text{ of } 60 \text{ days or} \\ \frac{1}{6} \text{ of } 6 \text{ days} \end{array}}$$
$$37 \text{ days}$$

LEARNING EXERCISES

What time combinations of 60 days will yield the following periods?

1. 80 days
2. 40 days
3. 33 days
4. 69 days
5. 26 days
6. 76 days
7. 53 days
8. 57 days
9. 27 days
10. 17 days
11. 19 days
12. 100 days
13. 99 days
14. 94 days
15. 126 days
16. 183 days
17. 117 days
18. 38 days
19. 49 days
20. 133 days
21. 137 days

SECTION 3 Computing the Interest If the Period of Time Is Other Than 60 Days

Knowing how to combine 60 days with some of its fractional parts, it is possible to apply the banker's method of finding interest to periods of time other than 60 days.

Example 1: Find the interest on $840 at 6% for 96 days.
Solution:
$$\underline{\begin{array}{l} \$ 8.40 = 60 \text{ days' interest at } 6\% \text{ on } \$840 \\ 4.20 = 30 \text{ days' interest } (\frac{1}{2} \text{ of } 60 \text{ days or } \frac{1}{2} \text{ of } \$8.40) \\ + .84 = 6 \text{ days' interest } (\frac{1}{10} \text{ of } 60 \text{ days or } \frac{1}{10} \text{ of } \$8.40) \end{array}}$$
$$\$13.44 = 96 \text{ days' interest at } 6\% \text{ on } \$840$$

When outlining examples such as these, determine, first, the combinations of days that are to be used. These time combinations should serve as guides in determining the interest for each number of days.

Example 2: Find the interest on $750 at 6% for 24 days.
Solution:
$$\underline{\begin{array}{l} \$7.50 = 60 \text{ days' interest at } 6\% \text{ on } \$750 \\ \$2.50 = 20 \text{ days' interest } (\frac{1}{3} \text{ of } 60 \text{ days}) \\ +.50 = 4 \text{ days' interest } (\frac{1}{15} \text{ of } 60 \text{ days or } \frac{1}{5} \text{ of } 20 \text{ days}) \end{array}}$$
$$\$3.00 = 24 \text{ days' interest at } 6\% \text{ on } \$750$$

Although the interest for 60 days may not be used directly in finding the final interest, it is best always to write it down *first*, for this value is used to find all the other interest values in the solution. If the 60-day interest is not to be added to the others, draw a line below it to separate it from the remainder of the outline.

Example 3: Find the interest on $1,240 at 6% for 134 days.

Solution:

$$\begin{aligned}
\$12.40 \quad &= \quad 60 \text{ days' interest at } 6\% \text{ on } \$1,240 \\
12.40 \quad &= \quad 60 \text{ days' interest} \\
2.48 \quad &= \quad 12 \text{ days' interest } (\tfrac{1}{5} \text{ of } 60 \text{ days}) \\
+ \ .4133 \ &= \quad \ 2 \text{ days' interest } (\tfrac{1}{6} \text{ of } 12 \text{ days}) \\
\hline
\$27.6933 \ &= \ 134 \text{ day's interest at } 6\% \text{ on } \$1,240 \\
\text{Interest} &= \$27.69
\end{aligned}$$

LEARNING EXERCISES

Find the interest at 6% on each of the following loans by the banker's 60-day method.

1. $900 for 80 days	11. $518 for 23 days
2. $800 for 90 days	12. $746 for 89 days
3. $600 for 66 days	13. $591 for 73 days
4. $400 for 33 days	14. $375 for 49 days
5. $720 for 26 days	15. $246 for 117 days
6. $450 for 53 days	16. $195 for 126 days
7. $240 for 56 days	17. $321 for 157 days
8. $1,200 for 19 days	18. $473 for 186 days
9. $375 for 17 days	19. $916 for 129 days
10. $675 for 38 days	20. $584 for 143 days

SECTION 4   (Optional) Computing the Interest at a Rate Other Than 6%

The banker's 60-day method can be applied to combinations of days other than those that you have already learned. The time and effort involved in finding these combinations and then determining the interest is usually greater than that needed to apply directly the formula: $I = P \times R \times T$. Similarly, the 6% method can be applied to loans where the rate is other than 6%. Here, again, you will find that in most cases you could have determined the interest with greater ease had you used the interest formula. For some of the simpler situations, however, you may find this 6% method desirable.

Example 1: Find the interest on $600 at 3% for 54 days.

Solution: As the 3% rate is $\tfrac{1}{2}$ of the 6% rate, find the interest for 6%; then take $\tfrac{1}{2}$ of this amount for the 3% that is needed.

Outline: $6.00 = 60 days' interest at 6% on $600

$\underline{-.60 =\ \ 6 \text{ days' interest } (\tfrac{1}{10} \text{ of 60 days})}$

$5.40 = 54 days' interest at 6% on $600

$2.70 = 54 days' interest at 3% on $600 ($\tfrac{1}{2}$ of $5.40)

Outline the right side of each equation before completing the left side.

Example 2: Find the interest on $750 at 2% for 129 days.

Solution: As the 2% rate is $\tfrac{1}{3}$ of the 6% rate, find the interest for 6%; then take $\tfrac{1}{3}$ of this amount for the 2% that is needed.

Outline: $7.50 = 60 days' interest at 6% on $750

7.50 = 60 days' interest

.75 = 6 days' interest ($\tfrac{1}{10}$ of 60 days)

$\underline{.375 = 3 \text{ days' interest } (\tfrac{1}{2} \text{ of 6 days})}$

$16.125 = 129 days' interest at 6% on $750

$5.375 = 129 days' interest at 2% on $750 ($\tfrac{1}{3}$ of $16.125)

LEARNING EXERCISES

Find the interest on each of the following loans.

1. $600 @ 3% for 30 days
2. $540 @ 3% for 40 days
3. $750 @ 3% for 33 days
4. $870 @ 3% for 50 days
5. $756 @ 3% for 84 days
6. $4,500 @ 3% for 117 days
7. $900 @ 2% for 80 days
8. $630 @ 2% for 69 days
9. $570 @ 2% for 53 days
10. $810 @ 2% for 26 days
11. $654 @ 2% for 100 days
12. $725 @ 2% for 126 days
13. $669 @ 4% for 66 days
14. $348 @ 4% for 86 days
15. $186 @ 4% for 39 days
16. $439 @ 4% for 24 days
17. $593 @ 4% for 76 days
18. $3,475 @ 4% for 108 days

To find the interest at a rate other than 6%, find 6% first. Then add or subtract as the case may be. Thus, to find 5% interest, compute 6% interest first; then subtract 1% from 6% ($\tfrac{1}{6}$ of 6%). To find 7%, add 1% to 6%. To find 8% interest, find 6% and add 2% ($\tfrac{1}{3}$ of 6%), and so on.

UNIT 4   Finding the Time Lapse Between Two Dates

SECTION 1   Exact-Time Method

This method consists in counting the number of days from one date to the other, excluding the first day and including the last day.

This is done because in most states the interest is computed from noon on the first day to noon on the last day. To simplify the counting of days, the first day is excluded and all the last day is counted. Whether the first day is omitted in the count and the last day included, or the first day counted and the last day not counted, the total number of days between the dates in question is exactly the same.

Example 1: Find the number of days from January 12, 1958, to June 8, 1958, by the exact-time method.

Solution: There is no "simple" device for counting the number of days between dates. The following diagram aids in finding the total.

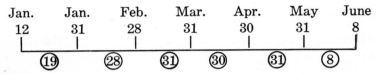

Since no interest is charged for the first day, subtracting the 12 from the 31 will enable you to find the number of days during the first month for which interest is charged. Exclusive of the first date and the last date, above the line, each of the other dates above the line represent the last day of each succeeding month. The numbers in the circles below the line indicate the number of days between these dates. These circled numbers, other than the first, can easily be found by merely observing the last day of each month. To complete the problem, add the numbers that are circled.

$$19 + 28 + 31 + 30 + 31 + 8 = 147 \text{ days}$$

Example 2: Find the number of days from October 19, 1957, to August 8, 1958, by the exact-time method.

Solution:

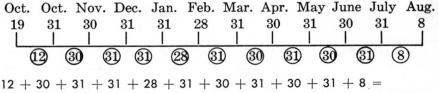

$$12 + 30 + 31 + 31 + 28 + 31 + 30 + 31 + 30 + 31 + 8 =$$
$$293 \text{ days}$$

LEARNING EXERCISES

Find the number of days from the first date through the second date in each of the following problems by the exact-time method.

1. May 5, 1957, to March 25, 1958 324
2. November 16, 1957, to February 19, 1958 95
3. March 22, 1958, to August 11, 1958 142 95
4. January 17, 1958, to April 1, 1958   74
5. August 10, 1957, to January 15, 1958
6. November 29, 1957, to March 18, 1958
7. April 30, 1958, to September 26, 1958
8. July 30, 1958, to November 14, 1958
9. February 9, 1958, to June 7, 1958
10. March 2, 1957, to February 13, 1958

SECTION 2   Finding the Exact Time with the Aid of a Table

You probably realized, from the length of time that it took you to determine the exact number of days between two dates, that no banker would consider devoting that much time to this computation for each loan. Even more important are the many opportunities that arise for making errors in the calculations. To shorten the time element and to lessen the possibility of error, several tables have been devised for finding the time lapse between two dates. You will learn how to use two of these tables.

Part 1—Time Table 1

The numbers in Time Table 1 represent the number of days between identical dates of any two months of the year. The method for applying this table can best be illustrated through the examples that follow the table.

TIME TABLE 1

| FINDING THE EXACT NUMBER OF DAYS FROM ANY DAY IN ONE MONTH TO THE SAME DAY IN ANY OTHER MONTH | | | | | | | | | | | |
Month	Jan.	Feb.	Mar.	Apr.	May	June	July	Aug.	Sept.	Oct.	Nov.	Dec.
January	365	31	59	90	120	151	181	212	243	273	304	334
February	334	365	28	59	89	120	150	181	212	242	273	303
March	306	337	365	31	61	92	122	153	184	214	245	275
April	275	306	334	365	30	61	91	122	153	183	214	244
May	245	276	304	335	365	31	61	92	123	153	184	214
June	214	245	273	304	334	365	30	61	92	122	153	183
July	184	215	243	274	304	335	365	31	62	92	123	153
August	153	184	212	243	273	304	334	365	31	61	92	122
September	122	153	181	212	242	273	303	334	365	30	61	91
October	92	123	151	182	212	243	273	304	335	365	31	61
November	61	92	120	151	181	212	242	273	304	334	365	30
December	31	62	90	121	151	182	212	243	274	304	335	365

Example 1: Find the exact number of days from April 5, 1958, to September 5, 1958.

Solution: 1. Follow the column headed "Month" downward until the name of the month of the first date is found. In this example, it is "April."

2. Follow the April row across until you reach the column headed by the name of the month of the second date. In this example it is "September."

3. The number at which your pointer has stopped—in this example 153—represents the exact number of days from April 5, 1958, to September 5, 1958. In fact, it represents the exact number of days from any date in April to the *same* numbered date in September. Thus, the number of days from April 17, 1958, to September 17, 1958, is also 153; or from April 23, 1958, to September 23, 1958, is the same number, 153.

Example 2: Find the number of days from April 5, 1958, to September 17, 1958.

Solution: Proceed exactly as you did in Example 1. The number 153, however, represents the number of days from April 5 to September 5. Since September 17 is 12 days beyond September 5, it is necessary to add 12 days to the 153 days, making a total of 165 days.

Outline: April 5 to September 5   153 days
                 September 5 to September 17   +12 days
                 April 5 to September 17   165 days

Example 3: Find the number of days from April 5, 1958, to September 2, 1958.

Solution: Again, follow the method in Example 1. The number 153 still represents the number of days from April 5 to September 5. Since September 2 is 3 days before September 5, it is necessary to subtract 3 days from 153 days, leaving 150 days, which is the exact number of days from April 5 to September 2.

Outline: April 5 to September 5   153 days
                 September 2 to September 5   −3 days
                 April 5 to September 2   150 days

LEARNING EXERCISES

Find the number of days from the first date through the second date in each of the following problems, using Time Table 1 on page 243.

1. May 12, 1958, to October 12, 1958
2. June 14, 1958, to October 18, 1958

3. February 3, 1958, to May 12, 1958
4. April 7, 1958, to August 23, 1958
5. July 12, 1958, to September 23, 1958
6. June 27, 1958, to December 5, 1958
7. January 31, 1958, to May 17, 1958
8. September 14, 1957, to February 20, 1958
9. July 3, 1957, to January 28, 1958
10. October 17, 1957, to June 9, 1958

Part 2—Time Table 2

Time Table 2 is designed to give the exact day of the year represented by each date of the year.

TIME TABLE 2

Finding the Exact Number of Days from Any Day of Any Month to Any Day of Any Other Month

Day of Month	Jan.	Feb.	March	April	May	June	July	Aug.	Sept.	Oct.	Nov.	Dec.
1	1	32	60	91	121	152	182	213	244	274	305	335
2	2	33	61	92	122	153	183	214	245	275	306	336
3	3	34	62	93	123	154	184	215	246	276	307	337
4	4	35	63	94	124	155	185	216	247	277	308	338
5	5	36	64	95	125	156	186	217	248	278	309	339
6	6	37	65	96	126	157	187	218	249	279	310	340
7	7	38	66	97	127	158	188	219	250	280	311	341
8	8	39	67	98	128	159	189	220	251	281	312	342
9	9	40	68	99	129	160	190	221	252	282	313	343
10	10	41	69	100	130	161	191	222	253	283	314	344
11	11	42	70	101	131	162	192	223	254	284	315	345
12	12	43	71	102	132	163	193	224	255	285	316	346
13	13	44	72	103	133	164	194	225	256	286	317	347
14	14	45	73	104	134	165	195	226	257	287	318	348
15	15	46	74	105	135	166	196	227	258	288	319	349
16	16	47	75	106	136	167	197	228	259	289	320	350
17	17	48	76	107	137	168	198	229	260	290	321	351
18	18	49	77	108	138	169	199	230	261	291	322	352
19	19	50	78	109	139	170	200	231	262	292	323	353
20	20	51	79	110	140	171	201	232	263	293	324	354
21	21	52	80	111	141	172	202	233	264	294	325	355
22	22	53	81	112	142	173	203	234	265	295	326	356
23	23	54	82	113	143	174	204	235	266	296	327	357
24	24	55	83	114	144	175	205	236	267	297	328	358
25	25	56	84	115	145	176	206	237	268	298	329	359
26	26	57	85	116	146	177	207	238	269	299	330	360
27	27	58	86	117	147	178	208	239	270	300	331	361
28	28	59	87	118	148	179	209	240	271	301	332	362
29	29	....	88	119	149	180	210	241	272	302	333	363
30	30	....	89	120	150	181	211	242	273	303	334	364
31	31	....	90	....	151	....	212	243	....	304	....	365

Without a table, you would know that January 17 is the 17th day of the year. However, it is unlikely that you would know what day of the year July 17 is. This can be found in the table as follows:

1. Go down the column headed "Day of the Month" until the number 17 is reached.

2. Follow this row across to the column headed "July."

3. The number 198 that you have just located indicates that July 17 is the 198th day of the year.

The value of this table in determining the number of days between two dates is shown in the examples that follow.

Example 1: Find the number of days from May 18, 1958, to November 14, 1958.

Solution: In Time Table 2 you will find that May 18 is the 138th day of the year and that November 14 is the 318th day of the year. Hence, the number of days between these dates can be found by subtracting 138 from 318. The difference (180) is the number of days from May 18 to November 14.

Outline:

November 14	318th day of the year
May 18	−138th day of the year
Number of days from May 18 to November 14	180

Example 2: Find the number of days between August 12, 1957, and March 3, 1958.

Solution: August 12 is the 224th day of the year. As there are 365 days in a year, then from August 12 until the end of the year there are 141 days (365–224). The time, however, does not expire until March 3, 1958. March 3 is the 62d day of the following year. Therefore, these 62 days must be added to the 141 days, making a total of 203 days between August 12, 1957, and March 3, 1958.

Outline:

December 31, 1957	365th day of the year
August 12, 1957	−224th day of the year
Number of days from August 12, 1957, to December 31, 1957	141
March 3, 1958	62d day of the year
Number of days from August 12, 1957, to March 3, 1958	203 (141 + 62)

LEARNING EXERCISES

Find the number of days from the first date through the second date in each of the following problems, using Time Table 2 on page 245.

1. May 14, 1958, to October 19, 1958
2. June 19, 1958, to October 3, 1958
3. February 8, 1958, to May 23, 1958

   4. April 7, 1958, to August 20, 1958
   5. July 9, 1958, to September 27, 1958
   6. June 27, 1958, to December 1, 1958
   7. January 22, 1958, to May 31, 1958
   8. September 24, 1957, to February 21, 1958
   9. July 29, 1957, to January 17, 1958
  10. October 17, 1957, to June 29, 1958

U N I T **5** **Computing Interest with the Aid of Time Tables**

The value of using time tables lies in the speed and accuracy with which it is possible to determine the number of days from one date to another. These tables become valuable assets when used as aids in determining the interest on a debt.

Business Transaction: Roger Bauman borrowed $800 from a friend on June 7, 1958, and returned the money on September 17, 1958. If he promised to pay interest at the rate of 5%, how large will the interest charge be? It was agreed that interest would be paid on the exact number of days during which the money was borrowed.

Solution: Using either Time Table 1 or 2, it is found that the number of days from June 7 to September 17 is 102. Applying the interest formula, $I = P \times R \times T$, the interest charge can be found.

Outline: → Known: Principal $800
                         Time   June 7 to September 17 — 102 Days
                         Rate   5%
             → To Find: Interest
             → Method: $I = P \times R \times T$
                         $= \$800 \times 5\% \times 102$ Days
                         $= \$800 \times \frac{5}{100} \times \frac{102}{360}$
                         $= \$\frac{34}{3}$
             Interest = **$11.33**

It was assumed in the solution of this problem that the 360-day, or banker's, year was to be used. Had the 365-day year, or the government year, been used, then the method would alter slightly.

$\rightarrow$ Method: $I = P \times R \times T$
$$= \$800 \times 5\% \times 102 \text{ Days}$$
$$= \$800 \times \tfrac{5}{100} \times \tfrac{102}{365}$$
$$= \$\tfrac{816}{73}$$
Interest $= \$11.18$

LEARNING EXERCISES

A. Using either Table 1 or 2 and the 360-day banker's year, find the interest on each of the following loans.

No.	Principal	Rate	Time to Run	Interest
1	$600	4%	Aug. 5, 1958, to Dec. 4, 1958	$xxx
2	800	6%	Sept. 25, 1958, to Dec. 10, 1958	xxx
3	500	$4\frac{1}{2}\%$	June 11, 1958, to Dec. 14, 1958	xxx
4	725	5%	July 25, 1958, to Dec. 26, 1958	xxx
5	650	$5\frac{1}{2}\%$	Mar. 12, 1958, to Sept. 19, 1958	xxx
6	275	$7\frac{1}{2}\%$	Feb. 3, 1958 to Nov. 15, 1958	xxx

B. Using either Table 1 or 2 and the 365-day government year, find the interest on each of the following loans.

No.	Principal	Rate	Time to Run	Interest
1	$ 300	6%	Aug. 17, 1958, to Dec. 20, 1958	$xxx
2	900	4%	Dec. 14, 1958, to Feb. 8, 1959	xxx
3	540	$5\frac{1}{2}\%$	May 18, 1958, to Oct. 23, 1958	xxx
4	250	$3\frac{1}{2}\%$	Apr. 23, 1957, to Feb. 21, 1958	xxx
5	375	7%	Nov. 1, 1957, to May 16, 1958	xxx
6	1,250	$4\frac{1}{2}\%$	Sept. 6, 1957, to July 7, 1958	xxx

C. *Problems to Be Solved*

1. A customer who promised to pay his debt of $370 on October 12, 1957, did not do so until March 1, 1958. How much interest did he owe on that debt if the rate of interest was 6% for the overdue period?

2. A firm in need of cash borrowed $1,000 on January 15, 1957, promising to pay interest at a rate of 5%. They agreed to return the money on June 1, 1957.

   a. Would the interest be more or less if the time used in computing the interest was based on the 360-day banker's year rather than on the 365-day government year?

   b. How much more or less would the interest amount be?

3. Mr. Wells borrowed $1,860 at an interest rate of 5% on October 19, 1957. He promised to return this money on May 27, 1958.

   a. How much interest will he be charged if the time is computed by the exact-time method and if the 360-day banker's year is used as a basis?

   b. What will the interest charge be if the time is computed by the exact-time method and if the 365-day government year is used as a basis?

UNIT **6**   **Computing Interest with the Aid of an Interest Table**

Considering the large number of loans that a bank makes each year, it would be time and effort consuming if the bank had to use the interest formula each time a person borrowed money. Therefore, tables like the one shown on page 250 were devised as an aid in determining the interest on a debt quickly and accurately.

This simple-interest table is based on loans of $100 but can easily be used to find interest on any other principal. Other tables are designed to give the interest on $1, $2, $3, and so on, as high as the banker may desire. No matter how the table was prepared, the basic principles for finding the interest in all the tables are similar to the procedure that will be explained in the examples that follow. Note, too, that the values in the table were found in terms of a 360-day banker's year. Tables are also constructed for the 365-day year.

Example 1: Find the interest on $100 at $5\frac{1}{2}\%$ for 21 days.

Solution: In the column headed "Time," find "21 days." Follow this row across until you reach the column headed "$5\frac{1}{2}\%$." The number under your pointer will be .3208, which represents the interest on $100 at $5\frac{1}{2}\%$ for 21 days. This amount is approximately $.32.

SIMPLE-INTEREST TABLE
($100 on a 360-Day-Year Basis)

Time	2½%	3%	3½%	4%	4½%	5%	5½%	6%	6½%	7%
1 day	.0069	.0083	.0097	.0111	.0125	.0139	.0153	.0167	.0181	.0194
2 days	.0139	.0167	.0194	.0222	.0250	.0278	.0306	.0333	.0361	.0389
3 days	.0208	.0250	.0292	.0333	.0375	.0417	.0458	.0500	.0542	.0583
4 days	.0278	.0333	.0389	.0444	.0500	.0556	.0611	.0667	.0722	.0778
5 days	.0347	.0417	.0486	.0556	.0625	.0694	.0764	.0833	.0903	.0972
6 days	.0417	.0500	.0583	.0667	.0750	.0833	.0917	.1000	.1083	.1167
7 days	.0486	.0583	.0681	.0778	.0875	.0972	.1069	.1167	.1264	.1361
8 days	.0556	.0667	.0778	.0889	.1000	.1111	.1222	.1333	.1444	.1556
9 days	.0625	.0750	.0875	.1000	.1125	.1250	.1375	.1500	.1625	.1750
10 days	.0694	.0833	.0972	.1111	.1250	.1389	.1528	.1667	.1806	.1944
11 days	.0764	.0917	.1069	.1222	.1375	.1528	.1681	.1833	.1986	.2139
12 days	.0833	.1000	.1167	.1333	.1500	.1667	.1833	.2000	.2167	.2333
13 days	.09C3	.1083	.1264	.1444	.1625	.1806	.1986	.2167	.2347	.2528
14 days	.0972	.1167	.1361	.1556	.1750	.1944	.2139	.2333	.2528	.2722
15 days	.1042	.1250	.1458	.1667	.1875	.2083	.2292	.2500	.2708	.2917
16 days	.1111	.1333	.1556	.1778	.2000	.2222	.2444	.2667	.2889	.3111
17 days	.1181	.1417	.1653	.1889	.2125	.2361	.2597	.2833	.3069	.3306
18 days	.1250	.1500	.1750	.2000	.2250	.2500	.2750	.3000	.3250	.3500
19 days	.1319	.1583	.1847	.2111	.2375	.2639	.2903	.3167	.3431	.3694
20 days	.1389	.1667	.1944	.2222	.2500	.2778	.3056	.3333	.3611	.3889
21 days	.1458	.1750	.2042	.2333	.2625	.2917	.3208	.3500	.3792	.4083
22 days	.1528	.1833	.2139	.2444	.2750	.3056	.3361	.3667	.3972	.4278
23 days	.1597	.1917	.2236	.2556	.2875	.3194	.3514	.3833	.4153	.4472
24 days	.1667	.2000	.2333	.2667	.3000	.3333	.3667	.4000	.4333	.4667
25 days	.1736	.2083	.2431	.2778	.3125	.3472	.3819	.4167	.4514	.4861
26 days	.1806	.2167	.2528	.2889	.3250	.3611	.3972	.4333	.4694	.5056
27 days	.1875	.2250	.2625	.3000	.3375	.3750	.4125	.4500	.4875	.5250
28 days	.1944	.2333	.2722	.3111	.3500	.3889	.4278	.4667	.5056	.5444
29 days	.2014	.2417	.2819	.3222	.3625	.4028	.4431	.4833	.5236	.5639
30 days	.2083	.2500	.2917	.3333	.3750	.4167	.4583	.5000	.5417	.5833
60 days	.4167	.5000	.5833	.6667	.7500	.8333	.9167	1.0000	1.0833	1.1667
90 days	.6230	.7500	.8750	1.0000	1.1250	1.2500	1.3750	1.5000	1.6250	1.7500
120 days	.8333	1.0000	1.1667	1.3333	1.5000	1.6667	1.8333	2.0000	2.1667	2.3333
150 days	1.0417	1.2500	1.4583	1.6667	1.8750	2.0833	2.2917	2.5000	2.7083	2.9160
180 days	1.2500	1.5000	1.7500	2.0000	2.2500	2.5000	2.7500	3.0000	3.2500	3.5070

Example 2: Find the interest on $275 at $5\frac{1}{2}\%$ for 21 days.

Solution: Proceed as in Example 1. The number found ($.3208) represents the interest on $100. Therefore, it is necessary to determine how many *hundreds* there are in $275. To do this, simply divide $275 by 100. This can be done by moving the decimal point in $275 two places to the left. The quotient 2.75 represents the number of hundreds in $275. For each $100 the interest is $.3208; hence, to find the interest for 2.75 hundreds, multiply 2.75 by $.3208. This product, $.8822, or $.88, will be the interest on $275 for 21 days at $5\frac{1}{2}\%$.

Outline: Interest on $100 = $.3208
Interest on $275 = 2.75 × $.3208
Interest on $275 @ $5\frac{1}{2}\%$ for 21 days = $.8822, or $.88

Example 3: Find the interest on $350 at 4% for 124 days.

Solution: The interest is found on $100 at 4% for 120 days, $1.3333; then on $100 at 4% for 4 days, $.0444. The sum ($1.3777) represents the interest on $100 at 4% for 124 days. To find the interest on $350, you must find the number of hundreds in $350. This is 3.5. Multiplying 3.5 by the interest for $100 ($1.3777) will give $4.82195. Thus, $4.82 is the interest on $350 at 4% for 124 days.

Outline:

$1.3333 = Interest on $100 for 120 days
\+ .0444 = Interest on $100 for 4 days
$1.3777 = Interest on $100 for 124 days
3.5 × $1.3777 = Interest on $350 for 124 days
$4.82195, or $4.82 = Interest on $350 for 124 days

LEARNING EXERCISES

A. Using the simple-interest table, find the interest on each of the following loans.

1. $300 @ 3% for 25 days
2. $800 @ $4\frac{1}{2}$% for 20 days
3. $2,400 @ $5\frac{1}{2}$% for 27 days
4. $3,000 @ 7% for 12 days
5. $750 @ $3\frac{1}{2}$% for 28 days
6. $625 @ 4% for 30 days
7. $1,250 @ 6% for 29 days
8. $500 @ $5\frac{1}{2}$% for 61 days
9. $200 @ $4\frac{1}{2}$% for 124 days
10. $550 @ $6\frac{1}{2}$% for 92 days
11. $375 @ 5% for 156 days
12. $2,725 @ 6% for 182 days

B. Find the interest on each of the following loans by using the simple-interest table and either of the time tables.

No.	Principal	Rate	Period of Loan	Interest
1	$ 600	4%	Apr. 5, 1958, to May 5, 1958	$xxx
2	900	6%	Aug. 17, 1958, to Sept. 15, 1958	xxx
3	400	5%	Feb. 14, 1958, to Mar. 15, 1958	xxx
4	300	$4\frac{1}{2}$%	June 12, 1958, to Aug. 16, 1958	xxx
5	1,400	$5\frac{1}{2}$%	Mar. 5, 1958, to June 23, 1958	xxx
6	350	6%	July 24, 1958, to Nov. 20, 1958	xxx
7	425	$3\frac{1}{2}$%	May 27, 1958, to Sept. 8, 1958	xxx
8	1,275	4%	June 10, 1958, to Nov. 18, 1958	xxx
9	302.50	$4\frac{1}{2}$%	Mar. 12, 1958, to May 15, 1958	xxx
10	451.36	7%	Apr. 9, 1958, to July 12, 1958	xxx

UNIT 7   **Compound Interest**

SECTION 1   Future Value of Money at Compound Interest

Thus far in this chapter, interest has been considered only from the point of view of the charge that a borrower has to pay on a loan. Just as important as this is the question, "How much money shall I have in the savings bank at the end of 3 years if I were to deposit $2,000 (or any other sum) today?" In this case, the person is not paying interest for the use of someone else's money but is receiving interest for allowing the bank to use his money.

You probably know that all savings banks credit their depositors with interest at least once a year. Therefore, using the preceding example as an illustration, after 1 year, the depositor would not only have his original $2,000 on deposit but also the interest that had been paid to him at the end of the first year. Hence, during the second year, he would collect interest on both the $2,000 and the first year's interest that he had allowed to remain in the bank. At the end of the second year, the new interest would be added to the old balance, again increasing the principal on which the interest is computed. This can be more clearly illustrated through the use of the following business transaction.

Business Transaction: Bernard Alden deposited $2,000 in the Guaranteed Savings Bank and allowed it to remain there for 3 years. If the bank paid its depositors 3% on their savings once each year, how much money did Mr. Alden have in the bank at the end of the 3 years?

Solution: Interest on $2,000 for the first year $= P \times R \times T$
$$= \$2,000 \times 3\% \times 1$$
$$= \$60$$

Hence, at the end of the first year, Mr. Alden had on deposit not only the original $2,000 but also the $60 in interest that he had received from the bank. This made a total of $2,060.

Interest on $2,060 for the second year $= P \times R \times T$
$$= \$2,060 \times 3\% \times 1$$
$$= \$61.80$$

Therefore, at the end of 2 years, Mr. Alden had on deposit $2,060 plus the second year's interest of $61.80, or a total of $2,121.80.

Interest on $2,121.80 for the third year $= P \times R \times T$

$$= \$2,121 * \times 3\% \times 1$$
$$= \$63.63$$

Thus, at the end of 3 years, Mr. Alden had $2,121.80 plus $63.63, or a total of $2,185.43 in the bank.

Outline:

At End of	Interest	Principal
First year	$60.00	$2,060.00
Second year	61.80	2,121.80
Third year	63.63	2,185.43

Whenever new interest is computed on the basis of the original principal plus the old interest, as was done in finding the second and third year's interest in the preceding business transaction, the method of computing interest is called the *compound-interest method,* or simply *compound interest.* Had the interest been found only once for the entire 3-year period, it would be computed as follows:

$$I = P \times R \times T$$
$$= \$2,000 \times 3\% \times 3 \text{ Years}$$
$$\text{Interest} = \$180$$

Therefore, the total amount of money that Mr. Alden would have had in the bank after 3 years would have been only **$2,180** instead of **$2,185.43.** When interest is found only once during the period, it is called *simple interest.* It is apparent, then, that a depositor receives more on his savings if interest is compounded than if it is computed as simple interest.

LEARNING EXERCISES

If a depositor neither adds any money to his account nor withdraws any from it, how large will his savings be at the end of the period indicated. Assume that interest is computed only once a year.

No.	Original Deposit	Interest Rate	Period of Deposit	Amount at End of Period
1	$4,000	3%	2 yrs.	$xxx
2	3,500	2%	2 yrs.	xxx
3	2,000	$2\frac{1}{2}\%$	2 yrs.	xxx
4	4,500	$3\frac{1}{2}\%$	3 yrs.	xxx
5	500	$3\frac{1}{4}\%$	3 yrs.	xxx
6	1,400	$2\frac{3}{4}\%$	3 yrs.	xxx
7	2,600	3%	4 yrs.	xxx
8	6,000	$2\frac{1}{2}\%$	5 yrs.	xxx

* Compound interest is not figured on amounts less than $1 by most banks and should not be so figured in the problems in this unit.

SECTION 2   Interest Compounded Semiannually or Quarterly

Most savings banks credit their depositors with interest more than once each year. If interest is credited twice a year, it is referred to as being *compounded semiannually;* or, as a few banks do, if credited 4 times a year, interest is said to be *compounded quarterly.* In Section 1, interest was compounded only once a year, or *annually.*

Earlier in this chapter it was pointed out that a rate of interest is quoted in terms of 1 year. Therefore, the bank that advertises its interest as being compounded semiannually at 3% is simply saying that every half year its depositors will receive interest on their deposits at a rate of $1\frac{1}{2}\%$ ($\frac{1}{2}$ of 3%).

Business Transaction: Henry Caldwell deposited $3,600 in the Regional Savings and Loan Association, which was paying its depositors interest at the rate of 3% compounded semiannually. If Mr. Caldwell allowed his deposit to remain untouched for 2 years, how much did he have on deposit at the end of that period?

Solution: An annual interest rate of 3% is the same as a semiannual rate of $1\frac{1}{2}\%$. Hence, at the end of the first half year, interest on Mr. Caldwell's deposit is found by multiplying $3,600 by $1\frac{1}{2}\%$. The product ($54) is added to the original deposit ($3,600), making the new principal $3,654 at the end of the first half year. Interest for the second half of the first year is computed on the $3,654. This same process is repeated for the first half of the second year and the second half of the second year.

Outline:

At End of	Interest	Principal
First half year	$54.00	$3,654.00
Second half year (1 year)	54.81	3,708.81
Third half year	55.62	3,764.43
Fourth half year (2 years)	56.46	3,820.89

LEARNING EXERCISES

In the following problems, if the depositor neither adds any money to his account nor withdraws any from it, how large will his savings be at the ends of the periods indicated?

No.	Original Deposit	Interest Rate	Compounded	Period of Deposit	Amount at End of Period
1	$ 400	2%	Semian.	2 yrs.	$xxx
2	1,000	3%	Semian.	2 yrs.	xxx
3	2,000	4%	Quarterly	1 yr.	xxx
4	3,600	3%	Semian.	$1\frac{1}{2}$ yrs.	xxx
5	4,000	$2\frac{1}{2}$%	Semian.	$2\frac{1}{2}$ yrs.	xxx
6	4,500	$3\frac{1}{4}$%	Semian.	$1\frac{1}{2}$ yrs.	xxx
7	800	2%	Quarterly	1 yr.	xxx
8	1,200	3%	Quarterly	$1\frac{1}{2}$ yrs.	xxx

SECTION 3   Computing the Future Value of Money by the Use of the Compound-Interest Table

By now you are aware that computing compound interest by the methods explained in Units 1 and 2 are time consuming. Because of this, tables have been devised to reduce the amount of work necessary to compute the amount of money that a person will have on deposit after a fixed period of time. The table on page 256 shows how much $1 will amount to if interest is compounded annually.

To illustrate: If $1 is placed on deposit at 3% compounded annually, after 12 years it will amount to $1.4258. This figure ($1.4258) was found by looking down the column headed by the word "Year" until the number 12 was reached and then following across this row to the column headed by the "3%." The number (1.4258) on which the pointer rested represents the value of $1 at the end of 12 years if interest is compounded annually at 3%.

This table can also be used to find the future value of $1 if interest is compounded either semiannually or quarterly. Thus, in the preceding illustration, if interest was compounded semiannually, the interest rate for the half year would be $1\frac{1}{2}$% (3% ÷ 2). Also, since the interest was given twice in 1 year, then in 12 years it would be given 24 times. This information is applied to the table by looking down the Year column to the number 24 (rather than 12) and across to the column headed by "$1\frac{1}{2}$%" (rather than 3%). The number found there (1.4295) represents the value of $1 at the end of 12 years if interest is compounded semiannually at 3%.

TABLE SHOWING AMOUNT OF $1 COMPOUNDED ANNUALLY

Year	1½%	2%	2½%	3%	3½%	4%	5%	6%
1	1.0150	1.0200	1.0250	1.0300	1.0350	1.0400	1.0500	1.0600
2	1.0302	1.0404	1.0506	1.0609	1.0712	1.0816	1.1025	1.1236
3	1.0457	1.0612	1.0769	1.0927	1.1087	1.1249	1.1576	1.1910
4	1.0614	1.0824	1.1038	1.1255	1.1475	1.1699	1.2155	1.2625
5	1.0773	1.1041	1.1314	1.1593	1.1877	1.2167	1.2763	1.3382
6	1.0934	1.1262	1.1597	1.1941	1.2293	1.2653	1.3401	1.4185
7	1.1098	1.1487	1.1887	1.2299	1.2723	1.3159	1.4071	1.5036
8	1.1265	1.1717	1.2184	1.2668	1.3168	1.3686	1.4775	1.5938
9	1.1434	1.1951	1.2489	1.3048	1.3629	1.4233	1.5513	1.6895
10	1.1605	1.2190	1.2801	1.3439	1.4106	1.4802	1.6289	1.7908
11	1.1779	1.2434	1.3121	1.3842	1.4600	1.5395	1.7103	1.8983
12	1.1956	1.2682	1.3449	1.4258	1.5111	1.6010	1.7959	2.0122
13	1.2136	1.2936	1.3785	1.4685	1.5640	1.6651	1.8856	2.1329
14	1.2318	1.3195	1.4130	1.5126	1.6187	1.7317	1.9799	2.2609
15	1.2502	1.3459	1.4483	1.5580	1.6753	1.8009	2.0789	2.3966
16	1.2690	1.3728	1.4845	1.6047	1.7340	1.8730	2.1829	2.5404
17	1.2880	1.4002	1.5216	1.6528	1.7947	1.9479	2.2920	2.6928
18	1.3063	1.4282	1.5597	1.7024	1.8575	2.0258	2.4066	2.8543
19	1.3270	1.4568	1.5987	1.7535	1.9225	2.1068	2.5270	3.0256
20	1.3469	1.4859	1.6387	1.8061	1.9898	2.1911	2.6533	3.2071
21	1.3671	1.5157	1.6796	1.8603	2.0594	2.2788	2.7860	3.3996
22	1.3876	1.5460	1.7216	1.9161	2.1315	2.3699	2.9253	3.6035
23	1.4084	1.5769	1.7646	1.9736	2.2061	2.4647	3.0715	3.8197
24	1.4295	1.6084	1.8087	2.0328	2.2833	2.5633	3.2251	4.0489
25	1.4509	1.6406	1.8539	2.0938	2.3632	2.6658	3.3864	4.2919

Business Transaction 1: If $400 is allowed to remain on deposit at 3½%, compounded annually for a period of 6 years, how much money will be in this account at the end of that period?

Solution: $1 at 3½% compounded annually for 6 years will amount to $1.2293. $400 will amount to 400 times $1.2293, or $491.72.

Outline:

Value of $1 @ 3½% compounded annually for 6 years = $1.2293

Value of $400 @ 3½% compounded annually for

6 years = 400 × $1.2293

= $491.72

Business Transaction 2: George Saylor deposited $3,700 in the First National Bank and allowed it to remain there for 11 years. If the bank paid its depositors interest at the rate of 3% compounded semiannually, how large was Mr. Saylor's savings at the end of the 11 years?

Solution: 3% interest rate compounded semiannually for 11 years implies that interest was given 22 times at a rate of $1\frac{1}{2}$%.

Outline:

Value of $1 @ $1\frac{1}{2}$% given 22 times = $1.3876

Value of $3,700 @ $1\frac{1}{2}$% given 22 times = 3,700 × $1.3876

= $5,134.12

LEARNING EXERCISES

A. If a depositor neither adds any money to his account nor withdraws any from it, how large will his savings be at the end of the period indicated in the following problems?

No.	Original Deposit	Interest Rate	Compounded	Period of Deposit	Amount at End of Period
1	$ 540	4%	Annually	6 yrs.	$xxx
2	750	$3\frac{1}{2}$%	Annually	9 yrs.	xxx
3	2,300	5%	Annually	15 yrs.	xxx
4	4,500	6%	Annually	12 yrs.	xxx
5	840	4%	Semian.	5 yrs.	xxx
6	925	6%	Semian.	8 yrs.	xxx
7	3,800	5%	Semian.	10 yrs.	xxx
8	690	6%	Quarterly	4 yrs.	xxx
9	940	6%	Quarterly	2 yrs.	xxx
10	2,600	6%	Quarterly	6 yrs.	xxx

B. *Problems to Be Solved*

1. How much interest will accumulate on an $800 deposit over 10 years if interest is compounded semiannually at 3%?

2. An amount of $4,000 is out on loan for 3 years at an interest rate of 5%.

    a. If the lender agrees to charge simple interest on this loan, how much will be returned to him at the end of the 3 years?

    b. If interest is compounded annually on this debt, how much will the lender receive at the end of the 3 years?

    c. How much more will the lender receive if interest is compounded rather than if simple interest is charged?

3. $5,000 is deposited in a building and loan association at a 6%

interest rate and allowed to remain there for 5 years. What will be the amount of money in the association at the end of this period if interest is compounded annually?

4. a. How much will a depositor gain in 5 years if his $5,000 were deposited in a bank where interest is compounded semiannually at 6%?

b. How much will he gain if interest is compounded quarterly at 6%?

5. Approximately how many years will it take for $1 to amount to $2 at an interest rate of 5% compounded annually?

6. Approximately how many more years will it take for $1 to amount to $2 at 3% interest compounded annually than at 6% compounded annually?

UNIT 8   What Have You Learned?

SECTION 1   Understanding Terms

Can you match the term in the column on the left with the proper definition in the column on the right?

Term	*Definition*
1. Principal of a debt	a. The time from the date the money was borrowed until the date it was returned.
2. Interest	b. A 360-day year.
3. Period of a loan	c. A 365-day year.
4. Banker's year	d. The banker's 60-day method of finding interest.
5. Borrower	e. Amount of money a person borrows.
6. Lender	f. The source from which the money is borrowed.
7. Government year	g. The amount returned to the lender.
	h. The person to whom the money is lent.
	i. The fee charged for borrowing money.

SECTION 2   You As a Borrower

How wisely would you borrow money? Can you make the correct selection in each of the following situations and justify your answer? If you cannot do so, review the pages indicated at the end of the problem.

1. You have the choice of borrowing $2,000 at 6% for 90 days either from the bank or from a private individual. The bank, as is customary, uses the "bank year" to determine the interest charge; the private lender, on the other hand, is willing to base his calculations on the "government year." From whom should you borrow the $2,000? (Pages 233 and 235.)

2. You have just received a shipment of merchandise valued at $850, for which you must pay cash. If you wait 30 days to make payment, there is a penalty charge of 2% of the invoice total. As you do not have the cash, should you pay immediately with money that can be borrowed from the bank for 30 days at an interest rate of 6%, or should you wait the 30 days and pay the penalty of 2%? (Page 233.)

3. You have just learned that you can buy the grand piano that you have always wanted at a discount of 20% off the list price of $3,200. You do not have the cash, and to save that much money would take you 2 years. From the point of view of savings only, would it be worth your while to borrow the amount you need from the bank, buy the piano, and pay off your debt to the bank at 6% at the end of 2 years? (Page 233.)

4. As the proprietor of a store, you have just received an invoice for merchandise purchased by you for $720, terms 2/10, n/30. Not having the money at present, should you borrow at 5% the amount you need to pay the invoice on the 10th day in order to take advantage of the 2% discount, or should you wait and pay the invoice when you have the money on the 30th day? (Pages 233 and 241.)

SECTION 3   Review Problems

1. Without the use of the time tables, find the exact number of days from March 14, 1958, to June 17, 1958. (Page 242.)

2. A merchant borrowed $425 at $4\frac{1}{2}$% interest rate from a friend for 3 months. What was the interest charge on this loan? (Pages 233 and 241.)

3. Arthur Todd borrowed $1,800 at 5% in order to buy a car. A year and a half later he paid off the debt. How much did he have to pay in interest? (Pages 233–234.)

4. Using the banker's 60-day method, find the interest on each of the following loans:

    a. $650 @ 6% for 90 days
    b. $208 @ 6% for 50 days
    c. $375 @ 6% for 123 days   (Page 239.)

5. On April 7, 1958, Fred Stanton borrowed $275 which he was supposed to repay on September 7, 1958. However, by receiving payment early for work he had performed, he paid off his debt on June 17, 1958.

  a. How many days did he actually keep the borrowed money? (Pages 241 and 243.)

  b. How many days' interest did he save by repaying the loan earlier than it was due? (Pages 241 and 243.)

  6. On March 17, 1958, Robert Arvin borrowed **$207** for the purchase of an automatic clothes washer. He paid off this debt on May 12, 1958, with interest at 7%. How much would Mr. Arvin have saved if he had had the cash to buy the washer? (Page 247.)

  7. Clark borrowed $1,200 from the bank for 90 days at 6%. If the bank deducted its interest charge from the loan at the time the money was borrowed, how much did Clark receive? (Pages 233 and 249.)

  8. William Brownley has $80,000, which he lends at $5\frac{1}{2}$% interest. How much money is it possible for Mr. Brownley's $80,000 to earn for him in 1 year, assuming that all the money is lent for the entire year? (Pages 233–234.)

  9. In need of **$375** to pay off an urgent debt, Robert Wharton borrowed this amount at $7\frac{1}{2}$% interest on November 12, 1957. On May 17, 1958, he paid back both the principal of the loan and the interest charges. How much did the loan cost him? (Page 247.)

SECTION 4   Testing Your Understanding

40 Minutes

  1. How many days are there from January 17, 1958, to April 12, 1958? Do *not* use the time tables. Show all your work.

  2. Using Time Table 2 on page 245, find the number of days from September 12, 1957, to May 9, 1958.

  3. The owner of a store paid off a debt to a distributor after 4 months. What was the charge if the interest rate was $5\frac{1}{2}$% and the principal of the debt was $450?

  4. After $2\frac{1}{2}$ years, Dorothy Kingsley paid off a debt of $1,800 on which she was paying interest at the rate of 4%. How much did it cost Miss Kingsley to borrow the money?

  5. Using the banker's 60-day method, find the interest on each of the following debts:

  a. $600 @ 6% for 80 days
  b. $750 @ 6% for 36 days
  c. $540 @ 6% for 183 days

6. Using the simple-interest table on page 250, find the interest on each of the following loans:

  a. $200 @ 5% for 25 days
  b. $350 @ 7% for 60 days
  c. $1,200 @ 4½% for 126 days

7. Robert Arnold borrowed $330 on May 9, 1958, and returned the money on August 12, 1958. Use the tables in this chapter to find the interest if the interest rate was 5½%.

$$\frac{\begin{array}{r} 14 \\ 28 \\ 31 \\ 12 \end{array}}{85}$$

U N I T **9**   General Review

SECTION 1   To Improve Your Speed and Accuracy

1. Addition: Copy and complete the following business form.

Weekly Payroll							
Department 43—Children's Clothes							
Week Beginning May 5, 19——							
Employee	Mon.	Tues.	Wed.	Thurs.	Fri.	Sat.	Total
English, A.	$10.76		$11.03	$10.20	$10.94	$11.50	$xxx
Fallone, G.		$11.24	10.86	10.72	11.49	11.86	xxx
Farah, R.	9.95	9.74	10.65		10.74	10.27	xxx
Glenfield, N.	12.14	12.58	11.62	12.93		13.20	xxx
Harbich, C.	14.50	15.21		16.01	15.73	16.18	xxx
Laskey, T.	11.24		12.87	10.92	11.15	11.83	xxx
Total	$ xxx	$ xxx	$ xxx	$ xxx	$ xxx	$ xxx	$xxx

2. Subtraction:

  a. 8,327
    2,374

  b. $4,250.00
      84.23

  c. $76\frac{1}{3}$
    $58\frac{2}{5}$

  d. $740 − $15.47

  e. $36\frac{2}{3} − 17\frac{2}{5}$

3. Multiplication:

  a. 4,378 × 694

  b. $5,275 × 1.06

  c. $17\frac{1}{2} × 56$

  d. $323.76 × .92

  e. $800 × 4\frac{3}{4}%$

4. Division:
   a. 36,742 ÷ 807   b. $642.42 ÷ .06   c. $58.98 ÷ 88%
   d. 56 ÷ $2\frac{1}{3}$ e. $75\frac{3}{4}$ ÷ 16

SECTION 2   Do You Remember These?

1. List Price = $78.50, Trade Discount Rate = 24%, Trade Discount = ?

2. List Price = $185, Discount Series = 25% and 5%, Net Price = ?

3. Find the single discount rate equivalent to the series 15% and 10%.

4. Marked Price = $147.90, Consumer Discount Rate = $33\frac{1}{3}$%, Retail = ?

5. Marked Price = $84, Retail Price = $72, Discount Rate = ?

6. Cost = $42, Retail = $56, Markup Rate Based on Cost = ?

7. Cost = $17.50, Retail = $15.50, Per Cent of Loss Based on Retail = ?

8. Cost = $120, Markup Rate Based on Cost = 32%, Retail = ?

9. Cost = $150, Markup Rate Based on Retail = 25%, Retail = ?

10. Retail = $60, Per Cent of Gross Profit Based on Retail = 42%, Cost = ?

11. Retail = $78.85, Per Cent of Gross Profit Based on Cost = $16\frac{2}{3}$%, Cost = ?

12. Retail = $99.95, Per Cent of Overhead Based on Retail = 18%, Overhead = ?

11

Discounting Notes and Drafts

PREVIEW

Before opening his men's-wear shop, George Barnard had the store completely redecorated. New, modern fixtures were installed. Chairs of Swedish design were placed strategically about the floor for the comfort of his customers. The windows were cleverly arranged to attract the eyes of passers-by. And, to supply an added touch, sections of the walls were covered with hand-painted murals in keeping with the masculine theme of the shop.

Unfortunately, Barnard's extravagant taste far outstripped his limited bank account. Hence, when work was half completed, he arranged to give the general contractor a written statement agreeing to pay for the unpaid portion of the work, which amounted to $2,500, 3 months after the store opened for business. He hoped that by that time the returns from his shop would cover the amount of his debt. A month after the contractor, Fred Wardell, had completed his work, he found himself in need of additional funds to conduct his own business. He could not demand the $2,500 from Barnard, for he had agreed to wait 3 months, not 1 month, for the money. In view of the circumstances, Wardell requested his bank to grant him a loan, offering as security the statement he had received from Barnard as promise of payment. The bank, knowing Barnard's and Wardell's reputations for honesty, accepted Barnard's written promise to pay and granted the loan. Did Wardell receive the full $2,500 from the bank?

For Class Discussion

1. What is the name of the written statement that George Barnard gave to Fred Wardell? *Promissory note*

2. What is the name of the charge that Wardell had to pay the bank?

3. If Fred Wardell had insisted that George Barnard pay him an additional fee for waiting 3 months for the $2,500, what would that fee be called?

4. What is the name of the transaction of selling a note to a bank as Wardell did?

5. From whom will the bank collect the $2,500 when payment is due?

6. If the person who promised to pay the money fails to do so, what may the bank do?

7. Could Wardell have legally demanded that Barnard pay him the $2,500 at the end of the first month?

Terms You Should Know

The slip of paper that George Barnard gave Fred Wardell, agreeing to pay the $2,500 in 3 months, resembled the form shown at the top of page 265.

This form is called a *promissory note*. The amount of money that is promised by the note is known as the *face value* of the note. The person who owes the money and who signs his name in the lower right-hand corner of the note is the *maker*. The person to whom the money is due or to whom payment is promised is the *payee*. The *period*, or *term*, of the note is the length of time the money was borrowed. The day the money was borrowed is written on the note and is simply called the *date* of the note, while the day the note must be paid is called the *maturity date* of the note.

To illustrate: Using George Barnard's note as a guide:
→$2,500 is the *face value*.
→George Barnard is the *maker*.
→Fred Wardell is the *payee*.
→3 months is the *period*, or *term*.
→July 29, 19—, is the *date*.
→October 29, 19—, is the *maturity date*.

Had Barnard borrowed the money directly from the bank in order to pay Wardell for his work, the note would be similar to the one shown here.

For lending him the money, the bank would have made a charge, usually computed as follows:

$$\$2,500 \times \frac{6}{100} \times \frac{3}{12} = \$37.50$$

The fee, $37.50, is deducted immediately by the bank from the $2,500 and only $2,462.50 turned over to the borrower, George Barnard. When the charge is taken off in advance, it is called, like all other deductions, a *discount*. The rate used to determine this charge, the 6% in this case, is referred to as a *discount rate*. The amount that was actually given to Barnard, the $2,462.50, is the *proceeds* of the note.

To illustrate: $400 was borrowed from the bank at a discount rate of 6% for 60 days.

→6% is the *discount rate*.
→$4 is the *discount* ($400 × 6% × 60 days).
→$400 is the *face* of the note.
→$396 is the *proceeds* ($400 − $4).

If the charge of $4 had been paid at the *end* of the 60 days when the note was due to be paid, the charge would be known as an *interest charge*. In this event, the person would pay back not only the $400, but he would also pay the interest charge of $4. The $404 is called the *value of the note at maturity*, or, simply, the *amount* of the note. Thus, the difference between the meanings of the words *interest* and *discount* lies in the fact that, in the case of interest, the charge is paid on the date when payment is due on the note; and in the case of discount, the charge is paid at the time the loan is made. The borrower never possesses the amount of the discount, for it is deducted from the face of the note before he is given the money.

The loan departments of most banks use a discount rate rather than an interest rate. In this way, it is possible for them to relend immediately to others the discount that was deducted at the time the loan was made. The process of deducting the discount from the face of the note and turning the proceeds over to the maker or borrower is called *discounting a note*. When a person borrows money from a bank, the note is discounted on the very day it is made out. This simply means that the bank deducts its charge before giving the borrower his money. In the preceding case, where Barnard borrowed $2,500 from the First National Bank, the note was discounted on July 29, 19— the day the money was borrowed.

Concerning This Chapter

Business would very likely come to a standstill if people were unwilling to trust one another in the delayed payment of debts.

To help bind these promises that payment will eventually be made, notes are drawn up, stating a promise to pay. These promises are not only moral obligations; they are also legal obligations. Banks recognize them as such, and being in business primarily to make money through the lending of money, they will lend money directly to private individuals or business concerns on the basis of these written promises. In addition, banks are usually willing to buy notes from persons who have lent money to others but are no longer willing or able to continue their own enterprises without the cash tied up in the loan.

In studying this chapter, you will learn how banks determine the value of a note at any time during the period of the debt. This knowledge will enable you to find the proceeds that are turned over to the borrower and the extent of the earnings of the bank. You will also discover another means that the businessman has for either delaying payment on a debt or collecting an overdue invoice.

U N I T 1   Finding the Maturity Date of a Note

The maturity date plays an important role in finding the discount on a note. Should a person desire to borrow money from a bank, it is necessary to determine first on what date the loan will be paid, that is, the maturity date. Then on the basis of this information, the bank will find the period of the note in *days*, not months.

Because of the importance that this date plays in computing the charge for borrowing money from a bank, there arises the need for a method of quickly finding the maturity date of a note. The following examples will illustrate this method.

Example 1: Find the maturity date of a 3-month note dated August 12.

Solution: Enumerate the months until you reach the third month after August. Thus, September is the first month; October is the second month, and November is the third month. November 12 is the maturity date.

Example 2: Find the maturity date on a 60-day note dated July 17.

Solution 1: Reference to Time Table 2 on page 245 will simplify the work very much. July 17 is the 198th day of the year; 60 days after this can be found by adding 198 to 60, making a total of **258**. Therefore, the note is due on the 258th day of the year. Again referring to the table for the 258th day of the year, you will find that this is September 15. Hence, the maturity date of the note is September 15.

Outline: July 17: 198th day of the year

$$\frac{+60}{258}$$

258th day of the year: September 15   Maturity Date

Solution 2: If the time table is not available, the maturity date may be found by counting forward from the date of the note the exact number of days, months, or years, as the case may be, after which date the note is to be paid.

Thus, in this problem, the maturity date is found by counting 60 days from July 17.

Outline: 60 days from July 17

$$\frac{14 \text{ days} \text{ left in July}}{46 \text{ days left}}$$

$$\frac{31 \text{ days} \text{ in August}}{15 \text{ days left in September}}$$

60 days from July 17 = September 15, Maturity Date

LEARNING EXERCISES

Find the maturity date in each of the following notes.

No.	Date of Note	Time to Run	No.	Date of Note	Time to Run
1	July 5	1 mo.	10	Feb. 25	90 days
2	Jan. 31	2 mo.	11	May 13	120 days
3	July 9	3 mo.	12	Jan. 21	108 days
4	Sept. 12	4 mo.	13	Mar. 3	75 days
5	Aug. 27	3 mo.	14	July 14	180 days
6	Oct. 4	6 mo.	15	Oct. 19	90 days
7	June 3	30 days	16	Nov. 22	90 days
8	July 6	30 days	17	Jan. 31	1 month
9	Apr. 7	60 days	18	Jan. 31	30 days

UNIT **2**   **Finding the Proceeds on a Note**

Business Transaction: On July 7, Theodore Hopkins borrowed $375 from the bank for 2 months. The bank discounted his note at 6% and turned over the proceeds to him.

    a. How much money did Hopkins receive from the bank (proceeds)?

    b. How much money did Hopkins return on the maturity date?

Solution: The charge for borrowing the money is found in exactly the same way that the interest was found in the preceding chapter, except that now, since the charge is collected on the day the money is borrowed, it is called *discount* rather than *interest*. The method employed is shown below:

    Discount = Principal × Rate × Time, or D = P × R × T

The discount is subtracted from the face of the note. The difference is the proceeds. The maturity date of the note is September 7. The term of the note is the number of days between July 7 and September 7 (2 months from July 7).

    Outline: → Known: Principal $375

                    Discount Rate   6%

                    Time   July 7 to September 7, 62 Days

        → To Find: Proceeds and Maturity Value

        → Method 1: D = P × R × T

$$= \$375 \times \tfrac{6}{100} \times \tfrac{62}{360}$$

                Discount = $3.88

                Proceeds = Face Value − Discount

$$= \$375 \quad\quad - \$3.88$$

            (a) Proceeds = $371.12

            (b) Maturity Value = $375, Face Value of the Note

    → Method 2: Using the simple-interest table on page 250:

                $1.0000 = Discount on $100 for 60 days

               +.0333 = Discount on $100 for 2 days

                $1.0333 = Discount on $100 for 62 days

      3.75 × $1.0333 = Discount on $375 for 62 days

                $3.88   = Discount on $375 for 62 days

Proceeds and maturity value can then be found in the same way as in Method 1.

It is important to remember that, when a bank discounts a note, it uses as its principal, not the amount that the borrower or maker receives, but the amount that he is expected to *return* when the note becomes due. Thus, in the preceding business transaction the principal of the debt was $375, not $371.12.

LEARNING EXERCISES

A. Using either the discount formula or the banker's 60-day interest method, find the discount, the proceeds, and the maturity value of each of the following notes. Check each answer by solving each problem again, using the simple-interest table on page 250.

No.	Face of Note	Time to Run	Discount Rate	Discount	Proceeds	Maturity Value
1	$600	60 days	6%	$xxx	$xxx	$xxx
2	400	90 days	6%	xxx	xxx	xxx
3	250	30 days	5%	xxx	xxx	xxx
4	325	120 days	$5\frac{1}{2}\%$	xxx	xxx	xxx
5	475	60 days	4%	xxx	xxx	xxx
6	255	32 days	6%	xxx	xxx	xxx

B. Find the proceeds of each of the following notes.

No.	Face of Note	Time to Run	Date of Note	Discount Rate	Term of Discount	Bank Discount	Proceeds
1	$500	1 mo.	June 9	6%	xxx	$xxx	$xxx
2	300	2 mos.	July 17	6%	xxx	xxx	xxx
3	600	2 mos.	Aug. 4	5%	xxx	xxx	xxx
4	420	3 mos.	Sept. 9	4%	xxx	xxx	xxx
5	250	1 mo.	Mar. 16	6%	xxx	xxx	xxx
6	350	2 mos.	Jan. 22	6%	xxx	xxx	xxx
7	175	3 mos.	Apr. 15	5%	xxx	xxx	xxx
8	600	4 mos.	May 7	$5\frac{1}{2}\%$	xxx	xxx	xxx

C. *Problems to Be Solved*

1. The following note was discounted at 5% discount rate at the bank on May 17. List the following information:

a. Maker	**d.** Maturity value	**g.** Bank discount
b. Payee	**e.** Date of maturity	**h.** Proceeds
c. Date of note	**f.** Term of discount	

...425^{00}_{xx}$...   Albany, New York....*May 17,*....19—..

Three months after date.....*I*.....promise to pay to the order of

..............*The Commercial Trust Company*.................

Four hundred twenty-five and $\frac{00}{xx}$·.......................Dollars

at...............*The Commercial Trust Company*..............

Value received.......................

No..*537*..   Due..*August 17,*..19—.... ..*Raymond Bauer*..

2. Jonathan Arnold borrowed $275 from the bank for 30 days at 6% discount rate. How much money did the bank actually give him?

3. On March 17, Fred Bender borrowed $340 from the bank for 2 months at a discount rate of $5\frac{1}{2}$%. What were the proceeds?

4. Ralph Warren needed $2,000 for 60 days.

    a. If he borrowed this money from a private individual at a 6% *interest* rate, what would the charge be?

    b. If he borrowed this money from the bank at a *discount* rate of 6%, what would the charge be?

    c. How much actual cash would he receive from the private individual?

    d. How much actual cash would he receive from the bank?

    e. From which source would it be advisable for him to borrow the money? Why?

UNIT **3** **Finding the Proceeds of a Non-Interest-Bearing Note**

      In the opening paragraphs of this chapter a situation was described in which George Barnard gave a note for $2,500 to contractor Fred Wardell, in payment of services the latter had rendered. After 1 month, Wardell sold the note to the bank. The point was raised as to how much Mr. Wardell would receive from the bank. You are now in a position to have this question answered. Before doing so, two important factors must be re-emphasized:

→**1.** The bank will charge interest only for the period of time during which the money was held by the borrower. This period is called the *discount period*, or *term of discount*.

→**2.** The discount charged by the bank is based on the maturity value of the note, *not* necessarily on the amount indicated on the face of the note.

Business Transaction: On July 29, George Barnard gave Fred Wardell a note for $2,500 for a period of 3 months. Wardell did not charge Barnard interest on the note. 1 month later, on August 29, Wardell discounted the note at the bank at 6%. How much did he receive from the bank?

Solution: In answer to the two points that were just emphasized above,

1. The bank received the note on August 29 and was paid for this note by George Barnard on October 29. The period of time for which the bank can charge discount is 61 days (the number of days from August 29 to October 29).

2. Since Fred Wardell did not charge George Barnard any interest on the note, the value of the note at maturity was $2,500. This was the amount the bank received on October 29. Notes like this one, where no interest is charged, are known as *non-interest-bearing notes*.

Outline: → Known: Maturity Value $2,500
                Discount Rate   6%
                Discount Period   August 29 to October 29,
                    61 Days
       → To Find: Proceeds
       → Method: $D = P \times R \times T$
                  = \$2,500 \times 6\% \times 61$ Days
         Discount = $25.42
         Proceeds = Maturity Value − Discount
               = $2,500   − $25.42
               = $2,474.58

Business Transaction: Find the proceeds of a $450 non-interest-bearing note dated April 7 and due in 3 months, if the note was discounted at the bank on May 15 at 5%.

Solution: 3 months from April 7 is July 7. The number of days from May 15 to July 7 is 53 days. Hence, the discount period, or time during which the bank had lent the money, was 53 days. It is for this period only that discount can be charged.

Outline: → Known: Maturity Value = $450
                     Discount Rate = 5%
                     Discount Period = May 15 to July 7, 53 Days
     → To Find: Proceeds
     → Method:

$4.50	= 60 days' discount at 6% on $450	
2.25	= 30 days' discount ($\frac{1}{2}$ of 60)	
1.50	= 20 days' discount ($\frac{1}{3}$ of 60)	
.225	= 3 days' discount ($\frac{1}{10}$ of 30)	
$3.975	= 53 days' discount at 6% on $450	
.6625	= 53 days' discount at 1% ($\frac{1}{6}$ of 6%)	
$3.3125	= 53 days' discount at 5% on $450	

$$\text{Proceeds} = \text{Maturity Value} - \text{Discount}$$
$$= \quad \$450 \quad - \quad \$3.31$$
$$\text{Proceeds} = \$446.69$$

The diagram shown here will be helpful in guiding your progress through the several steps in the solution.

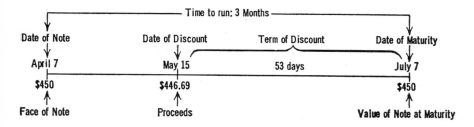

The dates above the line, reading from left to right, represent:
1. Date of the note
2. Discount date
3. Maturity date

The term of discount (in this transaction 53 days) is found after the discount date and maturity date are placed in the diagram. The face of the note, the $450 under "April 7," and the maturity value, the $450 under "July 7," are the same, for the note bore no interest. The proceeds of $446.69, which is the amount received on May 15, was based on the maturity value of $450 and the discount period of 53 days.

It is suggested that the time tables and the simple-interest table in the preceding chapter be used as much as possible in order *to lessen* the task of computation. The discount, however, can always be found by applying the discount formula as was shown earlier in the chapter (page 269).

LEARNING EXERCISES   *all problem*

Find the proceeds in each of the following notes.

No.	Face of Note	Time to Run	Date of Note	Discount Date	Discount Rate	Pro-ceeds
1	$200.00	2 mos.	June 17	July 12	6%	$xxx
2	300.00	3 mos.	Aug. 5	Aug. 20	6%	xxx
3	250.00	5 mos.	Mar. 12	May 3	6%	xxx
4	350.00	3 mos.	Sept. 9	Sept. 12	5%	xxx
5	175.00	2 mos.	Dec. 18	Jan. 3	5%	xxx
6	375.00	6 mos.	Oct. 23	Feb. 7	$5\frac{1}{2}\%$	xxx
7	402.00	1 mo.	July 10	July 25	6%	xxx
8	351.00	3 mos.	Jan. 3	Jan. 31	7%	xxx
9	276.00	9 mos.	Mar. 14	Aug. 3	$4\frac{1}{2}\%$	xxx
10	642.40	2 mos.	Aug. 18	Sept. 2	7%	xxx
11	816.35	3 mos.	Feb. 14	Feb. 27	7%	xxx
12	364.00	60 days	Aug. 8	Aug. 11	6%	xxx
13	580.00	75 days	July 25	Aug. 15	6%	xxx
14	800.00	90 days	Dec. 16	Jan. 8	6%	xxx
15	286.75	60 days	May 28	June 27	7%	xxx

UNIT 4   Finding the Proceeds of an Interest-Bearing Note

Thus far you have considered the discounting of non-interest-bearing notes—notes of the type given by Barnard to Wardell. Fred Wardell, for various reasons, did not charge George Barnard interest on the face value of the note. When the note was sold to the bank by Wardell, he lost money for he received less for the note than the amount of the debt. Though non-interest-bearing notes are common when delayed payment of debts for merchandise or services are involved, they are unlikely to occur in the actual lending of cash between two persons. People lend money for the purpose of earning money. Hence, most notes that are given when cash has passed from a lender to a borrower will draw interest. When these notes are discounted at a bank, a greater number of calculations are necessary than were previously used to determine the proceeds. This is so because the maturity value of the note is not the same as the face value.

Business Transaction: On July 29, George Barnard gave Fred Wardell a note for $2,500 payable in 3 months. At the end of the 3-month period, George Barnard was to pay back the $2,500 with interest at 5%. 1 month after the note was drawn up, Fred Wardell discounted the note at the bank at a 6% discount rate. How much did Wardell receive from the bank?

The note shown here was given by Barnard to Wardell. You will

$2,500 $\frac{00}{xx}$ Atlanta, Georgia, July 29, 19 —

Three months   after date I promise to pay

to the order of   Fred Wardell

Twenty-five hundred and $\frac{00}{xx}$ Dollars

Payable at   First National Bank

Value received with interest at 5%

No 183   Due October 29, 19 —   George Barnard

notice that the only difference between this note and the non-interest-bearing note on page 265 is that, following the printed words "Value received," is written the phrase "with interest at 5%."

Solution: Before attempting the solution, it is necessary for you to recall that the bank's charge depends on the maturity value of the note; that is, the discount is based on the amount that the bank will actually receive from the borrower when the note is due. Since this is an interest-bearing note, the value of the note increases constantly from the date of the note until the day the note is paid. To determine what it will charge, the bank must first determine what it will receive.

Had the money been borrowed directly from a bank, the bank would have found the exact number of days in the period. However, in view of the fact that the original transaction was between two private individuals, the period of the note remains in terms of months. The interest on $2,500 for 3 months at 5% amounts to $31.25. This means that the note will be worth $2,500 plus the interest of $31.25, or $2,531.25, on the day that George Barnard pays off the debt. It is this amount, $2,531.25, on which the bank will charge discount.

Outline: → Known: Face value $2,500
Period of note   3 Months
Discount period   August 29 to October 29,
61 Days
Interest rate   5%
Discount rate   6%
→ To Find: Proceeds on August 29
→ Method: $I = P \times R \times T$
$= \$2,500 \times 5\% \times 3$ Months
Interest $= \$31.25$
Maturity Value = Face Value + Interest
$= \quad \$2,500 \quad + \quad \$31.25$
$= \$2,531.25$
Discount = Maturity Value × Rate × Time
$= \$2,531.25 \times 6\% \times 61$ Days
$= \$25.73$

or

$\$25.3125 = 60$ days' discount at 6% on $2,531.25
$\underline{\quad.4218 = 1 \text{ day's discount } (\frac{1}{60} \text{ of } 60 \text{ days})\quad}$
$\$25.7342 = 61$ days' discount at 6% on $2,531.25

Proceeds = Maturity Value − Discount
$= \quad \$2,531.25 \quad - \quad \$25.73$
Proceeds $= \$2,505.52$

Again, this diagram will enable you to visualize the transaction.

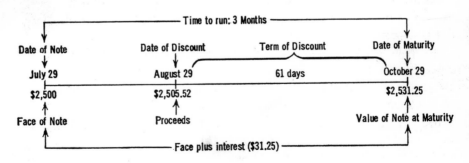

LEARNING EXERCISES

A. Find the proceeds of each of the following notes.

No.	Face of Note	Time to Run	Date of Note	Discount Date	Interest Rate	Discount Rate	Pro- ceeds
1	$ 600	3 mos.	Aug. 3	Aug. 14	6%	6%	$xxx
2	1,200	2 mos.	Nov. 17	Dec. 15	4%	5%	xxx
3	420	3 mos.	Apr. 12	May 12	5%	6%	xxx
4	3,450	4 mos.	Feb. 11	Feb. 19	7%	6%	xxx
5	1,900	60 days	May 5	June 2	8%	6%	xxx
6	2,400	90 days	June 27	July 10	6%	7%	xxx
7	1,375	6 mos.	Mar. 19	May 6	6%	6%	xxx

B. *Problems to Be Solved*

1. On July 24, Burke discounted at 6% a $725, three-month non-interest-bearing note that he had received from Fields on June 3. Find the amount received by Burke.

2. Find the bank discount at 5% and the proceeds of a 90-day, non-interest-bearing note for $5,860 that Ryan received from Lewis on August 18 and discounted on August 29.

3. A 5% interest-bearing note amounting to $620, dated July 28 and due in 90 days, is discounted at the bank on August 2 at 6%. Find the proceeds.

4. On August 11, Ellison received a 90-day, $4\frac{1}{2}$% interest-bearing note amounting to $5,870 from Fields and discounted the note on September 1 at 5%. Find the amount that he received from the bank.

5. If Cook discounted on June 29 an 80-day, 5% interest-bearing note amounting to $168.50, which he had received from Blaine on May 24, and the bank charged a 6% discount rate, how much did he receive for the note?

6. Find the proceeds on the following note if it was discounted January 17 at 6%.

....$7,200$\frac{50}{xx}$....	*Loomis, N. Y., Dec. 23, 19—....*

Sixty days after date......I......promise to pay to the order of

.....................*Elizabeth Allan*...................

Seventy-two hundred and $\frac{50}{xx}$ ....Dollars

Payable at.........*Manufacturers Banking Co.*...................

Value received.............

No...*347*..   Due..*Feb. 21, 19—*..   ..*Marcia Michaels*..

UNIT 5   **Collection of Debts Through the Use of Drafts**

Business Transaction 1: On May 14, the Donaldson Furniture Company of Paterson, New Jersey, sent 10 sofas and 15 living-room chairs to J. A. Stern, the proprietor of a furniture store in Miami, Florida. The Donaldson Company on September 14, after patiently waiting 4 months for either full or partial payment on its invoice of $2,250, completed the following form and deposited it at its bank for collection.

$ 2,250 oo/xx	Paterson, N. J., _September, 14_ _19 --_
_____ At sight _____	_pay to the order of_
Ourselves	
Twenty-two hundred fifty and 00/xx -_Dollars_	
Value received and charge to the account of	
_To_ _____ J. A. Stern _____	**DONALDSON FURNITURE COMPANY**
_____ Miami, Florida _____	_by_ _R. W. Donaldson_

This form is called a *sight draft*, or a *bill of exchange*. It is a written demand for payment. The collection of the draft would be attempted as follows. Donaldson's bank sends this draft to a bank in Miami. The Florida bank would then get in touch with J. A. Stern and request payment of the draft. If Mr. Stern accepts the draft by paying the $2,250, this amount, less a collection fee, will be returned to the Donaldson Company's bank and credited to its account. The payment, less the collection fee, is called the *proceeds* of the draft. Collection fees vary, ranging from as high as $\frac{1}{2}\%$ to as low as $\frac{1}{40}\%$ of the face value of the draft. Should Mr. Stern refuse to honor the draft, that is, pay it, his credit rating would no doubt be affected. The result would be that Mr. Stern would probably have difficulty whenever he tried to buy merchandise on credit.

Certain common terms are used in dealing with drafts. The *drawer* of the draft is the person who fills out the draft and signs his name in the lower right-hand corner. He is the person who is demanding that the money be paid. The person or company to whom he wishes the money to be paid is the *payee*. The one who is to pay it is the *drawee*.

To illustrate: In the preceding draft:

→Donaldson Furniture Company is the *drawer*.

→Ourselves is the *payee*.

→J. A. Stern is the *drawee*.

In this case, the drawer and the payee are the same person. Had the Donaldson Company directed Mr. Stern to pay the money to a third person, the third person would be the payee.

Business Transaction 2: A collection fee of $\frac{1}{8}\%$ was charged by the bank for collecting a draft of $2,250. How large was this fee?

Solution: 1% of $2,250 $= $22.50

$\frac{1}{8}$ of 1% of $2,250 $= \frac{1}{8}$ of $22.50

$\frac{1}{8}\%$ of $2,250 $= $2.81 Collection Fee

Business Transaction 3: A draft of $356.28 was collected by the National Trading Bank. If the collection fee was $\frac{1}{10}\%$, how much did the payee receive?

Solution: 1% of $356.28 $= $3.56

$\frac{1}{10}$ of 1% of $356.28 $= \frac{1}{10}$ of $3.56

$\frac{1}{10}\%$ of $356.28 $= $.36 Collection Fee

Proceeds = Face Value − Collection Fee

= $356.28 − $.36

Proceeds = $355.92

LEARNING EXERCISES

1. Find the collection fee on each of the following drafts.

No.	Face Value	Fee	No.	Face Value	Fee
a	$ 800.00	$\frac{1}{10}\%$	f	$ 627.50	$\frac{1}{8}\%$
b	600.00	$\frac{1}{3}\%$	g	873.26	$\frac{1}{10}\%$
c	2,800.00	$\frac{1}{2}\%$	h	948.42	$\frac{1}{6}\%$
d	450.00	$\frac{1}{10}\%$	i	4,376.00	$\frac{1}{4}\%$
e	525.00	$\frac{1}{8}\%$	j	9,547.50	$\frac{1}{5}\%$

2. Find the proceeds of each of the following drafts.

No.	Face Value	Fee	No.	Face Value	Fee
a	$850.00	$\frac{1}{10}\%$	d	$ 756.50	$\frac{1}{8}\%$
b	640.00	$\frac{1}{12}\%$	e	2,347.80	$\frac{1}{10}\%$
c	320.00	$\frac{1}{14}\%$	f	4,956.20	$\frac{1}{20}\%$

UNIT **6**   **Finding the Proceeds of a Time Draft**

Had the Donaldson Furniture Company desired to be more lenient with Mr. Stern, it might have changed the form of the draft to one like that shown here.

$ _____ 2,250 oo/xx _____	Paterson, N. J., _____ September 14, _19_ -
_____ Two months after sight _____	_pay to the order of_
	Ourselves
Twenty-two hundred fifty and 00/xx - - - - - - - - - - - - - - - - - - - _Dollars_	
Value received and charge to the account of	
_To_ _____ J. A. Stern _____	DONALDSON FURNITURE COMPANY
_____ Miami, Florida _____	_by_ _____ R. W. Donaldson _____

This draft differs from the one on page 278 in that the words "At sight" are replaced by the words "Two months after sight." This means that Mr. Stern is given 2 months in which to pay his debt after he is presented with the draft by the Miami bank. If he agrees to this condition, he writes the word "Accepted" across the draft, records the date of acceptance, and signs his name. The bank in Miami then holds the draft until the day of maturity. When payment is made the bank forwards the amount collected, less the collection fee, to the Donaldson Furniture Company. The date of maturity is computed from the *date of acceptance.*

Another alternative that the Donaldson Company had was to write the words "Two months after date" rather than "Two months after sight." Had this been done, the draft would have to be paid on November 14, which is 2 months after the draft was made out.

Drafts that delay payment until some future date are called *time drafts.* Once a draft is accepted by the drawee, it serves the same purpose as a promissory note, for it has now become a written promise to pay. Therefore, should the drawer desire, he can have the accepted draft discounted at the bank and receive the face value, less both the discount and collection fee. Discounting a draft is the same as discounting a non-interest-bearing note.

Business Transaction: Find the proceeds of this draft if it is accepted by Mr. Ellsworth on February 28 and discounted on March 3 at 6%.

$750 xx   *Jersey City, N. J., Jan. 29, 19 —*

Three months after date ———————— *pay to the order of*

      Henry Keller

Seven hundred fifty and xx ——————————— *Dollars*

Value received and charge to account of.

To William Ellsworth

  Newton, N. J.   *Fred West*

Accepted Feb. 28, 19——

Outline: → Known: Face Value $750

       Discount Period March 3 to April 29, 57 Days

       Discount Rate 6%

  → To Find: Proceeds

  → Method: D = P × R × T

        = $750 × 6% × 57 Days

        = $7.13 or

   $7.50 = 60 days' interest at 6% on $750

   −.375 = 3 days' interest ($\frac{1}{20}$ of 60 days)

   7.125 = 57 days' interest at 6% on $750

  Discount = $7.13

    Proceeds = Face Value − Discount

       = $750 − $7.13

       = $742.87

This diagram will enable you to visualize the transaction.

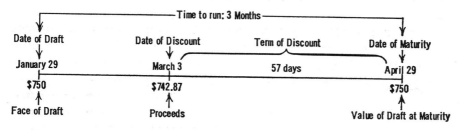

Time to run: 3 Months			
Date of Draft	Date of Discount	Term of Discount	Date of Maturity
January 29	March 3	57 days	April 29
$750	$742.87		$750
Face of Draft	Proceeds		Value of Draft at Maturity

LEARNING EXERCISES

1. Find the date of maturity, the term of discount, the bank discount, and the proceeds of each of the following drafts. When diagraming your problem for solution, show the maturity date, the discount period, and the bank discount, as well as the proceeds.

No.	Face of Draft	Date of Draft	When Due	Acceptance Date	Discount Date	Rate of Discount	Proceeds
a	$ 400.00	Feb. 15	3 mos. after date	Feb. 28	Mar. 21	5%	$xxx
b	700.00	Jan. 12	2 mos. after sight	Jan. 15	Feb. 11	6%	xxx
c	2,000.00	Mar. 16	2 mos. after sight	Mar. 17	Mar. 18	4%	xxx
d	1,500.00	Apr. 3	3 mos. after date	Apr. 19	May 2	$6\frac{1}{2}\%$	xxx
e	4,300.00	May 17	3 mos. after sight	May 30	June 21	8%	xxx
f	275.00	June 12	90 days after sight	June 18	June 21	5%	xxx
g	342.50	Feb. 18	4 mos. after date	Mar. 19	May 2	4%	xxx
h	4,375.40	June 21	60 days after date	June 22	July 9	7%	xxx

2. Find the proceeds of a 90-day sight draft amounting to $468.50, accepted December 18 and discounted December 24 at 6%.

3. On August 7, Johnson & Martin accepted a 60-day sight draft amounting to $860, drawn on them by Pomeroy & Company on August 2. Pomeroy & Company discounted the draft on August 28 at 5%. Find the proceeds.

4. How much will a bank pay on a $625 draft dated March 16, due 75 days after date, accepted April 7, if discounted May 2 at $6\frac{1}{2}\%$?

5. You draw a 3-month sight draft amounting to $267.75 on Cameron & Ronald, which they accept on June 30. If you discount the draft at your bank on July 21 at 6%, how much would you receive?

6. Assume that the following draft was accepted on November 29. Find the proceeds if the draft was discounted on November 30 at 5%.

....$5,000$^{00}_{xx}$....   Richmond, Va., Nov. 17, 19—....
Ninety days after sight........................pay to the order of
........................Charles Ryan........................
Five thousand and $\frac{00}{xx}$................................Dollars
Value received and charge to the account of
To.....Richmond Mailing Co......
.....Richmond, Va......   ....George Hall....

7. Assume that the following draft was accepted on April 30. Find the proceeds if the draft was discounted May 3 at 7%.

..$1,500$^{00}_{xx}$..   *Springfield, Mass., Mar. 15, 19—*....

Four months after date.....................pay to the order of

.....................*Joseph White*.......................

Fifteen hundred and $^{00}_{xx}$..............................Dollars

Value received and charge to the account of

To..*Charles Banworth*..

   ...*Boston, Mass.*....   ...*Wallace Brown*...

UNIT 7   What Have You Learned?

SECTION 1   Understanding Terms

Match the term in the column on the left with the proper definition in the column on the right.

Term	*Definition*
1. Promissory note	a. The person asking for payment of a debt.
2. Maker of a note	b. Date when note or draft was sold to bank.
3. Payee of a note	c. The date when the note was paid.
4. Drawer of a draft	d. A written promise agreeing to repay a debt.
5. Drawee of a draft	e. Charge paid for loan at time loan is repaid.
6. Maturity date	f. The person who lends the money.
7. Date of note	g. Amount of money given to the borrower by the bank.
8. Discount date	h. The person who borrows the money when a loan is made.
9. Discount period	i. Charge paid for borrowing money at the time the money is received.
10. Interest	j. The person in a draft who is being asked to pay the debt.
11. Discount	k. Value of a note on the day it is due.
12. Face value of a note	l. Period of a loan.
13. Proceeds	m. Number of days during which the bank holds the note.
14. Maturity value	n. Date when the money was borrowed.
	o. Amount of money that was borrowed.

SECTION 2   You As a Lender or a Borrower

How wisely would you lend the money you have or borrow the money you need? Can you make the correct selection in each of the following situations and justify your answer? If you cannot do so, review the pages indicated at the end of the problem.

1. You find yourself in possession of $10,000, which you would like to invest by lending it at a yearly rate of 6%. Would your returns be greater if you charged an interest rate or a discount rate? (Page 269.)

2. As the manager of the Loan Department of a bank, you have approximately $500,000 to lend at a yearly interest rate of 6%. Would it be better to make large loans for the entire year or small loans for short periods lasting no more than 3 months? In both cases the entire $500,000 will be out on loan. (Pages 233 and 269.)

3. You are in need of $500 for 6 months in order to make repairs on your home. The bank is willing to lend you the money at a discount rate of 6%. You have the choice of either borrowing the money for the entire 6 months or borrowing it for 3 months, paying the discount again, and renewing the note for another 3 months. Which choice would you make? (Pages 233 and 269.)

4. To pay off debts incurred through illness, you would like to borrow $200 for 3 months. Your credit is good at the bank; hence, it would be possible for you to borrow the money there at a discount rate of 6%. A neighbor who lends out small sums to increase his income is also willing to lend you the money, but he charges an interest rate of 6%. Where should you borrow the money? (Page 269.)

5. In order to increase their cash sales, Barker's Furniture Company allowed a discount of 6% for cash on all sales over $200. A living-room suite that you purchased there cost $450, but you could not pay them for 1 month. To allow you to take advantage of their discount on cash purchases, Barker's was willing to take your promissory note for 1 month for $450, less the 6% discount rate. Should you accept this offer if the discount rate on the note is 6%? (Pages 233 and 269.)

SECTION 3   Review Problems

1. Find the maturity date on notes that were dated as follows:
  a. June 7 for 30 days.
  b. July 5 for 6 months.
  c. September 17 for 120 days. (Page 267.)

2. Find the discount period for notes that were dated and discounted as follows:

   a. Dated May 3 for 3 months; discounted, June 7.

   b. Dated December 17 for 4 months; discounted, December 20.

   c. Dated August 12 for 60 days; discounted, September 3. (Pages 271–272.)

3. What are the proceeds of a $350, 60-day note if the discount rate is $5\frac{1}{2}\%$? (Page 269.)

4. On June 5, Edwin Barton borrowed $275 from the bank for 3 months at a discount rate of 6%.

   a. Find the period of the note in days. (Page 267.)

   b. Find the proceeds. (Page 269.)

5. Find the proceeds of a $420 non-interest-bearing note dated May 27, due in 3 months, if discounted June 3 at 6%. (Page 271.)

6. The Built-Well Furniture Company received a 90-day, non-interest-bearing note dated August 25, amounting to $864.75. As the company was in need of ready funds, it discounted the note at the bank on September 17 at 6%. Find the amount the company received. (Page 271.)

7. Theodore Wheeler borrowed $550 from Arthur Trent on March 11 for 2 months at an interest rate of 5%. On April 15, Trent discounted the note at the bank at 6%.

   a. What was the maturity value of the note? (Pages 274–276.)

   b. How much did Trent receive from the bank? (Pages 274–276.)

8. Find the proceeds of each of the following drafts:

   a. Face value, $946; collection fee, $\frac{1}{10}\%$.

   b. Face value, $427.39; collection fee, $\frac{1}{8}\%$.

   c. Face value, $2,875.98; collection fee, $\frac{1}{20}\%$. (Pages 278 and 279.)

9. Find the proceeds of a $274.50 non-interest-bearing note, due September 5, if it was discounted on July 15 at 6%. (Pages 271 and 272.)

10. A $463.75 time draft, due 3 months after sight, was accepted June 3 and discounted June 6 at 7%. To how much did the proceeds amount? (Page 280.)

11. In terms of the following note, give the information requested.

   a. Maker

   b. Payee

   c. Date of note

   d. Time to run

   e. Maturity date

   f. Face value

   g. Maturity value

   h. Proceeds, if discounted at the bank on June 18 at 6%

   (Page 274.)

..375^{00}_{xx}$..   *Franklin Square, N. Y.,   June 5...19—....*

..Four months...after date....I....promise to pay to the order of

.....................Michael Bush.....................

Three hundred seventy-five and $\frac{00}{xx}$.....................Dollars

at..............Mutual Trust Company.....................

Value received....*with interest at 5%....*

No...*184*..   Due..*October 5, 19—*..   ..*James Riley*..

---

12. In terms of the following draft, give the information requested.

....$1,550$^{00}_{xx}$....   *Chicago, Ill., Apr. 12, 19—....*

Ninety days after sight.................pay to the order of

.................John O'Connor.....................

Fifteen hundred fifty and $\frac{00}{xx}$.....................Dollars

Value received and charge to the account of

To....*Arthur Scanlon*....

          ....*Mound City, Ill.*.....   ....*Harold Larson*....

Accepted: May 6, 19—.

a. Drawer

b. Payee

c. Drawee

d. Time to run

e. Maturity date

f. Collection fee if the rate was $\frac{1}{8}$%

g. Discount if discounted at the bank on May 12 at 5%

h. Proceeds

          (Pages 278–279.)

SECTION 4   Testing Your Understanding

40 Minutes

1. Find the maturity date of a note dated April 17 and due in 90 days.

2. What is the discount period of a note dated August 9 and due in 6 months if the note was discounted at the bank on December 3?

3. Bernard Gange borrowed $245 from the bank on April 24 for 2 months at a discount rate of 6%.

    a. What is the term of discount?

    b. What are the proceeds?

4. On July 23, Anthony Trout discounted a $425 non-interest-bearing note at the bank at 5%. If the note was dated June 15 and was due in 4 months, how much did Trout receive from the bank?

5. What is the collection fee on a 60-day time draft amounting to $427.54 if the collection rate is $\frac{1}{8}\%$?

6. You receive a $1,360 draft from Martin on April 17, payable 4 months after date. How much would the bank pay you if you discounted the draft on May 15 at 6%?

7. In terms of the following note, give the information requested.

...$1,250\frac{00}{xx}$...   Canton, Ohio, July 18, 19—....
Three months..after date.....I.....promise to pay to the order of
.......................Herbert Fletcher...................
Twelve hundred fifty and $\frac{00}{xx}$.........................Dollars
Payable at.................Merchants State Bank.....
Value received....with interest at 6%..................
No....172...   Due..Oct. 16, 19—..   ...Robert Marks...

a. Maker   g. Interest on note

b. Payee   h. Maturity value

c. Date of note   i. Discount on note

d. Time to run   j. Proceeds, if discounted at the

e. Maturity date   bank on July 29 at 6%

f. Face value

UNIT 8   General Review

SECTION 1   To Improve Your Speed and Accuracy

1. Addition:

a.	b.	c.
428	$847.09	$37\frac{5}{6}$
593	56.73	$24\frac{2}{3}$
286	81.46	$32\frac{11}{12}$
744	3.58	
307	209.65	
658	78.20	
935	347.98	

d. $156 + $509.98 + $3.09 + $29 + $48.35

e. $26\frac{3}{8} + 43\frac{3}{4} + 38\frac{2}{3} + 8\frac{1}{2}$

2. Subtraction:

a. 83,904
    56,826

b. $20,905.00
    1,938.08

c. $56\frac{7}{8}$
   $25\frac{2}{3}$

d. $375 − $36.48

e. $85\frac{1}{2} − 49\frac{5}{8}$

3. Multiplication:

a. 57,026 × 285

b. $7,368 × 3.05

c. $27\frac{3}{4} × 72$

d. $425.09 × .96

e. $8\frac{1}{2} × 5\frac{3}{4}$

4. Division:

a. 100,000 ÷ 435

b. $927.35 ÷ .045

c. $86.50 ÷ $2\frac{3}{4}\%$

d. $72 ÷ 8\frac{1}{2}$

e. $35\frac{2}{3} ÷ 12$

SECTION 2   Do You Remember These?

1. Find the following products at sight.

a. 57.84 × 100   **b.** 394.82 × 1,000   **c.** 4,376 × 10

2. Find the following quotients at sight.

a. 63.70 ÷ 100   **b.** 3,750.75 ÷ 1,000   **c.** 675 ÷ 10

3. Using the straight-line method of depreciation, what is the annual depreciation on an article whose original value was $950 if, after 6 years, it was sold for $150?

4. An article originally cost $600. If a fixed yearly rate of 15% on the decreasing value is used in computing the depreciation on the article, what is the yearly depreciation for each of the first 2 years?

5. If a person's gross yearly salary is $3,958.76, how much is deducted for Social Security?

6. At time and a half for all work over 40 hours, what is the wage of a man who worked $43\frac{1}{2}$ hours at $2.26 an hour?

7. What are the weekly deductions for Social Security made from the salary of a man who works 39 hours at $2.06 an hour?

8. What is the interest on $650 for 2 months at an interest rate of 5%?

9. How many days are there between June 12 and October 23?

10. Using the banker's 6% 60-day method, find the interest on $325 that was borrowed for 90 days.

11. The catalogue price of an article is $56.50. If the trade discount rate is 38%, what is the net price of the article?

12. A discount series of 20% and 8% is equivalent to what single discount rate?

Began for Second Sem.

12

Installment Buying and Selling

PREVIEW

The large sign in the window of the automobile agency seemed to reach out like an enormous magnet and draw Bob Clark to it.

> **"ONLY $10.88 PER WEEK WILL BUY THIS CAR"**

Bob had found employment almost immediately after finishing school. His first few pay checks had been accompanied by that wonderful feeling of independence—a feeling that had brought him to the automobile agency. Now, for the small amount of $10.88 a week he could be the envy of his friends.

As this thought flashed through his mind, Bob stepped forward toward the door of the showroom. It was only then that the first disturbing thought clouded his beautiful dream—the sign had given no indication of how much money he was expected to leave as a down payment! What was even worse, nowhere did he see a reference to the number of weeks in which he was expected to pay the $10.88!

As he slowly backed away from the door, he had other sad misgivings. How much extra would he be charged for "paying off" the car in installments rather than buying it for cash?

Would he have to take out any special insurance on the car if he bought it on the installment plan?

How long would it take him to save the money if he decided to pay for it with cash?

If he should be unable to meet one of the payments, what would happen to the car?

Would there be any saving to himself if he borrowed the money he needed for the car from a bank rather than pay the dealer $10.88 a week?

Bob's better judgment finally got the upper hand. Although owning a car was something he had always desired, he felt that it would be wise to seek the answers to these questions before making a decision.

For Class Discussion

1. What is meant by the expression "buying on the installment plan"?

2. List several things the automobile finance company might do if Bob Clark should fail to meet his weekly payments.

3. What is the name for the additional charge that the buyer must pay when purchasing an article on the installment plan?

4. List several reasons why a merchant is justified in making an additional charge on installment purchases.

5. What are several advantages of buying articles on the installment plan?

6. What are several disadvantages of buying articles on the installment plan?

7. List several emergencies that might arise, making it necessary to purchase articles on the installment plan.

Why Use Installment Buying

Very often people are faced with the problem, "Shall I buy a new car on the installment plan now and pay interest on the money that I must borrow, or shall I wait until next year when I shall have the cash?"

How this question is answered is entirely a personal matter. If you are a salesman with an old car in such poor condition that the expense of keeping it an additional year would be more than the added installment charge, then by all means—buy now! On the other hand, it is difficult to justify the purchase, on credit, of a second family car that will not be used often.

Some buyers are indignant when told that they will have to pay an interest, or carrying, charge on their installment purchases. They feel that the seller has already made a profit on the cost of the article. Why, then, should the purchaser be asked to pay still more? Yet, if the prospective buyer would stop to consider the seller's point of view, he would find the following justifications for the carrying charge:

1. When the article is removed from the store, it is necessary for the merchant to replace it with another by either borrowing money or withdrawing money from the bank.

2. Additional employees must be hired to keep records of the periodic payments.

3. If payments are not made, the merchant will have to employ someone to reclaim the article.

4. As the buyer is, in a sense, borrowing money from the merchant to pay for the purchase, the merchant should have the right to charge interest on the loan.

Primarily, the greatest advantage of installment buying is that it permits people to acquire and enjoy goods *now* that they might have to wait years for if they were to purchase for cash.

Concerning This Chapter

Over 3 billion dollars' worth of merchandise is purchased on installment in the United States each month. Some of this purchasing is done wisely; some not so wisely. It is the purpose of this chapter to teach you how to determine the rate of interest you will have to pay each time you make an installment purchase. This knowledge should help you decide whether the installment purchase you may be contemplating is advisable. In addition, you will learn how to find the rate of interest on loans that are repaid on the installment plan. You will be able to compare the rates of interest charged by small-loan agencies with the rates charged by banks. Because some day you may wish to purchase an automobile on *time payments*, one unit—Unit 3—is devoted to presenting methods

by which such purchases are made. Unit 3 will also teach you how
to find the rate of interest on automobile loans. This chapter will
not only help you become a more intelligent buyer but it will also
help you to understand why installment buying is an important
activity in many business offices where you may be employed.

Terms You Should Know

Installment buying is not the least expensive way of acquiring
something you want. Almost always, the merchant increases the
selling price by a small amount, which he may call by such names
as *service charge, carrying charge, credit charge, installment charge,*
or simply *interest.*

Business Transaction: A sign in an electrical-appliance store
read: "Buy this dishwasher on easy terms; $15 down and $10.95
a month for only 16 months." Being interested in purchasing a
dishwasher, Mr. Weber inquired what the cost would be if he paid
cash. The reply was, "$159.50." How much could have been saved
by buying the dishwasher for cash?

Solution: If the article was purchased on the installment plan,
$10.95 would be paid each month for 16 months. Hence, the total
amount paid on the monthly installments alone would be 16 times
$10.95, or $175.20. In addition, the buyer was asked to pay $15
down immediately. Therefore, the complete cost of the dishwasher, if purchased on the installment plan, would be $175.20
plus $15, or $190.20. Since it could be bought for cash at $159.50,
Mr. Weber would save $30.70 ($190.20 − $159.50) if he should
decide to buy the washer by paying for it in a lump sum.

The cost of an article that is purchased on the installment plan
is called the *installment price* of the article. If the article is paid
for at the time of purchase by a lump-sum payment, that cost is
known as the *cash price* of the article. Using the figures in the
preceding business transaction:

→$190.20 is the *installment price.*

→$159.50 is the *cash price.*

→$30.70 is the *installment charge* ($190.20 − $159.50).

→$15 is the *down payment.*

UNIT 1   **Computing the Installment Charge**

Business Transaction: A lightweight English bicycle is advertised
at $47.25 cash or, if the buyer prefers credit, $7.25 down and $5.50

monthly. An inquiry at the store revealed the fact that **8** monthly
payments will have to be made.

    a. What is the installment price of the article?

    b. What is the installment charge on the purchase?

Solution: → Known: Down Payment   = $7.25

                    Monthly Payment   = $5.50

                    Number of Months = 8

                    Cash Price   = $47.25

      → To Find: Installment Price

                    Installment Charge

    → Method: Installment Price = Down Payment +

                              (Monthly Payment ×

                              Number of Months)

                          = $7.25 + ($5.50 × 8)

                          = $7.25 + $44

                          = $51.25

      Installment Charge = Installment Price − Cash Price

                       = $51.25   − $47.25

                = $4

LEARNING EXERCISES

A. Find the installment charge on each of the following purchases.

No.	Article	Cash Price	Terms of Installment Sale			Install-ment Charge
			Down Payment	Number of Payments	Amt. of Each Payment	
1	Suit	$ 55.00	$20.00	8	$ 5.00	$xxx
2	Portable radio	30.00	8.00	6	4.00	xxx
3	Record player	47.00	7.50	7	6.00	xxx
4	Fishing rod and reel	62.50	10.50	10	5.50	xxx
5	"Hi-Fi" set	112.75	12.75	12	8.75	xxx
6	Tape recorder	163.40	25.00	18	8.25	xxx
7	Set of en-cyclopedias	246.25	40.00	24	9.35	xxx
8	Sewing machine	210.95	10.95	16	12.85	xxx
9	Portable typewriter	79.98	7.50	20	3.95	xxx
10	Television set	269.95	29.95	30	8.97	xxx
11	Used car	575.00	57.50	18	31.34	xxx
12	Piano	776.50	50.00	36	21.84	xxx

B. *Problems to be Solved*

1. Roger Tyler bought a boat for $75 down and $40 a month for 6 months. If he had paid cash, it would have cost him $300. What was the installment charge on this purchase?

2. R. Lawrence and Company advertised a dining-room suite for $335.50 cash. Inquiry at the store showed that the suite could be purchased on the installment plan for no down payment and 25 monthly payments of $15.45 each. How much interest is an installment purchaser paying?

3. An oil-heater conversion unit can be purchased for a coal furnace for $399.95 cash or $49.95 down and $12.25 a month for 36 months. How large is the carrying charge that the installment purchaser will have to pay?

4. Burt's Fair Deal Auto Mart offered to sell a $275 used car for 10% down and $18.20 a month for 18 months. Find the installment charge if the car is purchased on the installment plan.

5. The Better-Buy Outlet Store advertised a color television set at $895 cash or 15% down and 30 months to pay. Prospective buyers were told that the monthly payments would amount to $29.42. If the set is purchased on the delayed-payment plan, what installment charge will the buyer have to pay?

U N I T 2   Computing the Rate of Interest on an Installment Purchase

You know that money deposited in a school bank earns $1\frac{1}{2}\%$ to $2\frac{1}{2}\%$ a year. If you had deposited your money in a savings and loan association, it might earn as high as $3\frac{1}{2}\%$ or 4%. On the other hand, if money is borrowed to purchase a house, interest from $4\frac{1}{2}\%$ to 6% a year must be paid. In addition, if a businessman borrowed money from the bank to help expand his business, he would doubtless have to pay a 6% rate on the loan. Keeping these rates in mind, it will be interesting to see what interest rate a buyer sometimes pays when he purchases an article on the installment plan.

Business Transaction: A clock-radio can be bought for $24.95 cash or, if purchased on the installment plan, for $4.95 down and $4.50 a month for 5 months. What rate of interest is the installment purchaser paying?

Solution:

Installment Price = Down Payment + (Monthly Payment ×
Number of Months)

$$= \quad \$4.95 \quad + \quad (\$4.50 \times 5)$$
$$= \quad \$4.95 \quad + \quad \$22.50$$
$$= \$27.45$$

Installment Charge = Installment Price − Cash Price

$$= \quad \$27.45 \quad - \quad \$24.95$$
$$= \$2.50$$

As was already noted, the installment charge on the purchase of an article may be considered as interest on a loan. The buyer is, in effect, borrowing money from the merchant to purchase the article. Hence, in this example, the buyer had to pay $2.50 interest for the money borrowed. What must be determined, however, is not the *interest*, but the *interest rate*. In order to compute this, it is necessary to know the principal of the debt.

Since the original price of the article was $24.95 and the buyer paid $4.95 down immediately, he still owes the merchant $20. Therefore, the amount that he has yet to pay ($20) is the principal of the debt. Because he plans to pay off the debt in 5 months, he must pay $4 each month on the $20 that he owes. Hence, on the $4 he returned at the end of the first month, he will have to pay 1 month's interest. On the $4 he returned at the end of the second month, he will have to pay 2 months' interest. The same would be true with each of the other $4 payments.

It should be clear to you, however, that interest for 1 month plus interest for 2 months plus interest for 3 months plus interest for 4 months plus interest for 5 months is the same as interest for 15 months (1 + 2 + 3 + 4 + 5). Therefore, it can be said that the buyer paid interest on $4 for 15 months. You have just learned that this interest amounted to $2.50. Hence, you have enough information now to apply the interest formula.

Interest = Principal × Rate × Time (in years)

$$\$2.50 = \quad \overset{1}{\$4} \quad \times \quad R \quad \times \overset{5}{\underset{1}{\cancel{\tfrac{15}{12}}}}$$

(The 15 months were changed to $\frac{15}{12}$ of a year.)

$$\$2.50 = 5 \times R$$

On pages 61 and 132 you learned that, if the product of two numbers is equal to a third, then either number divided into the third will give the other. In this business transaction, 5 times the rate will be $2.50; hence, if $2.50 is divided by 5; the quotient will be the rate. Therefore, .50, or

50% (2.50 ÷ 5), is the rate of interest on this installment purchase. This example can now be outlined as follows:

Outline: Monthly Principal = Total Debt ÷ Number of Months
$$= (\$24.95 - \$4.95) \div 5$$
$$= \quad\quad \$20 \quad\quad\quad \div 5$$
$$= \$4$$

The total interest of $2.50 consists of:

Interest on $4 for 1 month
+Interest on $4 for 2 months
+Interest on $4 for 3 months
+Interest on $4 for 4 months
+Interest on $4 for 5 months

or Interest on $4 for 15 months

Hence: $I = P \times R \times T$
$$\$2.50 = \$4 \times R \times \tfrac{15}{12}$$
$$\$2.50 = 5 \times R$$
$$.50 = R$$
$$50\% = R \quad \text{(Rate of Interest)}$$

It is important to remember that the $4.50 monthly payment is not the monthly principal of the debt, since the $4.50 includes part payment on the debt plus the interest due for that month. The monthly principal is found by dividing the original debt by the *number* of monthly payments. The original debt is the amount the buyer still owes after he makes the down payment; thus:

Original Debt = Cash Price − Down Payment

The following short cut may help simplify your computation. Instead of adding the numbers 1, 2, 3, 4, and 5, as was done in the outline above, multiply the last number by the next consecutive number (in this case you would multiply 5 by 6). If this product is then divided by 2, the answer will the the same as the sum that was found earlier (15). This short cut is particularly helpful if the number of monthly payments is large, such as 24. In this case, you simply multiply 24 by 25, getting a product of 600; dividing this number (600) by 2 results in a quotient of 300. This number (300) represents the sum of the whole numbers from 1 through 24. Obviously, this method of finding the sum is far easier than actually adding the numbers.

Business Transaction: An electric refrigerator is offered at $250 cash, or, on the installment plan, for $50 down and 24 monthly payments of $10 each. Find the rate of interest paid by the buyer if the refrigerator is purchased on the installment plan.

Outline: → Known: Down Payment $= \$50$
Monthly Payment $= \$10$
Number of Months $= 24$
Cash Price $= \$250$
→ To Find: Interest Rate
→ Method:

Installment Price = Down Payment + (Monthly Payment ×
Number of Months)

$$= \quad \$50 \quad + \quad (\$10 \times 24)$$
$$= \quad \$50 \quad + \quad \$240$$
$$= \$290$$

Installment Charge, or Interest = Installment Price − Cash Price

$$= \quad \$290 \quad - \quad \$250$$
$$= \$40$$

Original Debt = Cash Price − Down Payment

$$= \quad \$250 \quad - \quad \$50$$
$$= \$200$$

Monthly Principal = Original Debt ÷ Number of Months

$$= \quad \$200 \quad \div \quad 24$$
$$= \frac{\$200^*}{24}$$

Total Period for Which Monthly Principal Was Borrowed

$$= 1 + 2 + 3 + \ldots \ldots + 22 + 23 + 24$$
$$= \frac{24 \times 25}{2} \text{ (See short cut on page 296.)}$$

Total Period = 300 Months

Interest = Principal × Rate × Time

$$\$40 = \frac{\$\cancel{200}^{25}}{\cancel{24}_3} \times R \times \frac{\cancel{300}^{25}}{\cancel{12}_1}$$

$$\$40 = \frac{625}{3} \times R$$

$$\$40 \div \frac{625}{3} = R$$

$$.192 = R$$

$$19.2\% = R \text{ (Yearly Rate of Interest)}$$

LEARNING EXERCISES

A. What rate of interest will an installment purchaser have to pay on each of the following articles?

* Often, leaving the actual monthly principal in its fractional form, as is done in this case, will make the computation in the interest formula easier.

No.	Article	Cash Price	Installment Terms				Rate of Interest
			Down Pay-ment	Number of Pay-ments	Monthly Pay-ments	
1	*Desk*	$ 60.00	$15.00	5	$10.00	xxx%
2	*Watch*	42.00	12.00	4	8.00	xxx%
3	*Flute*	75.00	25.00	6	9.00	xxx%
4	*Vacuum cleaner*	90.00	15.00	5	16.00	xxx%
5	*Radio combination*	135.00	35.00	12	9.10	xxx%
6	*Dishwasher*	159.50	34.50	12	11.25	xxx%
7	*Clothes drier*	175.95	25.95	18	9.05	xxx%
8	*Sofa*	210.00	45.00	20	9.75	xxx%

B. *Problems to Be Solved*

1. Bob Stillman bought an electric coffee percolator for his mother at $5.50 down and $3 a month for 6 months. If he had paid cash, the percolator would have cost him $21.50. What yearly rate of interest did he have to pay?

2. Joe Wilson needed a tuxedo for the senior prom. He did not want to rent a suit, nor did he have the $65 with which to buy one. He, therefore, decided to buy a tuxedo on the installment plan at $5 down and $4 a month for 16 months. What rate of interest was Joe paying?

3. Mr. Atwater bought a bicycle for his son "on time" by paying $7.50 down and $5.50 each month for 6 months. If he had paid for the bicycle outright, the price would have been $37.50. What rate of interest was Mr. Atwater paying on this purchase?

4. The Merchant's Mart advertised a blender at $25.98. An installment purchaser, however, could buy it with no down payment and $9 a month for 3 months. If the blender was purchased on the installment plan, what rate of interest would the buyer pay?

5. For her trip to Bermuda, Mary Bryant purchased a set of matched luggage that was advertised at $59.50 cash. As she needed all the money she had saved for the expenses of her trip, she bought the luggage on the installment plan by making a $9.50 down payment and agreeing to make 9 monthly payments of $6 each. What rate of interest did Mary have to pay?

6. The Handy Hardware Company ran an after-Christmas sale on an electric sander, allowing a discount of 25% off the list price of $40. A person who did not have the ready cash could buy the sander at list by paying for it over a period of 10 months at $4 a month. What rate of interest would the installment buyer be paying?

UNIT 3

Computing the Rate of Interest on the Installment Purchase of an Automobile

As a graduation present, Robert Jarrett's father decided to buy Robert a used car. They visited a used-car lot and selected an automobile that was satisfactory to both of them. The cost, however, was somewhat larger than Mr. Jarrett cared to pay.

To overcome his prospective buyer's resistance, Bill Snead, the salesman, quickly suggested that the car be bought "on time."

"In fact," said he, "our rates for lending money are exactly the same as the bank's—6%. Let me show you how much it would cost you if you paid $50 down and the balance, $300, over a period of 18 months.

"Since you would owe us only $300 after you made the down payment of $50, the principal would be this $300. As the rate is 6% and the time 18 months, therefore:

$$\text{Interest} = \text{Principal} \times \text{Rate} \times \text{Time}$$
$$I = \$300 \times \tfrac{6}{100} \times \tfrac{18}{12}$$
$$\text{or} \qquad I = \$27$$

"If this interest is added to the $300, you will owe us a total of **$327**. Should you pay off this amount in 18 months, your monthly payments will be only **$18.16** ($327 ÷ 18)."

Most installment purchasers of cars, like Mr. Jarrett, have the impression that the rate of interest that they are paying on the debt is only 6%. Close examination of the method for finding the interest will disclose that this is not so. You will notice that the **$27** represents the interest on the entire $300 for *all* 18 months. After the first month, however, Mr. Jarrett will have paid back **$18.16**; hence his debt the second month will be only **$281.84**. At the end of the second month, having paid another **$18.16**, his debt would be reduced to **$263.68**. But he is still paying interest on the original $300, for, as was pointed out earlier, the **$27** was found by using the principal of $300 for the entire 18 months. And the same holds true for each succeeding month.

Realizing that Mr. Jarrett is not paying 6% on an installment purchase of a car, you are faced with another problem—what rate is he paying? The method developed for finding the rate of interest on installment purchases can be applied here.

Outline: Interest = $27

$$\text{Original Debt} = \text{Cash Price} - \text{Down Payment}$$
$$= \quad \$350 \quad - \quad \$50$$
$$= \$300$$

Monthly Principal $= \frac{300}{18}$

Total Period for Which Monthly Principal Was
$$\text{Borrowed} = 1 + 2 + \ldots\ldots + 17 + 18$$
$$= \frac{18 \times 19}{2} \text{ (See short cut page 296.)}$$
$$= 171 \text{ Months}$$
$$I = P \times R \times T$$
$$\$27 = \tfrac{300}{18} \times R \times \tfrac{171}{12}$$
$$\$27 = \tfrac{475}{2} \times R$$
$$\$27 \div \tfrac{475}{2} = R$$
$$.113 = R$$
$$11.3\% = R \text{ (Rate of Interest)}$$

This is a good deal more than the rate of interest that Mr. Jarrett was supposed to be paying. In fact, it is almost twice as much!

Most automobile dealers sell cars under terms similar to those just described. Occasionally, a dealer will claim that his rates are better than a bank's by charging the buyer what he calls a "5% plan." In recent years, the banks have tried to attract part of this large market by introducing "auto loans" at rates as low as $3\frac{1}{2}\%$. If the computation is examined closely, however, it can be discovered that invariably the $3\frac{1}{2}\%$, 5%, or whatever rate is quoted is taken on the original debt, and not on the decreasing principal.

Business Transaction: Mr. Davis financed the purchase of his new car at 5% over a period of 30 months. If the amount that Mr. Davis still owed after making the down payment was $2,400:

    a. What was the amount of his monthly payments?
    b. What rate of interest was he actually paying?

Solution: → Known: Total Principal $2,400
                Interest Rate Taken on Total Principal   5%
                Time   30 months
    → To Find: **(a)** Monthly Payments
              (b) Rate of Interest

$\rightarrow$ Method: $I = P \times R \times T$

$$= \$2{,}400 \times \tfrac{5}{100} \times \tfrac{30}{12}$$
$$= \$300$$

Total Debt $=$ Total Principal $+$ Interest
$$= \quad \$2{,}400 \quad + \quad \$300$$
$$= \$2{,}700$$

Monthly Payment $=$ Total Debt $\div$ Number of Payments
$$= \quad \$2{,}700 \quad \div \quad 30$$
$$= \$90 \quad (\text{Answer to } \textbf{a.})$$

Monthly Principal $=$ Original Debt $\div$ Number of Payments
$$= \quad \$2{,}400 \quad \div \quad 30$$
$$= \$80$$

Total Period for Which Monthly Principal
Was Borrowed $= 1 + 2 + \ldots + 29 + 30$
$$= \frac{30 \times 31}{2} \quad \begin{array}{l}(\text{See short cut on} \\ \text{page 296.})\end{array}$$
$$= 465 \text{ Months}$$
$$I = P \times R \times T$$
$$\$300 = \$80 \times R \times \tfrac{465}{12}$$
$$\$300 = \$3{,}100 \times R$$
$$\$300 \div \$3{,}100 = R$$
$$.097 = R$$
$$9.7\% = \text{Rate} \quad (\text{Answer to } \textbf{b.})$$

LEARNING EXERCISES

A. Find the monthly payment and rate of interest on each of the following car loans.

No.	Original Cost	Down Payment	Period	Rate Quoted	Monthly Payment	Rate of Interest
1	$2,000.00	$ 400.00	12 mos.	6%	$xxx	xxx%
2	1,800.00	600.00	18 mos.	4%	xxx	xxx%
3	2,650.00	650.00	2 yrs.	5%	xxx	xxx%
4	2,895.00	795.00	$2\frac{1}{2}$ yrs.	6%	xxx	xxx%
5	3,756.45	1,256.45	36 mos.	5%	xxx	xxx%

B. *Problems to Be Solved*

1. Fred Young traded in his car for a foreign sports car listed at $3,495. The dealer allowed Fred $1,295 on the trade-in and turned over the new car for no additional down payment. The monthly payments were spread over a 3-year period at a 4% interest rate. How large were the monthly payments, and what actual rate of interest was Fred paying?

2. When Super-Fine Highway Sales sold Arthur Benson his car, Arthur was impressed by the friendly, quick service he received. The dealer required no down payment on the used car priced at $875 and allowed Arthur 36 months to pay for it. In addition, Super-Fine Highway Sales informed Arthur that they were charging only the "bank rate" of 6% as a carrying charge. What actual rate of interest was Arthur paying?

3. Fred Sims bought a new car for $2,350. In addition to the trade-in of $975 on his old car, Fred withdrew $640 from his savings account to leave as a down payment. The remainder he financed through the bank at 4% for 20 months.

    a. How large were the monthly payments?

    b. What rate of interest was Mr. Sims actually paying?

4. The First National Bank arranged an auto loan for Mr. Phillips for $1,850 at $3\frac{1}{2}$%, to be paid back monthly over a period of 2 years. What rate of interest was Mr. Phillips paying on the decreasing balance?

U N I T **4**	**Computing the Interest Rate Charged by Small-Loan Agencies**

Tom Clark had become disturbed by the many payments that he had to make each month on his television set, radio-phonograph, dishwasher, and the doctor's bill for his wife's appendectomy. One evening he noticed a large advertisement in the newspaper:

LOANS

Get a FRESH START with $25 — $500. Now, employed men and women can cut monthly payments and clean up bills with a personal loan. Loan hand-tailored to *your* situation. Phone for a loan on your first visit.

Cash You Get	Pick Your Own Payment	
	15 Month Plan	20 Month Plan
$100	$ 8.08	$ 6.41
300	24.23	19.24
500	39.26	30.92

This, he thought, was the answer to his financial problems! If he simply borrowed $300 on the 20-month plan, he could clear up all his debts.

In order to determine just how clever Tom was in getting that fresh start, it will be necessary to find the rate of interest that he will be paying on the $300 loan.

Solution: According to the table in the advertisement, Tom's monthly payments for the $300 loan over the 20-month period will be $19.24. Hence, over the entire period, he will return to the loan agency $19.24 times 20, or $384.80. Since he plans to borrow only $300, Tom would be charged $84.80 in interest ($384.80 — $300). Applying the method for finding the rate of interest that had been developed in Units 2 and 3, the rate on this loan can be found.

Outline:

$$\text{Monthly Principal} = \text{Original Debt} \div \text{Number of Payments}$$
$$= \$300 \div 20, \text{ or } \$\tfrac{300}{20}$$

Total Period for Which the Monthly Principal Was
$$\text{Borrowed} = 1 + 2 + 3 + \ldots\ldots + 18 + 19 + 20$$
$$= \frac{20 \times 21}{2} \text{ (See short cut on page 296.)}$$
$$= 210 \text{ Months}$$

$$I = P \times R \times T$$
$$\$84.80 = \tfrac{300}{20} \times R \times \tfrac{210}{12}$$
$$\$84.80 = \tfrac{525}{2} \times R$$
$$\$84.80 \div \tfrac{525}{2} = R$$
$$.323 = R$$
$$32.3\% = R \quad \text{(Rate of Interest)}$$

Apparently, Tom was getting himself out of many small debts only to find himself tied to one very large debt. Also, the interest on the loan from the agency was probably much more than that which he was paying on any of the small sums he owed.

Concerns that lend small amounts of money are called *small-loan agencies*. Their dealings are regulated by law in most states. Interest rates vary from state to state, depending on the size of the loan and the laws of the state. Originally, loans up to $300 were considered to be small loans in most areas. Now, however, that amount has been increased to as much as $1,500 in some states.

These concerns appeal to the borrower because of the little that is required in the form of security. A few agencies will even lend money on the mere signature of the borrower, without requiring others to vouch for him. To compensate for this service, as you may have already noticed, their charge of 2½% or 3% a month is a great deal more than the 6% a year that many banks charge. It would be unfair not to point out that the risk these agencies take—that the loan may not be paid—is considerably greater than that of a bank. A bank requires better security. Therefore, the need for the small-loan agency to charge a higher rate seems to be justified. The borrower, in terms of his own need, will have to decide whether that rate is fair.

LEARNING EXERCISES

In the problems that follow you are asked to "find **A, B, C**." These letters mean:

A. The total amount repaid to the loan agency.

B. The interest paid on the loan.

C. The yearly rate of interest on the decreasing balance.

1. On the basis of the following Furniture Finance Company advertisement:

a. Find **A, B, C** on a $100 loan to be repaid in 18 monthly payments.

b. Find **A, B, C** on a $500 loan to be repaid in 6 monthly payments.

Furniture Finance Company

Cash You Get	20 Payments	18 Payments	6 Payments
$100	$ 6.41	$ 6.97	$18.15
200	12.83	13.93	36.31
500	30.92	33.69	89.53

2.

First Choice of Wise Car Buyers—FIDELITY TRUST COMPANY

Amount of Note	You Receive	You Repay Monthly	Amount of Note	You Receive	You Repay Monthly
$1,044.00	$1,007.46	$ 87.00	$1,080.00	$1,004.40	$45.00
1,560.00	1,505.40	130.00	1,608.00	1,495.44	67.00

a. Using the information in the Fidelity Trust Company advertisement, determine **A, B, C,** (1) on the $1,044 note that is to be repaid in 12 monthly payments; and (2) on the $1,080 note that is to be repaid in 24 monthly payments. Important: The amount that the borrower actually receives should be considered the principal of the debt.

b. The loans were advertised as a $3\frac{1}{2}\%$ automobile financing plan. Would you consider this to be the rate charged on these loans? Justify your answer.

c. In view of the $3\frac{1}{2}\%$ rate that the borrower was supposed to be charged, how were the numbers in the You Receive column determined?

3.

	Phone for a Loan—**National Banking Company**		
You Borrow	Charge for 12 Months	You Receive	12 Monthly Payments
$108	$ 6.48	$101.52	$ 9.00
216	12.96	203.04	18.00
492	29.52	462.48	41.00

a. Which column in the preceding table should be considered to be the principal of the debt? Justify your answer.

b. Determine **A, B, C:** (1) on the $108 loan that is to be repaid in 12 monthly payments; (2) on the $492 loan that is to be repaid in 12 monthly payments.

UNIT 5   What Have You Learned?

SECTION 1   Understanding Small-Loan Agency Borrowing

The following questions are designed to help you gain a better understanding of debt payment on the installment plan. They should be answered individually by each student and then discussed in class.

1. What do you consider was the reason that the loan agencies in Unit 4 advertised different types of cash loans?

2. Why do some people borrow money from a loan agency rather than from a bank in spite of the fact that it would be cheaper to borrow from a bank?

3. Give two reasons why loan agencies may prefer to advertise their interest rates on a monthly basis rather than on a yearly one, as is commonly done?

4. What is meant by the statement, "No indorsers or guarantors required"?

5. Under what conditions do you think it might be advisable to pay off a number of small debts by borrowing money from a loan agency?

6. Why should a small-loan agency charge a higher rate of interest than a bank?

7. Find several loan-agency advertisements in your newspaper.

a. Do any of these agencies advertise the lending of the same amount of money for the same period of time?

b. Compare the rates charged by these agencies with those in this chapter.

8. Do any of the banks in your city offer auto loans or home improvement loans? If so:

a. What rate of interest do the banks advertise that they charge on these loans?

b. What actual rate are they charging on the decreasing balance?

c. How do these rates compare with the rates they charge on their normal business loans?

d. How does the normal business-loan rate of these banks compare with the rate of interest they give their savings-account depositors?

SECTION 2   You As a Borrower

How wisely would you borrow money? Can you make the correct selection in each of the following situations, and justify your answers? If you cannot do so, review the pages indicated at the end of each problem.

1. You are in urgent need of $600 in cash. Inquiry at the bank shows that you can borrow the money there at a 6% interest rate for 3 months. You also learn that a loan agency would be willing to lend you the same amount at a 5% interest rate if you agreed to pay the money back in 3 equal installments over the 3-month period. Which of these loans would it be better for you to accept? (Pages 302–303.)

2. As the owner of a small shoe store, you are expecting a shipment of shoes valued at $200. If you pay the driver of the delivery truck for the merchandise, the manufacturer will grant you a 5% discount. On the other hand, he will allow you to delay payment for as long as 6 months without making any additional charges on the $200. Would it be to your advantage to borrow the $200 from the Furniture Finance Company, whose loan table appears on page 304, and pay the driver at the time of delivery, or to delay the payment for 6 months? (Pages 302–303.)

3. You are considering the purchase of a living-room sofa, the cash price of which is $217.95. Lacking that much money, you have been told that this sofa can be bought on the installment plan for $17.95 down and $14.50 a month for 18 months. Would it be better for you to use this installment plan or borrow the money from the Furniture Finance Company, whose advertisement appears on page 304? (Pages 292, 293–303.)

4. It is possible for you to buy a television set for cash at $224.50 or, on the installment plan, for $24.50 down and $27.50 a month for 8 months. Since you do not have the cash, would it be better for you to accept the dealer's installment plan or borrow $200 from the bank at the usual rate of 6%? (Pages 233, 292–293.)

SECTION 3   Review Problems

If you are unable to do the following problems, review the pages indicated within the parentheses.

1. A radio-phonograph can be purchased at $79.50 cash or, on the installment plan, for $10.50 down and $2.05 a week for 38 weeks. What is the installment charge on this purchase? (Pages 292–293.)

2. An oil burner is advertised for $295 cash or, on the deferred-payment plan, for $25 down and $30 a month for 10 months.

   a. How much more does the installment purchaser have to pay than the buyer who pays cash? (Pages 292–293.)

   b. What rate of interest is the installment purchaser paying? (Pages 294–297.)

3. A gas range is offered for sale on the monthly-payment plan for $15 down and $15 a month for 8 months. The gas range can be purchased for $120 cash. Find the rate of interest charged if the purchase is made on the installment plan. (Pages 294–297.)

4. A man bought a living-room suite for $260 on the following terms: $10 down and $12.50 a month for 20 months. He could have purchased the same suite for $235 cash. What rate of interest was he paying on the installment purchase? (Pages 294–297.)

5. In order to purchase a new car, Bernard Daly borrowed $1,800 from his bank on an auto loan of 4% taken on the original debt. He paid off the debt in 18 equal monthly installments.

   a. How large was each of the monthly payments? (Pages 299–301.)

b. What rate of interest was he actually paying on the decreasing balance? (Pages 299–301.)

6. When Jack Coty bought his new car for $2,675.24, he received $875.24 as a trade-in on his old car. He financed the balance over a period of 30 equal monthly payments with interest on the original loan for that period at 6%.

a. How large were Jack Coty's monthly payments? (Pages 299–301.)

b. What rate of interest was he actually paying? (Pages 299–301.)

7. The following advertisement appeared in a newspaper.

Loans on Your Signature				
	Amount of Monthly Payment for			
Amount of Loan	9 Months	12 Months	15 Months	20 Months
$ 85	$10.66	$ 8.29	$ 6.07	$5.45
150	18.82	14.62	12.11	9.62
Family Loan Corporation				

Consider the loan of $150 for 15 months.

a. How much will the borrower pay back to the loan agency?

b. What was the amount of interest on this loan?

c. What rate of interest was he charged? (Pages 302–304.)

8. What rate of interest was being paid by a borrower on a loan of $85 for 20 months from the Family Loan Corporation in Problem 7? (Page 302–304.)

SECTION 4   **Testing Your Understanding**

40 Minutes

1. A bookcase can be purchased for $120 cash or, on the installment plan, for $15 down and $2.50 a week for 46 weeks. What is the installment charge on this purchase?

2. Find the rate of interest that is charged on each of the following purchases:

a. A 9-by-12 rug: cash price, $150; installment price, $45 down and 8 monthly payments of $15 each.

b. A three-speed record player: cash price, $84; installment price, $18 down and 6 monthly payments of $12 each.

3. A new car that listed at $3,271.56 was purchased by making a down payment of $1,271.56 and financing the balance on a 5% auto-loan plan over a period of 24 months.

a. How much interest was the purchaser paying on this loan?

b. What actual rate of interest was he paying on the decreasing balance?

4. A small-loan agency placed the following advertisement in a newspaper.

For Fast Money See Us First

MARLOWE for MONEY

	Select Your Payment Plan	
Cash You Get	15 Months	20 Months
$200	$16.15	$12.80
400	32.04	24.36

What rate of interest is the borrower of $200 for 20 months paying?

UNIT 6 General Review

SECTION 1 To Improve Your Speed and Accuracy

1. Addition:

a. 367	**b.** $ 36.74	**c.** $24\frac{2}{3}$
784	29.36	$17\frac{1}{2}$
492	8.57	$48\frac{3}{4}$
576	103.28	
843	.35	
731	86.39	
507	354.76	

d. $396.74 + $87 + $42.05 + $9.57 + $137

e. $12\frac{1}{4} + 17\frac{1}{3} + 48\frac{1}{2} + 59\frac{2}{3}$

2. Subtraction:

| **a.** 56,742 | **b.** $10,000.00 | **c.** 87 |
| 43,807 | 7,346.27 | $59\frac{3}{4}$ |

d. $250 − $73.46

e. $72\frac{1}{6} − 15\frac{3}{4}$

3. Multiplication. Check your answers by casting out 9's.
    a. 374 × 26   b. 4,007 × 39   c. 6,439 × 507
            d. $34.76 × .05   e. $107.58 × .83

4. Division. Check your answers by casting out 9's.
    a. 4,275 ÷ 39   b. 87,246 ÷ 107   c. $10,000 ÷ .085
            d. 59.72 ÷ 42   e. .005736 ÷ 92

SECTION 2   Do You Remember These?

1. Change the following numbers to per cent values.

    a. .042   b. 3.26   c. 9

2. Change the following per cents to decimals.

    a. 28%   b. 124%   c. .3%

3. 15% of $234 is how much money?
4. $150 is what per cent of $275?
5. If a person's gross weekly salary is $92.50, how much is the Social Security deduction?
6. At $1.68 an hour, what is the weekly salary for 46 hours if time and a half is paid for all work over 40 hours?
7. Find the cost of 750 pounds of sugar at $8.32 a cwt.
8. What did Mr. Tyler's yearly earnings over the last 4 years average if he earned $4,375.75, $4,729.43, $5,062.29, and $5,824.37, respectively?
9. Using aliquot parts of $1, find the cost of each of the following purchases:

    a. 30 qts. @ $66\frac{2}{3}$¢   c. 56 doz. @ 75¢
    b. 24 lbs. @ $37\frac{1}{2}$¢   d. 48 yds. @ $83\frac{1}{3}$¢

10. A 25% discount rate was given on an article listing at $24.40. What was the net cost of the article?
11. Successive trade discounts of 25% and 10% were granted by the manufacturer on an article whose catalogue price was $80. What net price did the dealer have to pay?
12. An article was sold at a 40% markup on the cost to the dealer. If the merchant purchased the article for $32.95, at what price did he sell it?

13

The Arithmetic of Insurance

PREVIEW

George Kirk had been driving his car very carefully the day of the accident. It had been a beautiful Sunday afternoon—ideal for a drive in the country. Under pressure from the children, Mrs. Kirk had prepared a picnic lunch, and the entire family took off for their favorite outing spot. Unfortunately, half the state must have had the same plans, for the roads were crowded with cars.

As often happens, impatience finally overtook an oncoming driver, a Mr. Gardner. In trying to pass another driver, he mis-

311

judged his distance, swerved beyond the center line in the roadway, and struck the Kirk car. Only the comparatively slow speeds at which both cars were traveling prevented a major smashup. As it was, the left rear door of the Kirk car was badly dented and the rear left fender and rear bumper were completely ripped off the car. Bob Kirk, who was sitting in the rear seat on the left side of the car, was the only casualty. He suffered a broken arm. A front fender and headlight of the Gardner car were also demolished in the collision. The initial feeling of relief that overcame Mr. Gardner when he learned that no one had been injured seriously was followed by one of anxiety. Which, if any, of the many insurance policies that he carried would cover the cost of his folly that day?

For Class Discussion

1. What is an insurance policy?

2. Why do people insure themselves?

3. Can you give five different types of losses against which people insure themselves?

4. What is the name of the insurance that Mr. Gardner would have had to carry to protect himself against the cost of any damage that he caused to the Kirk car?

5. What type of insurance will cover the cost of the injury to Bob Kirk?

6. Is there any insurance that Mr. Gardner may have owned that would pay for the damage to his own car? If so, what is the name of this insurance?

7. Are there any laws in your state requiring motorists to carry automobile insurance? If so, to what extent must they be insured?

8. If Mr. Gardner was not insured, mention several things that Mr. Kirk could do to collect for the damages to his car and the injuries to his son.

Concerning This Chapter

The major purpose of all insurance is protection against an unexpected financial loss that may befall a person. Instead of one person having to bear a loss alone, many people join together, each person contributing a small share, to cover a large loss that may befall one of their members. As a very simple illustration:

Assume that in a town of 5,000 families each family owned its own home. Over the years, it was found that fire damaged only one house each year to an extent of $10,000. Hence, each family agreed to contribute $2 each year to a common fund to cover the fire loss that might be incurred that year. In that way, the family whose home was burned that year would not suffer a $10,000 loss, but merely a $2 loss, the amount of its contribution.

Basic to every variety of insurance are two principles:

→1. The uncertainty as to the person on whom the loss will fall.

→2. The certainty that the loss will occur to someone in a large group.

For example, if Edward Bryant, a resident of the town mentioned, knew that his home could not possibly burn during the coming year, there would be no need for him to join the others in insuring himself against a fire loss. Unfortunately, this prediction can never be made with absolute certainty. Realizing this, Mr. Bryant fears to carry the risk of a $10,000 loss alone and prefers to join the group by making his small payment. On the other hand, although it is not known which particular individual will suffer the loss, years of experience have shown that fires do start and do cause a great deal of damage year after year.

No matter what the nature of the insurance may be, whether it be protection against financial loss due to loss of life, fire damage, automobile damage, sickness, theft, or hailstorm damage, insurance companies, using the two principles just stated, are able to predict fairly accurately how great the loss will be during a coming year. On this prediction, they determine how large each person's contribution must be in order to cover the total loss that will occur that year. That contribution, which is the cost of the insurance, is called the *insurance premium*, or simply the *premium*. It should be noted that the premium must include more than the insured person's share of the year's loss. Part of the insurance premiums has to be used to pay for the operating expenses of the company, such as salaries, rent, taxes, heating, and the like.

Ranking high among the losses against which people insure themselves are fire, automobile accidents, and loss of life. It is to the insurance that covers these mishaps that this chapter will be devoted. You will learn how to compute the premiums on each of these types of insurance. Within each group, you will find that there is a variety of policies that a person may purchase. Thus, there is not just one kind of automobile insurance but several kinds, to cover the different types of losses against which a person may protect himself. The advantages and several of the disadvantages of each will be pointed out. The type of insurance that is best for all people is a question that cannot be answered, for insurance is an individual concern. The type of insurance that is beneficial to one person may be entirely inadequate for another.

UNIT 1   **Fire Insurance**

SECTION 1   Computing the Premiums

No matter what kind of insurance a person may purchase, the cost of that insurance is always based on the risk that the insurance company is taking. Thus, during a war, the cost of insurance against the possibility of loss caused by the sinking of a ship would be considerably more than the cost of the same insurance during a period of peace.

In fire insurance on homes, insurance companies feel that the risk they are taking depends on two factors:

→**1.** The material that was used in the construction of the house; that is, whether it is a brick or a wooden (frame) structure.

→**2.** The degree of fire protection that is available in the community in which the dwelling is located. As an example, does the fire department consist of permanently employed firemen who have received professional training, or is it manned by volunteers? Are there fire hydrants in the community, or must the water be drawn from wells?

Fire insurance companies determine their premiums in accordance with the degree of these risks. Thus, in one of the states, communities have been divided into nine groups, according to how adequate the fire protection has been in those communities in the past. The accompanying table shows the premium rates for these groups.

Annual Fire Insurance Rates (Based on each $100 of insurance)		
Community	Type of Dwelling	
	Brick	Frame
A	$.08	$.12
B	.085	.125
C	.09	.13
D	.095	.135
E	.10	.14
F	.11	.15
G	.15	.19
H	.28	.30
K	.34	.38

You will notice that rates in the H and K communities are much higher than those in the other groups. The fact that communities H and K have no hydrants is responsible for their comparatively high rates.

Business Transaction 1: Find the yearly premium for $15,000 worth of fire insurance on a brick house in a group D community.

Solution: According to the table, the rate will be $.095 for each $100 worth of insurance. To determine the number of hundreds in $15,000, $15,000 is divided by 100. The quickest way of doing this is by moving the decimal point 2 places to the left in the dividend (15,000). The quotient (150), the number of hundreds in $15,000, is then multiplied by the cost of each $100 worth of insurance ($.095). The product ($14.25) is the yearly premium.

Outline: → Known: Amount of Insurance $15,000
　　　　　　　　　　Brick House in a D Community
　　　　　　→ To Find: Yearly Premium
　　　　　　→ Method: Yearly Cost per $100 = $.095
　　　　　　　　　　Number of Hundreds in $15,000 = 15,000 ÷ 100
　　　　　　　　　　　　　　　　　　　= 150
　　　　　　　　　　Yearly Premium = 150 × $.095
　　　　　　　　　　　　　　　= $14.25

In order to encourage homeowners to insure their property for a period of time longer than 1 year, insurance companies offer "discount" rates on periods of 2, 3, 4, or 5 years. Thus, the cost of a 3-year policy is $2\frac{1}{2}$ times the annual premium. Similarly, a person who buys a 5-year fire insurance policy will pay only 4 times the amount he would have had to pay for a 1-year policy. This table gives the fire insurance rates on policies having a period greater than 1 year.

Fire Insurance Rates for Periods Greater Than 1 Year	
Period	**Rate**
2 Years	1 3/4 times the yearly premium
3 Years	2 1/2 times the yearly premium
4 Years	3 1/4 times the yearly premium
5 Years	4 times the yearly premium

Business Transaction 2: A frame house is located in a group F community. It is insured for $18,500 for a period of 4 years. Find the premium paid by the homeowner.

Solution: Find the yearly premium as in Business Transaction 1, and multiply the amount by $3\frac{1}{4}$.

Outline: → Known: Amount of Insurance $18,500
              Frame House in an F Community
              Period   4 Years
        → To Find: Premium
        → Method: Yearly Cost per $100 = $.15
              Number of Hundreds in $18,500 = 18,500 ÷ 100
                                               = 185
              Yearly Premium = 185 × $.15 = $27.75
              Four-Year Premium = $3\frac{1}{4}$ × $27.75
                               = 3.25 × $27.75
                               = $90.1875, or $90.19

LEARNING EXERCISES

A. Find the annual premium on each of the following policies.

No.	Amt. of Insurance	Community	Structure	Annual Premium
1	$16,000	A	Brick	$xxx
2	18,000	C	Frame	xxx
3	24,000	D	Frame	xxx
4	12,500	H	Brick	xxx
5	13,500	F	Frame	xxx
6	18,200	B	Frame	xxx
7	16,850	G	Brick	xxx
8	14,750	K	Frame	xxx

B. Find the premium on each of the following policies.

No.	Amt. of Insurance	Community	Structure	Period in Years	Premium
1	$17,000	C	Brick	5	$xxx
2	14,000	G	Frame	3	xxx
3	21,000	E	Brick	2	xxx
4	18,500	H	Frame	4	xxx
5	10,800	B	Frame	5	xxx
6	25,000	K	Frame	2	xxx
7	8,400	F	Frame	3	xxx
8	37,500	A	Brick	4	xxx
9	19,700	D	Brick	5	xxx
10	24,800	B	Brick	3	xxx

C. *Problems to Be Solved*

1. A brick dwelling is insured for $17,300 for 4 years in the state where fire insurance rates are as given in the tables on pages 314–315. If the community in which the house is located is classified as group H, what premium will the owner have to pay?

2. Mr. Crawford insured his frame house against fire for $21,000 for 5 years. The community in which he lives is classified as group G. How much would Mr. Crawford have saved in fire insurance premiums for a 5-year period if his house had been a brick structure instead of a wooden one?

3. How much less is the 3-year premium on a $16,000 fire insurance policy on a brick house located in a group A community than on one in a group K community?

4. How much less will Mr. Davenport have to pay on a 5-year fire insurance policy on a brick house in a group C community than on a frame house in a group H community? The cost of each house was approximately the same, and Mr. Davenport planned to carry $18,500 insurance.

5. If fire hydrants are installed in a group H community, it would be reclassified as a group F community. How much would the owner of a brick house that is insured for $23,500 for 5 years save by the installation of hydrants?

SECTION 2   Computing Premiums for Periods Less Than 1 Year

Rarely, if ever, does a homeowner sell his property on the very day that his fire insurance policy expires. Therefore, the insurance company must return to him that part of the premium that covers the period during which he no longer owns the house. The part of the yearly premium retained (held) by the insurance company appears in the scale shown on page 318. Since the homeowner paid the entire year's insurance when he bought the policy, a check for the remainder is sent to him when the house is sold. This table can be used only when the original policy was purchased for 1 year and the policy was canceled by the purchaser.

STANDARD SHORT-RATE SCALE FOR COMPUTING PREMIUMS FOR TERMS LESS THAN 1 YEAR

DAYS IN FORCE	PER CENT	DAYS IN FORCE	PER CENT	DAYS IN FORCE	PER CENT
1	5	92- 94	36	215-218	68
2	6	95- 98	37	219-223	69
3- 4	7	99-102	38	224-228	70
5- 6	8	103-105	39	229-232	71
7- 8	9	106-109	40	233-237	72
9- 10	10	110-113	41	238-241	73
11- 12	11	114-116	42	242-246 (8 mos.)	74
13- 14	12	117-120 (4 mos.)	43	247-250	75
15- 16	13	121-124	44	251-255	76
17- 18	14	125-127	45	256-260	77
19- 20	15	128-131	46	261-264	78
21- 22	16	132-135	47	265-269	79
23- 25	17	136-138	48	270-273 (9 mos.)	80
26- 29	18	139-142	49	274-278	81
30- 32 (1 mo.)	19	143-146	50	279-282	82
33- 36	20	147-149	51	283-287	83
37- 40	21	150-153 (5 mos.)	52	288-291	84
41- 43	22	154-156	53	292-296	85
44- 47	23	157-160	54	297-301	86
48- 51	24	161-164	55	302-305 (10 mos.)	87
52- 54	25	165-167	56	306-310	88
55- 58	26	168-171	57	311-314	89
59- 62 (2 mos.)	27	172-175	58	315-319	90
63- 65	28	176-178	59	320-323	91
66- 69	29	179-182 (6 mos.)	60	324-328	92
70- 73	30	183-187	61	329-332	93
74- 76	31	188-191	62	333-337 (11 mos.)	94
77- 80	32	192-196	63	338-342	95
81- 83	33	197-200	64	343-346	96
84- 87	34	201-205	65	347-351	97
88- 91 (3 mos.)	35	206-209	66	352-355	98
		210-214 (7 mos.)	67	356-360	99
				361-365 (12 mos.)	100

Business Transaction 1: 19 days after purchasing a 1-year fire insurance policy that cost $24.78, the policy was canceled by the purchaser. How much money was returned to the policy owner?

Solution: According to the scale, the per cent of annual premium that is kept by the insurance company to cover the cost of the 19 days' insurance is 15%. Therefore, 15% of $24.78, or $3.72, is retained by the company. The difference between the annual premium ($24.78) and the $3.72 is sent to the policyholder. This is $21.06.

Outline: Per Cent of Premium Retained by the Company = 15%

Amount of Premium Retained by the Company = 15% of $24.78

$$= .15 \times \$24.78$$
$$= \$3.7170$$

Amount Returned to the Policyholder = $24.78 − $3.72

$$= \$21.06$$

The Standard Short-Rate Scale is used also to compute the premium on a policy that is purchased for a period of less than 1 year. The cost is determined in exactly the same way as in Transaction 1.

Business Transaction 2: Mr. Tarbell rented a one-family frame dwelling on June 15. Because of business commitments, he knew that on October 1 he would have to move to another section of the state. According to his agreement with the owner of the house, Mr. Tarbell was to insure the dwelling for $27,000 for the period during which he would occupy it. If the house was located in a group H community, what was the cost of the insurance?

Solution: Premium Cost per $100 = $.30

Number of Hundreds in $27,000 = 270

Annual Premium = 270 × $.30

= $81

Period from June 15 to October 1 = 108 days

Rate on 108 Days = 40%

Amount Charged by Company = 40% of $81

= .40 × $81

= $32.40

Explanation: The exact number of days from June 15 to October 1 can be found by using either Time Table 1 or 2 on pages 243 and 245.

LEARNING EXERCISES

A. Find the amount of the premium returned to each policyholder if the annual policy was canceled by the policyholder at the end of the period indicated.

No.	Annual Premium	Days in Force	Premium Returned
1	$18.56	45	$xxx
2	23.48	225	xxx
3	38.62	285	xxx
4	26.39	43	xxx
5	32.08	86	xxx
6	29.73	275	xxx

B. Find the premium on the following short-term policies.

No.	Annual Premium	Period of Policy	Premium
1	$28.52	75 days	$xxx
2	43.84	7 mos.	xxx
3	37.46	315 days	xxx
4	25.08	34 days	xxx
5	59.23	100 days	xxx
6	46.88	261 days	xxx

C. Find the premium on each of the following short-term policies.

No.	Amount of Insurance	Date of Purchase	Date of Expiration	Com- munity	Structure	Pre- mium
1	$12,000	Feb. 10	June 10	A	Frame	$xxx
2	14,000	Mar. 16	May 20	E	Brick	xxx
3	23,000	July 15	Sept. 10	G	Brick	xxx
4	16,500	June 8	Aug. 28	F	Frame	xxx
5	27,400	May 12	Oct. 23	B	Frame	xxx
6	38,800	Jan. 23	Sept. 7	D	Brick	xxx

D. Find the amount of the premium returned to the policyholders if these annual policies were purchased and canceled by the policyholders on the dates indicated.

No.	Amount of Insurance	Date of Purchase	Date of Cancellation	Com- munity	Structure	Pre- mium
1	$16,000	Apr. 18	July 18	E	Brick	$xxx
2	20,000	Mar. 1	Aug. 1	G	Brick	xxx
3	34,000	Feb. 16	Sept. 26	F	Frame	xxx
4	12,500	Jan. 27	June 20	H	Frame	xxx
5	17,200	July 5	Oct. 31	B	Brick	xxx
6	28,400	Oct. 17	Mar. 20	A	Frame	xxx
7	21,500	Nov. 3	Apr. 17	D	Frame	xxx

E. *Problems to Be Solved*

1. The merchandise in a store was insured for $22,700 for 80 days at an annual rate of $1.15 per $100. Find the amount of the premium paid.

2. A political party rented a vacant store on August 15 to be used as its headquarters until Election Day on November 8. The party insured its files and the store fixtures against fire loss for $5,200, for the period that it would occupy the store. If the annual insurance rate was 65 cents per $100, what premium was paid?

3. During a period of specialized training, an army officer rented a house near the camp from July 12 to February 25 of the following year. He insured the house for $18,600 during his stay. If the house was a wooden structure in a group E community, how much was the premium?

4. Knowing that he would soon sell his house, Mr. Welker insured it on March 23 for 1 year only. On May 12, he sold the house and canceled

the policy. How much money did the insurance company return to him if the amount for which the structure was insured was $28,400 and the annual rate was 18½ cents per $100?

SECTION 3   Computing the Indemnity

In an *ordinary* fire insurance policy, the insurance company will pay the insured for any loss up to the amount of the insurance that he carries. The amount of the loss that is paid by the company to the insured is called the *indemnity;* the total amount of insurance on the property is called the *face value* of the policy. If a person insures his property for $6,000 and suffers a $5,000 fire loss, in an ordinary policy the company will pay the entire indemnity of $5,000. On the other hand, if the fire resulted in a $10,000 loss, the company would pay the insured only the face value of his policy, or $6,000.

Rarely will a person insure his home for the full value of the property because, even if the structure were completely destroyed by fire, the basement and the land could not possibly be damaged. These two items help comprise the total cost of his property. Thus, if his home were valued at $25,000, the basement and the land on which the building is constructed are probably worth $5,000. Hence, the owner would have nothing to gain by insuring the house for more than $20,000. Many homeowners feel, however, that fire will seldom destroy more than 50% of the value of their property. Thus, the owner of the $25,000 home might insure it for only $12,500.

To encourage property owners to insure their property for a larger per cent of its value than they might otherwise do, insurance companies offer discount rates on policies that contain a special agreement. This agreement is commonly called an **80% clause**. Through this statement in the policy, the homeowner agrees to share part of his fire loss with the insurance company if he insures his property for less than 80% of its value. The insurance company, on its part, agrees to reduce the premium rates by approximately 25% if the 80% clause is included in the policy. In some states, laws require that this clause appear in every fire insurance policy. In other states, this clause is not allowed to appear in policies affecting private homes of four families or less.

Computing the indemnity on a policy containing an 80% clause can best be illustrated through an example. Under this clause, a house valued at $20,000 must be insured for at least 80% of its value, or $16,000. If the house is insured for less than $16,000—say for $12,000—

the insurance company will pay only 12,000/16,000 of any fire loss and the property owner must carry the remainder of the loss. If the property is insured for $15,000, then the insurance company will bear 15,000/16,000 of the loss, and the owner must bear the rest. Should it be insured for the full $16,000, the company will pay for the entire loss but never more than the face value of the policy, which in this case would be $16,000. The owner may insure for more than $16,000 if he desires. In that event, the insurance company will pay for any fire loss up to the face value of the policy. An insurance company will never pay more than the amount of insurance carried on the property.

On the basis of this illustration, the following principle can be stated:

→Under the 80% clause, the part of the loss paid by the insurance company is equal to:

$$\frac{\text{Face of the Policy}}{80\% \text{ of the Value of the Property}}$$

Business Transaction: Property valued at $24,000 is insured for only $16,000. Fire damages the property to the extent of $5,400. If the policy contained an 80% clause, how much of the loss will be covered by the insurance company?

Solution: 80% of $24,000 is $19,200. As the property was insured for only $16,000, the company will pay only 16,000/19,200 of the loss of $5,400.

Outline:
Value of the Property = $24,000
80% of the Value = .80 × $24,000
= $19,200
Face Value of the Policy = $16,000
Fraction of Loss Paid by Insurance Company = 16,000/19,200
Indemnity Paid by Insurance Company = 16,000/19,200 × $5,400
= $4,500

If the property owner had been insured for $19,200 or more, the insurance company would have paid the entire loss of $5,400.

Other clauses, such as a **90% clause** or a **100% clause**, can be included in fire insurance policies. These clauses would carry with them greater discounts on the premium than is given for the 80% clause. The fraction of the insurance that the owner would be required to carry, however, would be greater in these cases than that under the 80% clause. Clauses providing that the insured share with the insurance company in the cost of any loss to his property are called *coinsurance* clauses. *Coinsurance* simply means "insuring together." It is important to remember that in the ordinary fire insurance policy the company will pay the full loss of any fire up to the face value of the policy; the loss covered by a policy containing a coinsurance clause, however, is shared in the manner outlined in the preceding Business Transactions.

LEARNING EXERCISES

A. In each of the following cases find the indemnity paid by the insurance company under an *ordinary* policy.

No.	Value of Property	Face Value	Fire Loss	Indemnity
1	$10,500	$ 7,500	$ 7,100	$xxx
2	16,000	12,500	15,000	xxx
3	19,500	20,000	14,750	xxx
4	33,000	25,600	27,500	xxx
5	25,000	25,000	13,500	xxx
6	42,000	36,000	38,500	xxx
7	10,500	12,000	10,500	xxx
8	5,000	3,500	4,200	xxx

B. In each of the following cases find the indemnity paid by the insurance company under a policy containing an **80%** *clause*.

No.	Value of Property	Face Value	Fire Loss	Indemnity
1	$15,000	$10,000	$10,800	$xxx
2	12,800	9,600	10,400	xxx
3	25,000	18,000	17,500	xxx
4	30,000	20,000	18,600	xxx
5	12,000	9,000	8,400	7 8xx5
6	8,000	12,300	8,000	xxx
7	9,000	6,400	5,400	xxx 00
8	17,000	12,800	10,200	9xxx00

C. Find the premium on each of the following policies containing an 80% clause if the insurance company grants a 25% discount when this clause is included in the policy. (Use tables on pages 314–315.)

No.	Face of Policy	Community	Structure	Period	Premium
1	$20,000	C	Brick	1 yr.	$xxx
2	15,000	F	Frame	1 yr.	xxx
3	18,500	G	Frame	1 yr.	xxx
4	12,600	B	Frame	1 yr.	xxx
5	16,000	E	Brick	3 yrs.	xxx
6	27,800	H	Brick	3 yrs.	xxx
7	34,000	A	Frame	5 yrs.	xxx
8	14,800	K	Frame	5 yrs.	xxx
9	39,200	C	Brick	4 yrs.	xxx
10	35,700	D	Brick	2 yrs.	xxx

D. (Optional) Problems to Be Solved

1. The stock of a department store was damaged to the extent of $40,000. The owner had insured his merchandise for $60,000, although its total value was $80,000. If the insurance policy contained an 80% clause, how large was the indemnity paid by the insurance company?

2. Although his home was worth $30,000, Mr. Arnold insured it for only $20,000 against a fire loss. Fire damaged his property to the extent of $5,600. How much of this loss did Mr. Arnold have to cover himself if his policy contained an 80% clause?

3. If a 90% clause is included in a policy, the insured will receive successive discounts of 25% and 5% off the premium that is charged on an ordinary fire insurance policy. If the 3-year premium on an ordinary policy amounted to $68.50, what would be the cost of the same policy if it contained a 90% clause?

4. Assuming that the discounts received in Example 3 apply here, what is the premium on a fire insurance policy containing a 90% clause if the face value of the policy is $22,500? (The house is a frame structure in a group C community.)

5. A house valued at $18,000 is insured for $14,000. If fire destroys the property to the extent of $2,340, what indemnity would the owner receive if he was covered by:

    a. An ordinary fire insurance policy?

    b. A policy containing an 80% clause?

    c. A policy containing a 90% clause?

UNIT **2**   **Automobile Insurance**

There are four major varieties of *coverage*—that is, insurance —that an automobile owner will usually consider purchasing for his car. These are:

1. Bodily-injury liability
2. Property-damage liability
3. Collision or upset
4. Comprehensive

The type of protection that the insured receives under each of these policies will be examined in the following sections.

SECTION 1   **Bodily-Injury Liability and Property-Damage Liability Insurance**

Bodily-injury liability insurance or, as it is frequently called, *public liability insurance*, protects the driver of an automobile against the cost of injuries that he might inflict on other people through the use of his automobile. The basic bodily-injury insurance coverage limits are commonly known as *5 and 10*. These numbers are abbreviations for the numbers $5,000 and $10,000. The owner of a 5-and-10 liability policy is protected to a maximum payment of $5,000 to any one person, and to a maximum payment of $10,000 for any one accident in which he may have injured more than one person. Thus, if during an accident the insured injured one person, who sued him for $7,000, and the injured person was awarded this amount by the court, the insurance company would pay only $5,000. The remaining $2,000 would have to be paid by the insured. Had the injured party been awarded $4,500 by the court, the insurance company would have paid the entire $4,500. If four persons were injured in this accident and all four were awarded a total of $14,000 for injuries, the insurance company would pay only $10,000. The remaining $4,000 would have to be paid by the insured. Of this

$10,000 paid by the insurance company, no more than $5,000 will be paid to any one of the four injured parties. Had the award to the four persons been for less than $10,000, the company would have covered the entire amount. Again, no one of the four persons can receive more than $5,000 from the insurance company. Summarizing, in a 5-and-10 bodily-injury liability policy, the insurance company agrees to pay up to $5,000 to each person injured by the insured but no more than $10,000 to all persons injured during any one accident.

Should the automobile owner desire, it is possible for him to purchase bodily-injury insurance having higher maximum limits. Should he buy 10-and-20 coverage, the insurance company will pay up to $10,000 to each person injured by the insured, but no more than $20,000 to all persons injured during the same accident. Still higher limits, such as 25-and-50, 50-and-100, or 100-and-300, are frequently purchased by the owners of automobiles.

Property-damage liability insurance covers exactly what is implied by its name. Should the insured damage anyone else's property (not his own)—such as an automobile, a house, a lawn, a bicycle, or any other object—his insurance company will pay for the damage. As with bodily-injury insurance, the company will pay no more than the maximum agreed on in the policy. The basic maximum limit in property-damage insurance is $5,000. Rarely will a person consider purchasing this type of insurance with a limit higher than $5,000, for rarely will the extent of damage to property during an accident exceed $5,000. Even were the insured to demolish another person's car completely, the cost of the damage would probably still be less than $5,000.

Rates for both bodily-injury and property-damage insurance depend on two factors:

→1. The frequency with which accidents occur in the area in which the insured lives.

→2. The manner in which the car is used.

Thus, in the rate table shown:

1. Class 1A indicates that the automobile is *not* used in driving to or from work.

2. Class 1B indicates that the automobile is used to drive to and from work and that the distance is less than 10 miles each way.

3. Class 1C indicates that the automobile is driven to and from work and that the distance is more than 10 miles each way.

4. Class 2A indicates that there is a driver under the age of 25 who uses the car.

Rate Table for
Bodily-Injury Liability Insurance—Maximum Limits: $5,000 and $10,000
Property-Damage Liability Insurance—Maximum Limit: $5,000

Class	Territory 1		Territory 2		Territory 3		Territory 4	
	B.I.	P.D.	B.I.	P.D.	B.I.	P.D.	B.I.	P.D.
1A	$41	$23	$ 55	$26	$37	$28	$26	$20
1B	48	27	64	31	43	32	30	24
1C	59	33	77	37	52	39	37	29
2A	76	43	100	48	67	51	47	37

Notice that the 2A rates that apply when there is a driver under the age of 25 are almost double the 1A rates. In some states the 2A rates apply only to male drivers under the age of 25. Apparently, insurance companies have found that an excessive number of accidents are caused by male drivers under the age of 25.

If higher limits than the 5-and-10 limits for bodily injury or the $5,000 property-damage maximum limit are desired, they are computed with the aid of this table.

Increased Coverage			
Bodily-Injury Liability		Property-Damage Liability	
Maximum Limits	Per Cent of 5-and-10 Rates	Maximum Limit	Per Cent of $5,000 Rate
$ 10,000 and $ 20,000	120%	$10,000	110%
25,000 and 50,000	136%	25,000	120%
50,000 and 100,000	145%	50,000	125%
100,000 and 300,000	154%		

Business Transaction 1: Find the total premium paid by the owner of an automobile for 5-and-10 bodily-injury insurance and a $5,000 property-damage policy. He lives in Territory 3 and is classified as a 1B driver.

Solution: Bodily Injury for Class 1B, Territory 3 = $43
Property Damage for Class 1B, Territory 3 = $32
Total Premium = $43 + $32
= $75

Business Transaction 2: Thomas Carter insured his car for 50-and-100 bodily-injury liability and $10,000 property-damage liability. If the use to which the car was put was classified as 1C and Carter lived in Territory 2, what total premium did he pay for this coverage?

Solution: Bodily-Injury (5-and-10) = $77
Bodily-Injury (50-and-100) = 145% of $77
= 1.45 × $77
= $111.65
Property-Damage ($5,000) = $37
Property-Damage ($10,000) = 110% of $37
= 1.10 × $37
= $40.70
Total Premium = $111.65 + $40.70
= $152.35

Explanation: As in Business Transaction 1, the basic rates for 5-and-10 bodily-injury and $5,000 property-damage coverage were found in the rate table for these coverages. In the Increased Coverage Table, it was found that the cost of 50-and-100 bodily injury is 145% of the premium on 5-and-10. Hence, the cost of $77 for 5-and-10 was multiplied by 145%. The cost of the $10,000 property-damage coverage was computed in a similar manner.

LEARNING EXERCISES

A. Find the indemnity paid by the insurance company in each of the following accidents.

No.	Property-Damage Coverage	Extent of Damage	Indemnity Paid by Company
1	$ 5,000	$ 2,340	$xxx
2	5,000	6,750	xxx
3	10,000	12,400	xxx
4	25,000	21,376	xxx
5	10,000	9,825	xxx

B. Find the premium on each of the following policies.

No.	Bodily-Injury Coverage	Class	Territory	Premium
1	5-and-10	1A	2	$xxx
2	5-and-10	1C	4	xxx
3	5-and-10	2A	3	xxx
4	10-and-20	1B	1	xxx
5	10-and-20	1C	2	xxx
6	25-and-50	1A	4	xxx
7	25-and-50	2A	3	xxx
8	50-and-100	1B	1	xxx
9	50-and-100	1C	3	xxx
10	100-and-300	2A	4	xxx

C. Find the premium on each of the following policies.

No.	Property-Damage Coverage	Class	Territory	Premium
1	$ 5,000	1A	3	$xxx
2	5,000	1C	2	xxx
3	10,000	1B	1	xxx
4	10,000	2A	4	xxx
5	25,000	1A	2	xxx
6	25,000	1C	1	xxx
7	50,000	2A	2	xxx
8	50,000	1B	4	xxx

D. *Problems to Be Solved*

1. How much more will a class 1C driver in Territory 3 have to pay for 25-and-50 bodily-injury coverage than he would if he were a class 1A driver?

2. How much more will a driver under age 25 have to pay for a 25-and-50 bodily-injury liability insurance policy in Territory 3 than he would if he were over age 25 and classified as a 1A driver?

3. A class 1A driver in Territory 1 will pay how much less for a $10,-000 property-damage policy than a class 1C driver?

4. During an accident, T. Waldo injured two persons. They sued and were awarded $6,000 and $4,000, respectively, by the court. If Mr. Waldo carried a 5-and-10 bodily-injury policy, how much did the insurance company pay the injured parties?

5. While driving, Mr. Bartner lost control of his car. It went over the curb, knocked down a boy standing on the sidewalk, and demolished the front porch of a house belonging to the boy's father. The boy's father sued Mr. Bartner and was awarded $5,600 for injuries to his son and $875.26 for damages to his house. If Mr. Bartner's insurance coverage was a 5-and-10 bodily-injury policy and a $5,000 property-damage policy, how much did this accident cost him?

6. As a result of a blowout, Bill Smith's car swerved and struck another car, injuring 5 persons. Through court action, he was required to pay the following amounts to the 5 injured persons: $27,000, $14,000, $6,000, $5,000, and $2,700, respectively. If he carried 50-and-100 bodily-injury insurance, how much did his insurance company have to pay?

SECTION 2   **Collision and Comprehensive Insurance**

The two kinds of automobile insurance that you studied in Section 1 of this unit covered the cost of damage that the insured may cause some other person or someone else's property. In this section, you will study types of coverage designed to protect the insured against damage to his own car.

The first of these is called *collision* or *upset insurance*. Under this coverage, the insurance company will pay the cost of any damage to the insured's car caused by collision of the car with another object or by the car's being upset. The entire cost of the damage, however, is not paid by the insurance company because these policies always contain a *deductible clause*. Thus, a *$50-deductible collision* policy means that the insured will pay for the first $50 of any damage to his car and the insurance company will pay the rest. As an example, if the owner of a $50-deductible collision policy damages his car in a collision so that the cost of repairs to his car is $140, the owner would pay $50 of the cost, and the insurance company would pay the remaining $90. Had the cost of the repairs been $50 or less—say, $49—then the insured would have had to cover the entire loss himself.

Another common type of collision insurance is the *$100-deductible* variety. In this coverage, the owner will pay for the first $100 of the damage to his car, and the insurance company will pay the balance. Although it is possible to purchase a *$25-deductible collision* coverage policy, people seldom do so because the cost is comparatively high.

All damage other than collision, upset, or mechanical failure that might occur to an automobile is frequently grouped under a coverage called *comprehensive* insurance. The most important coverages in this group are protection against loss caused by *fire* or *theft*. Other damages to his car for which the insured is also covered under the comprehensive policy are those caused by lightning, transportation, windstorm, hail, earthquake, explosion, riot, falling parts, flood, malicious mischief, and vandalism.

The cost of comprehensive and collision insurance depends on three factors:

→1. The number of accidents that occur in the community in which the insured lives.

→2. The cost of the car when new.

→3. The age of the car.

This table gives both the comprehensive and the collision rates for five makes of cars in an average community in the United States.

Make of Car	Comprehensive and Collision Insurance Rates								
	Age: New			Age: 6 to 18 months			Age: 18 to 30 months		
	Comp.	Collision		Comp.	Collision		Comp.	Collision	
		$50	$100		$50	$100		$50	$100
A	$18	$58	$38	$17	$55	$36	$14	$52	$34
B	20	63	43	18	60	41	15	57	39
C	23	70	50	20	67	48	17	63	45
D	26	76	57	23	72	54	19	68	51
E	30	78	58	27	74	55	22	70	52

Business Transaction: Find the total premium on both comprehensive coverage and $100-deductible coverage on a D-make car that is 10 months old.

Solution: The 10-month age of the car would place it in the 6-to-18-month age group. Hence, the comprehensive coverage would cost $23 and the $100-deductible coverage would cost $54.

Outline: Comprehensive Premium = $23
              $100-Deductible Collision Premium = $54
                          Total Premium = $23 + $54
                                    = $77

LEARNING EXERCISES

A. Find the premium on each of the following comprehensive coverages.

No.	Age	Make	Premium
1	New	D	$xxx
2	12 mos.	E	xxx
3	23 mos.	A	xxx
4	New	C	xxx
5	1 year	B	xxx

B. Find the total premium on comprehensive coverage and collision coverage on each of the following policies.

No.	Age	Make	Collision Coverage	Comprehensive Premium	Collision Premium	Total Premium
1	New	B	$ 50	$xxx	$xxx	$xxx
2	10 mos.	C	100	xxx	xxx	xxx
3	15 mos.	A	100	xxx	xxx	xxx
4	26 mos.	E	50	xxx	xxx	xxx
5	New	D	100	xxx	xxx	xxx
6	30 mos.	A	50	xxx	xxx	xxx

C. Problems to Be Solved

1. In an accident, Mr. Harding damaged another's car to the extent of $265.73 and his own car to the extent of $273.76. How much did his insurance company have to pay if he carried $50-deductible collision insurance and $5,000 property-damage insurance?

2. During a strike at his plant, Mr. Volk's car was overturned. Repairs to the car amounted to $346.50. Although Mr. Volk carried $50-deductible collision insurance, he did not have comprehensive coverage on the car. How much did the insurance company pay for the damage?

3. How much would a person save by buying $100-deductible rather than $50-deductible collision insurance on a new E-make car? Assuming that he was involved in only one accident during the year and that damages to his car in this accident amounted to more than $100, would he gain or lose by buying the cheaper insurance?

4. How much less will Mr. Bartner pay in premiums on both comprehensive coverage and $50-deductible collision coverage on his

E-make car when it is 2 years old than he paid when it was new?

5. How much less does the owner of a new A-make car pay for both his comprehensive and $100-deductible collision insurance than does the owner of a new E-make car? Which of these two cars is the more expensive? Justify your answer.

6. Carl Mardens, the owner of a new D-make car, purchased a $50-deductible collision insurance policy. During the year his car was involved in an accident that caused $80 damage to his car. How much did the insurance company gain or lose on Mr. Mardens that year?

7. As a result of an accident in which he was at fault, Kenneth Cartwright injured three passengers of another car, badly damaged that car, and smashed the front end of his own car. Through court action, he was required to pay $12,500, $2,300, and $1,500, respectively, to the injured persons and also $1,240 for the damage to the car he struck. Damage to his own car amounted to $810. He carried 10-and-20 bodily-injury coverage, $5,000 property damage, $100-deductible collision, and comprehensive coverage insurance. Explain how and through what policies the indemnities were paid.

UNIT 3   Life Insurance—Kinds of Coverage

In order that you may be better able to understand the differences between the various types of life insurance policies, it will be necessary to explain a few simple terms. The first of these, the word *premium*, has the same meaning as it had when used earlier in connection with fire insurance and automobile insurance. *Premium* merely denotes the cost of the insurance to the insured. Life insurance premiums, however, may be paid annually, semiannually, quarterly, monthly, or weekly. As you will learn later, the more frequently the premiums are paid, the greater will be the cost of the insurance, because more employees must be hired to keep records of the additional payments.

The *face value* of the policy is the amount of money that the insurance company agrees to pay at the time of the death of the insured or, in some cases, after a fixed period of time. The person to whom this money is paid is called the *beneficiary* of the policy.

All life insurance policies can be divided into four major groups:

1. Term insurance
2. Straight-life or whole-life insurance

3. Limited-payment life insurance

4. Endowment insurance

1. *Term Insurance:* Under a term insurance policy, premiums are paid for a fixed period of time. Thus, in a 10-year term policy having a face value of $5,000, the insured agrees to pay premiums until his death or for 10 years, whichever occurs first. If he is still living at the end of the 10 years, he will no longer be insured, nor will he or his beneficiary receive any money from the insurance company. Should he die at any time during the 10-year period, his beneficiary will receive the face value of the policy, $5,000.

Term insurance can be purchased for periods other than 10 years. In fact, the most common variety of term insurance is that purchased by people who are planning either a boat or a plane trip. It is important to realize that, with term insurance, as with all life insurance coverages, even if the insured were to make but one payment and then die, his beneficiary would collect the entire face value of the policy. Were this not so, life insurance would be of no value.

2. *Straight-Life or Whole-Life Insurance:* Under a straight-life or whole-life insurance policy, the insured agrees to pay premiums for his entire life. At the time of his death, his beneficiary will receive the face value of the policy. After purchasing the policy, whether the insured lives but 1 day or 90 years, he must pay premiums all his life.

3. *Limited-Payment Life Insurance:* Under a limited-payment life insurance policy, premiums are paid for a fixed period of time. Thus, in a 20-payment life policy having a face value of $5,000, the insured agrees to pay premiums for 20 years or until his death, whichever occurs first. At the end of the 20 years, assuming that he is still alive, he no longer makes any payments but is insured for the remainder of his life. The beneficiary will receive the face value of the policy at the time of the insured's death. Limited-payment life insurance can be purchased for periods other than 20 years.

4. *Endowment Insurance:* Under an endowment insurance policy, as under the limited-payment policy, premiums are paid for a fixed period of time. Thus, in a 20-year endowment policy, the insured agrees to pay premiums until his death or for 20 years, whichever occurs first. However, should the insured still be alive at the end of this period, he himself would receive the face value of the policy. Having been paid this amount, he would no longer be insured. Were he to die during the 20-year period, however, his beneficiary would receive the face value of the policy.

The accompanying table shows typical rates that are charged by life insurance companies for the four different types of policies.

Annual Premiums per $1,000 Worth of Insurance							
Age at Issue	Term		Whole-Life	Limited-Payment		Endowment	
	10-Yr.	15-Yr.		20-Yr.	30-Yr.	20-Yr.	30-Yr.
15	—	—	$17.08	$28.67	$22.50	$51.05	$32.35
20	$ 7.77	$ 7.90	19.02	31.19	24.55	51.44	32.82
25	8.29	8.55	21.78	34.26	26.97	51.70	33.84
30	8.97	9.64	25.09	37.71	29.81	52.15	35.25
→35	10.49	11.78	28.75	41.04	32.82	53.11	36.86
40	13.32	15.49	33.57	45.25	36.76	54.91	39.51
45	18.12	21.57	39.84	50.47	42.05	57.77	43.70
50	25.82	30.01	48.08	57.02	49.18	62.13	50.02
55	36.08	—	58.89	65.50	58.89	68.71	59.22
60	—	—	72.93	76.54	—	78.29	—

Business Transaction 1: Find the annual premium on a $1,000 30-payment life policy that was purchased at age **35.**

Solution: 1. Follow the column headed "Age at Issue" down to the number **35.**

2. Follow this row across to the two columns headed "Limited Payment."

3. Since the policy is a 30-payment life, the 30-Yr. column under the words "Limited Payment" is selected.

4. The number **32.82**, where your pointer has come to rest, represents the annual premium on the $1,000 policy.

You will notice that term insurance is the least expensive of the various types of insurance that can be purchased. Therefore, a person at age **30**, who may have a great deal of family responsibility but very little money, might prefer this type of insurance to a 20-year endowment policy. It would be possible for him to purchase almost 6 times as much term insurance for the same premium that he would have to pay for the 20-year endowment policy (**$52.15 ÷ 8.97 = 6**, approximately). On the other hand, a single person who has no one to protect through insurance on his life might be inclined to purchase the endowment policy. In this way, he would not only be insured for the 20-year period but at the end of that time, he would also receive the face value of the policy. To him, and many other people, this type of coverage is considered to be a form of savings.

The majority of people prefer either the whole life or the limited-payment life policy. Under these policies, they are insured for the duration of their lives at a cost that is much less than the cost of an endowment policy.

Business Transaction 2: Find the annual premium on a $6,000 20-year endowment policy that is issued at age 30.

> **Solution:** Premium for $1,000 = $52.15
> Premium for $6,000 = 6 × $52.15
> = $312.90

It was pointed out earlier that, if the premiums were paid more often than once a year, the cost would be greater because of the increased bookkeeping expense. In fact, if the premiums are paid semiannually, the total amount paid each year would be 3% more than if they had been paid annually. If paid quarterly, the cost is 5% more than if paid annually; and, if paid monthly, the cost is 6% more than the annual payments. To compute semiannual, quarterly, or monthly premiums, insurance companies use the following table.

To Compute Periodic Premium	
If period is:	Multiply annual premium by:
Semiannual	.515
Quarter	.2625
Month	.08833

Business Transaction 3: Find the quarterly premium on a $5,000 whole-life policy issued at age 30.

> **Solution:** Annual Premium for $1,000 = $25.09
> Annual Premium for $5,000 = 5 × $25.09
> = $125.45
> Quarterly Premium for $5,000 = .2625 × $125.45
> = $32.93

LEARNING EXERCISES

A. Find the annual premiums on each of the following policies.

No.	Policy	Age at Issue	Face Value	Annual Premium
1	10-year term	30	$ 1,000	$xxx
2	20-payment life	45	1,000	xxx
3	30-year endowment	25	1,000	xxx
4	Whole-life	40	2,000	xxx
5	20-year endowment	20	4,000	xxx
6	15-year term	30	5,000	xxx
7	30-payment life	45	7,000	xxx
8	Whole life	30	12,000	xxx
9	30-year endowment	20	15,000	xxx
10	10-year term	45	25,000	xxx

B. Find the periodic payment on each of the following policies.

No.	Policy	Age at Issue	Face Value	Period	Premium
1	Whole life	25	$ 1,000	Semian.	$xxx
2	20-payment life	30	1,000	Semian.	xxx
3	30-year endowment	20	1,000	Semian.	xxx
4	15-year term	40	3,000	Semian.	xxx
5	30-payment life	45	4,000	Semian.	xxx
6	10-year term	25	1,000	Quarterly	xxx
7	20-year endowment	30	6,000	Quarterly	xxx
8	Whole life	15	5,000	Quarterly	xxx
9	20-year endowment	20	15,000	Monthly	xxx
10	30-payment life	25	18,000	Monthly	xxx

C. *Problems to Be Solved*

1. How much more will the premiums be on a $5,000 20-payment life policy issued at age 25 than on a 30-payment life policy?

2. How much less will a person pay each year if he purchases a $4,000 whole-life policy at age 20 than the person who purchases a $4,000 20-year endowment policy at the same age?

3. Mr. Thorber purchased a $10,000 20-payment life policy at age 30. If he had purchased the policy at age 20, how much less would his annual premium have been?

4. At age 50, Mr. Welker purchased an $8,000 30-year endowment policy. If he had purchased the policy at age 45, how much less would his annual premiums have been?

5. At age 25, Mr. Kirsten purchased a $5,000 30-payment life policy. After making 5 annual payments, he died.

    a. What was the total amount that he paid the insurance company in premiums?

    b. How much did his beneficiaries receive?

    c. How much more did his beneficiaries receive than Mr. Kirsten paid the insurance company?

6. Mr. Urban purchased a $2,000 20-year endowment policy at age 30. If he lived the entire 20 years, making 20 annual payments, how much more or less than he paid the company in premiums did he receive at the end of the period?

7. At age 20, Tom Baxter purchased a $1,000 20-payment life policy, agreeing to make annual payments.

    a. Should he live the 20 years, how much less than the face value of the policy will he have paid the company?

    b. Why is it possible for an insurance company to pay Tom's beneficiary more money than Tom contributed to the company, although Tom lived the entire 20 years?

8. At age 60, Robert Edwards purchased a $1,000 20-payment life policy, agreeing to make annual payments.

    a. If he lives the entire 20 years, how much more than the face value of the policy will he have contributed to the insurance company?

    b. Why should Mr. Edwards have to pay more than the face value of the policy while Mr. Baxter in Problem 7 paid less than the face value of the same type of policy?

UNIT 4   What Have You Learned?

SECTION 1   Understanding Terms

Can you match the term in the column on the left with the proper definition in the column on the right?

Term	*Definition*

1. Premium
2. Indemnity
3. Face value
4. Coinsurance clause
5. Bodily-injury liability insurance
6. Property-damage liability insurance
7. Collision insurance
8. Beneficiary
9. Straight-life insurance
10. Limited-payment life insurance
11. Endowment insurance

a. Life insurance where the insured pays premiums for a fixed number of years and is insured for this period only. At the end of the period he receives the face value of the policy.

b. Person designated by the insured to receive the face value of the policy in the event of the insured's death.

c. Periodic payment for insurance.

d. Life insurance where the insured pays premiums for a fixed period of years but is insured for his entire lifetime.

e. The amount of coverage for which the insured is protected for the remainder of his life should he cease making payments.

f. Agreement between the insured and the insurance company that the insured will share in any fire loss if certain conditions are not met.

g. The amount of the loss paid to the insured.

h. Protection against the cost of damage to someone else's property through the use of an automobile.

i. Protection against the cost of injury to a person through the use of an automobile.

j. Life insurance where the insured pays premiums all his life.

k. Protection against the cost of damage to one's own car that is caused by an accident.

l. The total amount for which the insured is protected.

SECTION 2   You As a Purchaser of Insurance

How wisely would you purchase insurance? Can you make the correct selection in each of the following situations and justify your answer? If you cannot do so, review the pages indicated at the end of the problem.

1. You have just purchased a home and are employed in a position from which it is unlikely that you will be transferred for at least 10 years. For what period of time should you purchase fire insurance on your home? Justify your answer. (Page 315.)

2. Your home is valued at $20,000. You feel, however, that $12,500 worth of fire insurance will adequately protect you. Through your insurance agent you learn that, if the 80% clause is included in your policy, you are entitled to a reduction of 25% on the premium. From the standpoint of savings on the premium, and in view of the additional amount of coverage, should you insure your property at 80% of its value or select the ordinary coverage for $12,500? (Pages 321–322.)

3. To protect yourself against the cost of possible damage to your new car, you purchased a $50-deductible collision insurance policy. During the year, you had one accident in which your car was damaged to the extent of $82. Disregarding the element of protection, would you have saved any money had you purchased the $100-deductible policy that year rather than the $50-deductible policy? The make of the car is classified as C. (Pages 330–331.)

4. You are 30 years old, are not married, and have no one dependent on you. Should you purchase a $16,000 15-year term policy or a $3,000 20-year endowment policy? The premiums on both are approximately the same. (Page 335.)

SECTION 3   Review Problems

1. Using the tables on pages 314 and 315, find the premium on each of the following ordinary fire insurance policies. (Pages 314–316.)

No.	Face of Policy	Community	Structure	Period in Years	Premium
a	$12,000	D	Brick	1	$xxx
b	14,000	B	Frame	3	xxx
c	20,500	F	Brick	5	xxx
d	26,800	H	Frame	4	xxx

2. Find the amount of the premium returned to the policyholder if the annual policies were canceled by the insured at the end of the period indicated. (Page 318.)

No.	Annual Premium	Days in Force	Premium Returned
a	$22.75	45	$xxx
b	29.56	18	xxx
c	37.84	230	xxx

3. A 1-year fire insurance policy purchased on June 17 was canceled by the insured on October 20. If the annual premium on the policy was

$29.58, how much of that premium was returned to the insured? (Page 318.)

4. Mr. Kent, who owned a brick dwelling in a class C community, purchased a 180-day short-term fire insurance policy having a face value of $16,000. What was the premium on this policy? (Page 318.)

5. In each of the following cases, find the indemnity paid by the insurance company under a policy containing an 80% clause. (Page 321.)

No.	Value of Property	Face of Policy	Fire Loss	Indemnity
a	$25,000	$22,000	$ 6,000	$xxx
b	18,000	14,400	15,000	xxx
c	20,000	8,000	2,000	xxx
d	23,500	16,000	3,200	xxx

6. Using the tables on page 327, find the total premium paid on each of the following automobile policies. (Pages 327–328.)

No.	Coverage		Class	Terri-tory	Premium		Total
	B.I.	P.D.			B.I.	P.D.	
a	5-and-10	$ 5,000	1B	3	$xxx	$xxx	$xxx
b	10-and-20	5,000	1C	2	xxx	xxx	xxx
c	50-and-100	10,000	1A	1	xxx	xxx	xxx

7. As a result of an automobile accident, Banghart was awarded $32,000 by the courts. If the owner of the automobile that struck Banghart carried a 25-and-50 bodily-injury liability insurance policy, how much did the insurance company pay Banghart? How much was paid by the owner of the car? (Pages 325–326.)

8. During an accident, Mr. York's car was damaged to the extent of $375.25. If he carried $50-deductible collision insurance, how much did the insurance company pay Mr. York for the repairs? (Page 330.)

9. If a man aged 25 purchased a $5,000 30-year endowment policy and lived the 30 years, how much more would he pay the company during that period than he would collect from them at the end of the 30 years? (Page 335.)

10. How much larger is the annual premium on a $4,000 30-payment life policy issued at age 20 than the premium on a comparable whole-life policy? (Page 335.)

11. If Mr. Kalter purchased a $10,000 10-year term policy at age 40 and died at age 47 after paying his premium that year, how much more will his beneficiary receive than Mr. Kalter paid to the insurance company? (Page 335.)

12. How much less will a person pay in 1 year if he makes his payments annually rather than semiannually on an $8,000 20-payment life policy issued at age 25? (Pages 335–336.)

SECTION 4   Testing Your Understanding

45 Minutes

In order to solve many of these problems, it will be necessary to refer to the tables in this chapter.

1. Find the premium on an $18,500 3-year ordinary fire insurance policy on a brick house in a C community.

2. Mr. Appleton purchased a 1-year fire insurance policy. The premium amounted to $36.84. After the policy had been in force for 124 days, he sold the house and canceled the policy. How much of the premium did the insurance company return to Mr. Appleton?

3. Roger Perrine rented a brick dwelling in a class E community for 9 months. Part of the agreement with the owner of the house required that he purchase a fire insurance policy for the period that he occupied the property. If Mr. Perrine insured the house for $22,000 for that period, what premium did he have to pay?

4. Fire caused $12,400 worth of damage to property valued at $25,-000. Although the policy contained an 80% clause, the owner had insured it for only $15,000. How much of the loss did the fire insurance company cover?

5. Out of his first earnings, Bill Carton purchased a secondhand car. He immediately insured the car for 25-and-50 bodily-injury and $5,000 property-damage liability insurance. As Bill was under 25 years of age, he was classed as a 2A driver. If he lived in a Territory 3 community, what was the cost of this insurance?

6. Bill Carton (of Problem 5) accidentally struck another car, causing $875 damage to that car. Two passengers in the other car were also injured somewhat severely. Lawsuits against Bill resulted in his being required to pay the injured parties $27,000 and $5,000, respectively. Explain how much of the indemnity was paid by the insurance company and through what policies.

7. How much greater is the cost of $50-deductible collision insurance on a new D-make car than the cost of $100-deductible collision insurance on the same car? In the event of an accident resulting in damages to the car amounting to more than $100, how much would the owner of the car have gained by having the $50-deductible policy rather than the $100-deductible policy?

8. A man, aged 30, purchased a $5,000 20-payment life policy and lived the entire 20 years, during which time he paid annual premium. How much less did he pay the company than his beneficiaries will eventually receive at the time of his death?

9. How much will Mr. Baxter save each year on his $5,000 20-year endowment policy by making annual payments rather than by making quarterly payments? The policy was issued to him at age 25.

UNIT 5   General Review

SECTION 1   To Improve Your Speed and Accuracy

1. Addition:

a. 4,573	b. $576.93	c. $37\frac{5}{8}$
7,819	87.46	$25\frac{5}{6}$
2,706	403.75	$18\frac{1}{2}$
5,488	9.54	
9,264	26.85	
6,753	750.37	
8,627	25.99	

d. $306.85 + $46.98 + $.75 + $53 + $27.05

e. $56\frac{2}{3} + 28\frac{5}{6} + 37\frac{1}{2} + 2\frac{3}{4}$

2. Subtraction:

a. 42,305	b. $2,500.00	c. $56\frac{3}{4}$
15,832	1,768.25	$47\frac{5}{8}$

d. $100 − $59.98   e. $93\frac{2}{3} − 47\frac{7}{8}$

3. Multiplication:

a. 509 × 86   b. 37.06 × .0059   c. $199.95 × .85

d. $\frac{2}{3} \times \frac{3}{4} \times \frac{5}{8}$ e. $12\frac{2}{3} \times 14\frac{1}{2}$

4. Division:

    a. 6,059 ÷ 85   **b.** 30,075 ÷ 208   **c.** $575.50 ÷ .92

    d. $37\frac{1}{2} \div \frac{5}{6}$ **e.** $16\frac{2}{3} \div 12\frac{1}{2}$

SECTION 2   Do You Remember These?

1. Change the following fractions to per cent values.

    a. $\frac{7}{20}$ **b.** $\frac{17}{50}$ **c.** $\frac{9}{200}$

2. 25% of how much money is $14?

3. 250% of $56 is how much?

4. An article that was purchased for $6.50 was sold for $10. What was the per cent of markup based on the cost?

5. An invoice amounting to $96.50 was dated May 12; terms, 2/10, n/30. If the invoice was paid on May 20, how large was the remittance?

6. A note dated June 23, due in 90 days, will mature on what day?

7. Find the number of days between March 17 and September 12 of the same year.

8. Using the banker's 6% 60-day method of computing interest, find the interest on $750 for 80 days.

9. An article that cost $125 was sold at a 60% markup based on the cost. What was the retail?

10. At $2.75 an hour with time and a half for overtime based on a 40-hour week, what would be the gross salary on a work week of 46 hours?

11. How large are the Social Security deductions on an annual salary of $5,000?

12. Find the installment charge on an article, the cash price of which is $109.95, if it is bought on the installment plan for $15 down and $7.50 a month for 14 months?

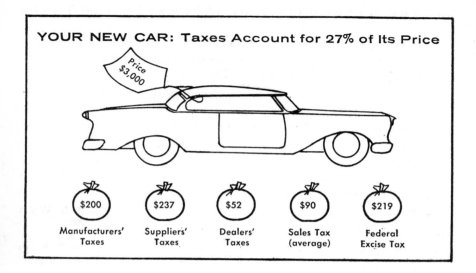

YOUR NEW CAR: Taxes Account for 27% of Its Price

Price $3,000

$200	$237	$52	$90	$219
Manufacturers' Taxes	Suppliers' Taxes	Dealers' Taxes	Sales Tax (average)	Federal Excise Tax

14

Property and Income Taxes

PREVIEW

Ralph Waldron and his wife had been married four years before they felt that they could afford to purchase their own home. Several months of search were finally rewarded when they found two houses that seemed to offer everything they were looking for. They were faced with the problem, therefore, of selecting one of these two equally attractive dwellings.

The houses were located in well-kept residential sections of neighboring communities, where the residents took pride in the appearance of their homes. The price of each house was the same, $21,000. In fact, there seemed to be no feature that made one house more desirable than the other. Mr. Waldron decided that, since the taxes were an important item in their budget, the choice should be determined by the amount of property tax on each house. After making inquiries at the tax departments of each of the communities, he learned that the tax rate in one community was $3.42 per $100, and in the other it was $5.76 per $100. This great difference between the tax rates convinced the Waldrons that their best interest would be served if they purchased the house in the first-mentioned community.

For Class Discussion

1. What is meant by the statement that the tax rate is $3.42 per $100?

2. Does the fact that the tax rate in the community where the Waldrons purchased their home was lower than the rate in the community they had decided against imply that their taxes will be lower in that community? Explain.

3. On what two factors does the property tax on a house depend?

4. How does a community decide what the tax rate will be?

5. What branch of the government receives the money that is paid in property tax by the homeowner?

6. What are five different uses for the property tax money?

7. On the basis of your answer to Question 6, explain why it is not always advisable to base the purchase of a home on the size of the tax.

8. Name several other types of taxes that individuals have to pay.

9. To what branch of the government are these taxes paid?

10. What use is made of the money collected through the taxes that you named in answer to number 8?

Concerning This Chapter

There are a number of ways in which people are taxed; however, most people are especially aware of three: property taxes, Federal income taxes, and state income taxes. These taxes stand out in their minds because they are so much larger than other taxes. Thus, a person will take greater notice of a $450 property tax than he will of a 7-cents-a-gallon tax on gasoline. The smaller taxes that he overlooks, however, add up to a considerable sum during the year.

This chapter is concerned with but two of the many taxes: property taxes and Federal income taxes. The income tax forms of those states that use this method of raising money are similar to the Federal income tax forms. Therefore, after you have learned how to fill out the Federal form, you will understand how to complete the state form. In the pages that follow, you will learn how property taxes are computed and the use to which this money is put. In addition, you will be shown how to fill out a simple income tax return—the type of return that is filed by the great majority of the people in the country.

UNIT 1 **Property Tax**

The major source of income to local governments for paying for the services to residents is a tax on buildings or land, called a *real estate tax,* or a *real property tax.* The money collected is frequently distributed in accordance with the sample budget shown here.

Town of Bloomfield, New Jersey
Analysis of 1956 Tax

Item	Per Cent of Tax
Local and State Schools	35.87
County Tax	18.90
Police and Fire Departments	16.18
Debt	2.20
Road, Sewer, Light, Scavenger Departments, and Public Grounds	8.77
Central Administration and Reserves	13.98
Library	1.36
Health and Charity	2.74

Property taxpayers should be interested not only in how large their taxes are but also in what they are receiving for their money. By paying somewhat more in taxes in one community than he would in a neighboring community, a taxpayer may be amply repaid for the larger expenditure in terms of better roads, more play areas for his children, more efficient police and fire departments, better schools, a more complete library, and the like.

SECTION 1   Computing the Tax Rate

It would obviously be unfair for each property owner to be charged with the same amount of tax. The person who owns $100,000 worth of property should pay more than the one who owns only $20,000 worth. Hence, in order to determine each person's share of the community's expenses, the total taxes that must be raised are divided among all the property owners in accordance with the value of the property that each one owns. To illustrate through the use of a simple situation—if the total value of all property in a certain town was $500,000 and the total expenses for the year were estimated at $25,000, then, for each dollar value of property, the town would have to raise 5 cents in taxes. This number (5 cents) was found by dividing the expenses by the total value of the property ($25,000 ÷ $500,000). A person who owns $10,000 worth of property will have to pay $500 as his share of the taxes, since he must pay 5 cents for each $1 value of his property. Similarly, a person owning $15,000 worth of property will have to pay $750 in taxes ($15,000 × .05).

The rate "5 cents for each $1 of property value" is called the *tax rate*. As the illustration shows, this rate simply indicates the number of dollars that a property owner will have to pay in taxes for each dollar in the value of his property. For the purpose of computing taxes, a value is given to the property by an official called a *tax assessor*, who is usually a local official. This value is called the *assessed value*, or *assessed valuation*, of the property. Frequently, the assessed value of property is far less than the actual value or market value of the property. A house having a market value of $20,000 may be assessed for as little as 10% of that amount, or $2,000, in some communities. It is on the total assessed value of a community's property, *not* on the market value, that the tax rate is determined.

Tax Rate = Total Expenses ÷ Total Assessed Valuation

Example 1

The total expenses that a city will have to meet during the coming year are estimated at $3,022,600 and the assessed valuation of all the property in the city is $63,500,000. Find the tax rate.

Solution: Tax Rate = Total Expenses ÷ Total Assessed Valuation

= $3,022,600   ÷ $63,500,000

= $.0476

Explanation: This number ($.0476) means that, for each $1 of the assessed value of a person's property, he will have to pay a tax of $.0476, or approximately 5 cents.

Though a tax rate is sometimes quoted in cents per $1, as was done in the preceding example, it is more common to find it quoted as dollars per $100 or even dollars per $1,000 of the assessed value of the property. In order to compare the tax rate of one community with that of another if different bases are used, it will be necessary to change the base on which one rate is determined to the base used for the other rate. Thus, if a tax rate of $.0476 per $1 is compared with one of $4.53 per $100, the first base would have to be changed from $1 to $100 or the second base from $100 to $1 before a comparison could be made.

Example 2

Express the tax rate of $.0476 per $1 as an equivalent rate in dollars per $100.

Solution: Since the base ($1) has to be multiplied by 100 to obtain the new base of $100, the same will have to be done with the number $.0476. The quickest way of multiplying this number by 100 is to move the decimal point two places to the right. Hence, a rate of $.0476 per $1 is the same as a rate of $4.76 per $100.

Example 3

Express the tax rate of $57.20 per $1,000 as an equivalent rate in cents per $1.

Solution: $57.20 per $1,000 is the same as
$.0572 per $1

Explanation: The number $1 was obtained from $1,000 by moving the decimal point 3 places to the left (or by dividing $1,000 by 1,000). Hence, it is necessary to move the decimal point 3 places to the left in the number $57.20, arriving at $.0572.

It is important to remember that, when the total expenses are divided by the total assessed value, the tax rate is found in cents per $1. From this rate, any other rate can be found by the methods shown in Examples 2 and 3.

LEARNING EXERCISES

A. Change each of the tax rates below to an equivalent rate in terms of the new base indicated.

No.	Tax Rate	New Rate	No.	Tax Rate	New Rate
1	$.0347 per $1	$xxx per $100	6	$5.74 per $100	$xxx per $1,000
2	$.0562 per $1	$xxx per $100	7	$45.80 per $1,000	$xxx per $100
3	$.0473 per $1	$xxx per $1,000	8	$8.66 per $100	$xxx per $1
4	$6.84 per $100	$xxx per $1,000	9	$5.03 per $100	$xxx per $1
5	$7.39 per $100	$xxx per $1,000	10	$.67 per $1,000	$xxx per $100

B. Find the tax rate in dollars per $100 for each of the communities listed below.

No.	Total Assessed Value	Total Expenses for Coming Year
1	$15,300,000	$ 483,000
2	87,900,000	5,714,000

C. *Problems to Be Solved*

1. The tax rate for one town was $5.23 per $100 and that of another was 6 cents per $1. Which town had the greater tax rate? Explain.

2. In a city where the total assessed value of the property was $70,000,000, the amount of money that had to be raised for the school budget was $2,000,000. How much of the tax rate in dollars per $100 of this town was devoted to education?

3. During a recent year, the budget requirements of a large city called for expenditures in the following departments:

Department	Requirement
Office of Mayor	$ 248,846
Department of Public Works	5,408,795
Police Department	4,510,268
Fire Department	2,952,575
Department of Health and Welfare	5,166,762

In dollars per $100, what part of the tax rate was needed for the budget of each of these departments? The assessed value of property in this city was $701,000,000.

SECTION 2   Computing Property Taxes

Two different kinds of property are taxed:

1. Real property—land or anything attached to it, as a building.
2. Personal property—furniture in a house or an office building.

A homeowner must pay both taxes, as he owns both the house and the furniture in it; on the other hand, the apartment dweller pays only the personal property tax. The tax rate in a community is the same for both types of property, as it is determined on the total assessed value of all property—real and personal.

Example 1

Find the tax paid by the owner of a house that is assessed for $7,300 if the tax rate is $6.24 per $100.

Solution: Since the owner must pay $6.24 on each $100 in the assessed value of the property, it is necessary to find how many hundreds there are in $7,300. To determine this, $7,300 is divided by 100, giving a quotient of 73. On each of these 73 hundreds, the owner must pay $6.24. Hence, on all 73, he will pay 73 times $6.24, or $455.52, in tax.

Outline: $\rightarrow$ Known: Tax Rate $6.24 per $100

$\qquad\qquad\qquad$ Assessed Value $7,300

$\rightarrow$ To Find: Tax

$\rightarrow$ Method: Number of Hundreds in 7,300 $= 7,300 \div 100$

$\qquad\qquad\qquad\qquad\qquad\qquad\qquad\qquad = 73$

$\qquad\qquad\qquad$ Tax $= 73 \times \$6.24$

$\qquad\qquad\qquad\qquad = \$455.52$

Often a low tax rate is confused with a low tax. The tax itself, as you will notice in the preceding example, depends on two factors: the tax rate and the assessed value of the property. If the tax rate is low, the tax may still be comparatively high, for property in that community may be assessed rather high. It was not enough for Mr. Waldron in the preview of this chapter to compare only the tax rates. If property is assessed much higher in the community where he purchased the house than in the community that he rejected, he may find that his actual taxes are higher in spite of the lower tax rate.

Example 2

The tax rate in the community where Mr. Waldron purchased his house is $3.42 per $100; in the other community it is $5.76 per $100. The market value of both houses is $21,000. The assessed value in the first community, however, is based on 60% of the market value; in the second community it is 35%. Compare the taxes of the two communities on these two houses.

Solution:

$$\text{Assessed Value of Mr. Waldron's House} = 60\% \text{ of } \$21,000$$
$$= \$12,600$$
$$\text{Assessed Value of Other House} = 35\% \text{ of } \$21,000$$
$$= \$7,350$$
$$\text{Tax on Mr. Waldron's House} = (\$12,600 \div 100) \times \$3.42$$
$$= 126 \times \$3.42$$
$$= \$430.92$$
$$\text{Tax on Other House} = (\$7,350 \div 100) \times \$5.76$$
$$= 73.50 \times \$5.76$$
$$= \$423.36$$

Thus, the tax on Mr. Waldron's home was $7.56 ($430.92 — $423.36) more than the house he rejected because of the higher tax rate.

LEARNING EXERCISES

A. Find the tax on each of the following properties.

No.	Assessed Value	Tax Rate		Tax
1	$ 6,000	$ 4.27	per $100	$xxx
2	7,400	5.36	per $100	xxx
3	12,300	4.98	per $100	xxx
4	15,650	2.27	per $100	xxx
5	7,800	54.20	per $1,000	xxx
6	10,500	85.70	per $1,000	xxx
7	25,400	17.60	per $1,000	xxx
8	8,700	.057	per $1	xxx
9	11,450	.0628	per $1	xxx
10	33,500	.072	per $1	xxx

B. *Problems to Be Solved*

1. Property in Marysville is assessed at 65% of its market value. If the tax rate is $4.57 per $100, what is the tax on a house that can be sold for $18,400?

2. The personal property in the branch office of a large insurance company is assessed at $125,000. If the tax rate is $7.24 per $100, how much tax will be paid on the property?

3. The total assessed value of all personal property in a large city during a recent year was $128,794,800. If the tax rate was $8.43 per $100, how much should the city expect to collect in personal property taxes alone?

4. Thomas Verner lived in a town where 28% of the property tax was passed along to the county government to help it meet its expenses. If Mr. Verner's property was assessed for $17,400, and the tax rate in the town was $24.90 per $1,000, how much of his tax was turned over to the county?

5. George Farrington purchased a home for $23,750 in Garden Town, where homes are assessed at approximately 38% of their market value. The tax rate in Garden Town is $8.42 per $100.

   a. If approximately 47% of the community's taxes is spent on schools, approximately how much of Mr. Farrington's tax will go toward the education of his children that year?

   b. There are three children of school age in the Farrington family. What will the education of each child cost Mr. Farrington for that year?

6. The real and personal property in a town was assessed at $2,600,000. The budget for the town amounted to $68,000.

   a. Find the tax rate in dollars per $100.

   b. How much tax will the owner of an office building have to pay if the building and the land were assessed at $35,000, and the furniture in the building was assessed at $5,200?

UNIT **2**   **Federal Income Tax**

      Income tax is the largest source of revenue that the Federal Government has. In fact, in 1957, approximately 32 billion dollars of the 66 billion that the Government collected came from individual income taxes. In turn, the Federal Government used the money that year for such services as:

   1. Protection (army, navy, air force, and so on), 42 billion dollars

   2. Civil benefits (highways, schools, parks, and the like), 14 billion dollars

   3. Interest on debts, 7 billion dollars

4. Civil operations (Government employees, and the like), 3 billion dollars

In the chapter on payrolls, you learned that a small fraction of an employee's salary was withheld each week for the payment of his income tax. This deduction is called a *withholding tax*. Actually, the Government is collecting the income tax from the wage earner on the installment plan. It was felt that were this payment made only once a year, many people would not have the money needed to pay the tax. Hence, the installment-plan method of tax collection was devised. Frequently, however, the sum of these payments does not equal the total yearly tax that a person owes the Government. Because of this, each year, by the 15th of April, everyone whose earnings were $600 or more during the previous year must file an income tax return wherein he shows his total income and the total of his installment payments. On the basis of this form, if the total of his installment payments is less than the actual yearly tax, he will have to send the Government a check for the additional amount he still owes. If, on the other hand, his payments were more than they should have been, the Government will refund to him his overpayment.

After January 1 of each year, every wage earner receives from his employer a form similar to the one shown here.

Apex Service Company 503 Main Street Belmont 2, Indiana Type or print EMPLOYER'S identification number, name, and address above.		WITHHOLDING TAX STATEMENT '1956 Federal Taxes Withheld From Wages *Copy A—For District Director*		
SOCIAL SECURITY INFORMATION		**INCOME TAX INFORMATION**		
$ 3,756.00 Total F.I.C.A. Wages* paid in 1956	$ 84.51 F.I.C.A. employee tax withheld, if any	$ 3,756.00 Total Wages* paid in 1956	$ 583.40 Federal Income Tax withheld, if any	
057-36-7942 Richard T. Brooks 76 Arbor Lane Belmont 2, Indiana Type or print EMPLOYEE'S social security account no., name, and address above.			EMPLOYER: See instructions on other side.	
			FOR USE OF INTERNAL REVENUE SERVICE	
			Employee's Copy and Employer's Copy compared	
FORM W-2—U. S. Treasury Department, Internal Revenue Service		*Before payroll deductions.	₀9—16—72856-1	

This form, called the *W-2 form*, shows the salary the employee earned during the year, the deductions made for Social Security, and the amount deducted for income tax. You will recall that deductions for Social Security are taken only from the first $4,200 of a wage earner's salary. Hence, if the yearly salary exceeded $4,200, the number above the words F.I.C.A. Wages would be $4,200; the number over the words Total Wages would be the person's actual earnings. In the W-2 form shown, Mr. Brooks's salary was $3,756. Therefore, the amount of F.I.C.A. wages and of total wages were the same.

The information on this form is needed to complete the income tax forms.

The methods explained in this unit will by no means make it possible for you to complete all income tax returns. They will, however, enable you to fill out those returns that the majority of individuals would be most likely to encounter. Each taxpayer has a choice of one of three forms on which to file his income tax return. Each of these returns will be examined separately.

SECTION 1   Form 1040A Return

Form 1040A is the simplest of the income tax forms to complete. It consists of a card, both sides of which are pictured here. The front of the sample form was completed on the basis of the information given on the W-2 form shown on page 354.

1. In answer to Question 4, Mr. Brooks, who owed no tax for previous years, simply placed an X in the square before the word "No."

2. On the reverse side, in answer to item 14, Mr. Brooks, who was single and under age 65, placed an X in the square that allowed him one exemption for himself. Since he had claimed only one exemption, he placed a 1 in the column at the right. Had he been over 65 years of age, he would have placed another X in the square directly below the one he had marked. Had this been done, he would have placed the number 2 in the column at the right.

After completing this form, Mr. Brooks mailed it to the District Director of Internal Revenue, where the card was sent through a machine to determine whether a refund should be made to Mr. Brooks or whether he owes the Government more money.

The word "exemption" used in the explanation merely means a deduction from his salary that the Government allows each taxpayer to make. For each relative that the taxpayer supports during the year, he is allowed 1 exemption. The most common of these exemptions are the taxpayer's wife, and children who are under 19 years of age. Other exemptions include the mother and father of the taxpayer if their income was less than $600 each and they received more than half their support from the taxpayer. Had Mr. Brooks been married and had two children, he would have listed their names in the space in item 15, written the word "child" in the column headed "Relationship" and placed a 1 in the column at the right for each child. In this way, the fill-in for item 16 would have been the number 4, representing 4 exemptions: himself, his wife, and two children. In order that the tax may be computed by the Government to Mr. Brooks's best advantage, his wife, too, must sign the form, even though she may not have any income.

The 1040A form may be used only if the total earnings of the husband and wife for the year are less than $5,000.

LEARNING EXERCISES

Using the information in the following table, complete 1040A forms obtained from the Internal Revenue Service. (If these forms are not available, copy the 1040A form shown on page 355.) Use the company name and address shown on the sample form.

No.	Taxpayer	Marital Status	Salary	Soc. Sec.	Income Tax
1	William C. Rogers	Single	$3,176.20	$71.46	$446.30
2	Joseph B. Lamb	Wife	3,847.00	86.56	456.25
3	Henry Kling	Wife and son	4,692.60	94.50	487.70
4	Raymond Larky	Wife and 2 sons	4,834.76	94.50	356.32
5	William Trent	Wife, 1 son, 2 daughters	4,582.06	94.50	247.56
6	Alfred Reese	Wife, mother, son	4,739.36	94.50	462.89
7	Frank Simon (aged 67)	Wife (aged 61)	3,972.46	89.39	239.17
8	Thomas Allen (Blind, aged 69)	Single	2,437.12	52.81	64.12

SECTION 2   Short Form 1040 Return

In filing the 1040A form, the taxpayer allows the Internal Revenue Service to determine his tax from the information that he has submitted. Should he desire to compute the tax himself, he may fill out the somewhat longer form called the *1040 form*, illustrated on page 358. You will notice that the information asked for in the upper section of this form, down to item 5, is almost identical with the 1040A form.

This form was completed, using the following information about Arthur Bailey: Salary, $4,823; Income Tax Withheld, $523.41; Dependents: wife, Sally, and son, William; no other source of income. The explanation for completing lines 6 through 19 follows:

Line 6: The law allows a person to subtract from his salary wages that he received when he was ill. The amount that he can deduct is only that part of his salary that he received after the first 7 days of illness. Other points have to be considered, too, such as whether the person was in the hospital at any time during the illness and the amount of salary that he received.

Line 7: Since Mr. Bailey received no "Sick Pay," the amount for line 7 is the same as for line 5.

Lines 8, 9, and 10: These are left blank because there was no other source of income.

Line 11: Since 8, 9, and 10 are blank, nothing had to be added (or subtracted) from line 7.

FORM 1040
U. S. Treasury Department
Internal Revenue Service

U. S. INDIVIDUAL INCOME TAX RETURN

For calendar year or other taxable year beginning *Jan. 1*, 1956, and ending *Dec. 31*, 1956

1956

PLEASE TYPE OR PRINT

Name
(If this is a joint return of husband and wife, use first names of both)
ARTHUR AND SALLY BAILEY

Your Social Security No. and Occupation
307-24-9621
Clerk

Home Address
(Number and street or rural route)
56 SPRUCE STREET

Wife's Social Security No. and Occupation
None —

(City or post office)   (Zone)   (County)   (State)
BELMONT 3   WEST ESSEX   INDIANA
None —

If Income Was All From Salaries and Wages, Use Pages 1 and 2 Only. If Such Income Was Less Than $5,000, You May Need to Use Page 1 Only. See Page 3 of the Instructions.

Exemptions

1. Check blocks which apply. { Regular $600 exemption .... ☒ Yourself ☒ Wife
   Check for wife if she had no income or her income is included in this return. { Additional exemption if 65 or over at end of taxable year ... ☐ Yourself ☐ Wife
   Additional exemption if blind at end of taxable year .... ☐ Yourself ☐ Wife

   Enter number of blocks checked ➤ **2**

2. List names of your children who qualify as dependents; give address if different from yours. *William*

   Enter number of children listed ➤ **1**

3. Enter number of exemptions claimed for other persons listed at top of page 2 .... **0**

4. Enter the total number of exemptions claimed on lines 1, 2, and 3 .... **3**

Income

5. Enter all wages, salaries, bonuses, commissions, and other compensation received in 1956, before payroll deductions. Outside salesmen and persons claiming traveling, transportation, or reimbursed expenses, see instructions, page 6.

Employer's Name	Where Employed (City and State)	Wages, etc.	Income Tax Withheld
Apex Service Co., Belmont, Indiana		$ *4,823 00*	$ *523 41*
Enter totals here ➤		$ *4,823 00*	$ *523 41*

6. Less: Excludable "Sick Pay" in line 5 (See instructions, page 6. Attach required explanation.) ....
7. Balance (line 5 less line 6) .... $ *4823 00*
8. Profit (or loss) from business from separate Schedule C ....
9. Profit (or loss) from farming from separate Schedule F ....
10. Other income (or loss) from page 3 ....
11. ADJUSTED GROSS INCOME (sum of lines 7, 8, 9, and 10) ..... $ *4823 00*

Special computation

Unmarried or legally separated persons qualifying as "Head of Household," see instructions, page 7, and check here ☐   Widows and widowers who are entitled to the special tax computation, see instructions, page 7, and check here ☐

If income on line 11 is under $5,000, and you do not itemize deductions, use Tax Table on page 16 of instructions. If income is $5,000 or more, or if you itemize deductions, compute your tax on page 2.

Tax due or refund

12. Enter tax from the Tax Table, or from line 9, page 2. Please check if you use Tax Table ☒ .. $ *509 00*

   If income was all from wages, omit lines 13 through 16
   { 13. (a) Dividends received credit from line 5 of Schedule J .. $
   { (b) Retirement income credit from line 12 of Schedule K ..
   14. Balance (line 12 less line 13) .... $ *509 00*
   15. Enter your self-employment tax from separate Schedule C or F ....
   16. Sum of lines 14 and 15 .... $ *509 00*

17. (a) Tax withheld (line 5 above). Attach Forms W-2 (Copy B) .... $ *523 41*
   (b) Payments and credits on 1956 Declaration of Estimated Tax (See page 8, instructions.) ●
   District Director's office where paid _____ $ *523 41*

18. If your tax (line 12 or 16) is larger than your payments (line 17), enter the balance here ➤ $
   Pay in full with this return; if less than $1.00, do not remit.

19. If your payments (line 17) are larger than your tax (line 12 or 16), enter the overpayment here ➤ $ *14 41*
   If less than $1.00, it will be refunded only upon application. See instructions, page 8.
   Enter amount of line 19 to be: Credited on 1957 estimated tax $ _____ ; Refunded $ *14.41*

Did you pay or agree to pay anyone for assistance in the preparation of your return? ☐ Yes ☒ No If "Yes," enter his name. _____

Is your wife (husband) making a separate return for 1956? ☐ Yes ☒ No If "Yes," enter her (his) name. _____

Do you owe any Federal tax for years before 1956? ☐ Yes ☒ No

Taxpayer sign here

I declare under the penalties of perjury that this return (including any accompanying schedules and statements) has been examined by me and to the best of my knowledge and belief is a true, correct, and complete return.

Arthur Bailey   *Feb 4 1957*
(Your signature)   (Date)

Sally Bailey   *Feb 4 1957*
(If this is a joint return, wife's signature)   (Date)

➤ To assure split-income benefits, husband and wife must include all their income and, even though only one has income, BOTH MUST SIGN.

Preparer (other than taxpayer) sign here

I declare under the penalties of perjury that I prepared this return for the person(s) named herein; and that this return (including any accompanying schedules and statements) is, to the best of my knowledge and belief, a true, correct, and complete return based on all the information relating to the matters required to be reported in this return of which I have any knowledge.

(Individual or Firm Signature)   (Address)   (Date)

Line 12: Since the amount on line 11 is less than $5,000, Mr. Bailey may use the tax table on pages 360 and 361 to compute his tax. When this table is used to compute income tax, the 1040 form is called the *short form.*

This table is read as follows: Notice that there are two columns headed by the words "But less than." Run your pointer down these columns until you come to the *first* number that is *larger* than the

"Adjusted Gross Income" that appears on line 11 of the 1040 form. In the case of Mr. Bailey, the "Adjusted Gross Income" was $4,823; the first number in the table that is larger than $4,823 is $4,850. Since Mr. Bailey claimed 3 exemptions, follow this row to the right until you come to the group of columns headed by the number 3.

Mr. Bailey could have filed a return for himself alone claiming all 3 exemptions, in which case his tax would be the number in the column headed by the words "Single or married person filing separately." The tax would then have been $519. The law, however, allows a husband and wife to fill out the same form, although the wife may have had no income. This is called a *joint return*. In most cases, filing a joint return is to the advantage of the taxpayer, for his tax will be somewhat lower. Mr. Bailey knew this and, having listed both his and his wife's names at the top of the return, he looked for his tax in the column headed by the words "A married couple filing jointly." The tax he found there was $509, a saving of $10 over the tax he would have had to pay had he filed "separately." This tax ($509) he wrote on line 12.

Lines 13 (*a*) and 13 (*b*) do not affect him.

Line 14: Same as line 12 because of the blank space in line 13.

Line 16: As he omitted line 15, since he was not self-employed, line 16 is the same as line 14.

Line 17 (*a*): This amount is the same as the "income tax withheld" number written on line 5.

Line 17 (*b*): As Bailey is not self-employed, this line and the one concerning the District Director's office would not concern him. Therefore, the sum of lines 17(*a*) and 17(*b*) would remain $523.41. This number is placed under the number $509.

Line 19: Since the amount withheld from Mr. Bailey's salary was greater than the tax he owed the Government, he omitted line 18 and found the number for line 19 by subtracting $509 from $523.41 ($14.41). Mr. Bailey wished the Government to return this money to him; so he filled in $14.41 next to the word "Refunded." Had the tax that was withheld from Mr. Bailey's salary been less than $509, he would have written the amount that he still owed the Government on line 18 and omitted line 19. From this point on, Mr. Bailey checked off the answers to a few simple questions, signed the form himself, and asked his wife to sign it also, since it was a joint return.

TAX TABLE FOR CALENDAR YEAR 1956

FOR PERSONS WITH INCOMES UNDER $5,000 NOT COMPUTING TAX ON PAGE 2 OF FORM 1040

Read down the income columns below until you find the line covering the adjusted gross income you entered on line 11, page 1, Form 1040. Then read across to the appropriate column headed by the number corresponding to the number of exemptions claimed on line 4, page 1. Enter the tax you find there on line 12, page 1.

If your adjusted gross income is— At least	But less than	And the number of exemptions is— 1	2	3	4 or more
		Your tax is—			
$0	$675	$0	$0	$0	$0
675	700	4	0	0	0
700	725	8	0	0	0
725	750	13	0	0	0
750	775	17	0	0	0
775	800	22	0	0	0
800	825	26	0	0	0
825	850	31	0	0	0
850	875	35	0	0	0
875	900	40	0	0	0
900	925	44	0	0	0
925	950	49	0	0	0
950	975	53	0	0	0
975	1,000	58	0	0	0
1,000	1,025	62	0	0	0
1,025	1,050	67	0	0	0
1,050	1,075	71	0	0	0
1,075	1,100	76	0	0	0
1,100	1,125	80	0	0	0
1,125	1,150	85	0	0	0
1,150	1,175	89	0	0	0
1,175	1,200	94	0	0	0
1,200	1,225	98	0	0	0
1,225	1,250	103	0	0	0
1,250	1,275	107	0	0	0
1,275	1,300	112	0	0	0

If your adjusted gross income is— At least	But less than	And the number of exemptions is— 1			2			3			4	5	6	7	8 or more
		And you are— Single or a married person filing separately	An un-married head of a house-hold	A★ married couple filing jointly	Single or a married person filing separately	An un-married head of a house-hold	A★ married couple filing jointly	Single or a married person filing separately	An un-married head of a house-hold	A★ married couple filing jointly					
		Your tax is—													
$2,325	$2,350	$301	$301	$301	$181	$181	$181	$61	$61	$61	$0	$0	$0	$0	$0
2,350	2,375	305	305	305	185	185	185	65	65	65	0	0	0	0	0
2,375	2,400	310	310	310	190	190	190	70	70	70	0	0	0	0	0
2,400	2,425	314	314	314	194	194	194	74	74	74	0	0	0	0	0
2,425	2,450	319	319	319	199	199	199	79	79	79	0	0	0	0	0
2,450	2,475	323	323	323	203	203	203	83	83	83	0	0	0	0	0
2,475	2,500	328	328	328	208	208	208	88	88	88	0	0	0	0	0
2,500	2,525	332	332	332	212	212	212	92	92	92	0	0	0	0	0
2,525	2,550	337	337	337	217	217	217	97	97	97	0	0	0	0	0
2,550	2,575	341	341	341	221	221	221	101	101	101	0	0	0	0	0
2,575	2,600	346	346	346	226	226	226	106	106	106	0	0	0	0	0
2,600	2,625	350	350	350	230	230	230	110	110	110	0	0	0	0	0
2,625	2,650	355	355	355	235	235	235	115	115	115	0	0	0	0	0
2,650	2,675	359	359	359	239	239	239	119	119	119	0	0	0	0	0
2,675	2,700	364	364	364	244	244	244	124	124	124	4	0	0	0	0
2,700	2,725	368	368	368	248	248	248	128	128	128	8	0	0	0	0
2,725	2,750	373	373	373	253	253	253	133	133	133	13	0	0	0	0
2,750	2,775	377	377	377	257	257	257	137	137	137	17	0	0	0	0
2,775	2,800	382	382	382	262	262	262	142	142	142	22	0	0	0	0
2,800	2,825	386	386	386	266	266	266	146	146	146	26	0	0	0	0
2,825	2,850	391	391	391	271	271	271	151	151	151	31	0	0	0	0
2,850	2,875	395	395	395	275	275	275	155	155	155	35	0	0	0	0
2,875	2,900	400	400	400	280	280	280	160	160	160	40	0	0	0	0
2,900	2,925	405	405	405	284	284	284	164	164	164	44	0	0	0	0
2,925	2,950	410	410	410	289	289	289	169	169	169	49	0	0	0	0
2,950	2,975	415	415	415	293	293	293	173	173	173	53	0	0	0	0

Tax table (left panel) — income $1,300 to $2,325

At least	But less than	1	2	3	4	5	6	7
1,300	1,325	116	0	0	0	0	0	0
1,325	1,350	121	1	0	0	0	0	0
1,350	1,375	125	5	0	0	0	0	0
1,375	1,400	130	10	0	0	0	0	0
1,400	1,425	134	14	0	0	0	0	0
1,425	1,450	139	19	0	0	0	0	0
1,450	1,475	143	23	0	0	0	0	0
1,475	1,500	148	28	0	0	0	0	0
1,500	1,525	152	32	0	0	0	0	0
1,525	1,550	157	37	0	0	0	0	0
1,550	1,575	161	41	0	0	0	0	0
1,575	1,600	166	46	0	0	0	0	0
1,600	1,625	170	50	0	0	0	0	0
1,625	1,650	175	55	0	0	0	0	0
1,650	1,675	179	59	0	0	0	0	0
1,675	1,700	184	64	0	0	0	0	0
1,700	1,725	188	68	0	0	0	0	0
1,725	1,750	193	73	0	0	0	0	0
1,750	1,775	197	77	0	0	0	0	0
1,775	1,800	202	82	0	0	0	0	0
1,800	1,825	206	86	0	0	0	0	0
1,825	1,850	211	91	0	0	0	0	0
1,850	1,875	215	95	0	0	0	0	0
1,875	1,900	220	100	0	0	0	0	0
1,900	1,925	224	104	0	0	0	0	0
1,925	1,950	229	109	0	0	0	0	0
1,950	1,975	233	113	0	0	0	0	0
1,975	2,000	238	118	0	0	0	0	0
2,000	2,025	242	122	2	0	0	0	0
2,025	2,050	247	127	7	0	0	0	0
2,050	2,075	251	131	11	0	0	0	0
2,075	2,100	256	136	16	0	0	0	0
2,100	2,125	260	140	20	0	0	0	0
2,125	2,150	265	145	25	0	0	0	0
2,150	2,175	269	149	29	0	0	0	0
2,175	2,200	274	154	34	0	0	0	0
2,200	2,225	278	158	38	0	0	0	0
2,225	2,250	283	163	43	0	0	0	0
2,250	2,275	287	167	47	0	0	0	0
2,275	2,300	292	172	52	0	0	0	0
2,300	2,325	296	176	56	0	0	0	0

↑ ★

Tax table (right panel) — income $2,975 to $5,000

At least	But less than	1	2	3	4	5	6	7
2,975	3,000	419	298	178	58	0	0	0
3,000	3,050	426	305	185	65	0	0	0
3,050	3,100	435	314	194	74	0	0	0
3,100	3,150	445	323	203	83	0	0	0
3,150	3,200	454	332	212	92	0	0	0
3,200	3,250	464	341	221	101	0	0	0
3,250	3,300	473	350	230	110	0	0	0
3,300	3,350	482	359	239	119	8	0	0
3,350	3,400	492	368	248	128	17	0	0
3,400	3,450	501	377	257	137	26	0	0
3,450	3,500	511	386	266	146	35	0	0
3,500	3,550	520	395	275	155	44	0	0
3,550	3,600	530	404	284	164	53	0	0
3,600	3,650	539	413	293	173	62	0	0
3,650	3,700	549	422	302	182	71	0	0
3,700	3,750	558	431	311	191	80	0	0
3,750	3,800	567	440	320	200	89	0	0
3,800	3,850	577	449	329	209	98	0	0
3,850	3,900	586	458	338	218	107	0	0
3,900	3,950	596	467	347	227	116	5	0
3,950	4,000	605	476	356	236	125	14	0
4,000	4,050	615	485	365	245	134	23	0
4,050	4,100	624	494	374	254	143	32	0
4,100	4,150	634	503	383	263	152	41	0
4,150	4,200	643	512	392	272	161	50	0
4,200	4,250	653	521	401	281	170	59	0
4,250	4,300	662	530	410	290	179	68	0
4,300	4,350	671	539	419	299	188	77	0
4,350	4,400	681	548	428	308	197	86	0
4,400	4,450	690	557	437	317	206	95	0
4,450	4,500	700	566	446	326	215	104	0
4,500	4,550	709	575	455	335	224	113	2
4,550	4,600	719	584	464	344	233	122	7
4,600	4,650	728	593	473	353	242	131	11
4,650	4,700	738	602	482	362	251	140	16
4,700	4,750	747	611	491	371	260	149	20
4,750	4,800	756	620	500	380	269	158	25
4,800	4,850	766	629	509	389	278	167	29
4,850	4,900	775	638	518	398	287	172	34
4,900	4,950	785	647	527	407	—	—	38
4,950	5,000	794	656	536	416	296	176	56

★ This column may also be used by certain widows or widowers who qualify for special tax rates.

U. S. GOVERNMENT PRINTING OFFICE : 1955—O—355293

(handwritten margin notes: 4540, 4627, 4621)

LEARNING EXERCISES

A. Using the tax table on pages 360 and 361, find the income tax due the Government in each of the following cases. If the person is married, assume that he and his wife are filing a joint return.

No.	Adjusted Gross Income	Marital Status	Income Tax
1	$4,700	Married, 2 children	$xxx
2	2,250	Single	xxx
3	4,965	Married, 2 dependent parents	xxx
4	2,474	Married	xxx
5	3,545	Single	xxx
6	4,480	Married	xxx
7	4,400	Single	xxx
8	2,285	Married, 1 child	xxx
9	3,360	Married, 3 children	xxx
10	790	Single	xxx

B. In each of the following problems, how much money should be returned to the taxpayer by the Government. If the amount withheld from the taxpayer's salary was less than the tax due, how large a check will the taxpayer have to send to the District Director of Internal Revenue. Indicate whether a refund is to be made to the taxpayer or a check sent to the Government. Assume that married persons are filing a joint return.

No.	Adjusted Gross Income	Marital Status	Tax Withheld	Income Tax	Refund or Add. Pay.
1	$2,356.00	Single	$327.00	$xxx	$xxx
2	3,724.00	Wife	347.12	xxx	xxx
3	3,915.81	Wife and son	306.28	xxx	xxx
4	4,401.46	Wife and 2 sons	339.47	xxx	xxx
5	4,898.15	Wife and 3 children	256.12	xxx	xxx

SECTION 3   Long Form 1040 Return

In addition to the deductions that a taxpayer may take for each of his exemptions, he is allowed other deductions, such as:

1. Contributions: Church, Salvation Army, Red Cross, community chest, hospitals, organized charities, and so on. In general, the deductible contributions cannot be greater than 20% of a person's income.

2. Interest on mortgages or other debts.

3. Taxes: Personal property tax, real estate tax, state tax, sales tax, gasoline tax, cigarette tax, and so on (no Federal tax).

4. Certain medical expenses.

5. Certain expenses connected with a person's employment.

6. Losses from theft, fire, or accident that were not covered by insurance.

The figures in the tax table on pages 360 and 361 are computed on the basis that every taxpayer will have deductions of 10% of his income. However, should a taxpayer's total deductions be more than 10% of his income, it would be advisable for him to list them on page 2 of the 1040 form. As an example, Mr. Bailey's income was $4,823; 10% of this amount is $482.30. If, when Mr. Bailey itemized his deductions the sum was less than $482.30, it would have been best for him to have used the 1040 short form as he did in Section 2 of this unit. If, however, the itemized deductions totaled more than $482.30, it would have been to his advantage to complete page 2 of the 1040 form as shown on page 364. By doing this, he is filing the *1040 long form.*

Example 1

Taxpayer: Arthur Bailey; Salary: $4,823; Tax Withheld: $523.41; Dependents: Wife, Sally; son, William. File Mr. Bailey's return, using the long 1040 form.

Solution: Lines 1 through 11 of the long form are completed in exactly the same manner as on page 358. Then Mr. Bailey would turn to page 2 of the 1040 form where he would find and complete the form shown on page 364.

The deductions are itemized as is shown in the upper part of this form. The explanation for completing each of the lines of the lower section follows:

Line 1: The $4,823 is simply the "Adjusted Gross Income" that Mr. Bailey had written on the front page of the 1040 form.

EXEMPTIONS FOR PERSONS OTHER THAN YOUR WIFE AND CHILDREN					Page 2
Name	Relationship	Number of months dependent lived in your home. If born or died during year also write "B" or "D"	Did dependent have gross income of $600 or more?	Amount YOU spent for dependent's support. If 100% write "All"	Amount spent by OTHERS including dependent from own funds
				$	$

Enter on line 3, page 1, the number of exemptions claimed above.
➡ If an exemption is based on a multiple-support agreement of a group of persons, attach information described on page 5 of instructions.

ITEMIZED DEDUCTIONS—IF YOU DO NOT USE TAX TABLE OR STANDARD DEDUCTION

If Husband and Wife (Not Legally Separated) File Separate Returns and One Itemizes Deductions, the Other Must Also Itemize

Describe deductions and state to whom paid. If more space is needed, attach additional sheets. Please put your name and address on any attachments.

Contributions	Church $150 Red Cross $35 Crippled Children's Hospital $35		
	Total (not to exceed 20% of line 11, page 1, except as described on page 8 of instructions)	$	210 00
Interest	Interest on mortgage—Fidelity Bank $120		
		Total	120 00
Taxes	Real Estate Tax $237 State Gasoline Tax $21 Auto License $23 State Income Tax $47.90		
		Total	328 90
Medical and dental expense (If 65 or over, see instructions, page 9)	Submit itemized list. Do not enter any expense compensated by insurance or otherwise. 1. Cost of medicines and drugs, in excess of 1 percent of line 11, page 1 .... $ 2. Other medical and dental expenses .... $ 3. Total .... $ 4. Enter 3 percent of line 11, page 1 .... $ 5. Allowable amount (excess of line 3 over line 4). (See instructions, page 9, for limitations.)		
Child care	Expenses for care of children and certain other dependents not to exceed $600 (See page 10 of instructions and attach statement)		
Casualty losses	Stolen watch—not covered by insurance $42.50 Total losses (not compensated by insurance or otherwise) .. 0		42 50
Miscellaneous	Chamber of Commerce dues $12		
		Total	12 00
	TOTAL DEDUCTIONS (Enter on line 2 of Tax Computation, below)	$	713 40

TAX COMPUTATION—IF YOU DO NOT USE THE TAX TABLE

1. Enter Adjusted Gross Income from line 11, page 1	$	4,823 00
2. If deductions are itemized above, enter total of such deductions. If deductions are not itemized *and line 1, above, is $5,000 or more:* (a) married persons filing separately enter $500; (b) all others enter 10 percent of line 1, or $1,000, whichever is smaller		713 40
3. Balance (line 1 less line 2)		4,109 60
4. Multiply $600 by total number of exemptions claimed on line 4, page 1		1,800 00
5. TAXABLE INCOME (line 3 less line 4)		2,309 60
6. Tax on amount on line 5. Use appropriate Tax Rate Schedule on page 11 of instructions...		461 92
7. If you had capital gains and the alternative tax applies, enter the tax from separate Schedule D		
8. Tax credits. If you itemized deductions, enter: (a) Credit for income tax payments to a foreign country or U. S. possession (Attach Form 1116)....... $ (b) Tax paid at source on tax-free covenant bond interest and credit for partially tax-exempt interest...		
9. Enter here and on line 12, page 1, the amount shown on line 6 or 7 less amount claimed on line 8	$	461 92

Line 2: Mr. Bailey copied the "Total Deductions" that he had computed on the upper part of this form.

Line 3: Subtracting $713.40 from $4,823, the amount $4,109.60 on line 3 was found.

Line 4: Mr. Bailey had claimed three exemptions. For each of these exemptions he is allowed to take a $600 deduction from his income. Hence, $1,800 was found by multiplying $600 by 3.

Line 5: Subtracting $1,800 from $4,109.60 leaves a balance of $2,309.60, on which Mr. Bailey must pay his tax.

Line 6: In order to compute his tax, Mr. Bailey had to refer to one of the three tables shown on page 366. Since he was a married person filing a joint return with his wife, he looked at Schedule II. As the amount on line 5 of his return was only $2,309.60, which is less than $4,000, he found 20% of $2,309.60. This amount ($461.92) is his tax.

Line 9: Lines 7 and 8 did not apply to Mr. Bailey; so he recopied on line 9 the amount he had written on line 6.

This tax ($461.92) was then transferred to line 12 of page 1 of the return. If you will refer to the tax form on page 358, you will find that, by itemizing his deductions, Mr. Bailey's tax was lower than it was when he used the short 1040 form because his itemized deductions were greater than 10% of his income. The remainder of page 1 of the 1040 form is completed in the same manner as was done when the short 1040 form was prepared.

All taxpayers whose income is greater than $5,000 a year must file the long 1040 form. They need not, however, itemize their deductions. Their deductions can be computed by the directions given on line 2, page 2, where the items concerning Tax Computation are listed.

Example 2

Find the tax of a single taxpayer whose taxable income shown on line 5 was $9,467.23.

Solution: Referring to Schedule I for Single Taxpayers, it is found that $9,467.23 is between $8,000 and $10,000. Hence, this taxpayer must pay $1,960 plus 34% of his salary over $8,000. The amount of his salary over $8,000 is $1,467.23 ($9,467.23 − $8,000). 34% of $1,467.23 is $498.86. Hence, his total tax is the sum of $1,960 and $498.86.

Outline: Tax on First $8,000 = $1,960
Amount over $8,000 = $9,467.23 − $8,000
= $1,467.23
Tax on $1,467.23 = 34% of $1,467.23
= $498.86
Total Tax = $1,960 + $498.86
= $2,458.86

I. (A) SINGLE TAXPAYERS WHO DO NOT QUALIFY FOR RATES IN TABLES II AND III, AND (B) MARRIED PERSONS FILING SEPARATE RETURNS

If the amount on line 5 is: Not over $2,000...... 20% of the amount on line 5.

Over—	But not over—	Enter on line 6:	of excess over—
$2,000	$4,000	$400, plus 22%	$2,000
$4,000	$6,000	$840, plus 26%	$4,000
$6,000	$8,000	$1,360, plus 30%	$6,000
$8,000	$10,000	$1,960, plus 34%	$8,000
$10,000	$12,000	$2,640, plus 38%	$10,000
$12,000	$14,000	$3,400, plus 43%	$12,000
$14,000	$16,000	$4,260, plus 47%	$14,000
$16,000	$18,000	$5,200, plus 50%	$16,000
$18,000	$20,000	$6,200, plus 53%	$18,000
$20,000	$22,000	$7,260, plus 56%	$20,000
$22,000	$26,000	$8,380, plus 59%	$22,000
$26,000	$32,000	$10,740, plus 62%	$26,000
$32,000	$38,000	$14,460, plus 65%	$32,000
$38,000	$44,000	$18,360, plus 69%	$38,000
$44,000	$50,000	$22,500, plus 72%	$44,000
$50,000	$60,000	$26,820, plus 75%	$50,000
$60,000	$70,000	$34,320, plus 78%	$60,000
$70,000	$80,000	$42,120, plus 81%	$70,000
$80,000	$90,000	$50,220, plus 84%	$80,000
$90,000	$100,000	$58,620, plus 87%	$90,000
$100,000	$150,000	$67,320, plus 89%	$100,000
$150,000	$200,000	$111,820, plus 90%	$150,000
$200,000	....	$156,820, plus 91%	$200,000

II. (A) MARRIED TAXPAYERS FILING JOINT RETURNS, AND (B) CERTAIN WIDOWS AND WIDOWERS. (SEE ABOVE)

If the amount on line 5 is: Not over $4,000...... 20% of the amount on line 5.

Over—	But not over—	Enter on line 6:	of excess over—
$4,000	$8,000	$800, plus 22%	$4,000
$8,000	$12,000	$1,680, plus 26%	$8,000
$12,000	$16,000	$2,720, plus 30%	$12,000
$16,000	$20,000	$3,920, plus 34%	$16,000
$20,000	$24,000	$5,280, plus 38%	$20,000
$24,000	$28,000	$6,800, plus 43%	$24,000
$28,000	$32,000	$8,520, plus 47%	$28,000
$32,000	$36,000	$10,400, plus 50%	$32,000
$36,000	$40,000	$12,400, plus 53%	$36,000
$40,000	$44,000	$14,520, plus 56%	$40,000
$44,000	$52,000	$16,760, plus 59%	$44,000
$52,000	$64,000	$21,480, plus 62%	$52,000
$64,000	$76,000	$28,920, plus 65%	$64,000
$76,000	$88,000	$36,720, plus 69%	$76,000
$88,000	$100,000	$45,000, plus 72%	$88,000
$100,000	$120,000	$53,640, plus 75%	$100,000
$120,000	$140,000	$68,640, plus 78%	$120,000
$140,000	$160,000	$84,240, plus 81%	$140,000
$160,000	$180,000	$100,440, plus 84%	$160,000
$180,000	$200,000	$117,240, plus 87%	$180,000
$200,000	$300,000	$134,640, plus 89%	$200,000
$300,000	$400,000	$223,640, plus 90%	$300,000
$400,000	....	$313,640, plus 91%	$400,000

III. UNMARRIED (OR LEGALLY SEPARATED) TAXPAYERS WHO QUALIFY AS HEAD OF HOUSEHOLD

If the amount on line 5 is: Not over $2,000...... 20% of the amount on line 5.

Over—	But not over—	Enter on line 6:	of excess over—
$2,000	$4,000	$400, plus 21%	$2,000
$4,000	$6,000	$820, plus 24%	$4,000
$6,000	$8,000	$1,300, plus 26%	$6,000
$8,000	$10,000	$1,820, plus 30%	$8,000
$10,000	$12,000	$2,420, plus 32%	$10,000
$12,000	$14,000	$3,060, plus 36%	$12,000
$14,000	$16,000	$3,780, plus 39%	$14,000
$16,000	$18,000	$4,560, plus 42%	$16,000
$18,000	$20,000	$5,400, plus 43%	$18,000
$20,000	$22,000	$6,260, plus 47%	$20,000
$22,000	$24,000	$7,200, plus 49%	$22,000
$24,000	$28,000	$8,180, plus 52%	$24,000
$28,000	$32,000	$10,260, plus 54%	$28,000
$32,000	$38,000	$12,420, plus 58%	$32,000
$38,000	$44,000	$15,900, plus 62%	$38,000
$44,000	$50,000	$19,620, plus 66%	$44,000
$50,000	$60,000	$23,580, plus 68%	$50,000
$60,000	$70,000	$30,380, plus 71%	$60,000
$70,000	$80,000	$37,480, plus 74%	$70,000
$80,000	$90,000	$44,880, plus 76%	$80,000
$90,000	$100,000	$52,480, plus 80%	$90,000
$100,000	$150,000	$60,480, plus 83%	$100,000
$150,000	$200,000	$101,980, plus 87%	$150,000
$200,000	$300,000	$145,480, plus 90%	$200,000
$300,000	....	$235,480, plus 91%	$300,000

LEARNING EXERCISES

A. The "taxable income" on line 5 of the 1040 return is shown in the second column of the table below. Compute the tax due in each case.

No.	Taxable Income	Type of Return	Tax
1	$ 3,750.00	Joint	$xxx
2	1,860.00	Single	xxx
3	3,900.00	Single	xxx
4	6,255.00	Joint	xxx
5	10,252.00	Joint	xxx
6	7,849.50	Single	xxx
7	12,295.25	Single	xxx
8	14,824.12	Joint	xxx

B. Copy the lower part of page 2 of the 1040 form, starting with the words "Tax computation—if you do not use the tax table." Using the information given here, fill out the 9 lines. (Deductions are not itemized.)

No.	Adjusted Gross Income	Number of Exemptions	Type of Return
1	$ 6,000	1	Single
2	6,200	4	Joint
3	7,320	2	Joint
4	8,946	3	Joint
5	12,395	4	Joint

C. Using the information given here, copy and complete all of page 2 of the 1040 form.

1. Adjusted Gross Income: $4,927.56.
   Deductions: Church, $75; Community Chest, $20; Polio fund, $12; Real estate tax, $265.40; Auto license, $27.50; Gasoline tax, $23; Cigarette tax, $12; Interest on mortgage, $237.42.
   Exemptions: 4 (joint return).

2. Adjusted Gross Income: $8,463.40.
   Deductions: Church, $250; Red Cross, $50; Salvation Army, $30; Interest on mortgage, $385.60; Real estate tax, $412.56; Auto license, $32.40; Gasoline tax, $18; Damage to car not covered by insurance, $176.25; Dues to professional organization, $24.
   Exemptions: 5 (joint return)

UNIT 3   **What Have You Learned?**

SECTION 1   You As a Taxpayer

How wisely would you pay your taxes? Can you make the correct choice in each of the following situations, and justify your answers? If you cannot do so, review the pages indicated at the end of each problem.

1. Two homes in two communities have a market value of $22,000. One of the homes is assessed at 40% of its value; the other is assessed at only 25% of its market value. The tax rate in the first town is $4.36 per $100; in the second, $5.49 per $100. Which homeowner will have to pay the smaller real estate tax? (Pages 351–352.)

2. In a community where the tax rate was $5.24 per $100, the homeowner had to pay $1.50 a month extra for refuse collection and $5.75 quarterly for sewage. In a neighboring community where the tax rate was $5.47 per $100, these charges were included in the taxes. In which community would the real estate tax be less on a $20,500 home if both communities assessed property at 35% of its market value? (Pages 351–352.)

3. You have a wife and two children. Your total income is $4,975. In filing your income tax return, you plan to use the short 1040 form. Would it be advisable for you to file a joint or a single return? How much would you save by using one form rather than the other? In both cases you would claim all the exemptions. (Pages 357 and 361.)

4. You have a wife and one child. Your total yearly income is $4,496. After itemizing your deductions, you find their sum to be $554.42. Should you use the short 1040 form or itemize your deductions and use the long 1040 form? How much would you save by using one form rather than the other? (Page 363.)

5. You are single with no dependents. Your salary is $6,754.50 a year. When filling out your income tax return, you find that the sum of your itemized deductions amounts to $437.62. Should you fill out the long 1040 form and itemize your deductions or the long 1040 form and *not* itemize your deductions? (Pages 363–366.)

SECTION 2   Review Problems

1. Change each of the tax rates below to an equivalent rate in terms of the new base indicated. (Page 349.)

No.	Tax Rate	New Rate
a	$.0458 per $1	$xxx per $1,000
b	43.70 per $1,000	xxx per $100

2. Find the tax rate in cents per $1 for a community where the total assessed value of all the property is $15,000,000 and the total budget for the coming year is $540,000. (Page 348.)

3. Find the tax on each of the following homes. (Page 351.)

No.	Assessed Value	Tax Rate	Tax
a	$ 8,400	$ 5.40 per $100	$xxx
b	14,750	67.50 per $1,000	xxx

4. In Branchville, where homes are assessed at 65% of their market value, the tax rate is $3.27 per $100. What is the tax on a home that can be sold for $18,600? (Pages 351–352.)

5. Real property in Ocean City is assessed at 35% of its market value and personal property is assessed at only 5% of its value. Mr. Turrell purchased a new home in Ocean City for $23,400 and spent $5,000 on furnishings. If the tax rate is $4.86 per $100, what will Mr. Turrell's total tax bill be? (Pages 351–352.)

6. The tax rates of two neighboring communities are $6.27 per $100 and $4.58 per $100, respectively. In the first community, real property is assessed at 25% of its market value; in the second, it is assessed at 40% of its market value.

   a. In which town would the taxes be greater on a new house whose market value was $24,000?

   b. How much greater? (Pages 351–352.)

7. Using the short 1040 form, how much income tax will each of the following persons have to pay? Assume that the married persons are filing a joint return. (Pages 357–361.)

No.	Adjusted Gross Income	Marital Status	Income Tax
a	$3,250	Single	$xxx
b	4,672	Wife and 2 children	xxx

8. During the year, $246.28 was withheld from John Lindsley's salary of $4,540 for income tax payments. When Mr. Lindsley filed his joint return at the end of the year, he used the short 1040 form.

a. Will Mr. Lindsley receive a refund from the Government, or had too little been withheld from his salary? (Pages 357–361.)

b. How large will the refund be, or how much money will he still have to pay?

9. Using the long 1040 form, how much tax will each of the following people have to pay? (Pages 363–366.)

No.	Taxable Income	Type of Return	Tax
a	$3,500	Joint	$xxx
b	7,468	Single	xxx

10. The itemized deductions of a taxpayer who earned $6,275 amount to $956.23. Should he use the long 1040 form and itemize his deductions, or should he file the long 1040 form but *not* itemize his deductions? Explain. (Pages 363–366.)

SECTION 3   Testing Your Understanding

50 Minutes

1. Change each of the tax rates below to an equivalent rate in terms of the new base indicated.

No.	Tax Rate	New Rate
a	$ .0327 per $1	$xxx per $1,000
b	$6.25 per $100	xxx per $1,000

2. In a community where property is assessed at $45,000,000, the anticipated expenses for the coming year amount to $1,800,000. What should the tax rate be in dollars per $100 for the coming year?

3. What is the tax on a house assessed at $9,200 if the tax rate is $6.54 per $100?

4. In a city where manufacturing plants are assessed at 48% of their actual value, a new factory was erected at a cost of $450,000. If the tax rate in that city is $8.64 per $100, how much tax will have to be paid on this building?

5. Which of the following two tax rates is the greater: $4.37 per $100 or $41.56 per $1,000? Explain.

6. How much income tax will each of the following people have to pay if they use the short 1040 form?

No.	Adjusted Gross Income	Marital Status	Income Tax
a	$2,857	Single	$xxx
b	4,796	Wife and 1 child (joint return)	xxx

7. In filing his joint income tax return, Mr. Harvey, who has a wife but no children, used the short 1040 form. If his income for the year was $4,248, and $547.23 had been withheld from his salary for income tax, how large a refund should he receive from the Government?

8. If each of the following taxpayers uses the long 1040 form, how much income tax will he have to pay?

No.	Taxable Income	Type of Return	Income Tax
a	$3,750	Joint	$xxx
b	8,596	Single	xxx

UNIT 4   General Review

SECTION 1   To Improve Your Speed and Accuracy

1. Addition:

a. 36,473
58,962
72,186
29,537
64,825
95,848

b. $4,593.67
284.98
1.75
3,096.09
47.15
.69

c. $48\frac{3}{4}$
$59\frac{5}{6}$
$36\frac{2}{3}$

d. $56,289.49 + $379.25 + $4.98 + $.39 + $48

e. $125\frac{3}{4} + 56\frac{1}{2} + 109\frac{5}{8}$

2. Subtraction:

a. 64,237
28,609

b. $5,325.00
2,863.49

c. $104\frac{2}{5}$
$85\frac{3}{4}$

d. $250 − $138.09

e. $81\frac{5}{6} − 47\frac{2}{5}$

3. Multiplication:

a. 38 × 407

b. $475.50 × 11.05

c. $1,450 × .045

d. $1\frac{1}{2} × 3\frac{1}{4} × \frac{2}{3}$

e. 1,524 × $83\frac{1}{4}$

4. Division:
   a. 43,578 ÷ 365   b. $150 ÷ 1.04   c. 2,375.75 ÷ .035
   d. 18 ÷ 4$\frac{1}{2}$ e. 34$\frac{3}{4}$ ÷ 6

SECTION 2   Do You Remember These?

1. Change the following per cent values to decimals.

   a. 15%   b. 3$\frac{3}{4}$%   c. 5.5%

2. 15 is what per cent of 45?

3. 125 is what per cent of 25?

4. A merchant purchased an article for $14.50 and sold it as a damaged article for $9.98. What was his per cent of loss based on the cost of the article?

5. $500 was borrowed from the bank for 92 days at a discount rate of 5$\frac{1}{2}$%. What were the proceeds on this note?

6. A note dated June 17, due in 4 months, was discounted at the bank on August 12. For what period of time did the bank charge discount?

7. The weekly salary of a wage earner is $76.20. How much is deducted from his salary each week for Social Security payments?

8. A merchant purchased a lamp for $35 and sold it at a 125% markup on the cost. What was the retail of the article?

9. Find the interest at 6% on a debt of $500 for a period of 40 days if computed by the banker's 60-day interest method.

10. A small-loan company advertised that a loan of $350 could be repaid by making 9 monthly payments of $43.75 each. How much interest did the borrower have to pay on this debt?

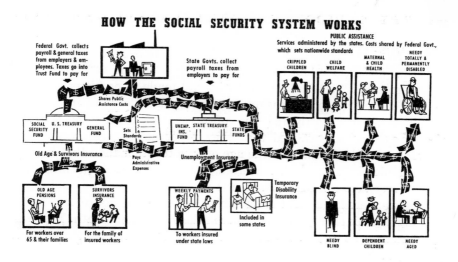

From "A Visual History of the United States," by Harold U. Faulkner & Graphics Institute; Abelard-Schuman.

15

Social Security Benefits

PREVIEW

As a result of an automobile accident, Tom Fowler hovered near death for seemingly endless weeks. As his strength slowly returned, he had time to contemplate what the course of events might have been had he not recovered. His hospitalization and medical and surgical insurance would have covered the cost of his stay in the hospital.

A long-established policy of the company for which he worked had been to pay the salaries of employees who were ill; hence, he had no fear of his income suddenly stopping. But, if he had not recovered, how would his wife have managed without his salary? What would become of Tom, Jr., who was a sophomore in high school, and of Nancy, who was in the fifth grade?

373

As these thoughts flashed through his mind, it occurred to him that deductions had been made weekly from his salary for some item called "OASI." Although he had made some bitter remarks on more than one occasion concerning this "loss" of income, he had never investigated the purpose these deductions served. Vaguely, Tom realized that they concerned his receiving some money after he reached the age of 65, but other than that he was completely in the dark concerning what other benefits he might receive. Since the OA in the OASI probably represented "old age," he wondered whether the remaining letters might not refer to benefits that his family would receive in the event of his death. This was a matter he was determined to investigate as soon as he was back on his feet.

For Class Discussion

1. What do the letters OASI represent?

2. What per cent of an employee's salary is deducted for Social Security?

3. Who else pays for this insurance other than the employee? What per cent does this other person pay?

4. Is an employee's contribution to Social Security based on his entire salary? Explain.

5. By what names other than OASI is this insurance called?

6. Can persons under 65 years of age benefit from the Social Security law? Explain.

7. Who, other than the insured, receive benefits at the time the insured reaches the age of 65?

8. Would Tom Fowler's wife and children have received any benefits under the Social Security law had Tom not recovered? If so, for what period of time would they have received these benefits?

Concerning This Chapter

In 1935, only 1 out of every 10 persons over the age of 65 was able to support himself without some financial assistance from relatives, private charities, or Government charities. To remedy this condition, the Social Security Act was passed in 1935, to provide for the payment of insurance benefits to "covered" employees who had reached the age of 65. By 1975, there will be over 20 million Americans aged 65 or over; 16 million, or 8 out of every

10 of these, will receive Social Security benefits. Most of these persons will be able to support themselves rather than be dependent on relatives or charitable organizations for financial help.

This Federal Act is known by various names. The most widely used of these names are:

1. Social Security
2. Federal Old Age Benefits (FOAB)
3. Federal Old-Age and Survivors Insurance (FOASI)
4. Federal Insurance Contributions Act (FICA)

In Chapter 7 you learned that through 1959 an employee pays $2\frac{1}{4}\%$ of his salary for the cost of the benefits that he will receive under this law. To this, his employer adds another $2\frac{1}{4}\%$ and forwards the total amount to the United States Treasury. The purpose of this chapter is to acquaint you with most of the important benefits that an employee is entitled to if he is covered by this insurance. You will learn that not only will the insured receive benefits at the time he reaches age 65 but that his wife and some of his children may also receive benefits. In the event of the death of a "covered" worker, his wife and children receive monthly benefits immediately, irrespective of the age of the deceased. Just how large these payments are and how they are computed will be shown in the course of this chapter.

Terms You Should Know

The word *covered* appeared frequently in the preceding paragraphs. There are two types of insurance coverage under the Social Security Act. A person can be either *fully insured* or *currently insured*. To understand these terms, it is necessary first to explain the meaning of the phrase: *a quarter of coverage.*

Should an employee earn at least $50 during the 3-month period January, February, and March and pay Social Security taxes during that period, he would be credited with *1 quarter of coverage.* This is true for any of the 4 periods shown in the chart.

FOUR
CALENDAR
QUARTERS

JAN FEB MAR APR MAY JUN JUL AUG SEP OCT NOV DEC

Thus, in a period of 1 year it is possible for an employee to earn 4 quarters of coverage by earning at least $50 in each of the periods. To be *fully insured*, the employee must have at least 40 quarters of coverage. The law has a special provision, however, for those who will reach the age of 65 before 1971. These persons can be fully insured with less than 40 quarters of coverage. A person may be *currently insured*, though, with only 6 quarters of coverage if he earned them within the preceding 3 years. A person who is only currently insured is not entitled to any of the retirement benefits that a fully insured person would receive after the age of 65. The greatest value of being currently insured is the benefits that the wife and children would receive in the event of the death of the insured.

The computation of the benefits that the insured will receive is based on an amount called the *average monthly salary*. To find this monthly salary, the sum of all the insured's earnings under Social Security from age 22 to age 65, or whenever later he retires, is found. This number is divided by the total number of months in this period, thus giving the *average monthly salary*. It is important to remember (see Chapter 7) that at no time will the yearly earnings that enter into this sum be more than $4,200, for Social Security deductions are made only on the first $4,200 of the yearly salary. In order to help increase this monthly average, however, the law allows the worker to drop the 5 years in which he earned his lowest salary. Other provisions are also made for those who are disabled, so that their average salary will not drop too low.

UNIT 1   **Computing Primary Benefits**

When the insured reaches the age of 65 and retires, he will receive monthly payments from the Government in return for all the contributions that he has made. Each of his monthly payments is called the *primary benefit*. It is computed in the following way:

55% of the first $110 of the average monthly salary
plus   20% of the remaining amount

Example 1

Find the primary benefit of a person whose average monthly salary is $275.

Solution:

$$55\% \text{ of } \$110 = \$60.50$$
$$+ \quad 20\% \text{ of } \$165 = \quad 33.00$$
$$\overline{\text{Primary Benefit} = \$93.50}$$

Explanation: From the average monthly salary of $275, $110 is subtracted; $165 remains. Hence, 20% of the amount over $110 would be 20% of $165.

It is important to note that at no time can the average monthly salary be larger than $350, for at no time are the contributions taken from more than $4,200 of a person's yearly salary. Thus, if $4,200 is the largest yearly salary from which deductions are taken for Social Security, then $4,200 ÷ 12, or $350, is the largest monthly salary.

Example 2

Find the primary benefit if the average monthly salary is $86.42.

Solution:

$$55\% \text{ of } \$86.42 = \$47.53$$
$$\text{Primary Benefit} = \$47.60$$

Explanation: Since the average monthly salary is less than $110, then 55% of the entire average monthly salary of $86.42 is determined. If the number of cents in the monthly benefit is not an exact tenth of a dollar, that amount is always changed to the next higher 10-cent value. In this example, 53 cents was changed to 60 cents.

If the primary benefit is found to be less than $30, the insured will receive $30. The law requires that the primary benefit be at least $30.

LEARNING EXERCISES

A. Find the primary benefit on each of the following salaries.

No.	Average Monthly Salary	Primary Benefit	No.	Average Monthly Salary	Primary Benefit
1	$200	$xxx	7	$ 42.00	$xxx
2	240	xxx	8	84.73	xxx
3	310	xxx	9	52.84	xxx
4	165	xxx	10	173.42	xxx
5	80	xxx	11	268.74	xxx
6	67	xxx	12	347.18	xxx

B. *Problems to Be Solved*   ~~Work Thru~~ .

1. What is the largest primary benefit that an insured can receive? Show all the computations necessary to arrive at your result.

2. During the months of January, February, and March, Jack Cahill earned \$462.57 in employment covered by Social Security. In April, May, and June, his total earnings were \$43.95; in July, August, and September, \$675.43; and in October, November, and December, \$63.25. How many quarters of coverage did Mr. Cahill earn that year?

3. During her summer vacation, Catherine Rawlings earned \$195.24 in June, \$227.56 in July, \$210.84 in August, and \$94.62 in September. How many quarters of coverage did Catherine earn that summer?

4. Explain how it would be possible for a person to be currently insured but not fully insured.

5. Explain how it would be possible for a person to be fully insured but not currently insured.

6. Can a person be both currently insured and fully insured? Explain.

UNIT **2**   **Computing Family Benefits After the Retirement of the Insured**

Not only will the insured himself, if he retires when he reaches the age of 65, receive monthly benefits from the Government, but also his wife, if she is at least 62 years of age, and dependent children, if they are under 18. All monthly payments to the various members of the family are computed on the basis of the primary benefit. Hence, it is important to understand thoroughly the method for determining the primary benefit that was explained in Unit 1. Retirement payments are made to the worker and to the members of his family only if the worker is fully insured. If the worker retires at age 65, Social Security benefits are paid to his family in accordance with the table on page 379.

In 1956, the Social Security law was amended so that disabled children, no matter what their age may be, are entitled to monthly benefits if the father or the mother is receiving benefits. This is true,

---

Monthly Retirement Payments

Person	Payment
Retired Worker	Primary Benefit
Wife, 65 or over	1/2 of the Primary Benefit
Child, under 18	1/2 of the Primary Benefit
Wife, regardless of age, if caring for a child entitled to benefits	1/2 of the Primary Benefits

---

however, only if the child was disabled before reaching his 18th birthday.

Example 1

Find the total monthly payment received by a family if the wife is taking care of a child who is under 18. The average monthly salary of the husband computed at the time of his retirement was $250.

Solution: Primary Benefit = $(55\% \times \$110) + (20\% \times \$140)$

$$= \$60.50 + \$28.00$$
$$= \$88.50$$

Husband's Benefit = $ 88.50

Wife's Benefit = 44.30 ($\frac{1}{2} \times \$88.50$)

  + Child's Benefit = 44.30 ($\frac{1}{2} \times \$88.50$)

Total Payment = $177.10

Explanation: According to the table, both the wife's and the child's benefits were ½ of the primary benefit of $88.50. Hence, each of their benefits was $44.25, which was changed to $44.30 in accordance with the regulation described on page 377.

The maximum amount of benefits that any one family can receive is $200. This maximum may be even lower. If the total monthly payment to one family is greater than 80% of the average monthly salary of the worker, then the family would receive no more than 80% of that average monthly salary. Thus, in Example 1, the total monthly benefit was $177.10. Since the $177.10 is less than both the $200 requirement and the 80% of the average monthly salary requirement, the family will receive the $177.10. Rarely does it occur that the family allotment is greater than either of these requirements.

Under the 1956 amendment to the Social Security law, the wife of a retired worker may apply for monthly benefits when she reaches the age of 62. If she does so, her monthly benefits would be only 75% of the amount she would receive had she waited until age 65.

Example 2

When Thomas Beatley retired at age 65, his average monthly salary was $312.50. When his wife became 62 years old, she applied for her Social Security benefits. What was the total amount of monthly benefits received by Mr. Beatley and his wife?

Solution: Primary Benefit $= (55\% \times \$110) + (20\% \times 202.50)$

$$= \quad \$60.50 \quad + \quad \$40.50$$

$$= \$101.00$$

Mr. Beatley's Benefit $= \$101$

Mrs. Beatley's Benefit $= 75\%$ of ($\frac{1}{2}$ of $\$101$)

$$= \tfrac{3}{4} \times \tfrac{1}{2} \times \$101$$

$$= \$\tfrac{303}{8}$$

$$= \$37.875, \text{ or } \$37.90$$

Total Benefits $= \$101 + \$37.90$

$$= \$138.90$$

Explanation: The amount that Mrs. Beatley would have received had she applied for Social Security benefits at age 65 would have been $\frac{1}{2}$ of the primary benefit, or $\frac{1}{2}$ of $101, or $50.50. As she was only 62 when she applied for her benefits, she received only 75% of this amount, or $37.90. If Mrs. Beatley had decided to retire at some other time between her 62d and her 65th birthdays, her monthly benefit would have been somewhat higher than the $37.90 but not so high as $50.50.

As noted in the explanation of Example 2, a woman may apply for her monthly benefits at any time after reaching the age of 62. Between the ages of 62 and 65, however, the size of her payment will vary between 75% of the amount she would receive at age 65 and 100% of that amount, depending on her exact age at the time she files her application. If she herself had been a working woman and was fully insured, she may apply for monthly benefits at age 62 rather than wait until age 65. Her payments, however, would be only 80% of what she would have received had she waited until age 65. If, as a working woman, she retires at any time between age 62 and age 65, the size of her benefit will vary between 80% of her primary benefit and 100% of her primary benefit, depending, as before, on her exact age at retirement.

LEARNING EXERCISES

Find the monthly allotments to each of the following families.

No.	Average Monthly Salary	Wife, 65 or over	Number of Children under Age 18	Monthly Benefit
1	$220.00	Yes	None	$xxx
2	180.00	Yes	None	xxx
3	137.26	Yes	None	xxx
4	280.00	Yes	One	xxx
5	305.72	Yes	One	xxx
6	260.00	No wife living	One	xxx
7	185.64	No wife living	One	xxx
8	240.00	Wife under 62	None	xxx
9	300.56	Wife under 62	One	xxx
10	334.18	Wife under 62	Two	xxx

UNIT 3 **Computing Survivors Benefits in the Event of the Death of the Insured**

Social Security deductions from an employee's salary have a twofold purpose: (1) retirement benefits, and (2) survivors benefits.

In Unit 2, you learned how to compute the benefits that a covered worker would receive at the time of his retirement at age 65. In this unit, you will examine the benefits that an employee's family would receive in the event of his death. When the worker dies, both his wife and children will receive monthly payments in accordance with the following table.

Monthly Survivors Payments

Person	Payment
Widow, age 62 or over	3/4 of the Primary Benefit
Widow, under 62, if any child is under 18	3/4 of the Primary Benefit
If only one dependent child under 18	3/4 of the Primary Benefit
If more than one child under 18	1/2 of the Primary Benefit*
Additional amount to be divided equally among all children under 18	1/4 of the Primary Benefit

Each child is entitled to $\frac{1}{2}$ of the primary benefit.

The widow, if she is under 62 years of age, will receive her monthly payment *only* if there is a child under the age of 18. In addition, should she be employed, her monthly allotment may be reduced. This will depend on the amount she is earning. At the time of her husband's death, the widow also receives a lump-sum payment called a *death benefit*, equal to three times the primary benefit, but not more than $255.

In order that his dependents may receive the death benefit and all survivors benefits, the worker had to be fully insured. If he was only currently insured at the time of his death, his widow would not be entitled to any survivors benefits other than death benefits, irrespective of her age, unless there was a disabled child in her care or a child under 18 years old.

Example 1

When Bill Edwards died, his wife was 35 and his two children were 12 and 14 years of age, respectively. If his average monthly salary had been $275, what survivors benefits would his family receive? Mr. Edwards was fully insured at the time of his death.

Solution: Primary Benefit = (55% × $110) + (20% × $165)

$$= \$60.50 + \$33.00$$

Primary Benefit = $93.50

Survivors Benefits

Widow's Benefit = $ 70.20 ($\frac{3}{4}$ × $93.50)

Benefit for Child of 12 = 46.80 ($\frac{1}{2}$ × $93.50)

Benefit for Child of 14 = 46.80 ($\frac{1}{2}$ × $93.50)

+Additional $\frac{1}{4}$ for both children = 23.40 ($\frac{1}{4}$ × $93.50)

Total Family Benefit = $187.20

The family will receive this benefit until the older child reaches the age of 18. This will be in 4 years. The family benefit will then be reduced by $46.80, which is the payment that this child is receiving. When the older child is 18, the younger child will be 16; hence, for 2 additional years, the family will receive $140.40 ($187.20 − $46.80). After this, as the children will have reached the age of 18, the family will receive nothing until Mrs. Edwards reaches the age of 62. At that time her monthly payments will begin again.

At the time of Mr. Edwards' death, the death benefit was computed at 3 times the primary benefit of $93.50. Although this product is $280.50, the family received only $255, for $255 is the largest lump-sum payment provided for under the Social Security law.

Example 2

Compute the benefits due the family of a deceased worker if his average monthly salary was $195. The age of his wife at the time of his death was 37, and the ages of his three children were 10, 14, and 15 years, respectively. The deceased worker was only currently insured at the time of his death.

Solution: Primary Benefit = (55% × $110) + (20% × $85)

$$= \qquad \$60.50 \qquad + \qquad \$17$$

$$= \$77.50$$

Death Payment = 3 × $77.50

$$= \$232.50$$

Widow's Benefit =	$ 58.20	($\frac{3}{4}$ × $77.50 = $58.13)
Benefit for Child of 15 =	38.80	($\frac{1}{2}$ × $77.50 = 38.75)
Benefit for Child of 14 =	38.80	($\frac{1}{2}$ × $77.50 = 38.75)
Benefit for Child of 10 =	38.80	($\frac{1}{2}$ × $77.50 = 38.75)
+Additional $\frac{1}{4}$ for All Children =	19.40	($\frac{1}{4}$ × $77.50 = 19.38)
Family Benefit =	$194.00	

On page 379 you learned that a family allotment can never be more than 80% of the average monthly salary. In this case, 80% of $195 is $156.

Therefore,

Family Benefit for First 3 Years = $156

Family Benefit for Next 1 Year = $155.20 ($194 − $38.80)

Family Benefit for Next 4 Years = $116.40 ($155.20 − $38.80)

After this, the family receives nothing.

If the wife is age 62 or over at the time of her husband's death, she will receive both the death payment and a widow's benefit. If there are children under the age of 18, they will receive benefits in accordance with the method described in Examples 1 and 2. The widow can receive a widow's benefit after the age of 62 only if the husband was fully insured or if she has dependent children.

LEARNING EXERCISES

In the problems that follow, it is assumed that the employee is both fully insured and currently insured, so that he is entitled to all the Social Security benefits.

A. Find the death payment and the widow's monthly benefit in each of the following cases. If the widow is not entitled to her monthly benefits immediately, state how long she will have to wait before she receives them. There are no children under the age of 18 in any of the families.

for Friday

No.	Average Monthly Salary	Age of Widow	Death Payment	Widow's Benefit
1	$190.00	67	$xxx	$xxx
2	215.00	64	xxx	xxx
3	86.23	69	xxx	xxx
4	324.46	65	xxx	xxx
5	295.06	60	xxx	xxx
6	312.51	54	xxx	xxx

B. Compute the benefits that the family will receive at the death of the worker in each of the following problems.

No.	Average Monthly Salary	Age of Widow	No. of Children	Ages of Children	Death Payment	Family Benefit
1	$260.00	34	1	12	$xxx	$xxx
2	180.00	42	1	16	xxx	xxx
3	346.72	38	1	15	xxx	xxx
4	245.00	36	2	14, 12	xxx	xxx
5	197.43	40	2	16, 10	xxx	xxx
6	184.16	26	2	5, 1	xxx	xxx
7	320.00	35	2	17, 15	xxx	xxx
8	240.00	37	3	15, 14, 11	xxx	xxx
9	186.00	31	3	10, 8, 3	xxx	xxx
10	342.00	36	3	19, 16, 14	xxx	xxx

C. *Problems to Be Solved*

1. Martin Thomas retired at age 66. His wife was 65 at the time. The Social Security Agency found that his average monthly salary had been $276.28. Mr. Thomas died at age 72, being survived by his wife. Describe the Social Security benefits that both Mr. Thomas and his wife received.

2. Gregory Kilburn died at age 57. Mrs. Kilburn was 56 at the time. When she filed her claim at the Social Security office, it was found that Mr. Kilburn's monthly income had been $312.47. Describe Mrs. Kilburn's benefits.

3. When Mr. Tracy died on June 17, he was survived by a wife aged

39 and a son who had celebrated his 16th birthday on April 30 of that year. If Mr. Tracy's average monthly income had been $348.26, how much did the benefits received by his family total?

4. Frank Atwood died at age 57, leaving a wife aged 52 and a completely disabled son, Clarence, aged 24. Clarence had been injured at age 5 and would never be able to provide for himself. Social Security records showed that Mr. Atwood's average monthly income was $317.18. Compute the benefits that Frank Atwood's wife and son would receive.

UNIT 4   What Have You Learned?

SECTION 1   Understanding Terms

Do you know the meaning of each of the following terms? If not, review the pages in parentheses.
1. Fully insured (Page 376)
2. Currently insured (Page 376)
3. A quarter of coverage (Page 375)
4. Primary benefit (Page 376)
5. Average monthly salary (Page 376)
6. Survivors benefits (Pages 381–382)
7. Maximum family benefit (Page 379)

SECTION 2   Review Problems

1. Find the primary benefit in each of the following cases, if the average monthly salary is as indicated: (Pages 376–377.)
    a. $265   b. $316.75   c. $82.64   d. $48.93
2. During the year, Mr. Torrence was employed as a teacher in a state where teaching was not covered by Social Security. When school recessed for vacation on June 22, he went to work in a chemical plant, where he earned $92.74 a week. If he held this position until August 27, how many quarters of coverage did he earn? (Pages 375–376.)
3. What are the retirement benefits for both a husband and his wife if both are over 65 and the wife did not claim her benefits until age 65? The husband's average monthly salary was $287.54. (Pages 378–379.)

4. A wife, aged 62, claimed her monthly benefits at the same time that her husband claimed his. If his average monthly income was $196.28, how large was her allotment? (Pages 378–380.)

5. At 65, Mr. Kenyon claimed his retirement benefits. His wife was 50 at the time, and he had one son aged 15.

a. If Mr. Kenyon's average monthly salary was $207.14, compute the benefits that the family received. (Pages 378–379.)

b. If Mr. Kenyon's son had been completely disabled since birth, how would that have affected the amount of benefits just computed? (Pages 378–379.)

6. Mrs. Templeton was 63 when her husband died. If Mr. Templeton had been receiving Social Security benefits based on an average monthly salary of $296.19, how much would Mrs. Templeton receive after his death? (Page 381.)

7. Mr. Drury died, leaving a wife of 46 but no children. If his average monthly salary had been $324.41, compute any benefits Mrs. Drury would receive. (Pages 381–382.)

8. Carl Johnson died at age 49, leaving his wife aged 47 and two children 20 and 15 years of age. When Mrs. Johnson filed her claim at the Social Security office, it was found that her husband's average monthly income had been $328.32. Compute the benefits that the family would receive. (Pages 381–382.)

9. Mrs. Merkle was left with the care of two children, Fred, aged 14, and Ruth, aged 10, at the death of her husband. Records at the Social Security office showed that Mr. Merkle's average monthly salary had been $295.80.

a. Compute the benefits that the Merkle family would receive. (Pages 381–382.)

b. If Mr. Merkle's average monthly salary had been $345.80, compute the benefits that the family would receive. (Page 379.)

SECTION 3   Testing Your Understanding

40 Minutes

1. Find the primary benefit in each of the following cases if the average monthly wage is as indicated:

a. $140   **b.** $89.56   **c.** $297.43

2. How many quarters of coverage would a person receive if he worked only during the following months under covered employment? The salary received was: February, $76.40; March, $186.25; June, $45.26; August, $242.70; September, $236.84; November, $356.25.

3. Mr. Egan is 72 and his wife, 66. Both are receiving Social Security payments. Mrs. Egan did not apply for her benefit until age 65.

a. If Mr. Egan's average monthly salary had been $195.90, how much did each receive?

b. What will Mrs. Egan's monthly allotment be after her husband dies?

4. As soon as Mrs. Farrow reached the age of 62, she applied for her Social Security benefit under her husband's coverage. If Mr. Farrow had been receiving his payment based on an average monthly salary of $163.56, how much will Mrs. Farrow receive?

5. A worker whose average monthly salary was $286.57 died, leaving a wife, aged 42, and a daughter, aged 10.

a. Compute the benefits that the family will receive.

b. If the daughter was so disabled that she would never be able to work, how would that affect the benefits just computed?

6. At the time of Paul Kelton's death his wife was 27 years of age and his two children, 5 and 2. His average monthly income had been $295. Compute the benefits that his family would receive.

UNIT 5   General Review

SECTION 1   To Improve Your Speed and Accuracy

1. Addition:

a. 56,394	**b.** $3,578.05	**c.** $139\frac{3}{5}$
82,497	604.68	$265\frac{1}{2}$
39,825	956.73	$154\frac{3}{10}$
74,706	39.27	
63,869	9,485.82	

d. $3,582 + $476.75 + $8.07 + $175 + $.98

e. $24\frac{3}{8} + 57\frac{3}{4} + 15\frac{1}{2} + 34\frac{5}{8}$

2. Subtraction:

a. 43,006	**b.** $75,000.00	**c.** $43\frac{5}{6}$
27,208	8,283.76	$27\frac{3}{4}$

d. $25 − $19.98

e. $36 − 18\frac{2}{3}$

3. Multiplication: Check your answers by casting out 9's.
    a. 483 × 57   b. 5,608 × 83   c. 27,845 × 609
    d. $8.54 × 1.08   e. $475.25 × .92
4. Division: Check your answers by casting out 9's.
    a. 24,766 ÷ 58   b. 63,005 ÷ 204   c. $1,000 ÷ .065
    d. 74.38 ÷ 8.6   e. .0493 ÷ .75

SECTION 2   Do You Remember These?

1. Change the following per cent values to fractions.
    a. $33\frac{1}{3}\%$ b. $87\frac{1}{2}\%$ c. $62\frac{1}{2}\%$ d. $83\frac{1}{3}\%$

2. Find the average of the following weekly salaries: $67.28; $85.72; $73.95; $123.56; $96.15; $84.25; $104.95.

3. How much change is given when a $10 bill is offered in payment of an article that sells for $3.98?

4. What is the cost of 2 dozen ties at $1.98 a tie?

5. What is the cost of 7,500 wire hangers at $9.50 per M?

6. At sight, give the cost of each of the following purchases:
    a. 18 gals. @ $66\frac{2}{3}$¢   b. 24 lbs. @ $37\frac{1}{2}$¢   c. 36 yds. @ 75¢

7. $12 is what per cent more than $10?

8. $15 is what per cent less than $18?

9. A machine that was originally worth $5,625 now has a scrap value of $250. How much has it depreciated over the years?

10. At $2.56 an hour, what is the salary of a man who worked $36\frac{1}{2}$ hours during a week?

11. If the catalogue price of a chair is $58.85, less 35%, what is the net price?

12. Discounts of 25% and 10% are given off the list price of $37.50. What is the net price?

13. An article that was purchased at $24.50 was sold for $34.50. What was the per cent of markup if based on the retail?

14. $350 was borrowed for 80 days at a 4% interest rate. What was the interest on this loan?

15. A man borrowed $600 from a bank for 120 days at a 5% discount rate. What were the proceeds that he received?

NEW YORK STOCK EXCHANGE
CENSUS OF SHAREOWNERS

ADULT SHAREOWNERS BY AGE

26.9%
24.4%
20.5%
15.0%
13.2%

YEARS 21-34 35-44 45-54 55-64 65 and Over

16

Stock Purchases
and Stock Sales

PREVIEW

On reaching the age of 25, Robert Peters inherited $25,000 that
had been willed to him by his uncle several years earlier. He considered various ways in which this inheritance could be used to
earn money for him. Among the investments he considered was
the possibility of depositing the money either in a bank or in a
savings and loan association. Because of the relatively small return paid by banks and savings and loan associations, he sought
other investments that might yield him a greater profit.

389

The possibility of starting his own business was suggested to him; but this, too, he put aside, for he realized that he lacked the training and experience needed to conduct the enterprises that were of interest to him.

After much deliberation, Robert finally decided that it would be wisest for him to become a part owner of an established firm that was managed by skilled men. As a shareholder in a corporation, not only would he receive a share of the profits of the company, but also, as the company grew, so, too, would the value of his investment grow.

Although he had now decided how to invest his money, he was faced with the even larger problem of where to invest it. There are many, many thousands of companies all over the United States in which he could become a part owner. Which of these would yield the largest return, with the greatest degree of safety to his investment, was the question he had to answer.

For Class Discussion

1. What is meant by the phrase, "a person is a shareholder in a company"?

2. What is the name of the certificate that shows that a person is part owner of a company?

3. If the company in which Mr. Peters finally invested his money made no profit during the year, how much return would he probably receive on his investment?

4. If the company in which Robert Peters invested his money should become bankrupt, what will become of the money he invested?

5. Since Robert Peters and others run the risk of losing their investments, what advantages are there for them to become shareholders in a company?

6. What name is given to that part of the company's profit that is divided among the shareholders?

7. What can Robert Peters do if he should decide that he no longer wishes to be a part owner of the company in which he has invested his money?

8. What is the name that is applied to men who purchase and sell shares of a company for other people?

Terms You Should Know

One of the most common ways by which individuals may become part owners of a corporation is by buying certificates called *shares of stock.* These certificates indicate that the purchaser owns a fractional part of the company. Purchasers of stock are called *stockholders*. A photograph of a stock certificate appears here.

You will notice that the word "common" appears on this certificate. Although there is much similarity among the several kinds of stock that a company may issue, broadly speaking, stocks are divided into two major groups: *preferred stock* and *common stock*. Usually, the preferred stockholder is guaranteed a certain per cent of his investment each year if the company earns a profit that year. In any event, the preferred stockholder will receive his share of the profits before any of that year's profit is distributed among the common stockholders. If there is no money left to be distributed among the owners of common stock, they will receive none that year. On the other hand, should the company have a very prosperous year, then the common stockholders may gain more than the preferred stockholders, whose share of the profit is usually a fixed per cent. Also, usually, only the owners of common stock have the right to vote for those who will be the directors of the company.

The original value placed on a share of stock by the directors of the company is called the *par value* of the stock. This value is determined by the amount of money that the company needs to raise in order to begin its business. Thus, the inventor of an unbreakable baseball bat may feel that he needs $50,000 to build a factory to manufacture his product. To raise the money, he may print 5,000 stock certificates worth a *par value* of $10 each. This is the value that the inventor has marked on the stock for its first sale. If the company prospers, the value of the stock will increase. If no one is interested in purchasing unbreakable baseball bats, then the value of the stock will decrease.

Since very few stocks, if any, sell at their par value after they have been sold by the company, many common stocks are now issued at *no par value* or at a par value of $1 or $2. In this way, as you will learn later, it is possible to save money on Federal taxes. The value of each share of stock is determined by the company directors at the time the stock is first sold. After the stock is issued, its value will depend on how much a buyer is willing to pay for it or how little a seller is willing to take to part with it.

Concerning This Chapter

This chapter is designed to acquaint you with a few of the basic principles connected with the purchase and sale of stocks. As approximately 8 million people own some form of stock, it is likely that you may some day consider this means of investing money. In the following pages, you will learn how to interpret stock market quotations as they appear on the financial pages of a newspaper, how to determine broker's fees and Federal taxes and state taxes on the purchase or sale of stocks, and how to compute the rate of return on an investment in stocks.

UNIT 1   **Computing Dividends on Preferred and Common Stock**

The profits on each share of stock that are distributed among the stockholders is called the *dividend* on the stock. Depending on the policy of the company, these dividends are commonly distributed either quarterly (four times a year), semiannually (twice a year), or annually (once a year). The preferred stockholders receive their promised share of any profits that the company may have made during the year. If there is any profit remaining, it is usually divided so that each share of common stock receives exactly the same amount. The promised yearly rate of interest on preferred stock is based on the par value of the stock, although the stock is rarely purchased at that value.

Business Transaction 1: Thomas Kleinert purchased 80 shares of 5% preferred stock of the Commercial Transport Corporation at $83.50 a share. The par value of the stock is $100. That year the company earned enough profit to distribute its quarterly dividend among its 5% preferred stockholders. How large was Mr. Kleinert's quarterly dividend?

Solution: Since the dividends are determined on the par value ($100) of the stock, then the dividend on 1 share of stock would be 5% of $100, or $5. Hence, Mr. Kleinert's 80 shares would earn for him 80 × $5, or $400, for the entire year. His quarterly dividend, therefore, would have been $\frac{1}{4}$ of this amount, or $100.

Outline: Yearly Dividend on 1 Share = 5% × $100
$$= \$5$$
Yearly Dividend on 80 Shares = 80 × $5
$$= \$400$$
Quarterly Dividend on 80 Shares = $\frac{1}{4}$ × $400
$$= \$100$$

It is important to note that, in finding the dividend, the par value of the preferred stock was used, *not* the cost of $83.50.

Business Transaction 2: After distributing the dividends on the preferred stock, the Commercial Transport Corporation found that it had enough profit left over to distribute a quarterly dividend of $18\frac{1}{2}$ cents on each share of common stock. If Mr. Kleinert owned 65 shares of common stock, how large a dividend check did he receive on these shares?

Solution: Quarterly Dividend = 65 × $18\frac{1}{2}$¢
$$= \$12.02\tfrac{1}{2}, \text{ or } \$12.03$$

LEARNING EXERCISES

A. Find the dividends that the owners of the following shares of common stock would receive.

No.	Number of Shares	Dividend and Period	Total Dividends
1	50	25¢ Quarterly	$xxx
2	75	30¢ Semiannually	xxx
3	250	$1.40 Annually	xxx
4	125	1\frac{1}{2}$ Quarterly	xxx
5	385	3\frac{3}{4}$ Annually	xxx
6	350	62$\frac{1}{2}$¢ Quarterly	xxx
7	250	$\frac{3}{4}$ Extra Dividend	xxx
8	2,340	37$\frac{1}{2}$¢ Extra Dividend	xxx

B. Find the dividends that the owners of the following shares of preferred stock would receive for the period shown.

No.	Type of Preferred	Par Value	Number of Shares	Period	Total Dividends
1	5%	$100	60	Semian.	$xxx
2	4%	100	200	Quarterly	xxx
3	3%	80	75	Semian.	xxx
4	7%	50	250	Quarterly	xxx
5	4½%	50	100	Annually	xxx
6	5½%	20	375	Semian.	xxx
7	6¼%	25	2,000	Quarterly	xxx
8	5¾%	10	925	Semian.	xxx

C. *Problems to Be Solved*

1. Robert Porter bought 100 shares of 4½% preferred stock of the Transcontinental Transport Company at $92.75 a share. If the par value of the stock is $100 a share, what quarterly dividends did he receive?

2. Gilbert Thomas owned 75 shares of Mid-Ocean Oil common stock and 135 shares of its 5% $50 par-value preferred stock. At its quarterly meeting, the Board of Directors of the company declared a dividend on the preferred stock and a 35 cent dividend on each share of common stock. What was the total amount of dividends that Mr. Thomas received on his investment?

3. On July 23, Donald Richards purchased 350 shares of Colgate Products 4% preferred stock at $56.75. The par value of the stock is $50. At the following quarterly meeting, the Board of Directors declared the regular dividend on the preferred stock plus an extra dividend of 27 cents on each share of the stock. How large was the dividend check that Mr. Richards received?

4. General Allied Corporation declared its regular semiannual dividend on its 5¾% preferred stock, par value $100, and also a dividend of $1.60 on its common stock. How much would Mr. Bricker receive on 975 shares of preferred stock and 352 shares of common stock?

UNIT 2 | **Understanding the Newspaper Report of Stock-Market Quotations**

Most stocks are bought or sold through agents called *stockbrokers*. Stockbrokers perform duties similar to those of the commission merchants about whom you studied earlier. Whereas commission merchants buy or sell merchandise, such as vegetables, fruits, clothing, furniture, and so on, stockbrokers deal only in stock. Persons who wish to buy shares of stock in a certain company get in touch with their brokers. The brokers, in turn, make the purchases through a central agency where other brokers gather to buy or sell stock. The largest of these agencies is called the New York Stock Exchange, which handles about 85% of all the business that is done in stock trading in the United States. Not all stocks can be bought or sold at this exchange. Only those stocks can be traded here that have been approved by the stockbrokers who are members of the New York Stock Exchange.

The American Stock Exchange is another large exchange in the city of New York. Many stocks that are not listed on the New York Stock Exchange can be bought and sold at the American Stock Exchange. Other exchanges are located in Chicago, Philadelphia, New Orleans, Los Angeles, Toronto, and Montreal.

Because of the public interest in the value of stocks, the financial

—1957— High.	Low.	Stock and Div. in Dollars	Sls. 100s.	First.	High.	Low.	Last.	Net Chge
		D						
17⅜	12	DAN RIV M .80a	18	12⅜	12⅜	12⅛	12⅛	+ ⅛
55	47½	Dana Cp 3	8	49	49¼	49	49	+ 1
27⅛	22	Daystrom 1.20 .	19	24½	24½	24	24¼	− ½
49¼	44⅛	Day P&L 2.20...	1	47½	47½	47½	47½	− ½
29	20¼	Dayt Rub 1.40r.	27	27⅝	28⅛	27	28	+ ⅞
16⅜	14	Decca Rec 1 ..	18	14¼	14¼	14	14	− ¼
34⅞	25½	Deere 1¾e ...	23	25¾	25⅞	25½	25¾	+ ⅛
35⅜	29⅞	Deere pf 1.40 ..	6	31⅛	31¼	31⅛	31¼	+ ⅛
31¼	26¼	Del & Hud 1.60.	10	28	28¼	28	28¼	+ ¾
25¾	18¼	Del L&W 1⅞t..	24	21	21⅝	21	21½	+ ⅞
47	36⅞	Del P&L 1.60...	10	40½	40½	40½	40½	− ½
48	38⅛	Den & RGW 2½.	8	39⅝	39⅝	38½	39	+ ¼
36⅛	33⅞	Det Edis 1.80 ..	15	35	35	34⅞	35	+ ¼
19⅝	14⅛	Det Stl Cp 1 ...	27	18	18¼	17¾	18	+ ½
38	26¼	De Vilbiss 2	1	35⅞	35⅞	35⅞	35⅞	+ ½
60⅝	43½	Diam Alk 1½b.	15	50¾	51	50¼	50¾	+ ¾
44⅞	32½	Diam Mat 1.80.	6	35⅛	35½	35⅛	35½	+ ⅜
22⅜	17¼	Dia T Mot ½e..	3	20⅜	20⅝	20¼	20¼	+ ¼
16⅜	13⅜	Diana Str 1 ...	23	14¼	14⅜	14⅛	14¼	+ ⅛
39½	33¼	Dis C Seag 1.20a	17	33⅞	34¾	33⅞	34¾	+ 1⅛
13⅜	9	Divco Cp .60 ...	8	11¼	11½	11¼	11½	+ ⅜
60½	51¼	Dixie Cup 2 ...	2	52½	52½	52¼	52¼	+ 1
75	65	Dixie Cup pf 2½.	1	65	65	65	65	− ½
39¼	28¾	Dobeck 1.40	1	29¾	29¾	29¾	29¾	+ ¾
13	10⅛	Dr Pepper .60 ...	1	10½	10½	10½	10½	+ ⅜
16⅛	13⅛	Dome Min .70...	24	13⅜	13½	13⅛	13¼	+ ⅛
95⅝	72½	Doug Airc 2a ...	46	86½	87¼	85¼	86½	+ 1½
82⅞	57	Dow Chm 1.10r..	119	68½	69¼	68½	69⅛	+ 1¾
89½	49⅝	Dress Ind 3	29	84	85¼	83¾	85¼	+ 2
21⅜	17½	Drewrys 1.60 ...	2	18	18	18	18	+ ⅜
11¾	6¾	Duplan	22	7	7	7	7	+ ¼
237	188	duPont 4½e......	67	191	193	189½	192½	+ 1½
99½	89	duPont 3½ pf 3½	1	91⅛	91⅛	91⅛	91⅛	+ ⅛
38⅞	33	Duq Lt 2	26	34⅞	35¼	34¾	35¼	+ ⅝
54	49	Duq 4.20 pf 2.10	z100	50	50⅛	50	50⅛	+ ⅛
17½	14½	DWG Cigar .80..	1	14⅞	14⅞	14⅞	14⅞	..
		E						
47⅜	36⅛	EAGLE P 2.20..	11	41	42	41	42	+ 1¼
57¼	43⅛	East Air L 1b..	22	48½	49¼	48¼	48⅜	+ ⅝
37¼	26½	East Cp 1.20b..	1	29	29	29	29	+ 1
48¼	29⅛	East S Stl 1½..	27	43¼	44	43	43½	+ 1½
100¾	75¾	East Kod 2.65e...	27	87	87¾	86½	87¾	+ 1⅜
170	154	East Kod pf 6...	z 50	157	157	157	157	..
65⅜	51½	Eaton Mfg 3.....	3	60⅝	61¾	60⅝	61¾	+ 1½
30	23¾	Edis Br Str 1.60.	4	24⅛	24⅛	24	24	..
50	36½	Ekco Pd 2b......	8	38½	38¾	38½	38½	..
21	16½	Elas Stop N 1a..	1	18¾	18¾	18¾	18¾	..
41⅜	33⅛	El Auto L 2a....	25	35½	36⅝	35½	36½	+ 1½
4⅞	3¼	El & Mus .12e...	74	3¼	3⅜	3¼	3⅜	+ ⅛
44½	32	El Stor Bat 1½e.	9	39¼	39¾	39	39½	+ ⅝
17⅜	14	Elgin Wch 1.....	1	14¾	14¾	14¾	14¾	+ ¼
29¼	21⅝	Elliott 1.20	15	28⅛	28⅛	27¾	28	+ ½
52½	44½	Elliott cv pf 2½.	2	51½	51½	51½	51½	+ ¼
59½	43	El Paso N G 2...	42	51¾	52¼	51⅝	52⅛	+ 1
39⅜	25¾	Emer El 1.40b...	7	25¾	26	25¾	26	− ⅝
13¼	7	Emer Rad .30r...	8	7⅜	7⅜	7⅛	7⅜	+ ⅛
31⅜	27½	Emp D El 1.60...	1	28½	28½	28½	28½	
34⅞	31⅞	End John 2......	5	32⅝	32⅝	32⅛	32½	+ ⅝
32½	25½	Equit Gas 1½...	16	28	28⅜	28	28⅛	+ ⅛
23½	20	Erie RR 1½.....	26	20⅛	20½	20⅛	20½	+ ⅜
86	76	Erie RR pf 5 ...	1	76	76	76	76	− 3½
29¼	21½	Evans Pd 1.60...	39	23	23⅜	23	23⅜	+ ⅜
20	15⅛	Eversharp 1.20 ..	7	17¼	17¼	17⅛	17¼	+ ⅛
96	62¼	Ex-Cell-O 2	14	83	84	82¼	83½	+ 2
		F						
49¼	38⅛	FAIR MOR 1.05e.	12	45⅞	46	45⅞	46	+ ⅜
15⅝	11	Fairch E ¼e.....	32	11¾	11⅞	11½	11¾	+ ¼
14⅞	10⅞	Fajardo S .65e...	1	11	11	11	11	..
20	16⅜	Falstaff Br 1....	1	16⅝	16⅝	16⅝	16⅝	+ ⅛
25½	22¼	Fam Fin 1½....	3	22½	22½	22½	22½	..
51½	31	Fansteel 1	11	43	43½	42⅝	43½	+ 1¼
7⅞	6½	Fawick .30e	12	7	7	6⅞	7	..
13¼	10¼	Fedd Quig .45r...	10	10¼	10⅜	10¼	10¼	..
41⅞	31¼	Fed Mogul 2.40..	18	37	37	36½	36⅞	+ ⅛
19⅛	13⅛	Fed Pac El .80...	17	16⅞	17⅝	16⅞	17⅝	+ 1
36⅞	29¾	Fed Pap Bd 1.80.	1	31⅜	31⅜	31⅜	31⅜	+ ⅜
37⅞	30½	Fed D Str 1.60..	35	31	31⅛	30⅞	31⅛	+ ⅝
10¼	8½	Felt & Tarr......	5	9⅛	9⅛	9	9	− ⅛
34⅜	25	Fenestra 2	6	27	27¼	26⅝	27	+ ½
39½	28¾	Ferro Cp 1.20e...	6	29½	29½	29¼	29½	+ ½
43	30¾	Fibre Pap ¾e...	19	31½	32½	31½	32	+ 1
61	45⅝	Fid P Fire 2....	13	46¼	47⅞	46¼	47⅞	+ 1⅝
30½	26⅛	Fifth Av Lin 2a..	2	26⅞	26⅞	26⅞	26⅞	+ ⅛
91¾	59½	Filtrol 1.80	44	62¾	65½	62½	64½	+ 3½
93	68	Firest 2.60a xd...	21	81¼	83	81¼	82½	+ 2⅞
106¾	102	Firest pf 4½....	z 20	102½	102½	102½	102½	..
61	49¼	First N Str 2a...	7	52	52¼	51½	52¼	+ ⅝
12¼	10⅝	Firth Cpt .60....	15	11⅝	11¾	11⅝	11⅝	..
41	34½	Flintkote 2.40b ..	21	36¾	37	36⅛	37	+ ⅝
21¾	13	Florerr Stv	3	13	13	13	13	− ⅛
54¾	41¾	Fla Pw 1.60.....	5	47	47	46½	46½	+ ¾
50¼	36¾	Fla P&L 1.20....	6	44⅛	44¼	43¾	44	+ ¼
62	50½	Food Fair 1b....	15	52	52	51½	51¾	+ ¼
77	51	Food Mach 2....	32	61¾	62¼	61	62¼	+ ¾
100	87	Food M pf 3¾..	z 40	87	87	87	87	− 1½
159	109	Food M pf 3¼..	z430	127	127	127	127	..
63⅜	51⅝	Ford Mot 1.80e..	179	60	60½	59¾	60½	+ 1
21⅛	16⅝	Forem Dair 1b...	28	17¾	17⅞	17⅝	17⅞	+ ⅛
41¾	31	Fost Wheel 1.60.	15	32	32¾	32	32½	+ 1
13⅞	12⅛	Frank Str .80....	1	12¼	12¼	12¼	12¼	..
97¼	78	Freept Sul 3.....	10	88½	88¾	87½	87½	+ ½
16¾	14	Froedt Cp 1.....	7	15¾	16¼	15¾	16¼	+ ¾
38⅜	25¼	Frue Tra 1.40b..	310	26	27⅛	25⅞	27	+ 1½

G

9⅛	6⅝	GABRIEL .45e ...	1	6¾	6¾	6¾	6¾	− ¼
40¾	28⅝	Gair Rbt 1½....	24	33⅝	34	33	34	+ ⅞
124	107¼	Gair pf 4½.....	z110	110	110	109	109	..
11¼	9⅜	Gamble Sk .60...	10	9⅞	10	9⅞	10	+ ⅛
32⅜	25⅝	Gamewell 1.60 ..	1	29½	29½	29½	29½	+ ⅜
9⅝	6	Gar Wood	6	8¼	8⅜	8¼	8⅜	+ ¼
38	30¾	Gardner Den 1½.	22	32¼	33	31¼	33	+ 2
53½	38	Garrett 2	17	49⅝	50⅜	49⅝	50⅜	+ 1⅜
16½	14¾	Gen Accept 1....	5	15¼	15¼	15	15	− ¼
29⅝	25⅜	Gen Am In .30e..	11	28	28¼	27¾	28¼	+ ½
71½	60¼	G Am Tran 2.80a.	8	61¾	62½	61¾	62¼	+ 1
10⅞	9	Gen Bak .60.....	4	10	10	9⅞	9⅞	..
34½	24½	G Bronze 1½b...	1	24⅞	24⅞	24⅞	24⅞	..
37¼	24⅝	Gen Cable 1.70e..	52	33	33¾	32¾	33¾	+ 1½
36⅞	30½	Gen Cigar 1.40...	1	36¾	36¾	36¾	36¾	..
17⅝	14½	Gen Contract .20r	4	15¼	15⅜	15¼	15¼	..
79¼	56⅝	Gen Dynam 3....	93	70¾	71⅞	70⅜	71⅝	+ 1⅞
53	45⅛	Gen Dynam wi...	55	47⅛	47⅞	47	47¾	+ 1⅛
65½	52¾	Gen Elec 2.....	204	55⅞	57	55¾	57	+ 1⅜
19	17	Gen Finan .80...	6	18	18	17⅞	17⅞	− ⅛
50⅝	43	Gen Fds .45h....	22	43¾	44½	43⅜	44½	+ 1½
10⅛	7	Gen Instru ⅜e...	5	7	7¼	7	7	..
71¾	61	Gen Mills 3.....	6	67⅛	68½	67⅛	68½	+ 1¼
122½	113	Gen Mills pf 5..z	50	113⅝	113⅝	113½	113½	− 1½
49¼	40¼	Gen Motor 1½e..	289	46¼	46⅞	46	46¾	+ ¾
124½	115½	Gen Mot pf 5....	4	119¼	119½	119¼	119¼	+ ½
101¼	91½	Gen Mot pf 3¾..	1	93	93	93	93	+ ¼
37⅞	31	Gen Out Ad 2a...	1	32¾	32¾	32¾	32¾	+ ¼
75¾	50¼	Gen P Cem 1.80..	9	69½	69¾	68¼	68¼	+ ¼
53½	36¾	Gen Prec 2.40....	45	37⅜	37⅜	36¾	36⅞	− ⅛
5⅜	4½	Gen Pub Sv .05e.	35	5⅛	5⅛	5	5⅛	+ ⅛
38½	34	Gen Pub U 1.90..	20	36	36⅞	36	36⅞	+ 1⅝
90¾	61½	Gen Ry Sig 2.40a	2	85¼	86	85¼	86	+ 1¼
46¾	34⅝	Gen Refrac 2b...	3	44¼	45	44¼	45	+ ⅞
29⅝	24½	Gen Shoe 1½....	6	25	25¼	25	25¼	+ ¼
35⅞	32½	Gen Stl Cast 1.80	7	33½	33½	32½	32¾	− 1¼
46	38	Gen Tel 1.20e....	50	40½	40⅝	40⅛	40¼	+ ¼
33⅛	29½	Gen Time 2......	3	31¼	31¾	31¼	31¾	+ ¾
66¾	50	Gen Tire 2b......	16	52	53¼	52	53¼	+ 2¼
86½	80¾	Gen Tire pf 5...	z150	81	81	80¾	80¾	− ¼
21½	96½	Gen Tire pf 4½.z	60	99¾	101	99¾	101	+ 2¼
37⅛	28½	Ga Pac new......	115	30	30⅜	29¼	30⅜	+ 1
52¼	46½	Gerber 1.40	1	46¾	46¾	46¾	46¾	..
61	41	Getty Oil 2¼t...	22	46¼	47	46¼	46½	+ ½

54½	40⅛	Gillette 2a	20	45½	46½	45½	46⅛	+ 1⅛
28⅝	23⅛	Gimbel 1.40	57	28¼	28½	27⅞	28⅜	+ ½
41⅛	34½	Glidden 2	14	35¼	35¼	34⅝	35⅛	+ ½
5⅜	3	Goebel Br.........	7	3⅛	3⅛	3	3⅛	..
160¼	153	Gold & S 6.......	20	156	156	156	156	..
89¼	66	Goodrich 2.20 ...	51	69	69⅞	68½	69⅞	+ 3⅜
81½	60	Goodyear 2.40 ...	33	71¾	73	71½	72¾	+ 2¼
36	29½	Gould Bat 1.70..	3	30	30¼	30	30¼	+ ½
60¼	44¾	Grace & Co 2.40.	27	56¾	57¼	56⅝	57	+ 1⅛
2⅝	1¾	Grah Paige	26	1¾	1¾	1¾	1¾	..
20⅝	11⅝	Granby M ½....	7	12	12	12	12	+ ⅜
36½	29½	Grand Un .60b...	11	31	31	31	31	+ ¼
51⅜	34	Gran C Stl 1¾e..	67	46½	47⅞	46	47⅞	+ 2⅛
45	35	Grant 2	8	35¾	36½	35¾	36¼	+ 1¼
7¾	5¾	Grays Rob	9	6	6	5⅞	5⅞	..
41½	25½	Gt N Ir Ore 2¾g.	9	34	34¾	34	34½	+ ⅝
108½	87	Gt No Pap 2.40a.	1	88¼	88¼	88¼	88¼	+ ¾
46⅞	38⅜	Gt No Ry 2½....	38	38⅜	39½	38⅜	39⅛	+ ⅜
23½	19¼	Gt West S 1.20a.	3	19⅜	19⅜	19¼	19¼	− ¼
33⅜	27⅛	Green (H L) 2a..	9	27¼	27¾	27¼	27⅝	+ ⅜
17½	14¼	Greyhound 1	59	14½	14⅝	14½	14⅝	+ ⅛
35⅞	27½	Grum Airc 2b....	21	29	29½	29	29⅛	+ ½
39⅝	30⅜	Gulf Mob & O 2a	13	30⅞	31	30⅜	31	+ ½
147½	83¾	Gulf Oil 2½b....	97	113	113¾	112¼	113½	+ 1¾
109	106½	Gulf Oil wi	7	106½	109	106½	108¾	..
42¾	32⅝	Gulf SU 1.60....	45	33¼	33⅜	33¼	33¼	+ ⅝

H

24	20½	HALL PRINT 1.40	2	21¾	22	21¾	22	+ ¼
90¾	58½	Hallibur 2.40 ...	34	82¼	85¾	82¼	85	+ 3
27	19	Hamil Wat 1.40..	3	25	25⅜	25	25⅜	+ ⅞
42⅜	34	Ham Pap 1½ ..	1	34¼	34¼	34¼	34¼	+ ¼
64	48	Harb Walk 2.80..	9	58	60	58	60	+ 3
38⅛	29⅞	Harris Sey 1.80..	3	35	35⅜	35	35⅜	+ ½
43	31⅞	Harsco Cp 2b....	9	37½	38	37¼	38	+ 1⅞
35⅝	24½	Harshaw Ch ¾e..	13	25¼	25¾	25¼	25¾	+ ¼
39	25	Hart S&M 1.60b.	2	27⅝	27⅝	27⅝	27⅝	− ⅜
8	6	Hat Corp	3	6⅛	6⅛	6⅛	6⅛	+ ⅛
37	18¼	Haveg Ind st pd.	2	23¾	23¾	23¾	23¾	+ ⅝
17⅜	13½	Hayes Ind 1.20b.	1	15⅞	15⅞	15⅞	15⅞	+ ¼
60	50	Heinz 1.80	5	50¾	50¾	50¼	50¼	+ ¼
101	90	Heinz pf 3.65...z	20	90	90	90	90	− 3
20	16	Heller 1	2	18¼	18¼	18¼	18¼	..
26⅜	23¾	Helme 1.60a	4	24⅛	24⅛	23¾	23¾	− ¼
21⅛	17	Hercul Mot .80..	8	17¾	17¾	17¾	17¾	..
51½	38½	Herc Pdr .40h...	24	39½	39½	38½	38⅞	− ¼

pages of most newspapers contain a record of the daily transactions that occur at some of these exchanges. A section of one of these reports is shown on page 395 and above. In order to interpret the transactions listed in the illustration, the line containing Eversharp will be used.

Explanation:

a. The first two columns represent the highest and the lowest prices at which the stock was sold to that date during the year. Thus, until that day of the year, the highest price that a buyer had to pay for each share of Eversharp was \$20; the lowest was \$15⅛, or \$15.125.

b. The number \$1.20 that appears after the word "Eversharp" signifies the amount of dividends that the company declared on each share of stock.

c. The 7 indicates that 700 shares of stock were sold that day.

d. The 17¼ under the "First" means that the first sale of Eversharp stock made that day was at \$17.25 a share.

e. The 17¼ under the "High" signifies that the highest price paid by a buyer that day was \$17.25.

f. The 17⅛ under the "Low" signifies that the lowest price paid for a share of stock that day was \$17.125.

g. The $17\frac{1}{4}$ under the "Last" signifies that the last purchaser of the day paid $17.25 for each share of stock that he bought.

h. The "Net Change" of $+\frac{1}{8}$ signifies that the last price that day was $\frac{1}{8}$, or $12\frac{1}{2}$ cents, higher than was the closing price on the previous day. Hence, the closing price on the previous day must have been $17\frac{1}{8}$, or $17.125. If the "Net Change" had been $-\frac{1}{8}$, it would signify that the closing price that day was $\frac{1}{8}$ lower than the closing price of the previous day.

You will notice that the fractional parts of quotations listed in the table are in eighths, fourths, or halves of a dollar. These are the only fractional parts of a dollar in which shares of stock are sold.

Business Transaction: Using the table, find the cost of 200 shares of Emerson Radio if they were purchased at the low for the day.

Solution: The day's low was $7\frac{1}{8}$; hence,

$$\text{Cost of 200 shares} = 200 \times \$7\frac{1}{8}$$
$$= 200 \times \$7.125$$
$$= \$1,425$$

Before multiplying, the fractional parts of a dollar should be changed to a decimal as was done in the illustration ($\frac{1}{8}$ = $.125). It should be noted that the $1,425 does not include the broker's fees and other charges that are made.

LEARNING EXERCISES

A. Find the cost of each of the following purchases by referring to the table on pages 395 and 396.

1. If purchased at the opening price:

Stock	Number of Shares
a. Diamond T Motors	300
b. Equitable Gas	100
c. Fibre Paper	700

2. If purchased at the lowest price:

a. duPont $3\frac{1}{2}$% Preferred	100
b. Electric Auto Light	600
c. Flintkote	300

3. If purchased at the last price:

a. Douglas Aircraft	900
b. Dow Chemical	2,300
c. Food Machinery	2,700

B. On the basis of the stock quotations in the table, what was the highest price paid for a share of each of the following stocks that year?

1. Eagle-Picher
2. Eastman Kodak
3. Endicott Johnson
4. Dan River Mills
5. Decca Records
6. Diamond T Motors
7. Dow Chemical
8. Family Finance

C. *Problems to Be Solved*

To obtain your answer, use the quotations that appear in the table.

1. Jonathan Wright owned 500 shares of Evans Products. How much did he receive in dividends to date that year?

2. How much did the owner of 85 shares of Erie Railroad 5% preferred stock receive in dividends for the year if the par value of the stock was 100?

3. Jules Kemp owned 175 shares of Elliott Company cumulative preferred stock having a par value of $50.

  a. How much did Mr. Kemp receive in dividends that year?

  b. Why is the number 2½ listed as the dividends for this stock?

4. If Mr. Scanlon purchased 300 shares of Electric Storage Battery Company at the high that day and 400 shares of Fanwick Corporation at the low that day, what was the total cost of his purchase?

5. Theodore Brick owns 435 shares of common stock and 850 shares of preferred stock of the Dixie Cup Company. How much money did he receive in dividends from the Dixie Cup Company that year?

UNIT **3**   Computing Brokerage Fees

SECTION 1   Computing Commission on Round-Lot Orders

Like the commission merchant, a stockbroker charges a fee for his services in buying or selling stock. This fee is called a *commission,* or *brokerage fee.* Its size depends on the number of shares that are bought or sold by the broker for his customer. Brokerage firms that trade through the various stock exchanges are required to charge their customers a minimum fee that is established by the exchange. These minimum fees vary with the different exchanges. The minimum fees for the New York Stock Exchange are listed below.

For Stocks Selling at $1 Per Share and Above
On Transactions Involving 100 Shares or Less

Amount of Money Involved	Commission
Under $100..	As mutually agreed
$100 to $1,999..	1% plus $5
$2,000 to $4,999	1/2% plus $15
$5,000 and above	1/10% plus $35

If the amount involved in a transaction is $100 or more, the commission shall not be less than $6. The commission charge, however, shall not be more than $50 for the sale of 100 shares or less. In addition, the charge cannot be more than $1 per share.

The majority of stocks traded on any exchange are either in multiples of 100, such as 100 shares, 200 shares, 300 shares, and so on, or in multiples of 10, such as 10 shares, 20 shares, 30 shares, and so on. The members of the exchange decide whether the stock shall be traded in 10-lot units or 100-lot units. Since over 75% of the shares listed on the New York Stock Exchange are traded in 100-share units, it is these transactions that will be given attention in this section.

When the number of shares bought or sold is a multiple of 100, the order is called a *round-lot order*. On the other hand, an order to purchase 56 shares of stock is called an *odd-lot order*. The rates shown in the chart apply only to round-lot orders. Should a person notify his broker to buy 500 shares of stock for him, the brokerage fee is determined first for 100 shares. The fee for 100 shares is then multiplied by 5 to determine the fee for the 500 shares.

Business Transaction 1: Burton Vale asked his broker to purchase 700 shares of Phoenix, Limited. The broker made the purchase at $12\frac{7}{8}$ a share. How large was the commission?

Solution: Cost of 100 Shares $= 100 \times \$12\frac{7}{8}$
$$= 100 \times \$12.875$$
$$= \$1,287.50$$

Commission on 100 Shares $= 1\%$ of $\$1,287.50 + \$5$
$$= \$12.88 + \$5$$
$$= \$17.88$$

Commission on 700 Shares $= 7 \times \$17.88$
$$= \$125.16$$

Explanation: The cost of 100 shares was found first because the commission is based on this cost. The cost ($1,287.50) of 100 shares being between $100 and $1,999, the commission, according to the rate table, amounts to 1% of $1,287.50 plus $5. The commission on 700 shares amounts to 7 times the commission on 100 shares ($17.88), or $125.16.

Business Transaction 2: 300 shares of Auto-Cart Company stock were sold at 26¼ a share. Considering brokerage fees only, how much money did the broker turn over to the person for whom he sold the stock?

Solution: Selling Price of 100 Shares = 100 × $26¼
$$= 100 \times \$26.25$$
$$= \$2,625$$
Brokerage on 100 Shares = ½% of $2,625 + $15
$$= \$13.13 + \$15$$
$$= \$28.13$$
Brokerage on 300 Shares = 3 × $28.13
$$= \$84.39$$
Selling Price of 300 Shares = 3 × $2,625
$$= \$7,875$$
Net Proceeds of Sale = Selling Price − Brokerage
$$= \quad \$7,875 \quad - \quad \$84.39$$
$$= \$7,790.61$$

LEARNING EXERCISES

A. Find the brokerage on each of the following sales of stock.

No.	No. of Shares	Price per Share	Brokerage
1	200	$ 2	$xxx
2	400	3½	xxx
3	500	12¼	xxx
4	100	15¾	xxx
5	300	67⅛	xxx
6	600	97⅝	xxx
7	400	106⅞	xxx
8	100	165½	xxx *

B. Find the net proceeds of each of the following sales. In computing the net proceeds, the only fee to be considered in these problems is the broker's commission.

* Read the rate table very carefully.

No.	Number of Shares Sold	Price per Share	Commission	Net Proceeds
1	100	$ 5	$xxx	$xxx
2	400	16	xxx	xxx
3	200	$27\frac{1}{2}$	xxx	xxx
4	600	$56\frac{3}{8}$	xxx	xxx
5	500	$93\frac{3}{4}$	xxx	xxx

C. Find the cost, including the brokerage, of each of the following purchases.

No.	Number of Shares Bought	Price per Share	Brokerage	Total Cost
1	100	$ 17	$xxx	$xxx
2	300	$23\frac{3}{4}$	xxx	xxx
3	400	$5\frac{7}{8}$	xxx	xxx
4	600	$73\frac{1}{2}$	xxx	xxx
5	200	$117\frac{1}{4}$	xxx	xxx

SECTION 2   Computing Commission on Odd-Lot Orders

In recent years, many persons who formerly kept their savings in banks are now investing in stocks in order to receive a greater return on their money. Many persons, however, seldom have enough money to purchase round-lot orders of 100 shares or more. Because of this, a certain area of the New York Stock Exchange is reserved for transactions involving *odd lots* (transactions that do not involve multiples of 100 shares or, in some cases, multiples of 10 shares). At the New York Stock Exchange the commission rates on odd-lot transactions are exactly the same as those on round lots, except that, after the commission is computed, $2 is deducted from that amount.

Business Transaction: Find the brokerage on 56 shares of stock purchased at $26\frac{7}{8}$.

Solution: Cost of 56 Shares $= 56 \times \$26\frac{7}{8}$

$$= 56 \times \$26.875$$
$$= \$1,505$$

Brokerage $= 1\%$ of $\$1,505 + \$5 - \$2$

$$= \quad \$15.05 \quad + \$5 - \$2$$
$$= \quad \$20.05 \quad - \$2$$
$$= \$18.05$$

Explanation: The brokerage was determined as a round lot, except that $2 was deducted from the round-lot fee of 1% of $1,505 + $5. When computing the answer to this problem, it is advisable to express the brokerage as follows:

$$\text{Brokerage} = 1\% \text{ of } \$1,505 + \$3$$

rather than as shown in the solution. Similar reductions can be applied to the other commission rates.

LEARNING EXERCISES

A. Find the commission on each of the following stock transactions.

No.	No. of Shares Purchased	Price per Share	Commission Charge
1	6	$48½	$xxx
2	29	9	xxx
3	3	58¾	xxx
4	7	35	xxx
5	46	42¼	xxx
6	20	90	xxx
7	50	61¾	xxx
8	90	78⅞	xxx

B. Using the stock quotations in the table in Unit 2, find the net proceeds of each of the following sales. In computing the net proceeds, the only fee to be considered is the brokerage.

No.	Company	Number of Shares Sold	Price per Share	Brokerage	Net Return
1	Daystrom	26	High	$xxx	$xxx
2	Dobeck	32	First	xxx	xxx
3	Equit Gas	57	Last	xxx	xxx
4	Falstaff	64	First	xxx	xxx
5	Fifth Av Lin	78	High	xxx	xxx

C. Using the stock quotations in the table in Unit 2, find the cost, including the brokerage, of the stocks in each of the following purchases.

No.	Company	Number of Shares Bought	Price per Share	Brokerage	Cost
1	Dow Chm	15	First	$xxx	$xxx
2	East Air L	25	High	xxx	xxx
3	Elgin Watch	48	First	xxx	xxx
4	Eversharp	76	Last	xxx	xxx
5	Equit Gas	89	High	xxx	xxx

UNIT 4   Computing the Tax on the Sale of Stocks

A person who sells stock must not only pay a commission to his broker, but he must also pay a tax to the Federal Government. The amount of this tax depends on the par value of the stock that is sold. The Federal tax is paid by the seller only, not the purchaser, when the transaction involves a round-lot sale. A transaction involving an odd-lot sale, however, requires that both the seller and the buyer pay a Federal tax. Here is a rate table for this tax.

Federal Tax

Based on each $100 of the *par value* of the stock

Selling under $20 per share	Selling at or over $20 per share
5¢	6¢

A stock having no par value shall be considered to have a par value of $100.

Business Transaction 1: Find the Federal tax on the sale of 300 shares of stock at $16\frac{1}{4}$ if the par value of the stock is $10 a share.

Solution: The par value on each share is $10; therefore, the total par value on the 300 shares is 300 × $10, or $3,000. Since the seller must pay 5 cents on each $100 of the total par value, it is necessary to find the number of 100 dollars in $3,000. This is determined by dividing $3,000 by 100, obtaining 30 as the quotient. On each of the 30 hundreds, the seller pays 5 cents; hence, on all 30 he pays 30 × 5 cents, or $1.50.

Outline: Total Par Value = 300 × $10
= $3,000
Number of Hundreds in $3,000 = $3,000 ÷ 100
= 30
Federal Tax = 30 × 5¢
= $1.50

If, in computing the number of hundreds of dollars in the total par value, the quotient is found to be a decimal, this number is changed to the next higher whole number. Thus, if the number of hundreds of dollars was 56.3, the broker, in determining the Federal tax, would change this number to 57.

Business Transaction 2: William Arnold purchased 57 shares of American Natural Gas Company at 66⅜. If the par value of each share is $25, how much Federal tax did Mr. Arnold have to pay?

Solution: The total par value of all the shares will be 57 times $25, or $1,425. Since the par value of each share was over $20, Mr. Arnold had to pay a Federal tax of 6 cents on each $100 of the total par value. The number of hundreds of dollars in $1,425 is 1,425 divided by 100, or 14.25. The broker would change this number to 15. The tax on each of the 15 hundreds is 6 cents; hence, on all 15, it is 15 times 6 cents, or 90 cents. If Mr. Arnold had purchased a round lot of shares, he would not have had to pay a Federal tax. The seller also had to pay 90 cents, for the seller must *always* pay the Federal tax.

Outline: Total Par Value = 57 × $25
= $1,425
Number of Hundreds in $1,425 = $1,425 ÷ 100
= 14.25
Rounding Off 14.25 to the Next Higher Whole Number = 15
Federal Tax = 15 × 6¢
= 90¢

Several states—for example, Florida, Massachusetts, New York, Pennsylvania, South Carolina, and Texas—levy a tax on the seller of

Rate Table for the New York State Tax	
Selling Price of Shares	Tax per Share
Less than $5	$.01
$5 but less than $10	.02
$10 but less than $20	.03
$20 or more	.04

stocks (never the buyer) in addition to that collected by the Federal Government. Since all transactions on the New York Stock Exchange are subject to the New York State tax, it is this state tax that will be examined. You may have noticed that the New York State tax does not depend on the par value of the stock as does the Federal tax.

Business Transaction 3: Find the New York State tax on 275 shares of stock that sold at $15\frac{3}{4}$ a share.

Solution: $15\frac{3}{4}$ is between $10 and $20; hence, the state tax is 3 cents a share. For 275 shares, therefore, the tax will be 275 × $.03, or $8.25. This amount is paid *only* by the seller.

Outline: Tax per Share = $.03

Tax for 275 Shares = 275 × $.03

= $8.25

LEARNING EXERCISES

A. Find the total of the New York State and Federal tax paid by the seller of stock in each of the following transactions.

No.	Number of Shares	Par Value	Selling Price	Federal Tax	N. Y. State Tax	Total Tax
1	200	$10.00	$ 3	$xxx	$xxx	$xxx
2	500	25.00	$7\frac{1}{2}$	xxx	xxx	xxx
3	100	50.00	$15\frac{3}{4}$	xxx	xxx	xxx
4	400	20.00	$12\frac{5}{8}$	xxx	xxx	xxx
5	65	2.00	$5\frac{3}{4}$	xxx	xxx	xxx
6	87	No	$8\frac{7}{8}$	xxx	xxx	xxx
7	36	1.00	$72\frac{1}{4}$	xxx	xxx	xxx
8	45	2.50	$13\frac{3}{4}$	xxx	xxx	xxx
9	200	.50	$14\frac{1}{4}$	xxx	xxx	xxx
10	75	.10	$6\frac{3}{8}$	xxx	xxx	xxx

B. Find the total tax paid by the buyer in each of the transactions in Problem **A**.

C. Using the stock quotations in the table on pages 395–396, find the total tax paid by the seller in each of the following transactions.

No.	Par Value	Company	No. of Shares Sold	Price per Share	Fed. Tax	N. Y. State Tax	Total Tax
1	$10	Eagle P	200	First	$xxx	$xxx	$xxx
2	2	Eaton Mfg	100	Last	xxx	xxx	xxx
3	5	Fed Pap Bd	50	High	xxx	xxx	xxx
4	No	Duplan	700	First	xxx	xxx	xxx
5	100	East Kod pf	200	Low	xxx	xxx	xxx

UNIT **5**   **(Optional) Computing the Rate of Return on Stock Investments**

Many persons purchase stock for the purpose of selling it at some later date at a profit. An equally large number of people invest their money in stock because the rate of return that they receive is greater than that paid on bank deposits. Both types of persons are concerned with the rate of interest they receive on their investment. If the rate of return were no larger than that which the bank offered them, it would be to their advantage to keep their money in a savings account, because that would involve less risk than a stock investment.

As you have already learned, the profit that is shared by the stockholders is not called "interest," as it is in a bank, but *dividends*. Frequently, this same profit is called the *return on the investment*, or, simply, the *income on the investment*. The *rate of return, rate of income*, or, as it is sometimes called, the *rate of yield* on an investment resembles the rate of interest on a bank deposit. It is merely a per cent value that represents the number of dollars profit per $100 invested by the stockholder. To illustrate, if a person invested $200 in stocks that paid him $14 each year in dividends, then his rate of return, or rate of yield, would be $14 on $200, or $7 per $100, or, 7%.

Business Transaction 1: John Ormond purchased 100 shares of General Baking Company at $9\frac{3}{8}$. If Mr. Ormond received a 60-cent yearly dividend on each share, what rate of income was he receiving on his investment?

Solution: This example is simply an application of one of the formulas involving the base, the rate, and the percentage where the base and percentage are known but the rate must be found. In Chapter 6, this problem was presented in the form:

$$\$.60 \text{ is what per cent of } \$9\tfrac{3}{8}?$$

Hence, the base is $9\frac{3}{8}$ and the percentage is $.60

Outline: $\rightarrow$ Known: Base $= \$9\frac{3}{8}$ (Cost of a Share of Stock)

Percentage $= \$.60$ (Dividend on Each Share)

$\rightarrow$ To Find: Rate of Income

$\rightarrow$ Method: Rate $=$ Percentage $\div$ Base (See pages 132–133.)

$$
\begin{aligned}
&= \quad \$.60 \quad \div \; 9\tfrac{3}{8} \\
&= \quad \$.60 \quad \div \; 9.375 \\
&= \quad .064 \\
&= \quad 6.4\% \text{ (Rate of Income)}
\end{aligned}
$$

You will notice that the 100 shares purchased were not used in the solution of this example. Since dividends are always declared on the basis of one share, the cost of one share is all that is needed to determine the rate of yield.

In the purchase of preferred stock, the investor can usually predict what his rate of return will be. When these stocks are issued, the company pledges itself to pay a certain fixed rate of the par value of the stock if the earnings permit the payment of a dividend. Hence, on the basis of the rate pledged, the purchaser can determine the actual rate of return that he will receive.

Business Transaction 2: Robert Brant purchased 75 shares of Carrier Corporation $4\frac{1}{2}\%$ preferred stock at $45\frac{1}{4}$ a share. What rate of return was he receiving on this investment if the par value of the stock was $50?

Solution: His yearly dividends can be found by multiplying 50 by $4\frac{1}{2}\%$; this product will be $2.25. Since the return ($2.25) is known, the rate of return can be found as in Business Transaction 1.

Outline: Dividend per Share $= \$50 \times 4\frac{1}{2}\%$
$= \$50 \times .045$
$= \$2.25$

Rate of Return $=$ Percentage $\div$ Base
$= \$2.25 \div 45\frac{1}{4}$
$= \$2.25 \div 45.25$
$= .0497$
$= 4.97\%$

You may have noticed that, in finding the rate of return, neither the brokerage nor the taxes were included in the cost of the stock. Most investors feel that these charges are small in comparison with the cost of the stock; therefore, in computing the rate of return they usually ignore these additional fees. Similarly, brokers will frequently find the rate of return for their customers by rounding off the cost of each share of stock to the nearest dollar. Thus, in Business Transaction 2, the $45\frac{1}{4}$ would be considered as $45; if the cost per share had been $45\frac{7}{8}$, $46 would have been used in computing the rate of return. Although the rates found in Business Transactions 1 and 2 are only approximate, they are very close to the actual rate of return. This is the method that you should use in computing the rate of return.

LEARNING EXERCISES

A. Find the rate of return on each of the following stock purchases.

No.	Price per Share	Yearly Dividend	Rate of Return (%)
1	$75	$2.50	xxx
2	19	1.25	xxx
3	$58\frac{1}{2}$	3.35	xxx
4	$16\frac{3}{4}$	1.20	xxx
5	$18\frac{1}{8}$	1.60	xxx
6	$12\frac{3}{8}$	1.00	xxx
7	$8\frac{7}{8}$	.60	xxx
8	$62\frac{5}{8}$	.90	xxx

B. Find the rate of yield on each of the following preferred stock purchases.

No.	Price per Share	Par Value	Dividend Rate	Rate of Yield (%)
1	$ 91	$100	$4\frac{1}{2}\%$	xxx
2	42	50	$2\frac{1}{4}\%$	xxx
3	154	100	7%	xxx
4	$47\frac{1}{2}$	50	$3\frac{1}{2}\%$	xxx
5	$45\frac{1}{4}$	50	$4\frac{1}{2}\%$	xxx
6	$93\frac{3}{8}$	100	4.20%	xxx
7	$101\frac{7}{8}$	100	$5\frac{1}{2}\%$	xxx
8	$76\frac{5}{8}$	100	$3\frac{3}{4}\%$	xxx

C. Using the stock quotations in the table on pages 395–396, find the rate of return on each of the following purchases.

No.	Company	Purchased at	Dividend That Year	Rate of Return (%)
1	Dana Cp	Low	$xxx	xxx
2	Day P&L	High	xxx	xxx
3	Diam Mat	Last	xxx	xxx
4	Dress Ind	High	xxx	xxx
5	Duq Lt	First	xxx	xxx
6	Elgin Wch	Low	xxx	xxx
7	El Paso N G	Last	xxx	xxx
8	Eversharp	High	xxx	xxx

UNIT 6   Profit Sharing in a Partnership

Large companies, as you have learned, have a great many proprietors, because each of the stockholders is actually a part owner of the company. The profits that the company earns is shared by the stockholders in accordance with the number of shares of stock that each one owns. If the company is relatively small, it is usually owned by only two or three people. Instead of issuing stock certificates, an agreement is drawn up among the owners, called *partners*, stating what fraction of the business belongs to each and how the profits or losses will be shared among them. A business that is operated by a group of partners is called a *partnership*.

There are many ways in which the partners may agree to share the profits or losses of their company. Among the most common of these agreements are:

→1. The profits are shared equally among all the partners.

→2. The share of the profit that each partner receives is in accordance with the amount of money that each contributed to the business. To illustrate: Each of three partners contributed $10,000, $5,000, and $5,000 to start a business. The first, according to this type of agreement, would receive $\frac{1}{2}$ of the profits, for he contributed $\frac{1}{2}$ of the money ($10,000 out of $20,000). The second and third would each receive $\frac{1}{4}$ of the profits, for each contributed $\frac{1}{4}$ of the money ($5,000 out of $20,000).

→3. Each partner will receive interest on his investment. After the interest is deducted from the total profit, the remainder is shared equally among the partners.

Business Transaction 1: George Simon, Robert Betts, and William Kyte formed a partnership in which they agreed to share equally in any profit or loss that the company may have. The profits for the first year are $25,200. What is each partner's share?

Solution: Since they were to share equally, each will receive $\frac{1}{3}$ of the $25,200, or $8,400.

Outline: Simon's Share = $8,400   ($\frac{1}{3} \times$ $25,200)

         Betts's Share = $8,400   ($\frac{1}{3} \times$ $25,200)

         Kyte's Share = $8,400   ($\frac{1}{3} \times$ $25,200)

Business Transaction 2: Thomas Warner, Fred Black, and Alfred Drew invested $15,000, $10,000, and $5,000, respectively, in a business. They agreed to share the profits in accordance with the amount that each had invested. How much was each partner's share of the first year's profit of $16,800?

Solution: All three men invested $30,000 ($15,000 + $10,000 + $5,000). Therefore, Warner's investment of $15,000 is $\frac{1}{2}$ of the entire investment ($15,000 out of $30,000). Hence, Warner will receive $\frac{1}{2}$ of the profit for the year, or $8,400 ($\frac{1}{2}$ of $16,800). In the same way, Black's and Drew's share of the profit can be found.

Outline: Total Investment = $15,000 + $10,000 + $5,000
$$= \$30,000$$

Warner's Fraction of the Profit = $\frac{15,000}{30,000}$, or $\frac{1}{2}$

Warner's Share of the Profit = $\frac{1}{2} \times \$16,800$
$$= \$8,400$$

Black's Fraction of the Profit = $\frac{10,000}{30,000}$, or $\frac{1}{3}$

Black's Share of the Profit = $\frac{1}{3} \times \$16,800$
$$= \$5,600$$

Drew's Fraction of the Profit = $\frac{5,000}{30,000}$, or $\frac{1}{6}$

Drew's Share of the Profit = $\frac{1}{6} \times \$16,800$
$$= \$2,800$$

Business Transaction 3: When Richard Cross and John Darcy organized their business, Cross invested $25,000; but Darcy contributed only $15,000. They agreed that each would receive 6% interest on his investment and that this interest would be deducted from the profits. The remainder of the profits was to be divided equally between them. If the first year's profit amounted to $14,000, what was each partner's share?

Solution: Interest on Cross's Investment = P × R × T
$$= \$25,000 \times 6\% \times 1 \text{ year}$$
$$= \$1,500$$

Interest on Darcy's Investment = P × R × T
$$= \$15,000 \times 6\% \times 1 \text{ year}$$
$$= \$900$$

Total Interest = $1,500 + $900, or $2,400

Net Profit = Total Profit − Interest
$$= \quad \$14,000 \quad - \$2,400$$
$$= \$11,600$$

Each Partner's Share of the Net Profit = $\frac{1}{2} \times \$11,600$
$$= \$5,800$$

Cross's Share of the Total Profit = $5,800 + $1,500
$$= \$7,300$$

Darcy's Share of the Total Profit = $5,800 + $900
$$= \$6,700$$

LEARNING EXERCISES

A. If the profits of a company are to be divided equally among the partners, how much will each receive in the following partnerships?

No.	Investment of Each Partner	Total Profit
1	$6,000, $8,000, $10,000	$5,460
2	$17,000, $19,000	7,620
3	$5,300, $6,400, $7,000, $7,500	6,484

B. If the profits of a company are to be divided in accordance with the investment of each partner, how much will each receive in the following partnerships?

No.	Investment of Each Partner	Total Profit
1	$5,000, $5,000, $10,000	$5,200
2	$12,000, $18,000	9,600
3	$10,000, $15,000, $25,000	12,500
4	$7,000, $9,000	4,000
5	$6,000, $8,500, $8,500	6,900
6	$8,000, $10,000, $15,000	9,500
7	$5,000, $7,500, $10,000, $12,500	12,800
8	$2,300, $4,200, $5,400, $4,700	8,450

C. If the *net profit* of a company is to be divided *equally* among the partners after the interest on their investments has been deducted from the *gross profit*, how much of the gross profit will each of the partners receive in the following partnerships?

No.	Investment of Each Partner	Interest Rate	Gross Profit
1	$5,000, $10,000	6%	$6,000
2	$4,000, $6,000, $7,000	5%	7,500
3	$9,500, $12,500	7%	8,600
4	$6,400, $4,800	$5\frac{1}{2}\%$	4,300
5	$7,200, $9,400, $8,500	6%	7,600
6	$6,600, $8,200, $10,700	$5\frac{1}{2}\%$	8,400

D. *Problems to Be Solved*

1. Two partners, Meehan and Cramer, invested $11,500 and $17,250, respectively, in a business. The partnership agreement provided for profit sharing according to the original investment. To how much is each partner entitled if the profit for 1 year amounted to $7,500?

2. Nash and Weldon entered into a partnership, investing $10,000 and $7,500, respectively. The agreement provided for equal sharing of profits after 6% interest is paid each partner on the amount he invested. The business made a profit of $6,400 for the year. Find each partner's share of the profit, including interest on his investment.

3. Robert Evans and James Lord were partners, having invested $40,000 and $50,000, respectively, in a retail business. The partnership agreement provided that each would receive a salary of $600 a month for working in the company. In addition, each would receive interest at 4% on his investment, the interest to be deducted from the gross profit. The net profit that remained was to be shared equally between them. The gross profit for the first year was $25,000.

    a. What was Mr. Evans' total return for the first year?

    b. What was Mr. Lord's total return for the first year?

UNIT 7   What Have You Learned?

SECTION 1   Understanding Terms

Can you match the term in the column on the left with the proper definition in the column on the right?

Term	*Definition*
1. Stock certificate	**a.** Persons who buy or sell stock for other people.
2. Preferred stockholders	
3. Par value	**b.** The difference between the closing prices on two successive days.
4. Dividend	
5. Stockbrokers	**c.** Evidence of ownership in a corporation.
6. Brokerage fee	**d.** An order to buy shares of stock that is either in multiples of 100 or, in some cases, multiples of 10.
7. Round lot	
8. Net change—in reference to daily stock quotations	
	e. Persons who have been guaranteed a fixed amount of company profits will be divided

Definition (Continued)

among them before any profits are distributed among the other shareholders.

f. A fraction of the profit of a company that is distributed for each share of the stock.

g. Value placed on a share of stock by the seller of the stock.

h. Value placed on a share of stock by the directors of the company.

i. Commission charged by a brokerage firm for the service of buying or selling stock.

SECTION 2 You As an Investor

How wisely would you invest your money? Can you make the correct selection in each of the following situations, and justify your answer? If you cannot do so, review the pages indicated at the end of the problem.

1. If the stocks of two companies were equivalent in *every* respect, except that one paid a yearly dividend of $2 and the other paid a quarterly dividend of 50 cents, which would you prefer? (Pages 392–393.)

2. You are interested primarily in investing your money in stocks that do not vary much in price but have paid dividends regularly for many years. After much investigation, you select a 5% preferred stock that has a par value of $50. You can purchase this stock at $73\frac{1}{2}$. Should you make this purchase or deposit your money in a savings bank or in a savings and loan association? (Pages 392, 393, 406–407.)

3. On November 2, you purchase 100 shares of stock at $51\frac{1}{4}$. The following day, the value of the stock increases to $52\frac{1}{4}$. Should you sell the stock at the increased price in order to realize a profit of $75, or should you hold the stock? (Pages 398–405.)

4. You have $5,000 to invest in stocks for the purpose of receiving a yearly return. You finally limit your selection to two companies whose stocks have not varied much in price over the last few years. The first is a $4\frac{1}{2}$% preferred stock with a par value of $100 that can be purchased at $96\frac{1}{8}$; the second is a common stock selling at $42\frac{1}{4}$. The common stock has been paying a $2\frac{1}{2}$ yearly dividend for many years. Which selection should you make? (Pages 406–407.)

5. You sell, at $59\frac{3}{4}$, 100 shares of stock that you had purchased two years ago at $52\frac{1}{4}$. During that period the company paid no dividends to their shareholders. Would you have gained more had you kept your money in a savings bank that paid 3% interest rate to their depositors? (Pages 252–256, 398–400.)

SECTION 3   Review Problems

1. Find the dividends that the owners of the following shares of common stock would receive. (Pages 392–393.)

	Number of Shares	Dividend
a.	200	35 cents Quarterly
b.	52	62½ cents Semiannually

2. Using the quotations in the table on pages 395–396, determine the dividends that the owner of 300 shares of Equitable Gas would have received that year. (Pages 392–393.)

3. How large would the quarterly dividend be for the owner of 100 shares of $5\frac{1}{2}\%$ preferred stock that had a par value of $25? (Pages 392–393.)

4. Using the table on pages 395–396, find the cost of 500 shares of Dow Chemical if these shares were purchased at the low of the day. (Page 397.)

5. Using the table on pages 395–396, what was the last price of Ex-Cell-O Corporation on the day prior to that shown on the table? (Page 397.)

6. How large was the brokerage fee on a purchase of 200 shares of stock at $18\frac{3}{4}$ if the transaction took place on the New York Stock Exchange? (Pages 398–400.)

7. David Pierce purchased 57 shares of a stock that was listed on the New York Stock Exchange. If the cost of each share was $43\frac{3}{8}$, what was the broker's commission? (Pages 401–402.)

8. Find the Federal tax on 250 shares of stock that have a par value of $10 if each share sold for $22\frac{5}{8}$. (Pages 403–404.)

9. How large was the Federal tax on 75 shares of stock that sold at $12\frac{5}{8}$ if each share has a par value of $25? (Pages 403–404.)

10. Find the New York State tax in Problems 8 and 9. (Pages 404–405.)

11. What rate of return did the purchaser of 125 shares of stock at $27\frac{3}{4}$ receive if the company paid a yearly dividend of $1.20? (Pages 406–407.)

12. What is the rate of income on a 5% preferred stock whose par value is $50 but that is selling at $41\frac{3}{8}$? (Pages 406–407.)

SECTION 4   Testing Your Understanding

50 Minutes

1. Mr. Field owns 250 shares of the common stock of a company that declared a 12½-cent quarterly dividend. How large was Mr. Field's share of the company's profit?

2. The owner of 100 shares of the Dobeckmun Company stock listed in the table on pages 395–396 would have received how large a dividend that year?

3. Martin Franklin purchased 300 shares of El Paso Natural Gas Company at its low on the day listed on pages 395–396. What was the cost of this transaction to Mr. Franklin? (Do not include commission and taxes.)

4. How much would the commission be on 200 shares of stock purchased through the New York Stock Exchange at $35\frac{3}{8}$?

5. What is the cost, including brokerage fees, of 25 shares of the Dayton Rubber Company if the stock was purchased at the high of the day as listed on pages 395–396?

6. How large is the Federal tax on 150 shares of stock whose par value is $5 if each share is selling at $32\frac{3}{8}$?

7. What is the New York State tax on a sale of 85 shares of stock that sells at $17\frac{5}{8}$?

8. Harry Townsend purchased 80 shares of Ingersoll-Rand at $63\frac{1}{2}$. If the company has been paying a yearly dividend of $3, what rate of return can Mr. Townsend look forward to on his investment?

9. A $4\frac{1}{2}\%$ preferred stock having a par value of $50 is selling for $52\frac{3}{4}$. What rate of income would a purchaser of this stock receive?

UNIT 8   General Review

SECTION 1   To Improve Your Speed and Accuracy

1. Addition:

a.	4,732	b.	$273.54	c.	$36\frac{1}{2}$
	5,947		7.85		$59\frac{5}{8}$
	8,369		46.93		$47\frac{5}{6}$
	7,692		855.07		
	3,674		.48		

d. $372 + $46.95 + $.07 + $492 + $1.74

e. $18\frac{2}{3} + 17\frac{5}{6} + 12\frac{1}{3} + 8\frac{1}{2}$

2. Subtraction:

    a. 8,305   **b.** $500.00   **c.** $69\frac{2}{3}$

       2,978   49.56 $27\frac{3}{5}$

    d. $673.46 − $160.29   **e.** $36 − 17\frac{3}{16}$

3. Multiplication:

    a. 507×93 **b.** 125×3.04 **c.** $75\frac{3}{4} \times 16$

    d. $48 \times 15\frac{5}{6}$ **e.** $6\frac{2}{3} \times 5\frac{2}{5}$

4. Division:

    a. $367{,}842 \div 59$ **b.** $4 \div .0004$ **c.** $5{,}000 \div 1.05$

    d. $15 \div 2\frac{1}{2}$ **e.** $4\frac{2}{3} \div 7\frac{1}{2}$

SECTION 2   Do You Remember These?

1. A cash discount of 6% on a $432 bill amounts to how much money?

2. To what single discount rate are the successive discount rates of 25% and 10% equivalent?

3. What discount rate is granted on a purchase made on December 26 and paid for January 6 if the terms are 6/10, 4/30, n/60?

4. Goods costing $24, bought July 29, are paid for on August 8. How large was the payment if the terms were 5/10, 2/30, n/60?

5. Find the interest on $3,000 for 4 months at a 5% interest rate?

6. A note dated July 17 and due in 60 days will fall due on what date?

7. A man borrowed $400 from the bank at a 5% discount rate. What were the proceeds if the loan was made for 90 days?

8. Using the 6%, 60-day interest method, find the interest on $375 for 80 days at 6%.

9. What is the installment charge on a purchase on which a down payment of $5 was made and 7 monthly installments of $4.50 each were paid? The cash price of the article was $32.75.

10. A discount of $2 was given on an article that listed at $16. What discount rate did the purchaser receive if the rate is based on the list price?

11. What is the net price of an article that lists at $250 if successive trade discounts of 40% and 10% are granted to the "trade"?

12. An article that is purchased at $12.50 is sold for $18.50. What is the per cent of markup based on the cost?

$100,000

NassauCounty,N.Y.

2%

$10,000,000

Commonwealth of Puerto Rico

Public Improvement Bonds Series A

$6,000,000

Mississippi Power Company

First Mortgage Bonds, 4⅝% Series due 1987

$267,000

Central Vermont
Public Service Corporation

2¾% First Mortgage Bonds

$4,850,000

City of Providence, Rhode Island

3.40% Bonds

$250,000

Jacksonville Expressway
Authority, Florida

4¼% Bonds due July 1, 1992

$27,410,000

New Housing Authority Bonds

17

Bond Purchases
and Bond Sales

PREVIEW

By the time Arthur Peterson had reached the age of 60, he had accumulated $25,000 through wise investments in stocks. Now, however, he felt that it would be advisable for him to liquidate his stockholdings in favor of investments that involved less risk. Depositing his money in a savings bank did not appeal to him because not only was the interest rate much lower than he had been receiving, but also, under Federal law, only $10,000 of his deposit would be insured. After careful study, he finally decided to buy $4\frac{1}{2}\%$ first mortgage bonds of the Artright Manufacturing Company. He was able to buy these bonds through his broker at $108\frac{3}{4}\%$ of their par value of $1,000. How much greater was the interest rate on this investment than if the money had been kept in a bank at 3%?

For Class Discussion

1. What is meant by the phrase "to liquidate his stock holdings"?

2. How could Mr. Peterson have deposited his money in savings banks and have had all $25,000 insured?

3. What is the distinction between a bondholder of a corporation and a stockholder?

4. What is the meaning of the term "par value" of a bond?

5. Does a $4\frac{1}{2}\%$ bond mean that the purchaser will receive $4\frac{1}{2}\%$ interest on the amount that he invests or on some other amount? Explain.

6. Why is a bond investment considered to be less of a risk than a stock investment?

Terms You Should Know

Corporations can raise large sums of money in two ways. They can either issue stocks, as you learned in the preceding chapter, or they can borrow money. Frequently, however, the amounts they need are so large that a single individual or institution is unwilling or unable to lend that much. Thus, if a corporation desires to borrow 5 million dollars, it may issue 5,000 certificates worth $1,000 each by promising to return the money in 25 years. These certificates are called *bonds*. Hence, a bond is simply a promissory note in which the time for repaying the note covers a great many years. As for other notes, the borrower—in this case, the corporation—will give some sort of security to guarantee that the bondholder will not lose his money.

It is important to note that a bondholder is a person from whom a corporation has borrowed money, but that a stockholder is a part owner of the corporation. Should the corporation become bankrupt, the bondholders would be paid any money received from the sale of the company's property before any of the proceeds would be distributed among the stockholders. Only after the bondholders have been paid the full amount of their loan will the stockholders be allowed to share in what remains. If the company prospers, however, the interest that the bondholders receive always remains the same, for they have simply lent money at a fixed rate of interest.

Because it takes a great deal of money to buy a single bond, comparatively few people invest their savings in bonds. The par value (the meaning here is exactly the same as it was for stocks) is usually $1,000 although some companies do issue bonds for $500 or even $100. Hence, the amount needed to invest in bonds is much greater than that needed to purchase stocks. United States Government Savings bonds are among the few bonds that can be purchased for less than $100. Unlike most stocks, bonds vary little in price from day to day. They are, therefore, usually bought for the interest they will pay rather than for the possibility that their value will increase greatly. The daily value at which a bond is sold is called the *market value* of the bond.

Concerning This Chapter

Although you may never purchase *corporate,* or *corporation, bonds,* these bonds are, nevertheless, a vital part of the financial structure of most companies. Students of business mathematics should, therefore, know a few of the more important aspects of bond transactions. In this chapter you will learn how to read and interpret the bond-market quotations as they appear on the financial pages of a newspaper. As every investor is interested in knowing the interest and also the rate of interest he will receive on his investment, several units will be devoted to showing how this information is obtained. As bonds, like stocks, are purchased through a broker, you will learn how to determine the broker's fee. Because the method of computing the cost of a bond is somewhat different from that involved in computing the cost of a stock purchase, some time will be devoted to showing how the computation connected with bond purchases may be performed.

UNIT 1 **Computing the Interest Payment on a Bond**

As with preferred stock, interest on a bond is determined on the basis of the *par value* of the bond, not on its *market value.* Thus, a $5\frac{1}{2}\%$ bond that was purchased for $987.50 and that has a par value of $1,000 will have its interest computed on the $1,000, *not* on the $987.50. The $5\frac{1}{2}\%$ represents the rate of interest that the corporation is paying on its debt.

Business Transaction: James Kemper owns a $4\frac{1}{2}\%$ bond the par value of which is $1,000. If he purchased the bond for $987.50, how much did he receive on his semiannual interest payment?

Solution: I = P × R × T
= $1,000 × $4\frac{1}{2}\%$ × $\frac{1}{2}$ Year
= $22.50

Explanation: Since the interest that Mr. Kemper received was based on the par value of the bond, the price he paid for it is completely ignored. This being a half-yearly interest payment, the time (T) will be equal to $\frac{1}{2}$.

LEARNING EXERCISES

A. Find the interest due for the period shown in each of the following problems.

No.	Market Value	Par Value	Interest Rate	Period	Interest
1	$ 981.25	$1,000	5%	Annually	$xxx
2	975.00	1,000	$3\frac{1}{2}\%$	Annually	xxx
3	327.50	500	$4\frac{1}{4}\%$	Annually	xxx
4	785.00	1,000	6%	Semian.	xxx
5	307.50	500	$4\frac{1}{2}\%$	Semian.	xxx
6	677.50	1,000	$2\frac{1}{4}\%$	Semian.	xxx
7	1,040.00	1,000	$5\frac{3}{4}\%$	Semian.	xxx
8	495.00	500	3%	Quarterly	xxx
9	977.50	1,000	$3\frac{1}{2}\%$	Quarterly	xxx
10	886.25	1,000	$3\frac{3}{4}\%$	Quarterly	xxx

B. *Problems to Be Solved*

1. Fred Darton owned 5 $4\frac{1}{2}\%$ bonds of the Standard Mining Company, which he purchased at $955 each. If the par value of each of these bonds is $1,000, how large were the interest payments that Mr. Darton received each year?

2. On July 19, Roland Lind received his semiannual interest payment on the 3 $5\frac{1}{4}\%$ Western Railroad bonds that he owned. Although the par value of a bond was $1,000, Mr. Lind had paid $1,016.25 for each bond. What was the amount of interest that he received?

3. On March 1, the Atlantic Union Corporation mailed its quarterly interest checks to the owners of its $3\frac{3}{4}\%$ bonds that had a par value of $500. How large a check would the owner of 8 bonds receive?

4. Mr. Sherman Place owned 6 $3\frac{7}{8}\%$ coupon bonds of the Hudson Gas Company. Although the par value of these bonds was $500, he had purchased them for $375 each. On the date that the interest fell due, Mr. Place clipped the coupons from the bonds and presented the coupons at his bank for payment. How large an amount did he receive?

UNIT **2** | **Interpretation of the Bond-Market Quotations As Reported in the Newspapers**

A bond-market trading report as it appeared on the financial page of a newspaper is shown on pages 422–423. The interpretation of much of the material in this table is the same as that for the stock-market report. There are, however, a few major differences that will be explained by examining the line containing the Tex Corporation quotations.

Range			Sales in	Net			
High	Low		$1,000	High	Low	Last	Change
1 02	95½	TEX Corp 3s 65 31		97½	97¼	97½	+ ¾

Explanation:

a. The **3s** following the name of the corporation represents the rate of interest that the company is paying on these bonds; namely, 3%.

b. The **65** that follows the symbol 3s shows that the bonds will mature in 1965. The company will have to pay the par value of these bonds to the owners in that year.

c. The next number, **31**, represents the actual number of these bonds sold that day.

d. Unlike stock quotations, the number 97½ under "High" does not mean that the highest price paid for a bond of this company was $97.50. In all bond quotations, the decimal point is placed one digit farther to the left than it actually belongs. Hence, in this case, the high of that day would be $975.

TREASURY BOND

95.11	91.24	2½s 72-67 De..c..	5	91.24	91.24	91.24	—1.29

NEW YORK CITY BOND

Range, High.	Low		Sales in $1,000.	High.	Low.	Last.	Net Chge.
105.8	97.8	3s 80	1	98.16	98.16	98.16	— .80

DOMESTIC BONDS

	U. S. Govt. Bonds.	Other Dom. Bonds.	Foreign Bonds.	Total All Bonds.
Day's sales	$5,000	*$2,820,000	$130,000	$2,955,000
Monday	......	*2,700,000	210,000	2,910,000
Year to date	$220,000	*757,989,000	43,611,800	801,821,700
1955	14,000	*781,985,600	69,742,400	851,742,000

Range, High.	Low.		Sales in $1,000.	High.	Low.	Last.	Net Chge.
		A					
112½	111	ALLEG LUD 4s 81	107	111⅜	111	111⅜	+ ¼
105	97	Allied Chem 3½s 78	21	97¾	97½	97½	— ⅜
101¾	97½	Alcoa 3⅛s 64	15	108½	98	98½	..
105	100½	Alum Can 3⅞s 70	2	100¾	100¾	100¾	— ¾
97½	86¾	Am & F P 5s 2030	8	89	89	89	— ⅞
85	78	Am & F P 4.80s 87	5	79⅞	79¾	79¾	— ⅛
111¼	101¼	Am Mch & F 4¼s 81	96	111	110½	110½	..
138¼	125	Am T & T 3⅞s 67	18	126⅞	125¼	126⅞	+ 1⅞
101	99⅝	Am T&T 3⅞s 90	24	100¾	100½	100⅝	— ¼
104⅛	95¼	Am T & T 3⅜s 73	15	95⅞	95¼	95⅞	+ ⅛
102½	92⅛	Am T&T 3¼s 84	3	92¼	92¼	92¼	— ½
95⅜	86½	Am T&T 2¾s 75	6	88¼	88	88	— ¼
94	84	Am T&T 2¾s 80	8	84¾	84½	84½	— ¼
94¼	84	Am T&T 2¾s 82	1	84	84	84	..
90¾	81	Am T&T 2⅝s 86	1	81½	81½	81½	..
100⅝	95½	Am Tobacco 3s 62	14	95⅝	95½	95½	..
100⅜	93½	Am Tobacco 3s 69	1	93½	93½	93½	..
87½	77½	Armour 5s 84 f	28	79	79	79	+ ½
101⅝	94	Assoc Inv 3⅜s 62	4	95	94⅛	95	+ 1
118⅜	105	Atchison 4s 95	6	107¾	107¾	107¾	..
115	100¾	Atchison 4s 95 st	1	102	102	102	— 2
108½	100½	Atl Cst L 4½s 64	3	102½	102½	102½	..
		D					
101	90⅞	DEERE 3⅛s 77	1	90⅞	90⅞	90⅞	— 2¾
103½	97	Del & Hud 4s 63	1	98½	98½	98½	..
98	89½	D L&W 4s-6s 2042	1	89½	89½	89½	— ½
110¾	107⅝	Det Edis 3¾s 71	12	108¾	108⅝	108¾	..
142	135	Det Edis 3¼s 69	7	139	139	139	..
100¼	92½	Det Edis 3s 70	4	93¼	93¼	93¼	— ¾
94½	84	Det Edis 2¾s 82	1	84¼	84¼	84¼	+ ⅛
177½	123¼	Dow Chm 3s 82	7	156½	156½	156½	— 2
96½	85	Duq Lt 2¾s 77	10	86¾	86¾	86¾	— ⅝
		E					
128	104¼	EAST S STL 4½s 71	10	120	120	120	..
		G					
111¾	101¾	GEN DYNAM 3½s 75	74	107	106¾	106¾	— ¼
115¾	100½	Gen Am Tran 4s 81	2	108¼	108¼	108¼	+ ¼
102½	98¼	Gen Elec 3½s 76	17	98¾	98⅝	98¾	— ⅛
102½	99¾	Gen Mot Acc 4s 58	39	101	100¾	100¾	— ⅛
102¾	98⅞	Gen Mot Acc 3⅞s 61	43	99½	99⅜	99½	..
101¾	94¾	Gen Mot Acc 3⅝s 75	13	95⅜	95¼	95¼	— ¼
102½	95½	Gen Mot Acc 3½s 72	1	96⅝	96⅝	96⅝	+ ⅛
100½	96	Gen Mot Acc 3s 60	9	96⅛	96⅛	96⅛	+ ⅛
99½	89	Gen Mot Acc 3s 69	3	90	90	90	— ½
98	90	Gen Mot Acc 2¾s 64	13	92½	92	92	— ½
114¾	105	Gen Tel Cp 4s 71	48	107	106¾	107	+ ¼
100	92¾	Goodrich 2¾s 65	15	93½	92⅞	92⅞	+ ⅛
116	105¼	Grace & Co 3½s 75	20	113¼	113	113¼	+ ¼
120	106½	Gt Nor Ry 5s 73	1	108½	108½	108½	..
94	82¼	Gt Nor Ry 3⅛s 2000	10	83	82¼	82¼	— ¾

Range, High.	Low.		Sales in $1,000.	High.	Low.	Last.	Net Chge.
110¾	94½	Nat Tea 3½s 80	11	98	97¾	98	— ½
104½	100⅛	N Eng T&T 4½s 61	28	102	101⅝	102	+ ⅛
104⅜	101¼	NY Cen 6s 80	22	102	101⅝	102	..
91⅜	79⅝	N Y Cen 5s 2013	45	81¼	80¾	81¼	+ ⅛
83¼	72	N Y Cen 4½s 2013	45	73½	73⅛	73½	+ ½
76	67	N Y Cen 4s 98	16	67⅞	67⅝	67¾	— ¼
92	83	N Y Conn 2⅞s 75	2	83	83	83	..
69	49⅜	NYNHH 4½s 2022f	24	50¾	50¼	50⅜	+ ¼
73¾	59⅞	NYNHH 4s 2007	21	60	59⅞	60	..
7¼	3⅞	N Y O&W 4s 92f q	16	4¾	4¼	4¾	+ ⅛
49	42⅝	N Y Sus&W 4½s 2019f	3	46	46	46	..
118	103½	Norf & W 4s 96	2	105¾	105¾	105¾	..
110	104	Nor Cen 5s 74	1	104	104	104	— 4½
104	95½	Nor Pac 4s 84	5	97¾	97¾	97¾	+ ¼
79¾	65	Nor Pac 3s 2047	18	67¾	67	67	..
107	87¼	Northrop 4s 75	5	92⅛	92⅛	92⅛	— ⅜
		O					
101¼	96½	OR WASH RR N 3s 60	3	98⅛	97½	97½	..
		P					
99¾	89	PAC G&E 3s 74	3	91⅝	91⅝	91⅝	+ ⅜
99¼	87½	Pac G&E 3s 77	10	88⅛	88⅛	88⅛	— 2¾
98¾	87½	Pac G&E 3s 79	1	89½	89½	89½	..
95	82¾	Pac T&T 2⅞s 86	3	82¾	82¾	82¾	..
93¼	82½	Pac T&T 2¾s 85	1	83⅝	83⅝	83⅝	+ ⅛
99½	90⅞	Pen Pw & Lt 3s 75	9	91⅞	91	91	— ½
110½	101¼	Pen RR 5s 68	8	102½	102¼	102½	..
106½	101	Pen RR 4½s 60	7	102½	102¼	102¼	— ½
107½	100	Pen RR 4½s 65	28	101¼	101	101	— ⅛
105½	91	Pen RR 4¼s 81	20	92	92	92	..
105½	90¼	Pen RR 4¼s 84	5	92	91½	91½	+ ⅜
101¾	92¾	Pere Mar 3⅜s 80	1	92¾	92¾	92¾	..
98¾	91	Phil El 2¾s 67	1	92	92	92	— ⅝
108⅞	100	PCC&SL 5s 70	5	100½	100½	100½	— ½
208	180	Pub S E G 8s 2037	1	180	180	180	— 20¼
100½	94	Pub S E G 3s 63	1	94¼	94¼	94¼	— ¼

		B					
97	83	B & O 4½s 2010	32	87	86	86	+ ¾
92½	79¼	B & O 4½s A 2010	17	81	80⅛	81	+ ½
90	81½	B & O 4s 80 B	33	83½	83	83½	..
96¾	87⅜	B & O 3⅞s 70 A	18	88½	88¼	88½	+ ⅜
105	101	Bell T Pa 5s 60	50	102⅛	101⅞	101⅞	— ¼
129¼	115⅛	Beth Stl 3¼s 80	258	127⅞	126½	127⅞	+ ½
99½	89	Beth Stl 3s 79	1	89	89	89	— ⅛
68½	53¾	Bos & Me 4½s 70 f	4	54¾	54¾	54¾	+ ½
88⅜	74	Bos & Me 4s 60	6	74¾	74¾	74¾	— ⅛
95	83	Brk Un Gas 2⅞s 76	2	84⅝	84⅝	84⅝	— ⅜
		C					
107¾	101	CAN PAC 4s perp	5	101⅞	101⅞	101½	— ⅛
67	55⅛	Cen RR NJ 3¼s 87	6	56⅞	56½	56½	..
106	99⅝	Ches & Oh 3⅞s 73	1	100	100	100	..
103	93	Ches & O 3½s 96 D	10	93¾	93½	93½	— ¾
103⅛	99⅞	Chi B & Q 4s 58	15	100½	100½	100½	..
97½	85	Chi B & Q 3⅛s 85	1	85	85	85	— ½
97	86	Chi G W 4s 88	1	88	88	88	+ 1⅞
70¾	57¼	CMSP&Pac 5s 2055 f	34	59¼	58⅞	59	+ ⅛
86¾	78½	CMSP&Pac 4½s 2019	1	78½	78½	78½	— ½
74⅜	60½	CMSP&Pas 4½s 2044	20	62¾	62⅛	62¾	+ ¼
69¾	53¾	Chi&NW 4½s 99 f	88	54½	54⅛	54½	..
103¼	94½	Chi R I & P 4½s 95	5	94½	94½	94½	..
103¾	99⅞	CIT Fin 4s 60	10	100⅝	100⅝	100⅝	+ ⅜
103⅞	95	CIT Fin 3⅝s 70	5	95½	95½	95½	— ⅜
99	95	CIT Fin 2⅝s 59	5	97⅛	97⅛	97⅛	..
96½	89¼	Cin Un Term 2¾s 74	4	89¼	89¼	89¼	..
98	89½	Cities Svc 3s 77	7	91	90¾	90¾	..
101	93⅛	Clev El Ill 3s 70	20	94⅞	94⅞	94⅞	+ ⅜
128¼	115	Colum Gas 3½s 64	67	125¼	125	125	..
108½	96½	Combust Eng 3⅜s 81	68	103½	103¼	103¼	..
104⅞	96½	Con Edis 3½s 83	5	96½	96½	96½	..
96¼	86	Con GE Ba 2⅞s 81	6	86	86	86	— 6
98⅝	89	Consum Pw 2⅞s 75	7	90	89¼	90	+ ½
113½	95	Cont Bak 3⅝s 80	4	98½	98¼	98¼	+ ¼
97⅛	88½	Cruc Stl 3⅛s 66	1	88½	88½	88½	..
33½	28¾	Cuba RR 4s A 70f	1	32¾	32¾	32¾	..
		H					
51½	42½	HUD & M rfg 5s 57f q	38	51	49⅞	51	+ 1
30	23⅜	Hud & M inc 5s 57f q	46	24	24	24	..
		I					
104½	92½	INT MINER 3.65s 77	5	94	94	94	..
		K					
102	94	KOPPERS 3s 64	1	96	96	96	..
		L					
87	76	LEH VAL 5s F 2003f	1	77	77	77	..
93¾	92⅝	Lockheed 4½s 76	7	93	93	93	+ ⅜
112	101	Lockheed 3¾s 80	31	104⅜	104	104⅜	+ ⅜
101	93½	Lorillard 3s 63	1	94	94	94	+ ½
87	75	Lou & N 2⅞s 2003	2	75	75	75	..
		M					
103¼	98¾	MAINE CEN 5⅛s 78	1	98¾	98¾	98¾	— ¼
97⅞	84¼	Merr Chap & S 4½s 75	5	85	84¾	85	+ ⅛
87½	77¾	Mpls Moline 6s 86f	5	79¾	79¾	79¾	— ¼
68¼	59½	MSPSSM gm 4s 91f	14	61¼	61¼	61¼	+ ⅛
100½	86	Mo Kan T 5s 62	1	91¼	91¼	91¼	+ ¾
85⅛	68	Mo Kan T 5s 67f	6	68¼	68	68	— ⅛
94¼	77	Mo Kan T 4s 90	1	77	77	77	..
68¼	55⅞	Mo Pac 5s 2045f	24	60	59⅞	60	..
77¼	64⅝	Mo Pac 4¾s 2020f	6	70¼	70	70¼	+ ½
71⅞	61½	Mo Pac 4¾s 2030f	23	66⅜	66	66	..
96¼	80¼	Mo Pac 4¼s 90	44	82¼	81¾	82¼	+ ½
95¾	79⅛	Mo Pac 4¼s 2005	32	80¾	80½	80¾	+ ¼
68½	60	Mor & Es 3½s 2000	2	60⅞	60⅞	60⅞	+ ½
		N					
101⅞	94⅞	NAT DAIRY 3s 70	2	94⅞	94⅞	94⅞	..
97¾	90	Nat Dairy 2¾s 70	5	91	91	91	+ ¾
		R					
117⅛	98	RCA 3½s 80	110	103½	103	103	— ⅜
		S					
73½	70	ST L S F 5s 2006 f	13	71¼	71	71	— ¼
97	93¾	St L S F 4½s 2022 f	1	83¾	83¾	83¾	— 2¼
101	87	St L S F 4s 97	1	88¾	88¾	88¾	— ¼
113	100	Scott Pap 3s 71	36	104	103¾	104	+ ¼
94½	86½	Shell Un 2½s 71	15	88¾	88⅝	88¾	+ ⅝
163	127	Sinclair 3¼s 83	33	133½	132½	132½	— 1
99½	87¼	So Bell TT 3s 79	8	89	88¼	88¼	— 1¼
135¾	122¼	So Nat Gas 4½s 73	7	124	123¾	124	+ ⅝
106½	97¾	So Pac 4½s 69	27	100½	100	100¼	— ⅛
106½	94	So Pac 4½s 81	6	96⅞	96⅞	96⅞	..
107½	97½	So Pac Or 4½s 77	13	100	99½	100	— ¼
97½	81	Std Coil P 5s 67	1	82	82	82	+ 1
148⅝	114½	Std O Ind 3⅛s 82	14	133	131¾	131¾	— 2
148⅝	114½	Std O Ind 3⅛s 82 reg	4	90	90	90	— 1½
96⅞	89	Std O NJ 2¾s 74	4	90	90	90	— 1½
		T					
102	95½	TEX CORP 3s 65	31	97½	97¼	97½	+ ¾
99¾	88⅝	Tex & NO 3¼s 70	7	88⅝	88⅝	88⅝	— ⅞
39½	25½	Third Av 5s 60 f q	64	37⅞	37⅞	37⅞	..
		U					
103⅞	95½	UN EL MO 3⅜s 71	3	97	97	97	+ ¼
105⅜	97½	Un Gas Cp 3⅝s 71	3	98¼	98	98¼	+ ¼
		V					
105¾	102⅛	Vanadium 4¼s 76	73	105⅜	105	105⅜	— ⅛
103	100	Va & Sw 5s 58	5	100½	100½	100½	+ ¼
96	84⅝	Virg Ry 3s 95	4	85¼	85¼	85¼	— ¾
		W					
104½	97½	WEST PEN P 3½s 66	10	99½	99½	99½	+ 1
71¾	62½	W Shore 4s 2361	11	64⅝	64⅛	64⅝	+ ⅜
69⅞	62	W Shore 4s 2361 reg.	3	63¼	63¼	63¼	..
103½	96⅞	West Md 4s 69	1	99	99	99	..
116½	105	Wheel Stl 3¾s 75	64	109⅞	109⅜	109⅜	— ⅝

e. As with "High," the "Low" figure of 97¼, or **97.25,** means that the lowest price received for a Tex Corporation bond that day was **$972.50.**

f. The net change of +¾, or **.75,** signifies that the closing price that day was **$7.50** more than it had been on the previous day.

Business Transaction: Find the market value of two Lockheed Corporation 3⅜s bonds if they were purchased at the high for that day.

Solution: Quotation for the "High" = 104⅜, or 104.375

Market Value of 1 Bond = $1,043.75

Market Value of 3 Bonds = 3 × $1,043.75

= $3,131.25

LEARNING EXERCISES

A. Using the table on pages 422–423, find the maturity date, the rate of interest, and the "net change" in dollars for each of the following bonds.

No.	Company	Maturity Date	Rate of Interest (%)	Net Change
1	Allied Chm	xxx	xxx	$xxx
2	Armour	xxx	xxx	xxx
3	Brk Un Gas	xxx	xxx	xxx
4	Cont Bak	xxx	xxx	xxx
5	Gt Nor Ry	xxx	xxx	xxx
6	Lorillard	xxx	xxx	xxx
7	Nor Cen	xxx	xxx	xxx
8	RCA	xxx	xxx	xxx

B. Using the same table, find the market value of each of the following purchases.

No.	Company	Purchased at	Number of Bonds	Market Value
1	Armour	Low	2	$xxx
2	Cities Svc	Last	3	xxx
3	Dow Chm	High	4	xxx
4	Gen Dynam	Last	3	xxx
5	Grace & Co	Last	4	xxx
6	Nat Tea	Low	2	xxx
7	N Eng T&T	Low	3	xxx
8	Pac G&E 3s	High	2	xxx
9	N Y Cen 4s	Low	5	xxx
10	Third Ave	Last	8	xxx

C. Using the table on pages 422–423, find the interest received for the period indicated. Assume that all the companies are paying interest on their bonds.

No.	Company	Par Value	Number of Bonds	Period	Interest
1	Am Tobacco 3s	$1,000	2	Annually	$xxx
2	Cin Un Term	1,000	3	Semian.	xxx
3	Colum Gas	1,000	2	Semian.	xxx
4	Vanadium	1,000	4	Quar.	xxx
5	Combust Eng	1,000	2	Semian.	xxx
6	Pac T&T	1,000	4	Quar.	xxx
7	N Y Conn	1,000	3	Semian.	xxx
8	Int Miner	1,000	5	Semian.	xxx

UNIT 3 — Computing Brokerage Fees and Taxes on Bond Transactions

For his services for buying and selling bonds, the bond broker charges a fee called either *brokerage* or *commission*. The minimum size of this commission is governed by the exchange through which the bonds are purchased. The New York Stock Exchange has established the following rates for the sale or purchase of bonds.

New York Stock Exchange Commission Rates on Bonds				
	Commission per Bond			
Price	1 or 2 Bond Orders	3 Bond Orders	4 Bond Orders	5 or More Bond Orders
Selling under 10	$1.50	$1.20	$ .90	$ .75
At least 10 but under 100	2.50	2.00	1.50	1.25
At least 100 and above	5.00	4.00	3.00	2.50

The figures listed under "Price" do not represent the actual cost of the bonds. As with the bond quotations interpreted on pages 421 and 424, they would represent the cost of the bond if the decimal point were moved one place to the right. Therefore, the statement "At least 10 but under 100" should be interpreted as selling at $100 but under $1,000 for each bond. The bond prices are listed as they are shown in the table, so that they will be in keeping with the way prices are quoted on the bond exchange and on the financial pages of newspapers.

Business Transaction 1: Find the commission on the sale of 4 bonds at $98\frac{7}{8}$.

Solution: Since $98\frac{7}{8}$ is between 10 and 100, the commission on each bond of a 4-bond order is $1.50. For the 4 bonds, the commission will be 4 × $1.50, or $6.

Outline: Commission per Bond   = $1.50
Commission for 4 Bonds = 4 × $1.50
= $6

As the par value on most bonds is either $1,000, $500, or $100, the Federal tax on the sale of bonds is frequently given in terms of these denominations.

Federal Tax on the Sale of Bonds	
Par Value	Tax per Bond
$1,000	$.50
500	.25
100	.05

United States Savings bonds are among the few bonds the par value of which is other than that shown in the table. The sale of these bonds, however, is not taxable; nor is the sale of state or municipal bonds. In addition, the Federal tax is paid *only* by the seller, *not* by the buyer.

In this chapter, unless otherwise indicated, consider the par value of all bonds as $1,000.

Business Transaction 2: Find the total of the commission and the Federal tax that was paid on the sale of 2 bonds of New England T&T if they were sold at the low of the day shown in the table on pages 422–423.

Solution: Low of That Day = $101\frac{5}{8}$
Broker's Fee per Bond = $5 (See page 425)
Broker's Fee for Two Bonds = $10
Federal Tax on One $1,000 Bond = $.50
Federal Tax on Two $1,000 Bonds = $1
Broker's Fee + Federal Tax = $10 + $1
= $11

LEARNING EXERCISES

A. Find the total of the commission and the Federal tax on the following bond sales.

No.	No. of Bonds	Market Value	Commission	Federal Tax	Total
1	28	$95\frac{5}{8}$	$xxx	$xxx	$xxx
2	13	$103\frac{1}{2}$	xxx	xxx	xxx
3	45	$86\frac{3}{4}$	xxx	xxx	xxx
4	32	$52\frac{1}{2}$	xxx	xxx	xxx
5	6	$59\frac{7}{8}$	xxx	xxx	xxx
6	1	$131\frac{5}{8}$	xxx	xxx	xxx
7	12	$67\frac{1}{2}$	xxx	xxx	xxx
8	2	$176\frac{1}{4}$	xxx	xxx	xxx

B. Using the quotations in the bond table, find the total of the commission and Federal tax on the following bond sales.

No.	Company	Selling at	No. of Bonds	Commission	Federal Tax	Total
1	Alcoa	Low	1	$xxx	$xxx	$xxx
2	Armour	High	5	xxx	xxx	xxx
3	B & O 4s	High	5	xxx	xxx	xxx
4	Det Edis $3\frac{3}{4}$s	Low	2	xxx	xxx	xxx
5	Nor Pac 3s	High	3	xxx	xxx	xxx
6	So Pac $4\frac{1}{2}$s	Last	3	xxx	xxx	xxx

C. *Problems to Be Solved*

1. Allan Clayton purchased 2 Northern Pacific 3% bonds at $67\frac{3}{4}$. How much commission and Federal tax did he have to pay for this purchase?

2. How large was the Federal tax and the brokerage on the sale of 3 $500 par-value bonds that sold at $52\frac{5}{8}$ each?

3. Daniel Wesley sold 8 bonds of the New York, Ontario and Western Railroad at $4\frac{3}{4}$. If the bonds had a par value of $100, how much did Mr. Wesley pay in broker's fees and Federal tax?

4. What is the total of the brokerage fee and the Federal tax on the sale of 5 Italian Republic bonds that have a par value of $1,000 but that are selling for 62½?

5. If Mr. Maxwell sold 2 Cuba Railroad 4% bonds, par value $500, at 32¾, how much did he pay for commission and Federal tax?

UNIT **4**   **Computing the Accrued Interest on a Bond**

You have already learned that a bond is in reality a long-term note that is gathering interest continuously. The interest payments are made annually, semiannually, or quarterly. Thus, if these payments are made semiannually, the corporation may send out its checks on May 1 and November 1 each year. Should someone sell a bond of this corporation on June 15, it would be unfair to him if he did not receive the interest that accumulated on the note (or bond) from May 1 to June 15. Hence, the buyer has to pay the seller not only the market value of the bond but also all the interest that has accumulated on the bond from the date interest was last paid until the date that the bond is sold. This accumulated interest is called the *accrued interest* on a bond. Although the buyer pays the accrued interest to the seller at the time of the purchase, this money should not be considered as part of the cost of the purchase. The buyer will receive interest for the entire period on the next interest date and will thus have returned to him the accrued interest that he paid.

Business Transaction: How much accrued interest will the buyer have to pay the seller on the purchase of a 4½% $1,000 bond if the date of purchase was June 18 and the interest dates are May 1 and November 1?

Solution: Interest on this bond would have accrued from May 1 to June 18, or 48 days. Using the interest formula presented in Chapter 10, $I = P \times R \times T$, the accrued interest that the buyer will have to pay can be found.

Outline: Known: Principal $1,000

Rate   4½%

Time   48 Days (May 1 to June 18)

To Find: Accrued Interest

Method: $I = P \times R \times T$

$= \$1,000 \times 4\frac{1}{2}\% \times 48 \text{ days}$

$= \$1,000 \times \frac{9}{200} \times \frac{48}{360}$

$= \$6 \text{ (Accrued Interest)}$

An alternative method for finding the accrued interest would be to use the tables on pages 243, 245, and 250.

LEARNING EXERCISES

A. Find the accrued interest on each of the following bond transactions.

No.	Par Value	Interest Rate	Interest Dates	Sale Date	No. of Bonds	Accrued Interest
1	$1,000	6%	May 1 and Nov. 1	June 28	1	$xxx
2	1,000	4%	Apr. 1 and Oct. 1	July 6	2	xxx
3	1,000	$4\frac{1}{2}$%	Apr. 1 and Oct. 1	May 30	4	xxx
4	500	5%	June 1 and Dec. 1	Oct. 29	1	xxx
5	500	$5\frac{1}{2}$%	May 1 and Nov. 1	Dec. 17	2	xxx
6	1,000	$3\frac{3}{4}$%	Feb. 1 and Aug. 1	May 19	3	xxx

B. Using the quotations in the table on pages 422–423, find the accrued interest on each of the following sales. These transactions took place on October 16. Assume that all the companies in these problems have been paying their interest regularly.

No.	Company	Par Value	Interest Dates	No. of Bonds	Accrued Interest
1	Am Tobacco 3s	$1,000	Feb. 1 and Aug. 1	1	$xxx
2	Bell T Pa	1,000	Apr. 1 and Oct. 1	2	xxx
3	Colum Gas	1,000	June 1 and Dec. 1	1	xxx
4	Det Edis $3\frac{3}{4}$s	1,000	May 1 and Nov. 1	3	xxx
5	N Y Sus&W	500	Mar. 1 and Sept. 1	5	xxx
6	Int Miner	1,000	Apr. 1 and Oct. 1	4	xxx
7	Chi B & Q $3\frac{1}{8}$s	1,000	Feb. 15 and Aug. 15	3	xxx

UNIT **5** **Computing the Rate of Return on Bond Investments**

As bonds are usually purchased for the interest that the buyer will receive on his investment, the method by which the *rate of interest,* or *rate of return,* is found should be studied. The investor, with this knowledge, can then determine which bond purchase will yield him a higher rate of interest and plan his investment accordingly. It should be pointed out, however, that the rate of interest received on a bond investment is not the only item that a buyer considers before making a purchase.

Although every bond carries with it a fixed rate of interest, this is not necessarily the rate that the owner will receive on his investment. As you have already learned, the periodic interest payments are based on the par value of the bond. Bonds, however, are not purchased at their par value but at their market value. These two values are seldom the same. It is on his investment, not on the par value of the bonds, that the investor wants to know what his rate of return will be. In computing the rate of return, as with stock investments, charges other than the market value of the bond are commonly overlooked, for they are comparatively small.

Business Transaction: Francis Nelson purchased 3 $5\frac{1}{2}\%$ bonds at $95\frac{3}{4}$. If the par value of the bonds is $1,000, what rate of return is Mr. Nelson receiving?

Solution: In Unit 1 of this chapter you learned that the interest on bonds is found by multiplying the par value by the annual guaranteed rate of interest. After the actual yearly return is found, the rate of return can be determined in the same manner that the rate of return in a stock investment is found.

Outline: I = P × R × T

= $1,000 × $5\frac{1}{2}\%$ × 1 Year

= $1,000 × $\frac{11}{200}$ × 1

= $55 (Yearly Return per Bond)

Since Rate = Percentage ÷ Base (See pages 132–133)

Therefore, Rate of Return = Interest ÷ Market Value of Bond

= $55   ÷ $957.50

= .057

= 5.7%

The total bond purchase, 3 bonds, did not enter into the computation as the rate of return on 1 bond is the same as the rate of return on all.

LEARNING EXERCISES

A. Find the rate of return on each of the following bond purchases.

No.	Par Value	Market Value	Guaranteed Rate	Rate of Return
1	$1,000	94	4%	xxx%
2	1,000	102	$3\frac{1}{2}$%	xxx%
3	1,000	$97\frac{1}{2}$	$4\frac{1}{2}$%	xxx%
4	1,000	$105\frac{3}{4}$	$5\frac{1}{4}$%	xxx%
5	1,000	$84\frac{1}{4}$	3%	xxx%
6	500	$43\frac{1}{8}$	$3\frac{1}{2}$%	xxx%
7	500	$56\frac{5}{8}$	$4\frac{1}{2}$%	xxx%
8	1,000	$66\frac{1}{2}$	4%	xxx%
9	1,000	$78\frac{1}{4}$	$2\frac{7}{8}$%	xxx%
10	1,000	$92\frac{3}{4}$	4.60%	xxx%

B. *Problems to Be Solved*

1. On June 15, Paul Kernan purchased 2 $2\frac{3}{4}$% American Ore Corporation bonds at $88\frac{3}{4}$. What rate of return may Mr. Kernan expect on his investment?

2. Allison Foster purchased 1 bond each of General Motors 3% bonds maturing in 1960 and in 1969. If they were both purchased at the low of the day recorded on pages 422–423,

    a. What was the rate of return on each?

    b. How much larger was one rate than the other?

3. What rate of return would the purchaser of 3% Chile bonds receive on his investment if he purchased them at $46\frac{1}{2}$; par value of each bond is $1,000?

4. Adam Parker bought 5 $2\frac{3}{4}$% Canadian Government bonds at $92\frac{5}{8}$. What rate of income did he receive?

UNIT **6**   **What Have You Learned?**

SECTION 1   Understanding Terms

Can you match the term in the column on the left with the proper definition in the column on the right?

Term	*Definition*
1. Corporate bond	**a.** The date on which the bond is sold.
2. Market value	**b.** The original value at which a bond is issued.
3. Par value	**c.** The value that has accumulated in interest between the date that interest was last paid and the date that the bond was sold.
4. Maturity date	**d.** The date on which payment of the bond has to be made by the company.
5. Accrued interest	**e.** The value at which a bond is sold at the exchange.
	f. A long-term note issued by a corporation.

SECTION 2   You As an Investor

How wisely would you invest your money? Can you make the correct selection in each of the following situations and justify your answer? If you cannot do so, review the pages indicated at the end of the problem.

1. It is possible for you to purchase either one of two $1,000 par-value bonds at the same market price. Although they both pay the same interest rate of 5%, one pays its interest annually; the other pays it semiannually. If in every other respect they are the same, which would you purchase? (Pages 419–420.)

2. Assume that you are able to find bonds of two different companies which you feel are comparable in every respect except the price. The bonds of the first company are selling for 75½; those of the second company are selling for 95¾. The par values of both issues are the same, $1,000. The interest rate, however, on the first company's bond, is 3½%; that of the second company's is 5%. If you were going to invest the same amount of money in each, which would you choose? (Pages 429–430.)

3. According to the quotations listed on pages 422–423, the New York Central Railroad has issued 4 different bonds, all having a par value of $1,000, yet selling at different prices. Why should the market value on these bonds vary from 102 down to 67⅝? (Pages 421, 424, 429–430.)

4. According to the quotations listed in the table on pages 422–423, General Motors 3% 1960 bonds are selling for almost the same price as the higher rate 3½% General Motors 1972 bonds. On the other hand, the General Motors 3% 1969 bonds are selling for a good deal less than the 1972 bonds. How can you account for this? (Pages 421, 424, 429–430.)

SECTION 3 Review Problems

1. Find the interest for the period shown in each of the following problems. (Pages 419–420.)

No.	Market Value	Par Value	Interest Rate	Period	Interest
a	$97\frac{3}{4}$	$1,000	4%	Annually	$xxx
b	$52\frac{1}{2}$	500	$4\frac{1}{2}$%	Semian.	xxx
c	$101\frac{5}{8}$	1,000	$3\frac{3}{4}$%	Quarterly	xxx

2. How much annual interest is collected by the owner of 5 $3\frac{7}{8}$% $1,000 par-value bonds that were purchased at $92\frac{3}{4}$? (Pages 419–420.)

3. Using the bond quotations in the table on pages 422–423, answer the following questions. (Pages 421–424.)

a. What rate of interest is General Electric paying on its bonds?

b. In what year will the RCA bonds mature?

c. What was the highest price paid for a Dow Chemical bond that year?

d. How much less did the last buyer of a Northrop bond pay that day than the last buyer of the previous day paid?

4. What is the total market value of 3 Eastern Electric bonds that are purchased at $83\frac{5}{8}$? (Pages 421–424.)

5. Using the table on pages 422–423, how much interest should the owner of 3 Goodrich Corporation bonds receive at each semiannual interest period? (Pages 419–420.)

6. How much will Raymond King have to pay in brokerage fees and Federal taxes on the sale of 4 $1,000 bonds whose market value is $102\frac{1}{2}$? (Pages 425–426.)

7. If Michael Olin sold 3 Detroit Edison $3\frac{3}{4}$% bonds at the high of the day's transactions shown on pages 422–423, how much did he have to pay in broker's fees and Federal taxes? (Pages 425–426.)

8. What is the accrued interest on 2 $1,000 5% bonds that were purchased on July 16 if the interest is paid semiannually on May 1 and November 1? (Page 428.)

9. Assuming that the transactions recorded on pages 422–423 took place on October 16, find the accrued interest on all the Consolidated Edison bonds that were sold that day. The interest dates were February 1 and August 1. (Page 428.)

10. What rate of return will Charles Master receive on the purchase of a $4\frac{1}{2}\%$ North American Corporation bond at $87\frac{1}{4}$? The par value of this bond is $1,000. (Pages 429–430.)

11. What rate of return can the purchaser of $2\frac{3}{4}\%$ National Dairy bonds expect if the bonds were purchased the day of the transactions listed on pages 422–423? This date was October 16. (Pages 429–430.)

SECTION 4   Testing Your Understanding

40 Minutes

1. Helen Mead owns 2 $5\frac{1}{2}\%$ $1,000 par-value bonds that pay interest semiannually. How large will her interest checks be?

2. According to the bond quotations listed on pages 422–423, how much interest will the owner of 5 bonds of Columbia Gas receive annually?

3. If brokerage fees and accrued interest are not included, how much will the buyer of 3 bonds at $85\frac{7}{8}$ have to pay?

4. What are the broker's fees and the Federal taxes on 3 $1,000 bonds that were sold at $103\frac{1}{2}$?

5. How much did the seller of 2 United Gas Corporation bonds have to pay in brokerage fees and Federal tax if he sold these bonds at the low price on the day of the quotations shown on pages 422–423?

6. How large is the accrued interest on a $4\frac{1}{2}\%$ $1,000 par-value bond bought on April 12 if the interest dates are February 1 and August 1?

7. What rate of return will Stanley Rogers receive if he purchased a $3\frac{1}{4}\%$ $1,000 bond at $85\frac{1}{2}$?

8. What rate of income will the purchaser of the Philadelphia Electric bond receive if the bond was purchased on the day of the bond trading shown on pages 422–423?

UNIT 7   General Review

SECTION 1   To Improve Your Speed and Accuracy

1. Addition:

a	b	c
56,594	$4,756.04	$57\frac{3}{4}$
83,768	923.76	$86\frac{2}{3}$
27,384	8,007.19	$74\frac{1}{2}$
19,276	49.53	
75,627	275.58	

d. $59 + $126.75 + $1.29 + $.54 + $8

e. $12\frac{3}{8} + 5\frac{1}{4} + 7\frac{5}{6} + 3\frac{2}{3}$

2. Subtraction:

a. 83,409	**b.** $492.17	**c.** 36
27,256	56.25	$15\frac{5}{6}$

d. $10 − $3.47

e. $48\frac{1}{2} − 16\frac{5}{8}$

3. Multiplication:

a. 4,095 × 806   **b.** $127.56 × .75   **c.** .05 × .003

d. $3\frac{4}{5} × 5\frac{2}{3}$ **e.** $1,200 × $\frac{2}{3}$ × $\frac{3}{4}$

4. Division:

a. 26,754 ÷ 830   **b.** 236.84 ÷ 1.04   **c.** $14\frac{1}{2} ÷ 5$

d. $16 ÷ 3\frac{1}{2}$ **e.** $15\frac{3}{4} ÷ 4\frac{1}{2}$

SECTION 2   Do You Remember These?

1. An article that cost $48 was sold for $54. Find the per cent of markup based on the cost.

2. What are the discount and retail on an article that had a marked price of $52.50 but was selling at a discount of 25%?

3. If a man received $2.56 an hour, what was his salary during a week in which he worked $36\frac{1}{2}$ hours?

4. At time and a half for all hours over 40 hours a week, what salary did a man receive who worked 45 hours? His regular hourly wage was $1.96.

5. How much will be deducted for Social Security from the salary of a man who earned $123.74 a week?

6. Robert Wright worked a 48-hour week earning time and a half for all hours over 40. How large were his Social Security deductions if his regular hourly wages were $2.08?

7. $18 is what per cent more than $15?

8. $64 is what per cent less than $72?

9. Office equipment that cost $600 when new has a scrap value of $100 after 10 years. Using the straight-line method, what are the annual depreciation and the annual rate of depreciation?

10. What are the proceeds of a bank loan of $500 for 120 days if the money was borrowed at a discount rate of 6%?

18

Business Records

PREVIEW

In the early chapters of this book you followed Fred Wilson through his training period at R. C. Bond and Company. At that time you became familiar with several simple business forms, such as the bin ticket, inventory sheet, voucher-check register, daily sales record, sales slip, and invoice. Many of these forms are used only in the operation of a department store. There are, however, many forms that are a necessary part of every business.

Although a merchant conducting a small business may be able to get along without accurate records, larger concerns would soon find themselves in a great deal of difficulty without them. It is only on the basis of carefully kept records that the proprietors of a concern can judge whether or not their business is being operated profitably. In addition, Federal taxes, Social Security taxes, unemployment taxes, and many other similar items are computed on the basis of the records of the firm. Should a company fail to keep an accurate accounting of all its income and expenses, it is likely to be in difficulty with the Federal and state governments. The purpose of this chapter is to acquaint you with some of the business forms that are widely used in industry.

For Class Discussion

1. What is a profit and loss statement?

2. Explain how a family budget is similar to a profit and loss statement.

3. Can you name three other records kept by most business firms?

4. In what way do business records help in the preparation of income tax reports?

5. If a company operates at a loss during a certain year, how will the company's income and expenses compare in size?

6. What is the difference in meaning between "gross profit" and "net profit"?

7. What is meant by "petty cash"?

8. Can you name several reasons why a firm should pay most of its bills by check?

9. Name several bills that a company might receive where payment by check would be somewhat awkward.

10. Name three different courses of action that a merchant might consider taking if he received damaged goods from a manufacturer.

U N I T 1 | **Preparing a Statement of Income and Expenditures**

It is as important for a wage earner to keep a detailed record of his income and expenses as for a business or a professional man to do so. Much greater benefit and satisfaction can be derived from one's income if it is spent wisely. This result is possible only if each expenditure is thoughtfully planned and carefully recorded. Then waste and extravagance can easily be detected. Also, each person should keep a complete record of all his income and expenses for income tax purposes, so that he may have all the information needed for filling out the tax reports and for proving all expense claims if called upon by the tax examiner to do so.

A form similar to the following, on which to record income and expenditures, is often used.

WEEKLY RECORD OF INCOME AND EXPENDITURES

DATE	EXPLANATION	RECEIPTS	PAYMENTS	FOOD	CLOTH-ING	SHELTER	HEALTH	CHARITY	SAVINGS	RECRE-ATION	MISC.
19— June 1	Balance	230 00									
1	Salary	132 00	20 00						15 00		5 00
2	Rent		90 00			90 00					
3	Food		17 10	17 10							
3	Electric light		6 30			6 30					
3	Tailor bill		8 10		8 10						
4	Medication		3 95				3 95				
5	Red Cross		5 00					5 00			
6	Movies		2 70							2 70	
6	Car repairs		5 25								5 25
		362 00	158 40	17 10	8 10	96 30	3 95	5 00	15 00	2 70	10 25
6	Balance		203 60								
		362 00	362 00								
19— June 8	Balance	203 60									

All receipts are entered in the Receipts column; all payments in the Payments column. The difference between the totals of these two columns at any time represents the cash on hand. It should be noted that each expenditure is entered in the Payments column and also in a column showing the purpose of the payment. The sum of the totals of these classified columns must equal the total of the Payments column.

At the end of each week or month, as the case happens to be, all columns are added. The balance of the cash on hand is then added to the total of the Payments column to show that the sum of these two columns is equal to the total of the Receipts column. The balance is also entered in the Receipts column as the first entry for the new period.

LEARNING EXERCISES

1. On Monday, October 19, Herbert Allan had $167 cash on hand. During the week his income and household expenditures were as follows:

October 19 Water bill	$6.80	October 20 Novel	$2.75
19 Groceries	$8.15	21 Cleaning bill	$5.60

October 21 Community Chest $3	October 23 Dental bill $15
22 Maid $10	24 Salary $80
22 Dress $25.95	

On a form similar to the illustration on page 438, enter the preceding data. Complete the form, rule and total the columns, and show the cash balance at the end of the week.

2. On March 1, Eric Michael's cash record showed a balance of $309.50. During the first two weeks of March his income and expenditures were as follows:

> March 1 Paid rent, $90; light bill,
> $4.75; telephone bill, $11.20.
> Received salary check, $135.
> 3 Paid car repairs, $12;
> tailor, $3.50.
> 5 Grocery bill, $16.10.
> 6 Red Cross contribution, $5.
> 7 Lecture series, $5.
> 8 Cash dividend, telephone
> stock, $27.
> 11 Milk bill, $3.60.
> 12 Purchased radio, $27.50.
> 14 Butcher bill, $10.95

On a record of income and expenditures, enter the preceding data. Complete the form, rule and total the columns, and show the cash balance on March 14.

UNIT **2**   **Keeping a Petty Cash Book**

Nearly all business firms deposit in the bank all cash taken in and then pay all bills by check. In paying by check, the theft of funds is prevented and all payments can be proved by the canceled checks returned by the bank.

This is an excellent system; nevertheless, it presents a problem. Should a check be prepared to pay for a collect telegram? When 20 cents in carfare is to be given to a messenger sent on an errand? When 3 cents must be given to the mailman for insufficient postage on a letter?

Writing checks takes time and costs money. Banks try to discourage the writing of checks for small amounts. What, then, is the answer? How can these small expenditures be handled?

Most firms set up a *petty cash fund*, out of which fund these small expenses are paid. A check is drawn payable to "Petty Cash" for a set sum. This money is usually kept in a small metal box. All expenditures for carfare, postage, telegrams, express charges, incidental office supplies, and similar expenses are paid from the petty cash fund. A receipt, called a *petty cash voucher*, is prepared for each payment; this voucher or a receipted bill is proof that the money was paid as requested. The total payments, called *disbursements*, as shown by receipts and vouchers, plus the cash in the petty cash box should at all times equal the amount of the original fund set aside for petty cash.

Example

Total disbursements (receipted bills and vouchers)	$31.85
+ Cash remaining in cash box	18.15
= Original amount in fund	$50.00

If these figures do not check, an error has been made.

A record of the amount of petty cash that should be on hand and a summary of the petty cash payments, is often kept in a book called a *petty cash book*. Special columns are provided in this book so that each payment may be classified according to its particular purpose. Expenses that do not appear frequently are put in a Miscellaneous column.

Petty Cash Book

Petty Cash Fund Received	Paid Out	Date	Explanation	Carfare	Postage and Telegrams	Office Supplies	Miscellaneous
50 00		Apr. 1	Check for fund				
	1 25	2	Carbon paper			1 25	
	2 60	2	Carfare, porter	2 60			
	6 00	3	Stamps		6 00		
	70	4	Telephone, messenger				70
	6 75	5	Tire repairs, truck				6 75
	1 00	7	Typewriter ribbon			1 00	
	45	8	Carfare, messenger	45			
	9 35	9	Repairs to office machines				9 35
	1 15	10	Telegram		1 15		
	1 75	12	Repairs to lock				1 75
	19 00		Petty cash on hand				
50 00	50 00		Totals	3 05	7 15	2 25	18 55
19 00		Apr. 13	Petty cash on hand				
31 00		13	Check for total payments				

A section of a petty cash book in which a series of small expenditures is recorded is shown on page 440.

LEARNING EXERCISES

1. A $25 petty cash fund was set up by the Charleton Sales Company to be used to meet small miscellaneous expenses that may arise.

The following expenses were paid out by the fund during the week of July 18.

July 18 Paid $1.25 for manila envelopes.
18 Contributed $2.50 to Heart Fund.
19 Paid $1.50 for stamps.
20 Paid $1.39 for stencils.
21 Paid 40 cents for carfare.
21 Contributed $2 to Girl Scout fund.
22 Paid 79 cents for correction fluid.
22 Paid 30 cents for paper clips.
23 Paid 95 cents for filing folders.
23 Paid $1.35 for telegram.

Rule a petty cash book similar to the illustration on page 440, and enter all transactions affecting the petty cash fund. Balance and indicate cash on hand. Show the amount necessary to return the fund to the original amount of $25.

2. Record the following transactions in a petty cash book similar to the one on page 440. Balance and rule the petty cash book. Indicate the amount necessary to return the fund to the original amount.

March 1 Drew $50 to set up petty cash fund.
1 Paid 80 cents for carfare.
2 Purchased filing cards, 40 cents.
2 Paid collect telegram, 90 cents.
3 Bought typewriter ribbon, $1.25.
3 Contributed $3 to Red Cross.
4 Paid $1.87 for express charges.
4 Paid $2.25 for stamps.
5 Paid $1.75 for rubber stamp.
6 Purchased carbon paper, $1.85.
6 Contributed $2 to Boy Scout fund.
6 Paid $3.25 to repair typewriter.
6 Bought 1 dozen pencils, 84 cents.

UNIT 3   Preparing Purchases and Sales Records

SECTION 1   Preparing a Purchases Journal

The difference between success and failure in business may depend on the accuracy of the business records. An error in recording expenses or cost of goods can often be responsible for huge business losses instead of profits.

A well-run business checks and records carefully all invoices for goods received. The book in which the purchases are recorded is called the *purchases journal*.

A purchases journal in which a series of purchase invoices has been recorded is shown here.

Purchases Journal   Page 4

Date	Invoice No.	Name of Creditor	Address	Terms	F	Amount
Apr. 1	253	Jackson Products Co	New York	5/10, n/30		1 86 50
9	625	Linden Supply Co	Trenton	Net		9 56 5
12	310	Victory Mfg. Co	Chicago	2/10, n/30		3 50 00
23	786	Maxwell Brothers	Boston	n/30		3 16 70
30	525	Clark Supply Co	El Paso	2/10, n/60		2 49 00
		Total Purchases				11 97 85

LEARNING EXERCISES

1. The Hogan Plumbing Company made the following purchases during the first week in May:

May 1   Ohio Supply Company, Dayton; terms, 5/10, n/30; $416.

    3   Marine Manufacturing Company, Pittsfield; terms, net 60 days; $277.75.

    4   Hoosier Cabinet Company, Camden; terms, 2/10, n/30; $903.50.

    6   Wholesale Supplies, Inc., Buffalo; terms, 5/10, n/60; $519.75.

    7   Plumbers Equipment Company, Sioux City; terms, n/30; $840.80.

    8   Hilton Supply Company, Fort Worth; terms, 5/10, n/60; $372.25.

On a form similar to the one on page 442, record these purchases and find the total purchases.

2. Complete the following table. The total of the Net Purchases column must be equal to the difference between the total of Gross Purchases and that of Returns and Allowances.

Article	Gross Purchases	Returns and Allowances	Net Purchases
Tires	$462	$ 94	$xxx
Jacks	117	38	xxx
Seat covers	315	87	xxx
Tools	286	69	xxx
Radios	509	142	xxx
Heaters	163	37	xxx
Antifreeze	76	29	xxx
Total	$xxx	$xxx	$xxx

SECTION 2   Preparing a Sales Journal

Charge sales (goods sold on credit) are usually recorded by the merchant from the sales slips and charged direct to the customers' accounts.

Many firms, however, prefer to enter all charge sales in a special book called a *sales journal* before recording them in the individual accounts with customers. This sales journal provides a duplicate record of all transactions in case any slips should be lost.

A sales journal in which a series of sales slips has been recorded is shown here.

Sales Journal   Page 7

Date	Sale No.	Name of Customer	Address	F	Amount
19—					
July 1	22	John Campbell	83 Ocean Avenue		115 10
2	23	Henry Fahey	212 Linden Avenue		82 65
3	24	Charles Chase	93 Bentley Street		216 80
5	25	Henry Lloyd	113 Sherman Place		107 45
9	26	William Holsey	338 Hudson Street		98 75
10	27	Wilbur Ross	155 Dwight Street		346 35
13	28	Joseph Newman	20 Lincoln Road		73 40
14	29	Robert Irwin	87 Dwight Street		100 60
		Total Sales			1141 10

LEARNING EXERCISES

1. Complete the following sales record for the 6 months ending June 30, 19—. The total of the Net Sales column must be equal to the difference between the total of Gross Sales and that of Returns and Allowances.

Month	Gross Sales	Returns and Allowances	Net Sales
January	$716	$127	$xxx
February	487	109	xxx
March	590	89	xxx
April	936	247	xxx
May	872	186	xxx
June	698	109	xxx
Total	$xxx	$xxx	$xxx

2. On a form similar to the following, record the gross sales, the discount allowed, and the net sales in the transactions that follow. Total and check all columns.

Assume that each customer took advantage of the discount offered.

Net Sales Record

Date	F.	Customer	Terms	Gross Sales	Discount	Net Sales
19— Aug. 1		J. Kresh	Cash	$87.60	$1.75	$85.85

August 1 Sold to J. Kresh, for cash, merchandise for $87.60, less 2%.

1 Sold to H. Whalen goods for $175; terms, 2/10, n/60.

3 Sold to L. Burton, for cash, goods for $212.10, less 1%.

4 Sold to S. Stone, for cash, merchandise for $88.85, less 2%.

4 Sold to B. Feller goods for $246.75; terms, 2/10, n/30.

5 Sold to T. Steer goods for $319.60; terms, 3/10, n/60.

6 Sold to F. Walters, for cash, merchandise for $282.90, less 2%.

UNIT 4 Preparing a Profit and Loss Statement

The financial report showing the earnings, expenses, and profit or loss of a business is called a *profit and loss statement*. If the expenses are less than the income, the net profit is determined by subtracting the total expenses from the total income. If the expenses exceed the income, a net loss results.

Business Transaction 1: A florist had a total income of $1,225 in the month of March. His total expenses for the month were $970. (*a*) What was his net profit? (*b*) What effect does the profit have on his proprietorship? (*c*) If his proprietorship at the beginning of the month was $4,650, what is his present proprietorship?

(*a*) Total Income $1,225
    Total Expenses   970
    Net Profit $ 255

(*b*) The net profit increases his proprietorship by $255.

(*c*) His present proprietorship is $4,650 + $255, or $4,905.
    Beginning Proprietorship $4,650
    Net Profit   255
    Present Proprietorship $4,905

If the expenses of a business exceed the income, the difference is called the *net loss*. This loss has the effect of decreasing the proprietorship. Thus, if the total income was $910 and the expenses were $1,135, the net loss equals $1,135 minus $910, or $225.

If the proprietorship, or capital, at the beginning of the period was $5,615, the present capital would be $5,615 minus $225, or $5,390.

In ascertaining the net profit for a trading business, it is necessary to determine, first, the profit on sales, or gross profit, by subtracting the cost price from the selling price of merchandise, and then to find the net profit by subtracting the expenses from the gross profit.

Business Transaction 2: Thomas Cook, a tire dealer, sold all his $1,200 worth of stock for $1,500 and incurred $60 expenses in so doing. His net profit would be computed as follows:

Selling Price	$1,500		Sales	$1,500
Cost Price	1,200		Purchases	1,200
Profit on Sales	$ 300	or	Profit on Sales,	
Less Expenses	60		or Gross Profit	$ 300
Net Profit	$ 240		Less Expenses	60
			Net Profit	$ 240

It is not customary for an operating business to sell, during a business period, all the goods that it has purchased. There will usually be merchandise on hand at the end of the period. This merchandise is referred to as the *inventory.*

If, in the preceeding illustration, the dealer had sold only $1,050 worth of his goods, he would have an inventory remaining of $150. In determining the profit or loss, the inventory would be shown on the statement as follows:

THOMAS COOK
PROFIT AND LOSS STATEMENT
June 30, 19--

Income from Sales			
Sales		$1,500.00	100%
Cost of Goods Sold			
Purchases	$1,200.00		
Mdse. Inv., June 30	150.00		
Cost of Goods Sold		1,050.00	70%
Gross Profit		$ 450.00	30%
Operating Expense			
Expense		60.00	4%
Net Profit		$ 390.00	26%

From this statement, it can readily be seen that the cost of sales is found by subtracting the merchandise inventory from the purchases ($1,200 minus $150). If the cost of sales is less than the sales, the gross profit is the difference between the sales and the cost of sales ($1,500 minus $1,050). If the cost of sales is greater than the sales, a gross loss results. The net profit is the difference between the gross profit and the expense ($450 minus $60).

By using the net sales in a profit and loss statement as a base (100%), it is possible to find the per cent of sales that is taken up by the cost of goods sold, by the gross profit, by the operating expenses, and by the net profit. A comparison of the per cents for a given year with those of preceding years shows whether or not sales, cost of goods sold, expenses, and net profit are increasing or decreasing.

If Thomas Cook had incurred $560 expenses instead of $60, his profit and loss statement would show a net loss. The gross profit and net loss section of the profit and loss statement would be shown as follows:

Gross Profit	$450.00
Operating Expense:	
Expense	560.00
Net Loss	$110.00

This computation shows that the accurate determination of the profit or loss of a business depends almost entirely on a person's proficiency in using the fundamental operations of arithmetic.

LEARNING EXERCISES

Problems to Be Solved

1. A gasoline-station owner had a total income of $3,305 during the month of August. His total expenses for the month were $2,860. What was his net profit?

2. Ross, a wholesale produce dealer, sold fruits and vegetables during a current month for $5,645. If his total expenses amounted to $6,310, did the business show a profit or a loss during the month? How much?

3. During the month of May, Marker sold all his merchandise for $2,375. If the merchandise cost $1,635 and the expenses incurred in operating the business amounted to $290, how much did he gain or lose?

4. Hill, a merchant, sold goods during his first month of business for $5,105. His purchases had amounted to $6,895. He had $2,245 worth of goods on hand at the end of the month. If his expenses amounted to $120, did he incur a profit or a loss during the period? How much? Present this information on a form (profit and loss statement) similar to the one used in the business transaction on pages 445–446.

5. Assume that Hill's expenses in Problem 4 had amounted to $750. Prepare a profit and loss statement showing the effect of this item.

6. Roth's records for the month of April disclosed the following information: sales, $2,105; purchases, $2,415; merchandise inventory, $510; expenses, $220. Prepare a profit and loss statement.

7. Hilton's records for the month of July disclosed the following information: sales, $5,635; purchases, $6,870; merchandise inventory, $1,095; expenses, $285. Prepare a profit and loss statement.

8. A high school student operated a small business in his home, selling greeting cards, stationery, school supplies, and similar items. During the month of December, his sales amounted to $210.50, his purchases to $145, and his expenses to $28.70. If his inventory at the end of the month was worth $19.56, how much did he clear? (Show all information on a profit and loss statement.)

UNIT 5   Preparing a Balance Sheet

Books are kept by a business to provide the owner with a detailed record of all transactions. These records, if properly kept, disclose what the business owns (its assets), what it owes (its liabilities), how much the owner is worth (his proprietorship, or capital), and the income and expenses during a specific period of time. Each item of information is summarized in a statement called an *account*. To aid in determining the profit or loss and the proprietorship, or capital, the balances of the accounts are listed in two parallel columns, assets and expenses in one column; liabilities, capital, and income in the second column. Such a list is referred to as a *trial balance*.

The income and expense accounts in the trial balance are used in preparing a profit and loss statement. What the business owns (the asset accounts in the trial balance plus the inventory) minus what the business owes (the liabilities) represents what the owner is worth (proprietorship, or capital). A statement showing this information is called a *balance sheet*. Thus, assets minus liabilities equals net worth.

A business is considered *solvent* when its assets are sufficient to pay off all its liabilities. If its assets are not sufficient to pay off all its liabilities, the business is *insolvent*. The amount that would remain unpaid if all assets were used in paying off liabilities is referred to as the *net insolvency* of a business.

In the preparation of a balance sheet, list the assets first; then list the liabilities. If the assets are greater, the difference between the assets and the liabilities is the net worth, or proprietorship. If the liabilities are greater than the assets, the difference would represent the net insolvency of the business.

The list of the assets should include the item Cash first, followed by the total of all promissory notes owed to the business, recorded as Notes Receivable. The sum of all amounts due from customers is listed as Accounts Receivable. The total value of goods in stock is listed under the heading "Merchandise." Fixtures and Real Estate are recorded last under assets.

A similar list of liabilities is then recorded. All notes owed by the business are grouped together under Notes Payable. All other amounts owed by the business are listed under Accounts Payable.

Business Transaction: John Turner is the proprietor of an office-supply firm. A summary of the accounts on his books at the end of the month, May 31, disclosed the following information (trial balance):

	Assets and Expenses	Liabilities, Capital, and Income
Cash	720 00	
Due from Charles Semple	85 00	
Equipment	500 00	
Owed to Harold Darwin		105 00
John Turner, Capital (May 1)		1,320 00
Sales		1,875 00
Purchases	1,590 00	
Expenses	405 00	
	3,300 00	3,300 00

Unsold merchandise on May 31 (merchandise inventory) amounted to $535.

a. Prepare a profit and loss statement in order that Turner may learn whether he earned a profit during the month or suffered a loss.

JOHN TURNER
PROFIT AND LOSS STATEMENT
May 1—31, 19--

Income from Sales:		
Sales		$1,875.00
Cost of Sales:		
Purchases	$1,590.00	
Mdse. Inv., May 31	535.00	
Cost of Sales		1,055.00
Gross Profit		$ 820.00
Operating Expense:		
Expense		405.00
Net Profit		$ 415.00

b. From the information in the trial balance, determine Turner's present capital, or proprietorship.

JOHN TURNER
PRESENT PROPRIETORSHIP
May 31, 19--

What He Owns

Cash	$ 720.00	
Due from Charles Semple	85.00	
Equipment	500.00	
Merchandise Inventory	535.00	$1,840.00

What He Owes

Owed to Harold Darwin	105.00

What He Is Worth

John Turner, Present Capital	**$1,735.00**

Proof of Present Capital, or Proprietorship

John Turner, Capital, in Trial Balance	$1,320
Net Profit from Profit and Loss Statement	415
John Turner, Present Capital	$1,735

The formula: What He Owns minus What He Owes equals What He Is Worth may be stated as What He Owns (Assets) = What He Owes (Liabilities) + What He Is Worth (Proprietorship, or Capital). $A - L = N W$ or $A = L + N W$

This formula may be shown in the balance sheet as follows:

JOHN TURNER
BALANCE SHEET
May 31, 19--

Assets

Cash	$ 720.00	
Semple	85.00	
Equipment	500.00	
Merchandise Inventory	535.00	
Total Assets		$1,840.00

Liabilities

Harold Darwin	$ 105.00

Proprietorship

John Turner, Capital, May 1	$1,320.00	
Add: Net Profit	415.00	
John Turner, Present Capital		1,735.00
Total Liabilities and Proprietorship		$1,840.00

For Class Discussion

1. What is meant by "business insolvency"? Is John Turner's firm solvent or insolvent?

2. What is the proprietorship of a business? How is it represented?

3. What is the total that John Turner owned? What name is applied to the things a man owns?

4. What is the total that John Turner owed? What name is applied to the debts that a man has?

5. How is the proprietorship, or net worth, determined?

6. What is meant by the statement, "A business is solvent"?

7. John Turner's assets total $1,840; his liabilities, $105. What is his net worth?

8. If Mr. Turner's assets totaled $105 and his liabilities, $1,840, would his business be considered solvent? Why?

LEARNING EXERCISES

Problems to Be Solved

1. The accounts on the books of William Burke on June 30 disclosed the following information: cash, $1,375; due from customers, $255; furniture, $875; due creditors, $110; William Burke, capital, June 1, $3,655; sales, $6,655; purchases, $7,100; expenses, $815. Merchandise inventory on June 30, amounted to $1,805.

a. Prepare a trial balance.

b. Did William Burke's transactions during the month of June result in a net profit or a net loss? How much? (Prepare a profit and loss statement.)

c. What was Burke's proprietorship, or capital, on June 30? Prove. (Prepare a balance sheet.)

2. The following trial balance was taken from the books of Anthony Ellis on March 31.

ANTHONY ELLIS

TRIAL BALANCE, MARCH 31, 19—

Cash.	$1,665.00	
C. Cook.	272.50	
Fixtures.	1,350.00	
T. Thomas.		$ 150.00
Anthony Ellis, Capital (Mar. 1).		3,725.50
Sales.		2,815.00
Purchases.	3,090.00	
Expense.	313.00	
	$6,690.50	$6,690.50

The merchandise inventory on March 31 was $920.

a. Prepare a profit and loss statement.

b. Prepare a balance sheet.

3. From the following data, prepare a balance sheet as of December 31, showing Robert Walton's proprietorship: cash, **$315.85**; value of merchandise, $1,672.80; due from charge customers, **$276.40**; due from Thomas Duff, $100 on a promissory note; value of furniture, $2,400; owed to C. Rand, $84.80; owed to L. Fromm, $90.65; owed to the Franklin Trust Company, $500 on a promissory note.

4. The Square Music Shop has assets as follows: cash, **$611.25**; merchandise in stock, **$6,824**; store furnishings, **$2,775**; and other assets, $1,500. Its liabilities include a $600 note and $1,850 due creditors. Find the capital.

5. Prepare a balance sheet as of June 30 for Charles Wright, haberdasher. Assets: cash, $450; a promissory note signed by T. Drew, **$62.25**; a note by H. Hornung, $150; due from customers on charge accounts, **$511.75**; merchandise in stock, **$8,335**; furniture and fixtures, **$4,210**. Liabilities: owed J. Ellis on a note, $250; owed M. Brill, $85.

6. On December 31, the Women's Shop owns cash, $880.50; merchandise, **$6,445**; other assets, **$3,215**. Liabilities consist of a $780 note, $500 due the Teeners Dress Company, and $375 due the Hanover Shoe Company. Find the capital or net worth of the Women's Shop.

UNIT **6**   **What Have You Learned?**

SECTION 1   Understanding Terms

Can you match the term in the column on the left with the proper definition in the column on the right?

Term	*Definition*
1. Profit and loss statement	**a.** Merchandise on hand at any time.
2. Inventory	**b.** A statement showing the assets, liabilities, and capital of a business.
3. Solvent	
4. Net profit	**c.** A list of the accounts of a business arranged in two parallel columns.
5. Balance sheet	
6. Purchases journal	**d.** The financial report showing the earnings, expenses, and profit or loss.
7. Petty cash fund	

Term (Continued)	*Definition (Continued)*

8. Gross purchases
9. Sales journal
10. Trial balance

e. Amount remaining when the expenses are subtracted from the total income.

f. When the assets of a business are sufficient to pay off all its liabilities.

g. A record of all merchandise purchased.

h. The total of the purchases journal for any period.

i. A record of all sales returns and allowances.

j. The book in which all sales on credit are recorded.

k. The money used to pay small business expenses.

SECTION 2   How Well Do You Understand Business Records?

Some of the following statements are true and some are false. If you are not sure of their truth or falsity, review the information given on the pages indicated after each statement.

1. The difference between the assets and the liabilities of a business is the profit earned by the business. (Page 448.)

2. A profit and loss statement and a balance sheet can be prepared only from the information provided by a trial balance. (Pages 448–450.)

3. The amount of unsold merchandise on hand at any time is referred to as the inventory. (Page 446.)

4. Out of a total of $4,670 worth of goods purchased, $385 worth was returned because of defects; and a credit of $96.50 was received because of damaged goods. The net purchases totaled $4,188.50. (Page 443.)

5. If, in Problem 4, the merchandise inventory was $2,370, the cost of goods sold amounted to $6,558.50. (Page 446.)

6. An excellent method of handling small expenditures in a business and of eliminating much record keeping is to keep a sum of money in a drawer out of which these payments are to be made. (Pages 439–440.)

7. Terms of credit as 3/10, n/30 on a purchase invoice means that 3% may be deducted from the net amount of the invoice if it is paid in from 10 to 30 days. (Page 203.)

8. It is good business practice to pay all expenses by check no matter how small they may be. (Pages 439–440.)

9. By keeping detailed records of income and expenses, a wage earner, as well as a business or professional man, can always detect waste and extravagance. (Pages 445–447.)

10. Receipted bills and vouchers in the petty cash box totaled $37.86. If the cash box also contained $12.14 in cash, the original amount in the petty cash fund must have been $25.72. (Pages 439–440.)

11. Because the amount of returns and allowances in most businesses is relatively small, keeping separate records of this item would result in a waste of time and money. (Page 443.)

12. Sales of goods on credit are always recorded direct from the sales ticket to the account of the person who will have to pay for the goods. (Page 443.)

SECTION 3   Review Problems

1. On June 1, Clare Boyd had $276.50 cash on hand. During the week he paid the following household bills:

June 1	Butcher bill, $12.65.
1	Light bill, $4.76.
2	Cleaning bill, $2.75.
2	Bill for dental services, $15.
3	Red Cross contribution, $5.
4	Bag and shoes, $27.80.
5	Grocery bill, $8.98.
5	Maid services, $7.
6	Concert series, $6.50.
6	Car repair bill, $11.35.
6	Telephone bill, $9.95.

Enter the foregoing data in a record of income and expenditures. Complete the form and show the cash balance on June 6. (Page 438.)

2. Donald West entered the automobile-accessory business, purchasing $3,485 worth of merchandise. During the first month, his sales amounted to $1,816. If he had $2,338 worth of goods on hand at the end of the month and his expenses amounted to $308, did he make a profit or incur a loss? How much? (Show this information on a profit and loss statement.) (Page 446.)

3. The Beck Shoe Company set up a $25 petty cash fund. During the first week that the fund was used, the following expenses were paid out.

Dec. 1	Bought typewriter ribbon for $1.10.
1	Paid for telephone call made by messenger, 25 cents.
1	Contributed $1.50 to Volunteer Firemen's Fund.

Dec. 2   Paid 65 cents for carfare.
   2   Paid $4.30 for repairs to car.
   3   Bought stamps for $1.80.
   4   Paid $2.98 for expenses.
   4   Sent telegram; cost $1.45.
   5   Sent $3 contribution to Cancer Fund.
   6   Paid $1.75 for rubber stamp.
   6   Bought manila folders for $1.98.
   6   Paid 60 cents for cellophane tape.

Enter all transactions in a petty cash book. Balance and rule. Indicate amount necessary to replenish fund. (Page 440.)

4. The Dobbs Toy Shop has assets as follows: cash, $597.70; goods in stock, $4,091.15; furnishings and equipment, $2,100; other assets, $2,400. Its liabilities include a $420 note and $3,160 due creditors. Find the net worth of the business. (Page 450.)

5. Prepare a balance sheet as of December 31, 19—, for Clark Hawes, merchant. Assets: cash, $1,126; a note signed by Thomas Carroll, $195; a note by Elvis Drew, $250; due from customers, $828.60; merchandise on hand, $6,764; furniture and fixtures, $3,520. Liabilities: owed Mr. Newton on a note, $750; owed Harry Oliver, $162. (Page 450.)

6. The following trial balance was taken from the books of Stephen Carlton on June 30, 19—.

STEPHEN CARLTON
TRIAL BALANCE—JUNE 30, 19—

Cash	$1,008.50	
F. Brooks	125.80	
S. Henry	460.75	
Furniture	800.00	
B. Alton		$ 500.00
Sales		4,270.50
Purchases	6,539.00	
Expense	645.50	
Stephen Carlton, Capital (June 1)		4,809.05
	$9,579.55	$9,579.55

Merchandise inventory on June 30, $3,415.
a. Prepare a profit and loss statement. (Page 449.)
b. Prepare a balance sheet. (Page 450.)

SECTION 4   Testing Your Understanding

40 minutes

1. On July 1, Joel Allan's cash record showed a balance of $167.75. During the following week, his income and expenditures were as follows:

July 1	Salary check, $150; paid rent, $85; paid for maid service, $7.50.
2	Paid telephone bill, $9.70; received cash dividend on stock, $18.50.
3	Paid tailor bill, $8; paid grocery bill, $3.95.
4	Bought chair for $6.50 and ladder for $4.95.
5	Paid milk bill, $4.10; paid for new tire for car, $12.80.
6	Contributed $3 to March of Dimes. Paid for repairs to refrigerator, $9.

In a record of income and expenditures, enter the foregoing data. Complete the form and show the cash balance on July 6.

2. Maddock's records for the month of October disclosed the following information: sales, $3,365.50; purchases, $5,019; expenses, $258.60; merchandise on hand at end of month, $2,565.

Did these transactions result in a profit or a loss for the month? Show this information by preparing a profit and loss statement.

3. On June 30, Mark Brink's assets were as follows: cash $1,019.20; merchandise inventory, $3,383; store fixtures, $2,500; other assets, $2,000.

His liabilities included a $750 note due in 60 days and $1,700 due creditors. Prepare a balance sheet.

4. The records of the Economy Drug Company during the first month of business in March, 19—, showed that sales totaled $4,465. Total purchases amounted to $6,758; defective goods returned were valued at $283, and a $250 reduction in price was received as a credit because of damaged merchandise.

The value of goods on hand at the end of the month was $3,198. If the expenses amounted to $422.25, to how much did the profit amount?

5. Prepare a profit and loss statement and a balance sheet from the following information:

FRED HILL NOVELTIES
DECEMBER 31, 19—

Cash	$1,526.50	
Due from J. Lewis	250.00	
Furniture	1,200.00	
Sales		$3,880.75
Purchases	4,939.50	
Expense	685.00	
Fred Hill Novelties, Capital (Dec. 1)		4,720.25
	$8,601.00	$8,601.00

Goods on hand on December 31 were valued at **$2,793**.

UNIT 7 General Review

SECTION 1 To Improve Your Speed and Accuracy

1. Add:

a	b	c	d	e	f
$\frac{1}{2}$	$\frac{5}{8}$	$\frac{2}{3}$	$\frac{7}{12}$	$24\frac{1}{2}$	$72\frac{1}{6}$
$\frac{1}{3}$	$\frac{1}{2}$	$\frac{1}{6}$	$\frac{1}{4}$	$32\frac{1}{4}$	$58\frac{5}{12}$
$\frac{1}{4}$	$\frac{5}{6}$	$\frac{1}{2}$	$\frac{5}{6}$	$51\frac{2}{3}$	$93\frac{3}{4}$
$\frac{1}{5}$	$\frac{3}{4}$	$\frac{3}{16}$	$\frac{2}{3}$	$19\frac{5}{6}$	$84\frac{1}{3}$
$\frac{1}{6}$	$\frac{1}{3}$	$\frac{7}{8}$	$\frac{1}{8}$	$64\frac{1}{8}$	$64\frac{1}{2}$

2. Subtract:

a	b	c	d	e	f
$\frac{5}{6}$	176	$24\frac{2}{3}$	253	$82\frac{1}{3}$	$95\frac{5}{8}$
$\frac{3}{4}$	$\frac{7}{8}$	$\frac{1}{2}$	$164\frac{3}{5}$	$22\frac{3}{4}$	$76\frac{5}{6}$

3. Multiply:

a. $\frac{5}{6} \times \frac{3}{4}$ **d.** $84\frac{3}{4} \times \frac{5}{12}$

b. $42 \times \frac{5}{6}$ **e.** $96\frac{2}{3} \times 42$

c. $\frac{7}{8} \times 84$ **f.** $36\frac{2}{5} \times 45\frac{3}{4}$

4. Divide:

a. $\frac{5}{16} \div \frac{7}{12}$

b. $\frac{7}{8} \div \frac{3}{4}$

c. $54 \div \frac{5}{6}$

d. $36\frac{1}{2} \div 18$

e. $75 \div 32\frac{4}{5}$

f. $56\frac{3}{4} \div 48\frac{1}{2}$

5. Complete the operations indicated.

a. 25% of $68 = ?

b. 12% of 216 = ?

c. 125% of 96 = ?

d. $\frac{1}{2}$% of $524 = ?

e. $20 is what % of $120?

f. 15 cents is what % of 75 cents?

g. 8 boxes are what % of 48 boxes?

h. 260 is what % of 325?

i. 20 is 20% of what?

j. $36 is $33\frac{1}{3}$% of what?

k. 30 is $37\frac{1}{2}$% of what?

l. 100 is 50% of what?

SECTION 2   Do You Remember These?

1. A house that cost $12,000 was rented on a yearly basis of 9% of the cost. Find the annual rent and the monthly rent.

2. An investor received a return of $170.10 on an investment of $1,890. What is the per cent of return?

3. A merchant bought a radio for $32 less $37\frac{1}{2}$% discount. He sold the radio for $32 less 25% discount. What per cent of the retail is the profit margin?

4. A camera was advertised for $48 during a 25% reduction sale. What was the original price?

5. A pair of shoes sells today for 150% of its former price. If it sold for $8.50 formerly, what is the price now?

6. An automobile that cost $1,820 when new was sold after 3 years for $750. How much did the car depreciate? What was the average yearly depreciation? What was the rate of annual depreciation?

7. A machine that sells for $220 includes a 10% tax. What is the list price of the machine?

8. Lawrence Bell borrowed $960 and paid it back in 98 days with interest at 6%. How much did he pay back?

9. Alfred Hershey discounted at 5% a 90-day non-interest-bearing note amounting to $1,250. Find the proceeds.

10. William James retired on Social Security at age 65. If his average monthly wage was $310 a month, to how much did his primary monthly benefit amount?

11. A building worth $14,000 was insured for $11,200. If the policy contained an 80% coinsurance clause, how much will the insurance company pay if a $6,400 fire loss occurs?

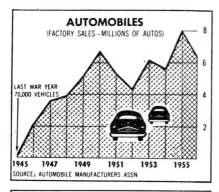

AUTOMOBILES
(FACTORY SALES -MILLIONS OF AUTOS)

LAST WAR YEAR·
70,000 VEHICLES

1945   1947   1949   1951   1953   1955
SOURCE: AUTOMOBILE MANUFACTURERS ASSN

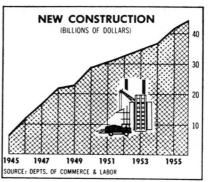

NEW CONSTRUCTION
(BILLIONS OF DOLLARS)

1945   1947   1949   1951   1953   1955
SOURCE: DEPTS. OF COMMERCE & LABOR

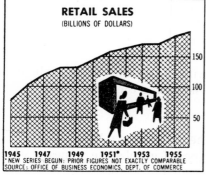

RETAIL SALES
(BILLIONS OF DOLLARS)

1945   1947   1949   1951*   1953   1955
* NEW SERIES BEGUN: PRIOR FIGURES NOT EXACTLY COMPARABLE
SOURCE: OFFICE OF BUSINESS ECONOMICS, DEPT. OF COMMERCE

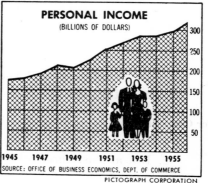

PERSONAL INCOME
(BILLIONS OF DOLLARS)

1945   1947   1949   1951   1953   1955
SOURCE: OFFICE OF BUSINESS ECONOMICS, DEPT. OF COMMERCE

PICTOGRAPH CORPORATION

19

Business Graphs

PREVIEW

After completing his dinner, Ronald Drake picked up the evening newspaper and retired to his easy chair in the living room. The day had been hot and muggy, so that at this hour Ronald was in no mood for any deep thinking. As he scanned page 15, his eye was attracted to and held by the graph shown on page 460. Always interested in what he was earning or what he thought he should be earning, Ronald lingered long enough to make a few mental notes. "Things aren't too bad for me," he thought, "it looks as if I'm earning twice as much now as I earned back in 1951 and 4 times

459

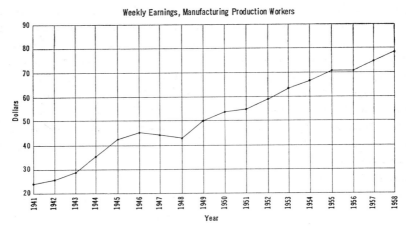

Weekly Earnings, Manufacturing Production Workers

as much as I did in 1941." And with these happy thoughts in mind, he turned the page to continue skimming the news.

For Class Discussion

1. By what special name is the graph shown here called?

2. List at least three other types of graphs the names of which you know.

3. According to this graph, did manufacturing workers earn twice as much in 1958 as they did in 1951? Explain.

4. Also, did manufacturing workers earn 4 times as much in 1958 as they did in 1941? Explain.

5. Mr. Drake is employed as a production worker in the Metal Arts Corporation. Is it possible to say from this graph that his salary was more in 1958 than it had been in 1954? Explain.

6. If Mr. Drake were a Federal civil-service employee, would he be correct in making the statements that he did? Explain.

7. From this graph, what can be said concerning the earnings of a manufacturing production worker in 1940? What can be said about his earnings in 1959?

UNIT **1**   **The Broken-Line Graph**

The graph shown at the beginning of this chapter is called a *broken-line* graph, because it consists of a series of lines drawn in different directions. These graphs are most easily constructed on paper that is ruled into small squares (quadrille ruling). The bottom line on the graph is known as either the *base line*, or *horizontal axis*. The vertical line at the left end of the horizontal axis is called the *vertical axis*. The lowest number on the vertical axis must *always* be 0. If this is not so, the reader will obtain a distorted picture of the data that has been graphed. You will notice that in the graph at the opening of this chapter, the lowest number was 20. This is *not* correct. A broken-line graph is read by comparing the distance from each of the points to the horizontal axis.

Most business charts depict conditions resulting from the passing of time. The years, months, days, or whatever the unit of time may be, are always noted along the horizontal axis.

Example

Draw a broken-line graph of the following data.

High School Enrollment in the United States

Year	Enrollment	Year	Enrollment
1900	699,000	1940	7,130,000
1910	1,115,000	1950	6,435,000
1920	2,500,000	1960	9,485,000
1930	4,812,000		(anticipated)

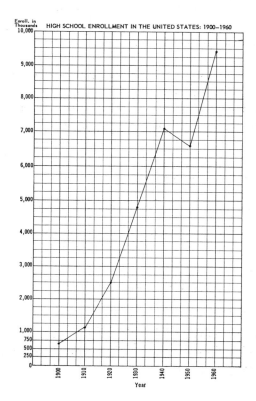

Solution: Since the enrollment for each year is a number containing 3 0's, it is advisable to drop the 0's and write the words "enrollment in thousands" at the head of the vertical axis, to make the computation easier. In the graph paper shown, there are 40 spaces along the vertical axis. Hence, the largest number (9,485) is divided by 40. This quotient is 237.125. Therefore, a more convenient larger number, such as 250, is used as the vertical unit.

LEARNING EXERCISES

A. What unit would you use for the vertical axis in each of the following cases?

No.	Number of Spaces	Largest Number to Be Graphed	No.	Number of Spaces	Largest Number to Be Graphed
1	20	100	6	30	867
2	40	160	7	40	5,657
3	25	500	8	75	24,394
4	20	74	9	80	75,946
5	50	242	10	100	256,840

B. Construct a broken-line graph for each of the following sets of data.

1. The population growth, in millions of persons, in the United States was:

Year	Population	Year	Population	Year	Population
1900	76	1920	107	1940	132
1905	84	1925	116	1945	140
1910	92	1930	123	1950	152
1915	100	1935	127	1955	165

2. The Federal debt, in billions of dollars, for the 16-year period from 1935 through 1950 was:

Year	Federal Debt	Year	Federal Debt
1935	34	1943	154
1936	37	1944	212
1937	39	1945	253
1938	41	1946	230
1939	43	1947	223
1940	45	1948	216
1941	56	1949	218
1942	102	1950	219

3. Personal savings, in hundreds of millions of dollars, in Canada from 1945 through 1955 were:

Year	Personal Savings	Year	Personal Savings
1945	16.2	1951	13.9
1946	9.9	1952	15.2
1947	4.3	1953	16.0
1948	10.1	1954	10.7
1949	10.1	1955	14.8
1950	6.5		

UNIT 2 The Bar Graph

Bar graphs are most frequently used to compare events that happen at the same time.

Example

A person interested in comparing the average individual personal incomes of persons in various sections of the United States in 1958 can do so through the use of a bar graph. These incomes are:

New England	$1,935	Central	$1,920
Middle East	2,000	Northwest	1,583
Southeast	1,233	Far West	2,094
Southwest	1,544		

Solution: Bar graphs are most easily constructed when drawn on paper divided into small squares. The unit on the vertical axis is found in exactly the same manner as was done for the broken-line graph. Thus, in the graph shown, 40 spaces were available along the vertical axis; hence, dividing 40 into the highest number ($2,094), the quotient is found to be $52.35. This quotient can be used as the vertical unit. A much more convenient unit, however, would be the number 60. Rather than draw lines between the points that have been located, as was done in the broken-line graph, rectangles are drawn from these points to the horizontal axis. The completed bars are then filled in with colored pencil.

It would have been meaningless to have presented the data in this example in the form of a broken-line graph, for the points bear no relation to one another. If you will refer to the graph of the high school enroll-

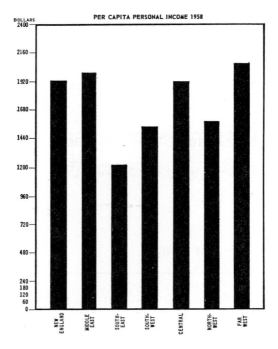

ment on page 461, it will be possible for you to approximate the enrollment for years that were not included in the data, such as 1925 or 1933. This can be done by reading the "in-between" points on the graph. Were the graph on this page a broken-line graph, points between the New England income and the Middle East income would have no meaning. Hence, sets of figures whose numbers are completely independent of one another are best graphed through a bar chart.

There are several points to keep in mind when a bar graph is being constructed.

→1. The width of the bars should be exactly the same. Were this not so, the reader would have difficulty in interpreting the picture. In the diagram shown here, it is impossible to know whether you are supposed

to compare the lengths of the bars, the widths of the bars, or perhaps even the areas of the bars. When the widths of the bars are the same, a comparison of their lengths is all that is necessary.

→**2.** From an artistic point of view, a bar graph is most pleasing to the eye if the distance between the bars is the same as the width of the bars.

The graph on page 464 is called a *vertical bar graph,* as each of the bars is drawn vertically. This same graph can be drawn horizontally by merely interchanging the vertical and horizontal axes. If this is done, the chart is called a *horizontal bar graph;* thus:

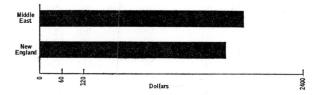

LEARNING EXERCISES

For Problems 1 and 2 construct vertical bar graphs presenting the data; for Problem 3 construct a horizontal bar graph.

1. The maximum weekly state unemployment benefits prescribed by law in nine states, Alaska, and Hawaii in 1957 were as follows:

Connecticut	$52	Michigan	$54	North Dakota	$35
Illinois	40	Nevada	50	Ohio	39
Maryland	38	New Mexico	30	Wyoming	36
	Alaska	$70	Hawaii	$35	

2. According to the 1950 census, the per cents of female employees between the ages of 14 and 64 who were working in the following occupations were:

Services (waitresses, practical nurses, laundresses, cleaners, and the like)	22.2%
Clerical and sales	36.0%
Managers and proprietors	5.0%
Professional and technical	12.0%
Operatives (packers, dressmakers, weavers, and so on)	19.0%
Farmers and farm laborers	3.8%
Craftsmen and forewomen	1.4%
Laborers	.6%

3. In 1957, the people in the United States purchased the following quantities of nondurable goods.

Goods	Millions of Dollars
Clothing and shoes	19.5
Food and alcoholic beverages	72.7
Gasoline and oil	7.0
Housefurnishings	2.4
Tobacco	5.3
Other	13.0

UNIT **3**   **The Rectangular Graph**

The rectangular graph is designed to show the reader how each single item in a group of items compares with the entire group.

Example

A family of 4 spends a yearly income of $4,500 in the following manner:

Food	$1,125	Recreation	$450
Rent	1,125	Health	225
Savings	675	Charity	225
Clothing	450	Miscellaneous	225

Draw a rectangular graph to show how these items compare with each other.

Solution: In constructing the rectangular graph, a single rectangle is divided into sections. The size of each section is found by comparing the item that represents that section with the sum of all the items. Thus, the cost of food ($1,125) in this budget is what per cent of the entire budget ($4,500)? By dividing 4,500 into 1,125 and changing the decimal to a per cent, it is found that food represents 25% of the budget. If the entire budget is to be represented by a rectangle 5 inches long, then the food item will cover 25% of the 5 inches, or $1\frac{1}{4}$ inches. The same procedure is followed for each of the remaining items. This information is then arranged in a table as follows:

Item	Cost	Per Cent	Length
Food	$1,125	25%	$1\frac{1}{4}$ inches
Rent	1,125	25%	$1\frac{1}{4}$ inches
Savings	675	15%	$\frac{3}{4}$ inch
Clothing	450	10%	$\frac{1}{2}$ inch
Recreation	450	10%	$\frac{1}{2}$ inch
Health	225	5%	$\frac{1}{4}$ inch
Charity	225	5%	$\frac{1}{4}$ inch
Miscellaneous	225	5%	$\frac{1}{4}$ inch

Rectangular Graph

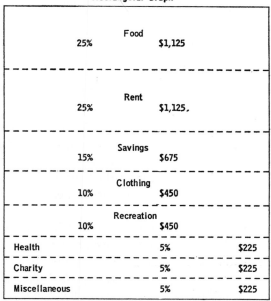

If different colors are used to represent each section, the graph will be both more appealing to the eye and easier to read. Secondly, if squared paper is available, the rectangular graph can be more readily constructed by counting squares rather than by measuring lines.

LEARNING EXERCISES

Construct a rectangular graph for each of the following sets of data.

1. Federal expenditures in 1956 are given in the following table:

Major National Security	64.8%	Interest	10.2%
Veterans	7.4%	All Other	17.6%

2. The expenses of the Provident Oil Company were distributed as follows:

Salaries and wages	58%	Taxes	4%
Rent	18%	Pension and insurance	3%
Advertising	10%	Heat, light, and power	2%
Replacements	5%		

3. Private investments abroad during a recent year were as follows:

Mining and smelting	11.7%	Public utilities	8.7%
Petroleum	30.2%	Trade	6.5%
Manufacturing	31.9%	Other industries	11.0%

UNIT 4   The Circle Graph

A *circle graph,* or *pie graph,* serves identically the same purpose as a rectangular graph—to compare a single item in a group to the entire group. The choice as to which type of graph should be used is entirely a matter of personal taste. Some persons believe that it is easier to compare the lengths of lines rather than the lengths of arcs. Others, however, contend that the circle makes a more appealing picture than the rectangle.

The computation that precedes the construction of a circle graph is exactly the same as for the rectangular graph, with one exception: the length of the rectangle is replaced by the length of the circle. Measured in degrees, the length of every circle is always 360 degrees. The instrument used to measure the length of an arc of a circle is a *protractor.* No circle graph can be drawn without the use of this instrument.

Example

Construct a circle graph showing the distribution of taxes collected by the Federal Government in 1957.

Tax	Billions of Dollars
Individual income	$34.1
Corporation income	21.2
Excise	9.2
Estate and gift	.9
Other	4.4
Total	$69.8

Solution: As with the rectangular graph, a table is designed as follows:

Tax	Amount	Per Cent	Degrees
Individual income	34.1	49	176
Corporation income	21.2	30	108
Excise	9.2	13	47
Estate and gift	.9	1.3	5
Other	4.4	6.3	23

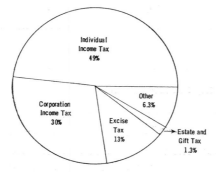

The values in the Per Cent column were found in exactly the same way as they were for the rectangular graph. The numbers in the Degrees column are based on the 360 arc degrees in a circle. Each of the numbers in the Per Cent column was multiplied by 360 degrees to find the corresponding number in the Degrees column. Using the excise tax as an example, 360 degrees was multiplied by 13%, obtaining the 47 degrees found in the Degrees column. The sum of the numbers in the Degrees column is slightly less than 360 degrees because the values in the Per Cent column were "rounded off."

LEARNING EXERCISES

Construct a circle graph for each of the following sets of data.

1. Of all the people in the United States that are 18 years of age or over, 3% are in the armed forces, 19% are veterans, and 78% have had no military experience.

2. In 1957, the Federal Government distributed its budget in the following manner:

Major national security	59%	Surplus	1%
Agriculture	8%	Other expenditures	22%
Interest on debts	10%		

3. United States investments throughout the world in 1957 were distributed as follows:

Manufacturing	33%	Public utilities	8%
Petroleum	30%	Trade	7%
Mining and smelting	11%	All other	11%

4. A budget for a family of 4 with an income of $6,000 is as follows:

Food	$1,500	Health	$180
Rent	1,200	Charity	420
Insurance and savings	900	Recreation	300
Clothing	600	Miscellaneous	900

5. In 1957, the United States male population was employed in the following occupations. (Numbers represent millions of employees.)

Skilled and semiskilled	17.5	Unskilled	4.8
Managerial and farmers	9.2	Professional and technical	3.8
Clerical and sales	5.7	Service	2.6

UNIT 5   Interpretation of Graphic Data

Frequently, a person will read into a graph information that may not be warranted by the picture. What conclusions can or cannot be drawn from a graph can best be illustrated by means of the accompanying broken-line graph. Several statements typical of those made during the examining of a graph such as the one shown are quoted, and the truth of these statements investigated.

1. "The per cent of women workers in 1950 is greater than the per cent of women workers in 1870." This statement is *true*, for the per cent values can actually be read from the graph and compared. Thus, in 1950 the per cent of women workers was 29%; in 1870 it was only 15%. Of course 29% is greater than 15%.

2. "Between 1870 and 1955 the per cent of employed women has steadily declined." This statement is *false*, for here again it is possible to read the points on the graph and actually see that for each 10-year period the per cent of employed women has either stayed the same or has increased.

3. "The per cent of women workers will be greater in 1960 than it was in 1950." Had the person said that the "per cent will *probably* be greater," he would have been on much firmer ground. Although the per cent of women employed has been steadily rising over the last 85 years, something unforeseen may occur during the next few years that may cause a dip in the graph. It

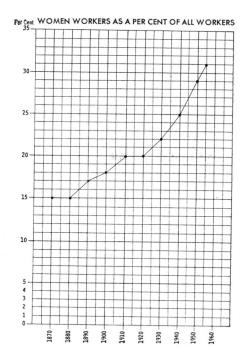

Per Cent WOMEN WORKERS AS A PER CENT OF ALL WORKERS

would be best to say that statements such as the one at the beginning of this paragraph are only "probably true." Predictions about the future or statements about the past, where the points are not actually on the graph, cannot be made with complete certainty.

4. "The per cent of women workers in 1860 was less than it was in 1870." The same analysis applies here as in Statement 3.

5. "The per cent of women workers in 1945 was less than that in 1950." Here the reader is trying to determine what happened during a year that fell between two points for which he had been given information. Again, he would have been far safer had he expressed himself in terms of "was probably less." It so happens that, in 1945, 35% of the workers were women; hence this statement would have been false. In general, however, it can be stated that, if the graph rises between two points where information is known, conclusions such as the one made at the opening of this paragraph will *probably* be true.

6. "The per cent of women employed in 1905 was greater than the per cent of women employed in 1910." On the basis of the analysis of Statement 5, it can be said that this statement is *probably false*. To say that the statement is *definitely* false would not be correct, however, for the graph gives no information concerning what occurred in 1905.

7. "A woman's place is in the home, not at work," "Women are absent from work more frequently than men," or "Women are better for detailed work than men." Statements such as these are purely a matter of personal opinion and should not be drawn on the basis of this graph. A graph gives information only about *numbers*, not about *opinions*.

8. "The rise in the per cent of women workers was caused by the need for

two salaries in a family in order to support the family." This statement, like the preceding one, cannot be made from an examination of the graph. The graph merely informs the reader that the numbers are either increasing, decreasing, or perhaps remaining the same. The graph does not show *why* this is occurring.

LEARNING EXERCISES

A. Using the accompanying graph—

1. Write 3 statements that are true.
2. Write 3 statements that are false.
3. Write 3 statements that are probably true.
4. Write 3 statements that are probably false.
5. Write 4 statements similar to those in Statements 7 and 8 above. These last four statements should merely express an opinion concerning the data. Show that they could not have been based on the graph.

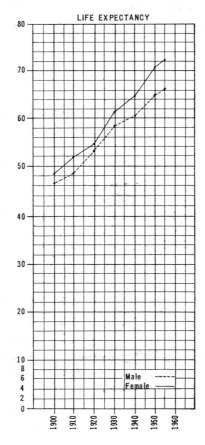

LIFE EXPECTANCY

B. Using the graphs on the following pages, list statements similar to those required in **A.**

1. Graph on page 464.
2. Graph on page 467.
3. Graph on page 469.

U N I T **6**   **What Have You Learned?**

SECTION 1   Understanding Terms

Can you match the term in the column on the left with the proper definition in the column on the right?

Term

1. Horizontal axis
2. Vertical axis
3. Vertical unit
4. Data
5. Pie graph
6. Protractor

Definition

a. An instrument designed to measure the size of arcs of a circle.
b. The difference between any two successive numbers along the vertical axis.
c. The set of numerical information from which a graph is drawn.
d. The leftmost line along which the vertical scale of a graph is written.
e. A rectangular graph.
f. The bottom line on a graph, sometimes called the base line.
g. A circle graph.

SECTION 2   How Well Can You Interpret Graphic Data?

Can you judge the truth or falsity of the statements that follow the accompanying graph? If you cannot do so, review pages 470 through 472. Each statement should be judged only in terms of this graph, not on the basis of any personal information that you might have.

    1. In 1957, the people of the United States spent more money for magazines and newspapers than they did for books and maps.

    2. In 1957, the people of the United States spent more money for

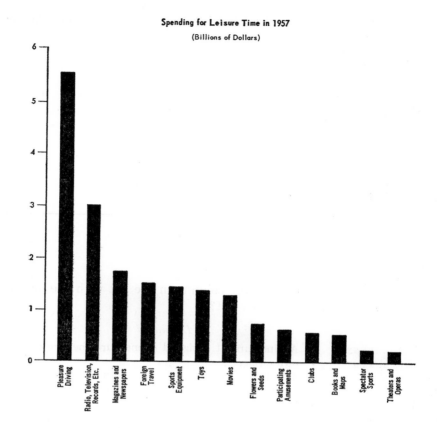

Spending for Leisure Time in 1957

(Billions of Dollars)

theater and opera tickets than they spent for admission to motion pictures.

3. In 1957, United States citizens spent more than twice as much in driving their cars in this country as they did for travel in foreign lands.

4. Not enough people were watching sports in the United States in 1957.

5. In 1957, less money was spent for opera tickets than for radios, television sets, and records.

6. People spent less money on flowers and seed than on foreign travel because flowers and seeds cost less.

7. In 1956, less money was spent for admission to sports events than on the purchase of sports equipment.

8. If people went to the theater more frequently, they would enjoy plays more than they enjoy motion pictures.

9. In 1957, more money was spent on pleasure driving than on radio sets, television sets, records, books, maps, flowers, and seeds.

10. The people who enjoy pleasure driving outnumber those who enjoy other leisure-time activities.

SECTION 3   Review Problems   *Chapter test*

1. The following data give the amount spent for new factories and equipment from 1948 through 1957. Construct a broken-line graph presenting this information. (Pages 460–461.)

	Billions of Dollars		Billions of Dollars
1948	9	1953	21
1949	15	1954	26
1950	21	1955	$26\frac{1}{2}$
1951	22	1956	28
1952	19	1957	27

2. The insurance premiums, to the nearest hundred, paid by a large manufacturing plant during an 8-year period were as follows:

1950	$37,400	1954	$25,600
1951	56,400	1955	24,800
1952	43,000	1956	33,400
1953	32,800	1957	44,200

Construct a bar graph on the basis of this information. (Pages 463–464.)

3. The Nation's timber is owned by the following groups:

Federal Government	44%	Farmers	15%
Private companies	37%	State and local governments	4%

Construct a circle graph using the above information. (Pages 468–469.)

4. People in the United States, other than farmers and miners, are employed as follows. (The figures represent millions of employed persons.)

Construct a rectangular graph showing this distribution. (Pages 466–467.)

Construction	2.6
Manufacturing	16.0
Transportation and public utilities	4.0
Wholesale and retail trade	10.4
Finance, insurance, and real estate	2.0
Service and miscellaneous	5.5
Government	6.6

SECTION 4   **Testing Your Understanding**

40 Minutes

1. The net income per person on the farm is given by the following table:

Year	Net Income	Year	Net Income
1939	$249	1949	$766
1941	350	1951	981
1943	654	1953	919
1945	722	1955	862
1947	834	1957	824

Construct a broken-line graph picturing this information.

2. The incomes of all families in the United States in 1955 were grouped as follows:

Family Earnings	Per Cent of Total Number of Families
Under $1,000	11%
$1,000 to $1,999	12%
$2,000 to $2,999	13%
$3,000 to $3,999	14%
$4,000 to $4,999	14%
$5,000 to $7,499	22%
$7,500 and over	14%

Construct a circle graph showing this distribution.

3. The 150 million people in the United States in 1950 could have been classified as follows. (The figures represent millions of people.)

Unemployed	3
Employed	59
Retired, dependent, and others	88

Construct a rectangular graph presenting this data.

UNIT 7 General Review

SECTION 1 To Improve Your Speed and Accuracy

1. Addition:

a. 736,083	**b.** $ 276.98	**c.** $43\frac{1}{3}$
695,487	49.07	$62\frac{1}{4}$
274,859	4,893.54	$7\frac{1}{2}$
947,675	604.75	$84\frac{1}{6}$
586,406	1.09	
158,398	26,725.50	

d. $.08 + $15.35 + $248 + $183.98 + $86

e. $12\frac{3}{4} + 14 + 15\frac{2}{3} + 26\frac{3}{8}$

2. Subtraction:

a. 100,000	**b.** $550.00	**c.** $57\frac{3}{4}$
43,756	23.78	$29\frac{5}{8}$

d. $273.50 − $46.86   **e.** $174\frac{2}{3} - 108\frac{5}{6}$

3. Multiplication:

a. 5,684 × 397   **b.** $4,375.50 × .045   **c.** 1.08 × .002

d. $17\frac{2}{5} \times 14\frac{1}{2}$ **e.** $1,500 × $\frac{6}{100}$ × $1\frac{1}{2}$

4. Division:

a. 375,843 ÷ 465   **b.** $325 ÷ .045   **c.** 2 ÷ .005

d. $12 \div \frac{1}{2}$ **e.** $\frac{1}{3} \div 12$

SECTION 2 Do You Remember These?

1. Men's hats were purchased for **$7.50** and sold for **$12.50**. What was the per cent of markup based on the cost?

2. Mechanical pencils that were purchased at **$1.65** each were sold at **$2.75** each. What was the per cent of markup based on the retail?

3. Money was borrowed from the bank on June 6 for a period of 90 days. What is the maturity date of the note?

4. **$500** was borrowed from the bank at $4\frac{1}{2}\%$ for a period of 120 days. What were the proceeds on the note?

5. A note dated May 14 due in 3 months was discounted at the bank on June 2. For what period did the bank hold the note?

6. An article can be purchased for $129.95 cash, or, on the installment plan, for $10.95 down and $11.50 a month for 1 year. What is the installment charge on this purchase?

7. A house valued at $25,000 was insured for $15,000 under a policy containing an 80% coinsurance clause. If fire caused damage to the property to the extent of $4,000, how large was the payment that the owner received from the insurance company?

8. If a worker's average monthly earnings for Social Security purposes are $245, what will his primary benefit be at the time he retires?

9. A man died leaving a wife and a child under 18. If the primary benefits amounted to $84.60, how much did the wife and the child receive?

10. Find the yearly dividends received on 500 shares of stock that pays a quarterly dividend of 15 cents.

11. Find the yearly rate of return on stock purchased at 45 that paid an annual dividend of $3.

12. What is the total market value of 5 bonds that are quoted at $92\frac{1}{2}$?

20

Cost of Shipping Merchandise

PREVIEW

After several months' experimentation, the engineers at the Bell Tool Manufacturing Company were successful in developing a lightweight, low-cost attachment for a portable saw they had been marketing. Not only this company, but all other firms producing portable saws, had been receiving complaints over a period of years concerning the danger of using these saws in "tight"

479

corners. The Bell Company attachment was designed to eliminate any chance of injury to the user.

Before developing this new piece of equipment, the company had limited its sales to the western seaboard area of the Nation. Knowing the appeal that this attachment would have to the large "Do-It-Yourself" market, the company decided to expand the territory in which to market their new invention. The response to advertisements placed in magazines with nationwide circulation among homeowners and amateur craftsmen was overwhelming.

This widespread response, however, created another problem that had been considered only lightly until then. How might the attachment be best shipped to customers in various parts of the country? Which of the many ways available would be the cheapest? If the least expensive way was used, would it be so slow that the customers would be annoyed by the delay in receiving their merchandise? Which of the shipping services would be the most convenient to the company and also to the purchaser? Would it be advisable to use one means of shipping under some conditions and another under other conditions? A good deal of the sales success of the Bell Tool Manufacturing Company's new appliance would depend on how these questions were answered.

For Class Discussion

1. What are several ways by which articles are shipped from one section of the country to another?

2. What is the name for the package delivery service conducted by the Federal Government?

3. What is the difference between railway freight service and fast freight service?

4. What is the difference between airmail and air freight?

5. What is meant by the term "motor freight"?

6. Which of the various ways of shipping merchandise is usually the cheapest? What is an important disadvantage of shipping merchandise by this means?

UNIT 1   **Shipping by Freight Train**

If shipments are made by land, shipping by freight train is less expensive than shipping by air or by truck. Shipping by freight train, however, is somewhat slow. The shipper who has less than a carload of merchandise to transport may find that his shipment is placed on a siding until the freight car is filled with other articles going to the same destination. This, among other things, tends to slow down freight-train service.

In computing the cost of freight shipments, articles are grouped in various classifications. Most merchandise is listed in Class 100, which implies that the *normal rates* will be applied to these articles. All other class numbers merely indicate the per cent of the normal rates that apply to the shipping costs of merchandise in these groups. Thus, an article listed in Class 82 will be shipped at rates that are 82% of the normal rates, or the Class 100 rates.

Freight rates depend not only on the class of each article but also on the distance that the article travels before it reaches the station at its destination. Hence, railroad companies prepare tables for each of their many depots listing the rates from that depot to each of the other depots. As no one railroad company services all sections of the country, freight cars are frequently rolled about the country by a great many railway companies before they reach their destinations. Therefore, the offices of railway depots must not only have rate tables covering the cost of shipments to the company's other depots but also rate tables covering transportation costs to all parts of the country. You may have often noticed a single engine pulling a large number of freight cars belonging to many different railway companies. This is due to the fact that the companies whose names appear on the box cars do not service the area where you had seen the trains. The railway that does service that area had taken over the movement of the car from the point where the previous company's service area ended.

A sample table for Class 100 articles that are shipped within the service area of a single railway company is shown on page 482.

Business Transaction 1: An article listed in Class 100 was shipped by the Pennsylvania Railroad Company from Newark, New Jersey, to Hagerstown, Maryland. What was the cost of transportation if the article weighed 4,500 pounds?

Solution: As the article weighed 4,500 pounds, which is less than 5,000 pounds, its shipping rate is found in the column headed "Less Than 5,000 Lbs." The rate for shipments from Newark, New Jersey, to Hagerstown, Maryland, is $1.93 per 100 pounds.

Outline: Rate per 100 Pounds = $1.93

Number of Hundred Pounds = 4,500 ÷ 100

= 45

Cost of 4,500 Pounds = 45 × $1.93

= $86.85

Pennsylvannia Railroad Company

From Newark and Harrison, New Jersey

Class 100 — Rate in Cents per Hundred Pounds

Includes Pickup and Delivery

Destination	Less Than 5,000 Lbs.	5,000 Lbs. and Over	Destination	Less Than 5,000 Lbs.	5,000 Lbs. and Over
Akron, Ohio	283	260	Mackinaw City, Mich.	369	346
Altoona, Pa.	213	194	Madison, Ind.	351	329
Baltimore, Md.	176	161	Nanticoke, Pa.	153	140
Barberton, Ohio	282	260	Natrona, Pa.	243	229
Canton, Ohio	277	255	Oil City, Pa.	254	233
Chester, Pa.	131	120	Olean, N. Y.	231	212
Dayton, Ohio	322	300	Penn Yan, N. Y.	213	194
Decatur, Ill.	391	369	Philadelphia, Pa.	131	120
Economy (Ambridge), Pa.	243	229	Reading, Pa.	148	135
Effner, Ill.	374	352	Richmond, Ind.	333	312
Fort Wayne, Ind.	339	317	St. Louis, Mo.	408	386
Franklin, Pa.	254	233	St. Marys, Pa.	225	206
Gary, Ind.	374	352	Tarentum, Pa.	243	229
Georgetown, Del.	179	164	Terre Haute, Ind.	369	346
Hagerstown, Md.	193	176	Uhrichsville, Ohio	277	255
Hanover, Pa.	176	161	Uniontown, Pa.	243	229
Indiana, Pa.	231	212	Vandergrift, Pa.	243	229
Indianapolis, Ind.	351	329	Van Wert, Ohio	328	306
Jeannette, Pa.	243	229	Washington, D. C.	183	167
Jeffersonville, Ind.	362	340	Weirton, W. Va.	260	239
Kalamazoo, Mich.	345	323	Xenia, Ohio	322	300
Kane, Pa.	231	212	York, Pa.	176	161
Lackawanna, N. Y.	237	218	York Haven, Pa.	168	153
Lancaster, Pa.	156	143	Zanesville, Ohio	287	265

Business Transaction 2: A shipment of 9,250 pounds of chemicals is transported from Harrison, New Jersey, to Reading, Pennsylvania. If chemicals are listed in Class 50, what is the cost of this shipment?

Solution: The rates for the shipment of articles in Class 50 are 50% of the rates in Class 100. Hence, the rate of $1.35 per 100 pounds for the transportation of articles in Class 100 from Harrison, New Jersey, to Reading, Pennsylvania, would be reduced to $.68 per 100 pounds in

Class 50 (50% of $1.35). Any fractional part of a penny is rounded off to the next higher amount.

Outline: Rate per 100 Pounds in Class 100 = $1.35
Rate per 100 Pounds in Class 50 = $.68
Number of Hundred Pounds = 9,250 ÷ 100
= 92.50
Cost of 9,250 Pounds = 92.5 × $.68
= $62.90

LEARNING EXERCISES

A. Find the cost of shipments by Pennsylvania Railroad from Newark, New Jersey, to each of the destinations listed below.

No.	Destination	Class	Weight, in Pounds	Cost
1	Tarentum, Pa.	100	3,000	$xxx
2	York, Pa.	100	8,000	xxx
3	Georgetown, Del.	100	2,400	xxx
4	Weirton, W. Va.	100	6,755	xxx
5	Penn Yan, N. Y.	80	4,600	xxx
6	Washington, D. C.	60	8,390	xxx
7	Altoona, Pa.	75	5,760	xxx
8	Canton, Ohio	84	26,700	xxx
9	York, Pa.	96	43,500	xxx
10	Gary, Ind.	68	1,275	xxx

B. *Problems to Be Solved*

1. What area of the country is serviced directly by the Pennsylvania Railroad Company?

2. 375 pounds of drugs are shipped from Harrison, New Jersey, to St. Louis, Missouri, by Pennsylvania Railroad freight. If drugs are listed in Class 50, what are the transportation costs?

3. A company shipped the following merchandise by Pennsylvania Railroad from Newark, New Jersey, to Mackinaw City, Michigan.

Weight	*Class*
524	100
486	82
695	94

Find the total cost of this shipment.

4. A carload of equipment going from Harrison, New Jersey, to Vandergrift, Pennsylvania, contained articles of the weights and classes indicated:

Weight	Class
6,275	100
2,562	100
7,948	95
14,367	84
9,572	58
36,486	75

Find the total cost of shipping this carload of goods.

UNIT **2**   **Shipping by Government Services**

SECTION 1   Parcel Post

Parcel post or, as it is sometimes called, fourth-class mail, is one of the most widely used means of shipping small articles from one section of the country to another. This service, like the delivery of letters (first-class mail), is provided by the Federal Government. Merchandise, printed matter, mailable live animals, and most other articles can be transported by parcel post. The Government, however, places limitations on the size and weight of the package being shipped. In most cases, packages mailed from a first-class post office have the following restrictions in weight.

→1. They cannot weigh more than 40 pounds if their destination is another first-class post office in a local, first, or second zone.

→2. They cannot weigh more than 20 pounds if their destination is another first-class post office in any other zone.

If the package is being delivered to a second-, third-, or fourth-class post office from any other post office, its weight cannot exceed 70 pounds. In addition, the size of the package is limited by the fact that the sum of its length and circumference at its thickest part cannot be more than 100 inches. If the mailing point and the destination are both first-class post offices, the package will not be accepted for delivery if this measurement exceeds **72** inches.

Post offices are ranked in four classes in accordance with the volume of mail that they handle. Those processing the largest quantity of mail are ranked as first-class post offices; those handling the least are fourth-class.

Parcel-post rates are based on two factors:

→1. The weight of the package.

→2. The distance from the mailing point to the destination of the package.

So that rates can be found as quickly as possible, the United States is divided into **8** zones. The word "zone," as used by the Post Office Department, simply means the distance from the mailing point to the destination of the article. Thus, rates for Zones **1** and **2** include packages that travel up to **150** miles from the post office where they were mailed.

Fourth Class (Parcel Post) Zone Rates

Weight, over 8 ounces and not exceeding:	Local	Zones						
		1 and 2	3	4	5	6	7	8
		Up to 150 miles	150 to 300 miles	300 to 600 miles	600 to 1,000 miles	1,000 to 1,400 miles	1,400 to 1,800 miles	Over 1,800 miles
1 pound.......	$0.18	$0.23	$0.23	$0.24	$0.26	$0.28	$0.30	$0.32
2 pounds......	.20	.27	.29	.31	.36	.40	.46	.51
3 pounds......	.21	.31	.34	.38	.45	.52	.61	.69
4 pounds......	.23	.35	.39	.45	.54	.64	.76	.87
5 pounds......	.24	.39	.44	.52	.63	.76	.91	1.05
6 pounds......	.26	.43	.49	.59	.73	.88	1.06	1.23
7 pounds......	.27	.47	.54	.66	.82	1.00	1.22	1.41
8 pounds......	.29	.51	.60	.73	.91	1.12	1.37	1.59
9 pounds......	.30	.55	.65	.80	1.00	1.24	1.52	1.77
10 pounds......	.32	.59	.70	.87	1.10	1.36	1.67	1.95
11 pounds......	.33	.63	.75	.93	1.19	1.48	1.82	2.13
12 pounds......	.34	.67	.80	1.00	1.28	1.60	1.98	2.31
13 pounds......	.36	.71	.85	1.07	1.37	1.72	2.13	2.49
14 pounds......	.37	.75	.90	1.14	1.47	1.84	2.28	2.67
15 pounds......	.39	.79	.96	1.21	1.56	1.96	2.43	2.85
16 pounds......	.40	.83	1.01	1.28	1.65	2.08	2.58	3.03
17 pounds......	.42	.87	1.06	1.35	1.74	2.20	2.74	3.21
18 pounds......	.43	.91	1.11	1.42	1.84	2.32	2.89	3.39
19 pounds......	.45	.95	1.16	1.49	1.93	2.44	3.04	3.57
20 pounds......	.46	.99	1.21	1.56	2.02	2.56	3.19	3.75
21 pounds......	.47	1.02	1.26	1.62	2.11	2.67	3.34	3.93
22 pounds......	.49	1.06	1.32	1.69	2.21	2.79	3.50	4.12
23 pounds......	.50	1.10	1.37	1.76	2.30	2.91	3.65	4.30
24 pounds......	.52	1.14	1.42	1.83	2.39	3.03	3.80	4.48
25 pounds......	.53	1.18	1.47	1.90	2.48	3.15	3.95	4.66

Zone 3 rates are for those packages that travel a distance of 300 to 600 miles. Greater distances apply to each of the other zones, with the very last, or Zone 8, including packages that are shipped over 1,800 miles. Each post office in the nation has a set of tables showing the distance from its location to every other post office in the country. A section of the parcel-post rate table is shown on page 485.

The Local column contains the rates for packages whose destinations are within the limits of the city in which they were mailed. Also note that no fractional parts of a pound are listed. A fraction of a pound is considered as an additional pound. For example, the rates for a package that weighs 16 pounds 2 ounces are found in the row for the 17-pound packages.

Business Transaction 1: William Burke mailed a package weighing 12 pounds 5 ounces from his local post office to a town 754 miles away. What did the postage cost?

Solution: As 754 miles is between 600 and 1,000 miles, the package was delivered to a Zone 5 distance. The weight of 12 pounds 5 ounces is considered as 13 pounds.

Outline: Cost of a 13-pound parcel to Zone 5 = $1.37

Should the sender so desire, he may insure parcel-post packages (as well as third-class mail) for an amount not exceeding $200. The cost of this insurance is given in the following table.

Amount of Insurance	Cost
$.01 to $5	$.05
5.01 to 10	.10
10.01 to 25	.15
25.01 to 50	.20
50.01 to 100	.30
100.01 to 200	.35

Business Transaction 2: A package weighing 17 pounds 3 ounces was mailed a distance of 1,475 miles. If the contents were insured for $200, what was the total mailing cost?

Solution: Cost of 18 pounds to Zone 7 = $2.89
Cost of Insurance for $200   =   .35
Total Mailing Cost   = $3.24

LEARNING EXERCISES

Find the cost of shipping the following packages by parcel post.

No.	Weight	Distance, in Miles	Insurance	Parcel-Post Fee	Insurance Fee	Total
1	17 lbs.	200	None	$xxx	$xxx	$xxx
2	12 lbs. 2 oz.	500	None	xxx	xxx	xxx
3	18 lbs.	675	$ 5	xxx	xxx	xxx
4	17 lbs. 12 oz.	1,600	50	xxx	xxx	xxx
5	23 lbs.	2,500	75	xxx	xxx	xxx
6	6 lbs. 10 oz.	Local	125	xxx	xxx	xxx
7	10 lbs. 7 oz.	120	25	xxx	xxx	xxx
8	$18\frac{1}{2}$ lbs.	1,123	55	xxx	xxx	xxx
9	$14\frac{1}{4}$ lbs.	367	8	xxx	xxx	xxx
10	$7\frac{3}{4}$ lbs.	Local	4	xxx	xxx	xxx

SECTION 2   Airmail

Airmail is not divided into classes like other postal services. Hence, the cost of transporting articles by airmail is computed in terms of the weight of the article and the distance it is shipped, not by any class.

Airmail Rates

Weight over 8 ounces, and not exceeding:	Rate					
	Zones 1, 2, and 3	Zone 4	Zone 5	Zone 6	Zone 7	Zone 8
1 pound................	$0.60	$0.65	$0.70	$0.75	$0.75	$0.80
2 pounds................	1.08	1.15	1.26	1.39	1.47	1.60
3 pounds................	1.56	1.65	1.82	2.03	2.19	2.40
4 pounds................	2.04	2.15	2.38	2.67	2.91	3.20
5 pounds................	2.52	2.65	2.94	3.31	3.63	4.00
6 pounds................	3.00	3.15	3.50	3.95	4.35	4.80
7 pounds................	3.48	3.65	4.06	4.59	5.07	5.60
8 pounds................	3.96	4.15	4.62	5.23	5.79	6.40
9 pounds................	4.44	4.65	5.18	5.87	6.51	7.20
10 pounds................	4.92	5.15	5.74	6.51	7.23	8.00
11 pounds................	5.40	5.65	6.30	7.15	7.95	8.80
12 pounds................	5.88	6.15	6.86	7.79	8.67	9.60
13 pounds................	6.36	6.65	7.42	8.43	9.39	10.40
14 pounds................	6.84	7.15	7.98	9.07	10.11	11.20
15 pounds................	7.32	7.65	8.54	9.71	10.83	12.00
16 pounds................	7.80	8.15	9.10	10.35	11.55	12.80
17 pounds................	8.28	8.65	9.66	10.99	12.27	13.60
18 pounds................	8.76	9.15	10.22	11.63	12.99	14.40
19 pounds................	9.24	9.65	10.78	12.27	13.71	15.20
20 pounds................	9.72	10.15	11.34	12.91	14.43	16.00
21 pounds................	10.20	10.65	11.90	13.55	15.15	16.80
22 pounds................	10.68	11.15	12.46	14.19	15.87	17.60
23 pounds................	11.16	11.65	13.02	14.83	16.59	18.40
24 pounds................	11.64	12.15	13.58	15.47	17.31	19.20
25 pounds................	12.12	12.65	14.14	16.11	18.03	20.00

The weight of packages is limited to 70 pounds, and the sum of the length and the circumference at the thickest part of a package cannot exceed 100 inches.

A section of the airmail rate table is shown on page 487.

In this table the zones represent the same distances as in the parcel-post table. Thus, Zones 1, 2, and 3 represent a distance up to 300 miles from the mailing point. Similarly, a package mailed to Zone 7 means that the article will travel 1,400 to 1,800 miles from the post office in which it was deposited.

Business Transaction: A package weighing 12 pounds 7 ounces is sent by airmail a distance of 927 miles. What is the postage for this shipment?

Solution: The cost of any fraction of a pound is charged on the basis of a whole pound; hence the cost of shipping 12 pounds 7 ounces by airmail is the same as the cost of 13 pounds. As 927 miles falls between 600 miles and 1,000 miles, the package is being delivered to a Zone 5 distance (see the parcel-post table).

Outline: Postage for 13 pounds to Zone 5 = $7.42

LEARNING EXERCISES

A. Find the postage on each of the following airmail deliveries.

No.	Weight	Zone	Cost
1	15 lbs.	4	$xxx
2	16 lbs. 8 oz.	7	xxx
3	8 lbs. 3 oz.	2	xxx
4	10 oz.	5	xxx
5	$5\frac{1}{2}$ lbs.	3	xxx

B. Find the postage on each of the following airmail deliveries.

No.	Weight	Distance, in Miles	Cost
1	12 lbs.	1,200	$xxx
2	17 lbs. 10 oz.	500	xxx
3	9 lbs. 3 oz.	2,425	xxx
4	10 oz.	257	xxx
5	$6\frac{1}{4}$ lbs.	752	xxx

C. How much greater is the cost of shipping the following articles by airmail than by parcel post?

No.	Weight	Distance	Airmail Cost	Parcel-Post Cost	Added Cost
1	9 lbs.	Zone 5	$xxx	$xxx	$xxx
2	17 lbs.	Zone 8	xxx	xxx	xxx
3	14 lbs. 6 oz.	Zone 3	xxx	xxx	xxx
4	12 lbs.	725 mi.	xxx	xxx	xxx
5	19 lbs. 14 oz.	2,635 mi.	xxx	xxx	xxx
6	15 oz.	1,493 mi.	xxx	xxx	xxx
7	16 lbs. 5 oz.	265 mi.	xxx	xxx	xxx

D. *Problems to Be Solved*

1. Richard Fiske sent a package weighing 14 pounds 3 ounces by parcel post from Omaha, Nebraska, to Seattle, Washington, a distance of 1,799 miles, insuring the contents for $125. If this package had been sent uninsured by airmail, how much greater would the cost have been?

2. From Billings, Montana, to Cleveland, Ohio, is a distance of 1,369 miles. How much greater is the cost of the airmail delivery of a 12-pound package than the parcel-post delivery of the same weight of package if both are insured for $75?

UNIT 3 What Have You Learned?

SECTION 1 Review Problems

1. What is the cost of shipping 7,395 pounds of merchandise in Class 82 from Harrison, New Jersey, to Hagerstown, Maryland? (Pages 481–482.)

2. A package weighing 16 pounds 2 ounces was sent by parcel post from Kansas City, Missouri, to Charleston, South Carolina, a distance of 1,115 miles. If the package was insured for $75, what was the total postage? (Pages 485–486.)

3. What is the airmail postage on a package weighing $17\frac{1}{2}$ pounds that is shipped from Raleigh, North Carolina, to Providence, Rhode Island, a distance of 670 miles? (Pages 487–488.)

4. Mrs. Carnahan, who lives in Knoxville, Tennessee, sent a package of preserves weighing 12 pounds to her daughter attending college in Burlington, Vermont. If the distance between the cities is 990 miles, how much did Mrs. Carnahan have to pay in airmail charges? (Pages 487–488.)

SECTION 2   Testing Your Understanding

40 Minutes

1. A crate of rifles weighing 970 pounds is shipped from Harrison, New Jersey, to Economy, Pennsylvania. What would be the shipping cost if the rifles, Class 95, are sent by freight?

2. The owner of a gift shop operates two stores—one in Atlantic City, New Jersey; the other in Miami, Florida. In November of one year, he shipped a package of his merchandise weighing 24 pounds from the Atlantic City store to the Miami store by parcel post. Atlantic City is 1,285 miles from Miami. What was the total postage on this shipment if it was insured for $200?

3. In reply to a rush order, Marleen's of Richmond, Virginia, sent a package of women's dresses weighing 15 pounds to New Orleans, Louisiana, by airmail (1,055 miles). What was the cost of this shipment?

4. So that his wife might receive her gift before her birthday, Tom Pelham sent it by airmail from Baltimore, Maryland, to his home in Memphis, Tennessee, 945 miles away. If the package weighed 1 pound 5 ounces, what was the cost of the postage?

5. A package weighing 9 pounds 4 ounces must be shipped from Hot Springs, Arkansas, to Norfolk, Virginia, a distance of 945 miles.

    a. What would the airmail postage be?

    b. What would be the cost by parcel post?

    c. How much greater is one than the other?

UNIT 4   General Review

SECTION 1   To Improve Your Speed and Accuracy

1. Addition:

a.	b.	c.
592,874	$ 5,624.50	24⅔
638,557	788.16	47⅚
704,639	17,935.98	31¾
387,962	67.09	56
846,143	6,275.25	
251,706	3.99	

    d. $295 + $43.27 + $.98 + $107 + $350.05

    e. $17\frac{5}{16} + 24\frac{3}{8} + 18\frac{1}{4} + 32\frac{1}{2}$

2. Subtraction:

a. 726,059	**b.** $20.00	**c.** 50
296,843	14.98	$17\frac{3}{4}$

    d. $1,000 − $238.75   **e.** $259\frac{4}{5} − 162\frac{3}{4}$

3. Multiplication:

    a. 5,083 × 509   **b.** $7,450.28 × .029   **c.** 30.05 × .04

    d. 375 × 5½¢   **e.** $2,400 × 4% × 3½

4. Division (check your answer by casting out 9's):

    a. 874 ÷ 26   **b.** 24,397 ÷ 304   **c.** 49 ÷ .23

    d. 5,097 ÷ 76.8   **e.** 59.35 ÷ .98

SECTION 2　　Do You Remember These?

1. Find the cost of 4,000 articles at $34.50 per M.

2. Using aliquot parts of $1, find the extensions in each of the following:

    a. 56 yds. @ 50¢   **c.** 24 qts. @ 16⅔¢

    b. 48 bu. @ 75¢   **d.** 45 pts. @ 40¢

3. At $2.54 an hour, what are the weekly earnings of a man who works 39½ hours?

4. 3¼% of $4,250 is how much money?

5. An article that lists at $59.50 can be bought at a 25% discount. What is the net price?

6. Successive trade discounts of 10% and 25% are equivalent to what single discount rate?

7. The price of an article was dropped from $19.98 to $14.98. What discount rate was being offered the buyer?

8. $500 was borrowed from the bank for 90 days at a discount rate of 5%. How much did the borrower receive?

9. A note dated May 5, due in 5 months, was discounted at the bank on June 11. For what period of time did the bank keep the note?

10. A loan of $150 was made by a small-loan agency. If the debt was to be paid off in 9 monthly installments of $18.75 each, how much interest was the borrower paying?

11. A man carried $50-deductible collision insurance on his car. If

the car was damaged during an accident to the extent of $247.50, how much did he collect from the insurance company?

12. At age 30, Mr. Johnson purchased a $3,000 whole-life insurance policy. After making 3 payments of $25.27 each, he died. How much money did his beneficiaries receive?

13. If the primary benefit that a retired worker is receiving is $74.60, how large will the lump-sum death benefit be at the time of his death?

14. Stock that was purchased at $52\frac{1}{2}$ pays a $3 yearly dividend. What rate of interest is the purchaser receiving on his investment?

Ewing Galloway

21

Cost of Public Utilities

PREVIEW

Mrs. Martin had spent a back-breaking spring, transplanting her perennial shrubs, sowing grass seed on the bare spots on her lawn, and planting flower seeds in the annual beds. The coming of summer failed to bring forth the dazzling array of color predicted by the seed catalogue. Rather, it ushered in a hot, dry spell that burned everything exposed to the sun. In desperation, Mrs. Martin made full use of the garden hose and her newly acquired automatic sprinkler system. Hour after hour water sprayed over her spindly plants, bringing to them what she hoped would be some badly needed nourishment.

Mrs. Martin's efforts were at last rewarded, for the fall flowers were even more colorful and more bountiful than she had dreamed they could be. But the coming of fall also brought with it the quarterly water bill. Mr. Martin's first reaction to its size was shocked amazement. "Surely an error had been made—this most certainly must be the bill for the soft-drink plant on the other side of town! If not that, then, at the very least, a computational error has occurred," he said.

His dash into the cellar to read the meter was brought to a sudden halt by the realization that the numbers on the dials were meaningless to him. Unless he could interpret the figures, he would not know whether this bill was really his.

For Class Discussion

1. By what unit of measure is water sold to the homeowner?

2. How frequently is the homeowner billed for the water that he has used?

3. How does the Water Department in a community determine how much water has been used by the occupants of a home?

4. What other utilities purchased by the homeowner are measured by meters in the house?

5. By what units of measure are these utilities purchased?

6. How frequently is the homeowner billed for the cost of the services listed in the answer to Question 4?

7. Is it possible for a homeowner to purchase these utilities from some company other than the one that is supplying him? Explain.

UNIT **1**   **Computing the Cost of Water**

Water is sold to the homeowner either by the gallon or by the cubic foot. If water is sold by the gallon, the meter that measures the quantity of water flowing into the house usually resembles the one shown here. The circular dial at the center of the meter measures quantities of water less than 10 gallons. This dial and the one containing the number 4 are often ignored when the meter is read by the rep-

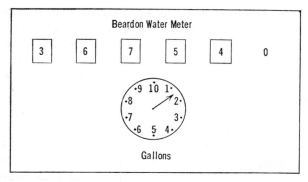

resentative from the Water Department. Thus, the number of gallons recorded in this meter would be read as 367,500. This number alone is not sufficient to enable a clerk to compute the bill. In addition, he must have the reading that was made at the end of the previous period. If this reading was 354,700, then, by subtracting 354,700 from 367,500, the number of gallons (12,800) that were consumed during that period will be found.

Billing periods for the purchase of water are usually on a quarterly basis (every 3 months). A typical rate table in communities where water is purchased by the gallon resembles the following:

Water Rates

Borough of West Camden

(per 1000 gallons per quarter)

First 30,000 gallons	50 cents
All over 30,000 gallons	45 cents

Minimum Charge $3

Business Transaction: In the community in which these water rates are used, a meter reading at the beginning of the quarter was 247,000. If the meter reading at the end of the quarter was 295,600, what was the amount of the water bill?

Solution: Number of Gallons Consumed = 295,600 − 247,000

= 48,600

Cost of First 30,000 Gallons = 30 × $.50

= $15

Cost of Remaining 18,600 Gallons = 18.60 × $.45

= $8.37

Cost of 48,600 Gallons = $15 +. $8.37

= $23.37

Explanation: As the cost of the first 30,000 gallons is computed at 50 cents per 1,000 gallons, it is necessary to find how many thousands are contained in 30,000. This is done by dividing 30,000 by 1,000. The fastest way of determining the quotient is to apply the short cut of moving the decimal point 3 places to the left. Moving the decimal point thus, the quotient 30 was found. After determining the cost of 30,000 gallons, the cost of the additional 18,600 gallons had to be found, for a total of 48,600 gallons had been consumed. This was computed in the same manner that the cost of the 30,000 gallons had been determined, with the one exception that the rate is 45 cents per 1,000 gallons rather than 50 cents. The sum of the two costs ($15 and $8.37) represents the total cost.

LEARNING EXERCISES

A. Using the water-rate table for the borough of West Camden shown on page 495, find the bill for the water consumed during each of the following quarterly periods.

No.	Meter Reading at Beginning of Period	Meter Reading at End of Period	No. of Gallons Consumed	Cost
1	562,000	573,000	xxx	$xxx
2	293,000	365,000	xxx	xxx
3	674,000	756,000	xxx	xxx
4	219,500	367,200	xxx	xxx
5	394,700	462,300	xxx	xxx
6	438,400	440,100	xxx	xxx

B. The quarterly water rates for the town of Mountainside are as follows:

Minimum: $3.00	
First 10,000 cu. ft.	$3.00 per 1,000 cu. ft.
From 10,000 to 100,000 cu. ft.	2.60 per 1,000 cu. ft.
Over 100,000 cu. ft.	2.00 per 1,000 cu. ft.

Meter readings on June 28 and September 29 are as follows. Find the cost of the water used during the third quarter by each of the three residents.

No.	June 28	September 29	Cubic Feet Consumed	Cost
1	375,400	396,000	xxx	$xxx
2	562,700	563,200	xxx	xxx
3	675,300	843,000	xxx	xxx

C. The Clear Brook Water Company charged its consumers the following rates per quarter:

Up to 6,000 cu. ft.	$2.60 per M. cu. ft.
Next 53,000 cu. ft.	2.40 per M. cu. ft.
Next 61,000 cu. ft.	2.10 per M. cu. ft.
Over 120,000 cu. ft.	1.80 per M. cu. ft.

Minimum: $2.00

Find the second quarterly water bill if the meter readings were as follows:

No.	March 23	June 20	Cubic Feet Consumed	Cost
1	637,000	641,000	xxx	$xxx
2	207,800	286,200	xxx	xxx
3	593,100	704,600	xxx	xxx

UNIT 2   Computing the Cost of Gas

Within recent years, gas has not only been purchased as a fuel for cooking, but it has also had widespread use as a fuel for heating the home and for providing refrigeration. Therefore, it has become a major item in the cost of maintaining a home.

Like water, gas is purchased by the cubic foot. Its consumption is measured by a meter that resembles the water meter.

Gas is most often sold in units of 100 cubic feet. Therefore, the two zeroes are usually omitted when the flow of gas is recorded or a consumer is billed for the purchase of gas. A reading of 638,300 would simply be indicated as 6,383, implying 6,383 hundred cubic feet of gas had passed through the meter since its installation.

Consumers are billed monthly for the purchase of gas rather than quarterly as for water. A typical rate table showing the cost of gas is shown here.

CONSUMER SERVICE ELECTRIC AND GAS COMPANY

Monthly Residential Gas Rates

First 4 hundred cu. ft. or less $1 Minimum

11¢ per hundred cu. ft. for next 10 hundred cu. ft.
9.5¢ per hundred cu. ft. for next 36 hundred cu. ft.
7.5¢ per hundred cu. ft. for next 50 hundred cu. ft.
6¢   per hundred cu. ft. in excess of 100 hundred cu. ft.

Business Transaction: Gas-meter readings on February 24 and March 25 were 3,672 and 3,754, respectively. If the rates in the preceding table are used, what is the cost of gas for this period?

Solution: It is important to remember that readings are recorded in hundreds of cubic feet. Hence, 3,672 means 3,672 hundred cubic feet.

Outline: Number of Hundreds of Cubic Feet Consumed

$$= 3,754 - 3,672 \quad = 82$$

Cost of First 4 Hundred cu. ft. = $1.00
Cost of Next 10 Hundred cu. ft. =   1.10 (10 × 11¢)
Cost of Next 36 Hundred cu. ft. =   3.42 (36 × 9.5¢)
Cost of Remaining 32 Hundred cu. ft. =   2.40 (32 × 7.5¢)
Cost of 82 Hundred cu. ft. = $7.92

In computing the cost of gas, as in this example, it is advisable to keep a tally of the number of cubic feet of gas the cost of which is being found at each step. Thus:

82 Total
−4 For $1
78 Remaining
−10 @ 11¢
68 Remaining
−36 @ 9.5¢
32 Remaining
−32 @ 7.5¢
0 Remaining

LEARNING EXERCISES

A. Using the Consumer Service Electric and Gas Company rate table on page 498, determine the monthly gas bill for each of the following purchases.

No.	Meter Reading at Beginning of Period	Meter Reading at End of Period	Cubic Feet Consumed	Cost
1	492	512	xxx	$xxx
2	357	426	xxx	xxx
3	462	537	xxx	xxx
4	2,380	2,432	xxx	xxx
5	1,653	1,841	xxx	xxx
6	3,425	3,836	xxx	xxx
7	5,682	6,107	xxx	xxx

B. In the area that it services, the Central States Gas Company is permitted to charge the following monthly rates:

First 600 cu. ft. or less	$1.25
Next 1,500 cu. ft.	12¢ per 100 cu. ft.
Next 2,400 cu. ft.	10.5¢ per 100 cu. ft.
Next 4,500 cu. ft.	8.5¢ per 100 cu. ft.
Next 11,000 cu. ft.	7¢ per 100 cu. ft.
Next 30,000 cu. ft.	$5\frac{1}{2}$¢ per 100 cu. ft.
Over 50,000 cu. ft.	5¢ per 100 cu. ft.

Find the cost of gas to each of the following consumers for the monthly period listed.

No.	Meter Reading at Beginning of Period	Meter Reading at End of Period	Cubic Feet Consumed	Cost
1	568	570	xxx	$xxx
2	394	436	xxx	xxx
3	1,272	1,385	xxx	xxx
4	2,609	2,786	xxx	xxx
5	4,905	5,362	xxx	xxx
6	6,957	7,348	xxx	xxx
7	3,006	3,867	xxx	xxx

UNIT **3**   **Computing the Cost of Electricity**

Gas and electricity are frequently purchased from the same company. For a number of reasons, including the desire to avoid the laying of an excessive number of electric wires or gas pipes, a community will grant a single company a monopoly on the sale of gas and electricity in its area. The company may also provide the community with service in the form of street lighting in return for the monopoly privilege.

Like gas, the consumption of electricity is recorded on a meter, and the consumer is billed monthly for the quantity that he used. The unit of electricity purchased is called a *kilowatt-hour* (abbreviated *KWH*). You are probably familiar with the fact that the electric light bulbs in your home are marked **25 watts, 40 watts, 60 watts, 100 watts,** or other values. Think of a very small bulb of 1 watt. If this bulb burned for 1,000 hours, it would consume 1,000 watt-hours of electricity, or 1 kilowatt-hour of electricity. Thus, 1,000 watt-hours and 1 kilowatt-hour have the same value and meaning. Similarly, if the 100-watt bulb in your home burned for 10 hours, it would consume 1,000 watt-hours of electricity (100 × 10 = 1,000), or 1 kilowatt-hour.

Electric meters that record the flow of electricity are similar to the illustration below. The dials indicate that **5,764 KWH** of electricity

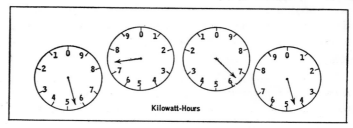

Kilowatt-Hours

have passed through this meter since its installation. Rate tables showing the cost of electricity are similar to the following.

CONSUMER SERVICE ELECTRIC AND GAS COMPANY
Monthly Residential Electric Rates

First 14 KWH or less $1 Minimun

3.8¢ per KWH for next 26 KWH
2.7¢ per KWH for next 60 KWH
2.5¢ per KWH for next 100 KWH
2¢ per KWH in excess of 200 KWH

Business Transaction: Electric-meter readings on January 31 and March 1 were 9,652 and 9,792, respectively. If the rates in the table are used, what is the cost of electricity for this period?

Solution: Number of KWH Consumed = 9,792 − 9,652   = 140

Cost of First 14 KWH	= $1.00	
Cost of Next 26 KWH	= .988	(26 × 3.8¢)
Cost of Next 60 KWH	= 1.620	(60 × 2.7¢)
Cost of Remaining 40 KWH	= 1.000	(40 × 2.5¢)
Cost of 140 KWH	= $4.608, or $4.61	

As in the computation of the cost of gas, a tally should be kept as the amount is determined.

```
 140 Total
− 14 For $1
 126 Remaining
− 26 @ 3.8¢
 100 Remaining
− 60 @ 2.7¢
  40 Remaining
− 40 @ 2.5¢
   0 Remaining
```

LEARNING EXERCISES

A. Using the Consumer Service Electric and Gas Company rate table, determine the monthly electric bill for each of the following purchasers.

No.	Meter Reading at Beginning of Period	Meter Reading at End of Period	Number of KWH Consumed	Cost
1	259	285	xxx	$xxx
2	4,502	4,604	xxx	xxx
3	498	618	xxx	xxx
4	1,892	2,042	xxx	xxx
5	3,561	3,795	xxx	xxx
6	5,374	5,861	xxx	xxx
7	6,287	6,300	xxx	xxx
8	1,276	1,280	xxx	xxx
9	3,063	3,791	xxx	xxx
10	7,004	7,862	xxx	xxx

B. Using the electric and gas rates of the Consumer Service Company, copy and complete the following bill.

	Consumer Service Electric and Gas Company			
Date	Meter Reading and Use		Charge for Service	
	Gas	Electricity	Description	Amount
Sept. 2	2692	1,690	Gas	$xxx
Aug. 3	2536	1,352	Electric	xxx
Quantity Consumed	xxx	xxx	Total	$xxx

C. Copy and complete forms similar to the one in **B** for each of the following examples.

No.	Meter Reading Dates	Gas Readings	Electric Readings
1	Oct. 29	2,753	2,047
	Sept. 27	2,694	1,688
2	Jan. 12	514	4,706
	Dec. 13	491	4,493
3	Mar. 1	2,221	9,786
	Jan. 31	1,764	9,592

UNIT 4 What Have You Learned?

SECTION 1 Review Problems

1. Using the water-rate table on page 495, find the cost of the water consumed during each of the following quarterly periods.

	Meter Reading at Beginning of Period	Meter Reading at End of Period	No. of Gallons Consumed	Cost
a	462,000	473,000	xxx	$xxx
b	573,200	592,600	xxx	xxx
c	108,800	376,500	xxx	xxx

2. Using the gas-rate table under Learning Exercises, section B, on page 499, determine the cost of gas consumed during the monthly periods shown below.

	Meter Reading at Beginning of Period	Meter Reading at End of Period	Cubic Feet Consumed	Cost
a	467	469	xxx	$xxx
b	5,764	5,832	xxx	xxx
c	1,553	1,846	xxx	xxx

3. Using the electric-rate table on page 500, find the cost of electricity consumed during the following monthly periods.

	Meter Reading at Beginning of Period	Meter Reading at End of Period	Number of KWH Consumed	Cost
a	375	386	xxx	$xxx
b	4,267	4,395	xxx	xxx
c	5,692	6,347	xxx	xxx

4. Copy and complete the following bill. Use the electric and gas rates given on pages 498 and 500.

Consumer Service Electric and Gas Company				
Date	Meter Reading and Use		Charge for Service	
	Gas	Electricity	Description	Amount
July 17	3,576	1,967	Gas	$xxx
June 18	3,484	1,821	Electricity	xxx
Quantity Consumed	xxx	xxx	Total	$xxx

SECTION 2   Testing Your Understanding

40 Minutes

1. Using the water-rate table given on page 495, compute the quarterly water bill for the period if the meter reading at the beginning of the period was **347,500** and the reading at the end of the period was **426,000**.

2. Using the gas-rate table under Learning Exercises, section B, on page 499, find the monthly bill to the consumer if the meter read 3,958 on September 14 and 4,075 on October 15.

3. Copy and complete the following electric and gas bill. Use the rates given on pages 498 and 500.

Consumer Service Electric and Gas Company				
Date	Meter Reading and Use		Charge for Service	
	Gas	Electricity	Description	Amount
Sept. 2	2,692	1,690	Gas	$xxx
Aug. 3	2,536	1,352	Electric	xxx
Quantity Consumed	xxx	xxx	Total	xxx

UNIT 5 General Review

SECTION 1   To Improve Your Speed and Accuracy

1. Addition:

a.	627,583	b.	$ 3,695.98	c.	$58\frac{3}{8}$
	480,749		307.49		$65\frac{1}{3}$
	168,536		48,525.09		$14\frac{3}{4}$
	793,358		69.95		$86\frac{5}{6}$
	835,494		482.50		
	359,182		4,909.24		
	540,729		7.67		

d. $36,809 + $58.24 + $104.95 + $.97 + $67

e. $15\frac{2}{3} + 47\frac{1}{2} + 6\frac{3}{5} + 29\frac{1}{6}$

2. Subtraction:

a.	674,058	b.	$16,575.00	c.	124
	283,462		12,849.95		$68\frac{3}{4}$

d. $400 − $293.75   **e.** $18\frac{3}{5} - 12\frac{5}{6}$

3. Multiplication:

a. 54,085 × 802   **b.** $657 × 1.045   **c.** 3.98 × .95

d. $\frac{5}{6} \times \frac{2}{3} \times \frac{3}{4}$ **e.** $425 × $\frac{5}{200}$ × $1\frac{1}{4}$

4. Division:
   a. 500,000 ÷ 674 b. .02 ÷ .0035 c. $29.95 ÷ .035
   d. 12½ ÷ 2½ e. ⅗ ÷ 15

SECTION 2 Do You Remember These?

In order to solve the problems in this section, it will be necessary for you to refer to the tables on the pages indicated.

1. If a man earns $123.46 each week and claims 4 exemptions, what are his weekly deductions for income tax? (Pages 172–173.)

2. What is the commission on 3 bonds whose market value is 85¾ each? (Page 425.)

3. Find the yearly premium on a 20-payment life policy for $5,000 that was taken out at age 40. (Page 335.)

4. From a weekly salary of $117.36, how much money will be deducted for Social Security tax? (Pages 168–169.)

5. Determine the number of days between March 12 and November 21 of the same year. (Pages 245–248.)

6. What is the cost of 5-and-10 bodily-injury liability insurance and $5,000 property-damage insurance for a person who is classified as a 1B driver if his home is located in a community listed as Territory 3? (Page 327.)

7. How large will the monthly retirement benefits be for a worker and his wife, both of whom are over 65 years of age, if the primary benefit is $84.60? (Page 379.)

8. If the adjusted gross income on the income tax return is $4,773.24, what is the tax for a person who claims 4 exemptions? (Pages 359–361.)

9. How large is the brokerage on the purchase of 200 shares of stock at 13½ a share? (Page 399.)

22

Practical

Measurements

PREVIEW

The linoleum on the kitchen floor of the Murchison home reached the point where it had become a safety hazard. Mr. Murchison, a "do-it-yourself" enthusiast, was greatly pleased at the prospect of removing the kitchen floor covering and replacing it with those "easy-to-apply" linoleum tiles. Mrs. Murchison, on the other hand, was willing to endure anything—even her husband's handiwork—in order to eliminate the unsightly appearance of her kitchen.

Shopping excursions to several linoleum stores revealed the fact that tiles for home use were usually purchased in the 9- by 9-inch size. After the quality, design, and color of the tiles had been decided on, Mr. Murchison returned to one of the shops to purchase the needed quantity. It was only when one of the clerks asked him how many tiles he needed that Mr. Murchison realized that he had not measured the kitchen floor.

This was more of a problem than he had bargained for. Cabinets projected into the room in several places. The breakfast bar that he had proudly displayed as a product of an earlier venture, ran right down the middle of the floor. "Just what am I supposed to measure?" thought he. "Will measuring the distance around the nooks and crannies help me find the number of tiles I need? The tiles are 9 by 9 inches, but all I'm measuring are the lengths of the cabinets. What value will these measurements serve?" Needless to say, at Mrs. Murchison's request, a representative from the floor-covering store was called to rescue Mr. Murchison from his predicament.

For Class Discussion

1. What did Mr. Murchison have to determine before he could compute the number of tiles that he needed?

2. Name several units that are used for the measurement of distance.

3. How would you interpret the statement that the length of a room is 14 feet?

4. If the number of inches in a foot were less than those in a standard foot, how would this affect the number of feet in the width of a room?

5. How would you interpret the statement that the area of the floor of a room is 124 square feet?

6. Name several square units other than the square foot.

7. What is meant by the volume of a box?

8. What are several units of measure that can be used in finding the volume of a box?

UNIT **1**   **The Linear Unit**

THE PERIMETER OF A RECTANGLE

When the sides of a closed figure consist of straight lines, the distance around that figure is called the *perimeter*. Thus, in the drawing shown, the distance around this figure is

5 feet + 3 feet + 6 feet + 4 feet + 3½ feet

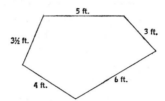

or a total of 21½ feet. A better definition of *perimeter*, then, is: The perimeter of a figure is the sum of the sides of the figure.

A figure that is encountered daily is the one shown here. It is called a *rectangle*.

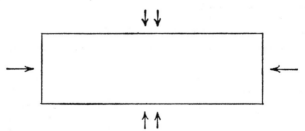

Two features distinguish this figure:

→1. The opposite sides are equal; in other words, the sides toward which the single arrows point are equal, and those toward which the double arrows point are also equal.

→2. The angles at each of the corners are *right* angles, meaning that they contain 90 degrees.

The perimeter of a rectangle is equal to twice the length of the rectangle plus twice its width,

or

$$P = 2L + 2W$$

This equation for finding the *perimeter of a rectangle* is merely a short way of writing the much longer principle.

Example

Find, in inches, the perimeter of a rectangle that is 15 feet 4 inches long and 11 feet 5 inches wide.

Solution: As the perimeter is to be found in inches, both the 15 feet and the 11 feet are first changed to inches by multiplying each by 12 (12 inches = 1 foot). Hence, 15 feet will be changed to 180 inches, making the length 184 inches (180 inches + 4 inches); and the 11 feet is changed to 132 inches, making the width 137 inches (132 inches + 5 inches). The perimeter is then found by multiplying the length (184 inches) and the width (137 inches) each by 2 and adding the products.

Outline: Known: L = 15 ft. 4 in. = 184 in.

W = 11 ft. 5 in. = 137 in.

To Find: Perimeter

Method: P = 2L + 2W

= 2 × 184 + 2 × 137

=   368   +   274

= 642 Inches

LEARNING EXERCISES

A. The lengths and widths of rectangles are given here. Find the perimeters in terms of the units indicated in the perimeter columns.

No.	Length	Width	Perim-eter	No.	Length	Width	Perim-eter
1	17 yds.	14 yds.	xxx yds.	10	19 yds. 2 ft.	15 yds. 1 ft.	xxx yds.
2	56 ft.	47 ft.	xxx ft.	11	48 yds. 2 ft.	43 yds. 2 ft.	xxx yds.
3	5 yds. 2 ft.	3 yds. 1 ft.	xxx ft.	12	36 ft. 9 in.	27 ft. 3 in.	xxx ft.
4	23 yds. 1 ft.	18 yds. 1 ft.	xxx ft.	13	53 ft. 5 in.	39 ft. 11 in.	xxx ft.
5	57 yds.	48 yds. 2 ft.	xxx ft.	14	3 yds. 2 ft. 4 in.	2 yds. 1 ft. 5 in.	xxx in.
6	9 ft. 3 in.	7 ft. 5 in.	xxx in.	15	7 yds. 1 ft.	5 yds. 4 in.	xxx in.
7	85 ft. 2 in.	54 ft. 7 in.	xxx in.	16	6 yds. 2 ft. 6 in.	4 yds. 1 ft. 6 in.	xxx ft.
8	127 ft.	96 ft. 11 in.	xxx in.	17	26 yds. 1 ft.	18 yds. 9 in.	xxx ft.
9	12 yds.	5 yds. 1 ft.	xxx yds.	18	75 yds.	62 yds. 4 in.	xxx ft.

B. *Problems to Be Solved*

1. Each night a man walked his dog around the block twice. If the length of the block was 75 yards 2 feet and the width 62 yards 1 foot, how many feet did the man walk?

2. Mrs. Teller purchased a 12-foot by 16-foot rug that was cut from a bolt. She paid **65** cents a foot for fringe with which to trim the rug. This price included both the material and the sewing. By how much did this increase the cost of the rug?

3. A demonstration is to be put on in a rectangular field measuring **125** yards 1 foot by **86** yards. In order to keep the spectators off the field, 3 strands of rope are strung completely around the field.

    a. How many yards of rope are needed?

    b. What would be the total cost of the rope at $7\frac{1}{2}$ cents a yard?

4. To enclose a pasture **165** by **125** feet, Mr. Brenman built a split-rail fence consisting of two parallel rails running completely around the field. If the rails cost **19** cents a foot, what did Mr. Brenman pay for the fence?

UNIT 2   The Square Unit

THE AREA OF A RECTANGLE

The area of a rectangle can be found by "ruling off" the rectangle and counting the number of squares contained therein.

As the accompanying rectangle shows, there are exactly the same

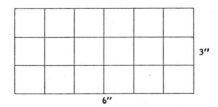

number of squares in each row (6). Hence, multiplying the number of squares in one row by the number of rows will yield the total number of squares in the entire rectangle. The diagram also shows that the number of squares in each row is exactly the same as the number of inches in the length of the rectangle, and that the number of rows is the same as the number of inches in the width of the rectangle. Therefore, without having to "rule off" the rectangle, but merely by looking at the numbers representing the length and the width, the number of squares in each row and the number of rows can be determined. Therefore, the following principle can be stated:

→The area of a rectangle can be found by multiplying the number of square units in one row by the number of rows
$$A = LW \quad \text{or} \quad A = L \times W.$$
The relationship between the common square measures is as follows:

Square Measure
144 square inches = 1 square foot
9 square feet   = 1 square yard

Example

Find the area of a rectangle whose length is 15 feet and whose width is 8 feet.

Solution: The length of 15 feet indicates that there are 15 square feet in each row, and the 8-foot width indicates that there will be 8 rows. Hence, applying the principle above, the area can be found.

Outline: Known: L = 15 ft.
          W = 8 ft.
    To Find: Area
    Method: A = LW
          = 15 × 8
          = 120 Square Feet

LEARNING EXERCISES

A. Find the area of the rectangles whose lengths and widths are as follows.

No.	Length	Width	Area	No.	Length	Width	Area
1	26 ft.	18 ft.	xxx sq. ft.	6	8 yds. 1 ft.	6 yds.	xxx sq. yds.
2	125 yds.	93 yds.	xxx sq. yds.	7	5 yds. 2 ft.	4 yds. 1 ft.	xxx sq. yds.
3	5 ft. 2 in.	4 ft. 5 in.	xxx sq. in.	8	17 ft. 3 in.	16 ft.	xxx sq. ft.
4	14 yds. 2 ft.	2 yds. 1 ft.	xxx sq. ft.	9	25 ft. 6 in.	18 ft. 9 in.	xxx sq. ft.
5	16 ft. 2 in.	14 ft. 7 in.	xxx sq. in.	10	5 yds. 1 ft.	2 yds. 7 in.	xxx sq. in.

B. *Problems to Be Solved*

1. Find the area of a square each side of which measures 5 feet 6 inches.

2. The floor of a bedroom was scraped and finished at 12 cents a square foot. If the dimensions of the room are 16 feet by 14 feet 3 inches, what was the cost of finishing this floor?

3. A rectangular playground is to be covered with asphalt at a cost of $2.25 a square yard. If the playground is 105 yards by 86 yards 2 feet in size, what will be the cost of this work?

4. The floors of the living room and the dining room of an apartment were scraped and finished at 11 cents a square foot. The dimensions of the rooms are: living room, 15 feet 8 inches by 12 feet; dining room, 12 feet 6 inches by 10 feet. What was the cost of this work?

UNIT 3   The Cubic Unit

THE VOLUME OF AN OBJECT

The space that an object occupies is called the *volume* of the object. To measure the volume of an object, it is necessary to compare the object with an object whose size is known. The standard that is used for comparison resembles a child's block or an ice cube that is 1 inch long, 1 inch wide, and 1 inch deep. This block is called a *cubic inch*. Hence, the statement that the volume of a box is 90 cubic inches simply means that the box is 90 times the size of a 1-cubic-inch toy block. This can also be interpreted as meaning that, if the blocks (or cubic inches) were placed within the box, layer on layer, it would take 90 blocks to fill the box completely.

→The volume of a rectangular solid is found by multiplying the number of cubic units in one column by the number of columns in the first layer. This product is then multiplied by the number of layers.

The formula for finding the volume of a rectangular solid can be expressed as:

$$V = L \times W \times H$$

Example

Find the volume of a box that is 1 foot 3 inches long, 1 foot wide, and 9 inches high.

Solution: By changing each of the measurements to inches, it is seen that the number of cubic inches in the first column is 15, the number of columns is 12, and the number of layers is 9. The product of these three numbers will give the volume.

Outline: Known: L = 1 ft. 3 in. = 15 in.

W = 1 ft. = 12 in.

H = 9 in.

To Find: Volume

Method: V = L × W × H

= 15 × 12 × 9

= 1,620 Cubic Inches

LEARNING EXERCISES

Monday

A. Find the volume of the rectangular solids whose lengths, widths, and depths are as follows:

No.	Length	Width	Depth	Volume
1	5 ft.	3 ft.	6 ft.	xxx cu. ft.
2	3 yds. 1 ft.	3 yds.	2 yds. 2 ft.	xxx cu. ft.
3	5 ft. 2 in.	4 ft. 7 in.	3 ft. 4 in.	xxx cu. in.
4	$8\frac{1}{3}$ yds.	6 yds.	$2\frac{1}{2}$ yds.	xxx cu. yds.
5	$7\frac{1}{4}$ ft.	$6\frac{1}{2}$ ft.	10 ft.	xxx cu. ft.
6	7 yds. 2 ft.	5 yds.	6 yds.	xxx cu. yds.
7	8 ft. 6 in.	6 ft. 4 in.	8 ft.	xxx cu. ft.
8	12 yds. 1 ft.	10 yds. 2 ft.	7 yds. 1 ft.	xxx cu. yds.
9	15 ft. 4 in.	13 ft. 6 in.	10 ft. 6 in.	xxx cu. ft.
10	3 yds. 2 ft. 3 in.	3 yds. 6 in.	2 yds. 2 ft.	xxx cu. ft.

B. *Problems to Be Solved*

1. The bottom of a rectangular solid is a square that is 7 inches on a side; the depth of the solid is 6 inches. What is the volume of the solid?

2. How many cubic feet of room will be occupied in a moving van by a trunk that is 5 feet 4 inches long, 2 feet 6 inches wide, and 2 feet 4 inches high?

3. Mr. Hall had a rectangular swimming pool built on his property. The dimensions of the pool were 65 feet by 25 feet by 6 feet. The pool was the same depth throughout.

a. What is the volume of the pool?

b. How many gallons of water will it take to fill the pool if 1 cubic foot will hold $7\frac{1}{2}$ gallons?

c. If water costs 50 cents per 1,000 gallons, what will be the cost of filling this pool?

4. How would you show that there are 27 cubic feet in a cubic yard?

UNIT **4**   **What Have You Learned?**

SECTION 1   Understanding Terms

Can you match the term in the column on the left with the proper definition in the column on the right?

Term	*Definition*
1. Unit of measure	**a.** The number of cubic units contained within a solid.
2. An inch	**b.** A straight line whose length is used as a unit for measuring distance.
3. A square inch	
4. Area	**c.** A four-sided figure in which the opposite sides are equal and the angles are right angles.
5. Volume	**d.** A standard used as a basis of comparison in measurement.
6. Perimeter	
7. Rectangle	**e.** The number of square units contained within the surface of a figure.
8. Square	
	f. The distance around a closed figure whose sides consist of straight lines.
	g. A rectangle all of whose sides are equal.
	h. A unit resembling an ice cube that is used for measuring the size of solid figures.
	i. A small square whose size is used as a unit for measuring the size of other flat figures.

SECTION 2   Review Problems

1. Find the perimeter and the area of the rectangles whose lengths and widths are as follows. (Pages 508–511.)

No.	Length	Width	Perimeter	Area
a	7 yds. 2 ft.	3 yds. 1 ft.	xxx ft.	xxx sq. ft.
b	10 ft. 7 in.	8 ft. 3 in.	xxx in.	xxx sq. in.
c	3 yds. 3 in.	2 yds. 1 ft.	xxx in.	xxx sq. in.
d	12 yds. 1 ft.	9 yds.	xxx yds.	xxx sq. yds.
e	14 ft. 4 in.	10 ft. 6 in.	xxx ft.	xxx sq. ft.

2. Find the volume of the rectangular solids whose lengths, widths, and depths are as follows. (Pages 512–513.)

No.	Length	Width	Depth	Volume
a	8 yds.	4 yds.	5 yds.	xxx cu. yds.
b	3 yds. 2 ft.	2 yds. 1 ft.	2 yds. 2 ft.	xxx cu. ft.
c	8 ft. 6 in.	6 ft.	4 ft. 3 in.	xxx cu. ft.

3. When remodeling the living room of his home, Mr. Brinker purchased molding to be nailed around the ceiling of the room. He paid 12 cents a foot for this molding. What was the cost of the molding if the dimensions of the room are 18 feet 4 inches by 13 feet 2 inches? (Page 508.)

4. Inlaid linoleum was purchased for a rectangular kitchen floor at a cost of $2.50 a square yard. This price did not include the cost of the installation. If the dimensions of the floor are 4 yards 1 foot by 3 yards 2 feet, what was the cost of the linoleum? (Pages 510–511.)

5. Fill dirt can be purchased at $2.25 a cubic yard. What would be the cost of filling in the cellar of a house destroyed by fire if the dimensions of the cellar are 32 feet by 27 feet by 8 feet? (Pages 512–513.)

SECTION 3   Testing Your Understanding

40 Minutes

1. Find the perimeter and the area of the rectangles whose lengths and widths are as follows.

No.	Length	Width	Perimeter	Area
a	5 yds. 2 ft.	4 yds. 2 in.	xxx in.	xxx sq. in.
b	16 ft. 4 in.	15 ft.	xxx ft.	xxx sq. ft.

2. Find the volume of the rectangular solids whose lengths, widths, and depths are as follows.

No.	Length	Width	Depth	Volume
a	9 yds. 2 ft.	7 yds.	5 yds. 1 ft.	xxx cu. ft.
b	12 yds. 1 ft.	9 yds. 1 ft.	6 yds.	xxx cu. yds.

3. In decorating a room for a party, crepe paper was strung around the ceiling. The cost of the paper was 6 cents a yard. What was the total cost of the paper if the dimensions of the room were 26 feet by 18 feet?

4. A man purchased a liquid crab-grass killer. The directions on the label of the bottle stated that the contents would cover 150 square feet of lawn. How many bottles would he have to use if the dimensions of his lawn are 73 feet by 64 feet?

5. A man purchased a level truckload of topsoil at $5 a cubic yard. If the dimensions of the section of the truck that carried the dirt are 8 feet by 5 feet by $2\frac{1}{2}$ feet, what was the cost of the topsoil?

UNIT 5   General Review

SECTION 1   To Improve Your Speed and Accuracy

1. Addition:

a. 458,736	b. $57,805.49	c. $49\frac{3}{5}$
593,284	2,796.58	$57\frac{2}{3}$
607,548	23.95	$84\frac{5}{6}$
875,958	9,344.27	$69\frac{1}{2}$
386,673	506.34	
965,164	26,987.68	
253,795	8.54	

    d. $5.35 + $164 + $27.96 + $5,648 + $1.98
    e. $18\frac{3}{8} + 14\frac{5}{6} + 37\frac{3}{4} + 65\frac{1}{2} + 19\frac{5}{8}$

2. Subtraction:

a. 493,307	b. $83,000.00	c. 75
187,692	17,486.98	$48\frac{7}{12}$

    d. $2,500 − $345.75   **e.** $84\frac{11}{12} - 27\frac{2}{3}$

3. Multiplication:

    a. 30,056 × 2,700   **b.** $250.75 × 2.035   **c.** 35.25 × .92
    d. $2\frac{1}{2} × 3\frac{4}{5} × 1\frac{2}{3}$ **e.** $1,500 × $\frac{17}{400}$ × $2\frac{1}{2}$

4. Division:

    a. 275,000 ÷ 439   **b.** .045 ÷ 1.06   **c.** $524 ÷ 1.25

    d. $16\frac{2}{3} \div 2\frac{1}{2}$ **e.** $18\frac{3}{4} \div 5$

SECTION 2   Do You Remember These?

1. Change each of the following fractions to per cent values.

    a. $\frac{3}{20}$ **b.** $\frac{7}{25}$ **c.** $\frac{27}{500}$

2. Successive discounts of 20% and 10% are given on an article that lists at $54. What is the net cost of the article?

3. An article was sold at 125% of its cost of $35. At what price was the article sold?

4. A machine that was originally purchased for $4,000 has a scrap value of $400 after 10 years. Using the straight-line method of depreciation, what is the yearly depreciation of the machine?

5. A motor whose original value was $800 depreciated 40% of its book value each year. What is the book value of this motor at the end of 3 years?

6. A man borrowed $800 from the bank for 62 days at a discount rate of 6%. What were the proceeds on this note?

7. A note dated May 17 and due in 6 months was discounted at the bank on July 9. What is the discount period on the note?

8. What are the Social Security deductions on yearly earnings of $3,756.18?

9. What rate of return will the purchaser of a 4% $1,000 par-value bond receive if he purchased the bond at 92?

10. What is the cost of 50 shares of a stock that was purchased at $34\frac{3}{4}$?

23

Farming, Petroleum, and Lumber Industries

PREVIEW

One evening as George Briggs was reading the school paper, his father asked him whether he would check the computations on an invoice he had received that day from the farm co-operative.

Mr. Briggs had recently purchased a tractor and 2 tons of fertilizer through the co-operative to which he belonged. As a member of the group, he was granted a discount of 15%. In addition, the terms of the invoice were 1/10, n/30.

George was interested to find that the computation was identical with that which he had learned in business mathematics. The only difference was in the names of the articles. Where the problems in the business mathematics course had been concerned with the purchase or sale of desks, furniture, or automobiles, those with which his father, as a farmer, was concerned were about tractors, fertilizer, or bags of potatoes. George had always thought of his father as a farmer only; but, as he glanced over other records on his father's desk, he realized that his father was a businessman, too. The problems that Mr. Briggs faced each day were basically no different from those of a merchant operating a store.

Concerning This Chapter

There are many industries throughout the United States in which terms peculiar to each industry are used. Fundamentally, however, the knowledge of business arithmetic that is needed by employees in these various fields is much the same. The clothing merchant sells dozens of socks; the dairy farmer sells gallons of milk; the lumberman sells board feet of lumber. Yet for all, per cent of gain, per cent of loss, discount, markup, markdown, have the same meaning. In this chapter, three large industries—farming, petroleum, and lumber—were selected for special study. Typical problems that occur in these fields were chosen so that you may see the similarity that exists between these problems and the problems in business arithmetic with which you are familiar. In many ways, this chapter will be a review of the topics you have already studied in this book.

UNIT 1   **Problems of the Farmer**

Problems to Be Solved

1. A Florida fruitgrower hauls his oranges and grapefruit 85 miles to market. His truck, with a capacity of 120 boxes, costs 16 cents a mile to operate. The fruitgrower pays 14 cents for each box in which he packs his fruit. Assuming that the incidental expenses in connection with the trip average $8.50, determine the marketing cost of each box of fruit.

2. A gross profit of $4,416.55 is realized by Parker from the sale of cotton and wheat. He paid 5% interest for 1 year on $975 that he borrowed to buy machinery; $3.50 for a subscription to a farm magazine; and $37.50 for farm-bureau dues. Other expenses amounted to $127.80. Find his total expenses and his net profit.

3. Howard Ely purchased a corn husker and shredder for $1,550, subject to discounts of 10% and 5%. If the freight charge was $65, how much did the equipment cost?

4. Dean bought a farm of 215 acres at $73.50 an acre. His estimated annual expenses included: depreciation of buildings and equipment, $310; taxes, $245; insurance, $39.50; repairs, $185; and interest on a $4,500 mortgage at 5%. He rented the farm to a tenant at $9.50 an acre.

    a. Find his annual net income.

    b. Find the rate of return on his investment.

5. A 210-acre farm was purchased in Iowa at $42.50 an acre. The terms were: 25% cash; balance in 3 notes of equal amount, with interest at 5%, payable in 1 year, 2 years, and 3 years, respectively.

    a. Assuming that the notes were met at maturity, what was the total cost of the farm, including interest?

    b. At what price an acre must the farm be sold in order that the farmer may realize a profit of 15% on his investment?

6. A commission merchant received from a farmer a consignment of 36 crates of strawberries, 24 crates of raspberries, and 40 crates of cherries. (Each crate contained 32 boxes.) The merchant sold the strawberries at $18\frac{1}{2}$ cents a box, the raspberries at $16\frac{1}{4}$ cents a box, and the cherries at $15\frac{3}{4}$ cents a box. The expenses were: freight charges, $59.82; cartage, 12 cents a crate; commission and collection, 9%. Find the amount remitted to the farmer by the commission merchant.

7. A farmer insured his barn, which cost $4,500, for $3,000, under a policy containing an 80% coinsurance clause. Fire damaged the barn to the amount of $1,500. How much did the farmer collect from the insurance company?

8. Lloyd, a farmer, had 47% of his land in wheat; 12% in rye; 15% in pasture; 21% in corn; and the remainder in meadow. If the total acreage of the farm was 700 acres, how many acres of each crop were under cultivation?

UNIT **2**   **4-H Clubs and Co-operative Marketing and Buying**

Problems to Be Solved

1. Michael Herberts, a member of a 4-H club, received $68.85 as the income from his pig project. He had invested 29 hours of labor and $35.70 in cash in the project. If his work is worth 75 cents an hour, find: (**a**) his profit or loss; (**b**) the per cent that the profit or loss was of his total investment; and (**c**) the per cent that the profit or loss was of his income.

2. Eric Fredericks, a member of a local 4-H club, was engaged in a pig project. The market price of the animals was $10.80 a hundred pounds. It is estimated that a bushel of corn fed to a pig will cause the pig to gain $12\frac{1}{2}$ pounds.

    a. If corn costs $1.20 a bushel, will Eric gain or lose by fattening the pigs on corn?

    b. Assuming that Eric owns 6 pigs, how much will he gain or lose by feeding the animals a total of 16 bushels of corn before selling them? (Show all work necessary to arrive at your solution.)

3. It is estimated that the experience gained by boys and girls in 4-H clubs results in an increase in their income, when they become adult farmers, of 12% a year. Assuming that the income of a farmer without this experience is $2,670 a year, how much would he probably earn if he had been a member of a 4-H club as a boy?

4. A co-operative association of woolgrowers sold for its members a wool crop amounting to $286,500. From this sum, the association deducted $7,600 for an addition to its warehouse and $2,500 for its reserve fund. It issued shares of stock to its members as evidence of their ownership in these assets of the association. The gross sales of Clerkin, a member, amounted to $3,220 for the year.

    a. How much should be charged to him for the deductions?

    b. How much did he receive for his crop?

5. Hilton, a member of a grain-marketing co-operative association, received 95 cents a bushel as an initial payment for the 5,370 pounds of wheat that he delivered to the association. A short time later, he was notified that his wheat had been sold for $1.96 a bushel and that expenses charged against his account amounted to $8.15. How much was due him in settlement? (1 bushel of wheat weighs 60 pounds.)

6. The goods sold in 1 year by a consumers' co-operative amounted to $718,650, and the profit amounted to $16,640. Of this profit, 15% was placed in a reserve fund, and the balance was distributed among the members.

    a. How much money was available for distribution as dividends?

    b. What rate of dividend did the directors declare, based on the sales?

7. The grain-storage charge paid by the members of a co-operative grain association was $1\frac{1}{2}$ mills a day for each bushel. John Milton, a member, stored 1,480 bushels of wheat with the association from September 12 to December 18. Find the amount of his storage bill.

8. A grain-marketing association paid its members a cash dividend of $8\frac{1}{2}\%$ on the grain marketed during the year. How much did Harding's dividend amount to if he received $6,489 as the market price of his grain at the time of the sale?

UNIT 3   Stock-Raising Problems

Problems to Be Solved

1. A farmer made "chop" feed by mixing corn and oats in the ratio of 3 to 5 by weight. How much corn and oats would he use to make 400 pounds of feed?

2. A bulletin of a local farm bureau recommends the following daily silage rations: sheep, $4\frac{1}{2}$ pounds; dairy cows, 42 pounds; calves, 21 pounds. Compute the number of tons of silage needed to feed 105 sheep, 60 cows, and 32 calves for 84 days.

3. Texas, the leading cattle-producing state of this country, had 6,550,000 cattle in a recent year. If there were 62,800,000 head of cattle in the United States, what per cent of this total number of cattle was found in Texas? (Carry to 4 decimal places.)

4. A dealer bought 840 sheep for $6,618.75. He sold 20% of them at $16.75 per head, 75% of the remainder at $15.20 per head, and the balance of the sheep at $13.80 per head. Find his total profit and the average profit on each sheep.

5. A farmer purchased a steer weighing 1,030 pounds at $10.35 a hundredweight. He fattened it at a feed cost of $49.05. If the steer gained 250 pounds, at what price per pound must the farmer sell the steer to gain 10% on his total investment?

6. Hull sold 98 hogs weighing 21,810 pounds to the stockyards at $14.85 a hundred pounds. If yardage per head was 23 cents and commission per head was 78 cents:

    a. What was the net amount received by Hull for the hogs?

    b. What was the average amount received by him for each hog?

7. A beef steer dressed 730 pounds, which was 58.4% of his live weight. Find his live weight.

8. According to recent figures issued by the United States Department of Agriculture, the gross income from livestock and livestock products in the United States is as follows:

Millions of Dollars		*Millions of Dollars*	
Horses	7	Cattle and calves	683
Mules	6	Eggs	472
Hogs	897	Milk	1,617
Sheep and lambs	108	Wool	50
Chickens	328	Honey	8

What per cent of the total gross income is the income from each item?

UNIT **4**   **Problems of the Poultry and Dairy Industries**

Problems to Be Solved

1. The Guernsey cows in a dairy averaged 36 pounds of milk each a day, testing 4.24% butterfat; the Holstein cows averaged 41 pounds of milk, testing 3.72% butterfat; and the Jersey cows averaged 30 pounds of milk, testing 5.35% butterfat. How many pounds of butterfat were produced by each cow daily?

2. Find the number of pounds of American cheese (also known as Cheddar cheese) that can be produced from 4,200 pounds of milk containing 4.73% butterfat. The number of pounds of cheese that can be produced from the milk is 2.9 times the number of pounds of butterfat in the milk.

3. A grain mixture used as a ration for dairy cattle consisted of 3 parts of ground corn, $1\frac{1}{2}$ parts of ground oats, and $1\frac{1}{2}$ parts of wheat bran. To prepare 1,500 pounds of this grain mixture, how many pounds of corn, oats, and bran would have to be used?

4. A farmer set 2,490 eggs, of which 69.6% hatched. Of the chickens that hatched, 86.7% were raised. Find the number of chickens raised.

5. Charters sent 720 dozen eggs to a commission merchant to be sold for him. The commission merchant sold them at 42 cents a dozen and sent the net proceeds to Charters, after deducting $12.60 for storage, $28.10 for transportation, and 6% for commission. How much did Charters receive for the eggs?

6. Turkey toms bring 35 cents a pound live or 42 cents a pound dressed. Assuming that the turkeys average 14 pounds in weight and lose $1\frac{1}{2}$ pounds in dressing, how much more would be received for 150 turkeys dressed than alive?

7. A farmer sent a consignment of 860 pounds of poultry to a commission merchant. The poultry was sold at 28 cents per pound. Drayage charges amounted to $12.60, and commission was $7\frac{1}{2}$%. Compute the gross proceeds, the commission, and the net proceeds.

8. An agent sold 600 pounds of butter for a farmer at 58 cents a pound. He charged 6% commission for selling. How much did the farmer receive if other expenses in connection with the sale amounted to $11.35?

UNIT **5**   **Problems of the Cotton Industry**

Problems to Be Solved

1. The cotton yield an acre on various types of land is as follows:

	Yield in Pounds
a. Marginal land too poor for profitable farming	64.5
b. Superior land	680
c. Lowest state average	98.3
d. The United States average	183.8
e. The highest state average	385.6

At 32.5 cents a pound, find the income on an acre of each type of land.

2. The cotton crop on Robert Baker's plantation is $\frac{1}{3}$ bale an acre. At 32 cents a pound, what is his income from 475 acres? (A bale contains 500 pounds.)

3. A tenant farmer sold the 36 500-pound bales of cotton produced on his land at 30.5 cents a pound. He paid the owner $\frac{1}{4}$ of the income from the crop as rent. What was the tenant farmer's income?

4. A cotton grower obtained a yield of 750 pounds of seed cotton an acre. He had 45 acres of cotton under cultivation. Assuming that 1,500 pounds of seed cotton make 1 500-pound bale of lint, what was the total amount received for the crop if the lint was sold for 31 cents a pound and the seed, which is the residue, was sold for $32 a ton?

5. The quantities of cotton ginned in the United States in a recent year, classified according to colors, were as follows:

	Bales		Bales
Extra white	485,500	Yellow-stained	1,400
White	12,465,400	Gray	19,900
Spotted	2,038,800	Blue-stained	3,000
Yellow-tinged	56,200	No grade	205,600
Light yellow-stained	3,587		

a. Find the total number of bales ginned.

b. Find the per cent that each quantity is of the total.

6. A company ginned 1,049,822 pounds of seed cotton in 1 year, from which it produced 706 bales of lint.

a. How many pounds of seed cotton were used for each bale?

b. At $1.75 per 100 pounds, how much did the company receive for ginning the seed cotton?

7. Statistics prepared by the United States Department of Agriculture for a recent year disclosed the following facts: that, out of a total United States crop of 16,847,000 bales of cotton, 8,842,000 bales were exported; that the cotton mills in the United States consumed 4,902,000 bales; that the total world crop was 28,250,000 bales.

a. What per cent of its total crop did the United States export?

b. What per cent of the world crop was produced in the United States?

c. The United States exports of cotton were equivalent to what per cent of the world crop?

d. What per cent of the total United States cotton crop was consumed by the cotton mills?

UNIT **6** | **Problems of the Petroleum and Lumber Industries**

Problems to Be Solved

1. By a process of refining, every barrel of crude petroleum is separated into the following products: gasoline, 30%; kerosene, 10%; gas, oil, and fuel, 45%; lubricating oil, 4%; paraffin, mineral oil, and the like, 6%; asphalt and other products, 2%; loss, 3%. How many barrels of each of the above products can be refined from 3,500 barrels of crude petroleum?

2. A giant sequoia tree contains 450,160 board feet of lumber. If an average of 12,000 board feet of lumber is required to build a 4-room bungalow, how many bungalows can be built from the lumber in this tree?

3. Gasoline taxes in a Northern state account for 24.27% of the money raised by state taxes. How much did the gasoline taxes amount to if $34,700,000 was raised in that state in 1 year?

4. A pipe-line company obtained 3,250,000 barrels of crude oil in 1 year, incurring the following operating expenses: transportation, $102,000; maintenance, $23,250; depreciation, $30,750; general expenses, $27,000. Find the total operating cost per barrel of crude oil.

5. The leading petroleum-producing states during a recent year were: Texas, 311 million barrels; Oklahoma, 233 million barrels; California, 193 million barrels; Kansas, $40\frac{1}{2}$ million barrels; Arkansas, 24 million barrels; and Wyoming, 21 million barrels. What per cent of the total production for the 6 states was the production of each state? (Carry each division to 3 decimal places.)

6. It is estimated that 37% of the wood in a tree is wasted in the forest, 21% in the mill, and 4% in the factory.

    a. How many board feet of lumber out of 60,000 board feet are wasted in the factory?

    b. Approximately how many board feet of standing lumber are consumed to produce 25,000 board feet ready for use?

7. In a recent year, 32,157,630 cords of fuel wood were cut from the farm forest land in the United States. How many tons of coal does this fuel wood replace if $1\frac{1}{2}$ cords of wood are equal in fuel value to 1 ton of coal?

NUMBER OF CIVIL SERVICE EMPLOYEES

ADMINISTRATION	COMPETITIVE	APPOINTED
ARTHUR 1884		
CLEVELAND 1897		
ROOSEVELT 1909		
TAFT 1913		
HOOVER 1933		
ROOSEVELT 1940		
EISENHOWER 1956		

Each symbol represents 150,000 employees

PICTOGRAPH CORPORATION

24

Civil Service and Employment Problems

The following problems are representative of those included in examinations for positions in private industry and in the state and Federal civil service. The purpose of including them here is to acquaint you with the kind of arithmetical reasoning that is considered important by some organizations. Your ability to solve these problems—or your lack of ability to do so!—is not a true indication of your understanding of business mathematics. Chances are, however, that if you have mastered the principles presented in this book, you will make a creditable showing on this type of test.

See how well you can do. Work the problem; then check your answers against those given in the key on page 532.

1. A freight train consists of 26 cars. Each car contains 82 barrels of flour, and each barrel weighs 196 pounds. How many pounds of flour are there in the entire cargo?

2. Mr. Black spends $48 a week, which is $\frac{3}{8}$ of his weekly income. Mr. Cutler spends $60 a week, which is $\frac{5}{6}$ of his weekly income. Which of them has the greater income and how much greater?

3. A man bought 425 acres of land at $56 an acre. He sold 125 acres at $50 an acre, 230 acres at $65 an acre, and the remainder at $75 an acre. What was his total gain?

4. A cloth merchant sold three lots of lining, the first containing 19 pieces of 28 yards each, at $1.75 a yard; the second containing 14 pieces of 27 yards each, at $1.87 a yard; and the third containing 40 pieces averaging 25 yards each, at $1.95 a yard. What was the value of the whole transaction?

5. A man sells eggs at 60 cents a dozen, which is $\frac{1}{4}$ more than he pays for them. What must he sell them for, to gain $\frac{1}{3}$ more than he pays for them?

6. On January 10, a merchant bought goods invoiced at $876.40 on the following terms: 4 months net or 6% off if paid within 10 days. What sum will pay the debt on January 15?

7. A person bought 8 building lots for $350 each and 12 for $525 each. What was the average price paid for each lot?

8. The occupants of 6 cottages used during the year $12\frac{1}{2}$, $14\frac{2}{3}$, $10\frac{1}{4}$, $12\frac{3}{4}$, 11, and $15\frac{1}{3}$ barrels of flour, respectively. Find the average number of barrels to a cottage.

9. If a letter carrier can sort letters at the rate of $1\frac{1}{3}$ letters a second, how many minutes will it take him to sort 1,840 letters?

10. Pictures marked at a discount of 20% were bought for $36. How many pictures would have to be bought to obtain a $135 discount?

11. If a drayman averages 4 loads of freight a day and receives $7.50 a load, how much will he earn in a month of 24 working days?

12. If 35% of a gang of men were discharged, and there were 52 men left, how many men were there in the gang originally?

13. A man purchased pencils at 6 for 25 cents. He bought 15 dozen pencils. How much change did he receive from a $10 bill?

14. A merchant put $5,000 in a business. At the end of the first year he gained $640; the second year he lost $390; and the next 3 years he gained $750 each year. How much was he worth at the end of 5 years?

15. A man bought a store and its contents for $4,720. He sold these

for $12\frac{1}{2}\%$ less than they cost him; then he lost 15% of the selling price in bad debts. Find his entire loss.

16. A man bought 156 barrels of flour for $1,573. Finding 32 barrels of flour worthless, he sold the remainder at $13.50 a barrel. Did he gain or lose, and how much?

17. A merchant sold a quantity of sugar for $1,180 and thereby gained $\frac{1}{4}$ of the cost. If he had sold it for $1,000, would he have gained or lost, and how much?

18. Out of a total of 2,476 applications filed for positions in the Federal civil service, only 1,988 applicants appeared for examination.

a. Find the per cent of those who filed applications who appeared for the examinations.

b. If 1,342 applicants passed the examinations, what per cent of those who appeared for the examinations passed?

19. Jones and Smith owned a fleet of taxicabs, each man having an equal interest. Jones sold $\frac{1}{4}$ of his share. They then had 42 left. How many taxicabs did they have to start with?

20. A man left his son $38,000, which was $\frac{2}{3}$ of the value of his estate. What was the value of his estate?

21. Dewey's checkbook balance on March 31 was $711.56. His bank statement showed a balance of $1,085.66. A $2.15 service charge had been made by the bank. Outstanding checks totaled $126.25. A deposit of $250 had not been recorded in the checkbook by error. Prepare a reconciliation statement.

22. Notebooks may be purchased at two for a quarter or, when purchased by the gross, at $13.80 a gross. How much is saved per dozen when the notebooks are purchased by the gross?

23. A realtor received 5% commission on all sales. If his total commission during a 3-month period totaled $4,180, to how much did his sales amount?

24. A manufacturer pays his salesmen 10% commission on all sales up to $5,000 a month and an additional commission of 6% on all sales in excess of this amount. Martin, a salesman, sold $6,495 worth of merchandise during the month of October. What was his total commission?

25. A 4-cycle power motor is sold for $136; terms, 25% down payment, balance in equal monthly payments of $8.50 each. How many monthly payments must be made?

26. A man received a dividend check for $270 on 60 shares of stock costing him $112.50 a share. What was the per cent of return on his investment?

27. Dover insured his plant for $35,000 with the Mutual Insurance Company and for $25,000 with the Home Insurance Company. A $19,500 fire loss occurred. How much would Dover receive from each company?

28. Norton drove his car from Monticello to Liberty, a distance of 12 miles, in 15 minutes. At this rate, what was his speed an hour?

29. A radio cost $27 after a discount of $33\frac{1}{3}\%$ was deducted from the marked price. What was the marked price?

30. A merchant went out of business owing creditors $64,800. The total net cash realized by him for the sale of all the assets of the business amounted to $19,440. If he distributed the money among his creditors, how much would be paid to a creditor to whom he owed $2,430?

31. A clothier sells topcoats at $48 each, which is a gain of 20% of cost. How many topcoats must he sell to realize a profit of $200?

32. A businessman deposited $\frac{4}{5}$ of his profits in a savings account. After he withdrew $\frac{1}{4}$ of his deposit, $3,270 remained. To how much did his total profits amount?

33. In the partnership of Herberts and Fredericks, Eric Herberts contributed $6,000 and Michael Fredericks $1\frac{1}{2}$ times as much as Herberts. If each contributes $2,500 additional, what per cent of the total invested capital will each have made?

34. Clark earned $4,200 and saved $\frac{1}{6}$ of his salary. Lewis saved the same amount, but it was only $\frac{1}{12}$ of his salary. How much more than Clark did Lewis earn?

35. A mail train is traveling at the rate of 1 mile in $1\frac{1}{3}$ minutes. How many miles an hour is the train going?

36. Find the total interest paid on a $250 loan if the loan is paid back in 10 equal monthly payments with interest at the rate of 1% a month on the unpaid balance.

37. A man purchased an automobile for $1,200. He estimated that the car depreciated 15% each year, based on the value of the car at the beginning of the year. During which year will its value shrink to less than $600?

38. There are 60 pounds in a bushel of wheat and 48 pounds in a bushel of barley. How many bushels of barley will weigh as much as 680 bushels of wheat?

39. Joe Spivis bought 2 farms. For one, he paid $4,560; for the other, twice as much as for the first. He spent $537 on each for improvements and paid taxes that amounted to $78. He sold both farms for $15,570. Did he gain or lose on the sale, and how much?

40. A real estate agent who charges 5% commission sold a lot and remitted to his principal $2,227.25, after deducting his commission and $43.25 selling expenses. For how much did he sell the lot?

41. A government employee earns $6,450 a year. If his pension rate is 4.6%, how much is deducted for pension from his semimonthly pay check?

42. A house valued at $13,500 is insured for $\frac{5}{6}$ of its value at $\frac{7}{8}$%. What is the amount of premium that must be paid?

43. A house costs $18,000. Expenses, including taxes, amount to $660. What monthly rent must the owner receive to clear 6% on his investment?

44. A family spends 30% of its income for food, 12% for clothing, 25% for shelter, 6% for recreation, 7% for education, and 5% for miscellaneous items. The weekly earnings are $140. How much can be saved in 1 year?

45. An estate cost $180,000; the tax valuation is 60% of its price. What is the tax to be paid if the rate is 6.75 cents a dollar?

46. Browning sells a certain article at $5.28 a dozen. He buys the articles for $60 a gross, less 20%, 10%, and 5%. What is his gross profit per dozen?

47. Login sold a building for $42,000, taking a loss of $12\frac{1}{2}$% on the price he paid. What did he pay for the building?

48. The partnership of Herbert and Frederick made a profit of $16,450. If Herbert's share of the profit is to be 75% of Frederick's, what is Herbert's share?

49. A widow had $64,000, which was $\frac{4}{5}$ of an estate. The balance was equally divided among 5 children. How much did each receive, and how much more did the widow have than each child?

50. Eric and Michael own a tract of land. They sell $\frac{1}{4}$ of the tract to one man and $\frac{1}{8}$ to another. What they have left is worth $4,500. At the same rate, what was the original tract worth?

51. A man rented his farm for $\frac{1}{4}$ of the crop and realized $1,320 rent. How much more would he have received had he rented the farm for $\frac{1}{3}$ of the crop?

52. An author received 10% royalty on a certain book. How many books must be sold at $3.20 each to yield an income of $2,400?

53. A refinery put 85,000 pounds of sugar in 10-pound, 5-pound, and 2-pound boxes, using the same number of each size. How many boxes of each size were used?

54. The total cost of two houses is $35,000. If one house cost $\frac{1}{3}$ more than the other, how much is paid for the higher-priced one?

55. A house is purchased for $19,000 on the following terms: $10,000 cash and a $4\frac{1}{2}\%$ mortgage on the property for the balance. To how much does the quarterly interest amount?

56. A man sold $\frac{5}{8}$ of his business for $36,000. At the same rate, what is his remaining business worth?

57. The yearly income on a 5% investment is $875. How much is the total investment?

58. Last year a firm distributed a bonus of $9\frac{1}{2}\%$ of its net income to its employees. If it distributed $22,800, to how much did its net income amount?

59. An airplane travels 184 miles in 40 minutes. How many miles will the airplane travel in $4\frac{1}{4}$ hours at the same rate?

60. A certain mail train picks up $3\frac{1}{2}$ times as many bags as it drops. If it picks up 266 bags, how many does it drop?

Answers to Civil Service and Employment Problems

1. 417,872 pounds
2. Mr. Black, $56
3. $2,650
4. $3,587.86
5. 64 cents
6. $823.82
7. $455
8. $12\frac{3}{4}$
9. 23 minutes
10. 15 pictures
11. $720
12. 80 men
13. $2.50
14. $7,500
15. $1,209.50
16. $101 gain
17. $56 gain
18. a. 80.29%
    b. 67.5%
19. 48
20. $95,000
21. $711.56 + $126.25 + $250 − $2.15 = $1,085.66

22. Savings, 35 cents a dozen
23. $83,600
24. $739.20
25. 12
26. 4%
27. Mutual, $11,375; Home, $8,125
28. 48 miles an hour
29. $40.50
30. $729
31. 25 topcoats
32. $5,450
33. Eric Herberts, $42\frac{1}{2}\%$ Michael Fredericks, $57\frac{1}{2}\%$
34. $4,200 more
35. 45 miles an hour
36. $13.75
37. Fifth year
38. 850 bushels
39. $738 gain
40. $2,390
41. $12.36

42. $98.44
43. $145
44. $1,092
45. $7,290
46. $1.86, Gross profit margin
47. $48,000
48. $7,050, Herbert's share
49. Each child received $16,000. Widow had $48,000 more
50. $7,200
51. $440 more
52. 7,500 books
53. 5,000 boxes
54. $20,000
55. $101.25
56. $21,600
57. $17,500
58. $240,000
59. 1,173 miles
60. 76 bags

SUPPLEMENTARY SECTION

GENERAL REVIEW OF BUSINESS MATHEMATICS

1. Find the sum in each of the following problems. Check your answer by the reverse-order method.

a	b	c	d
$3,482.14	$8,089.76	$82,915.80	$3,891.50
5,614.97	58.32	694.33	861.42
7,862.28	9.18	8,754.27	8,095.68
1,397.64	861.93	21,332.81	87.64
4,890.26	5,642.87	16.80	59.76
5,219.83	67.52	413.76	9,081.34
8,683.21	913.58	9,697.34	529.67
2,217.86	5,197.36	5,436.75	640.43

2. Find the difference in each of the following problems. Check each by adding the remainder and the subtrahend to get the minuend.

a	b	c	d	e	f	g	h
8,894	3,286	5,881	7,762	9,246	1,357	8,254	4,163
2,295	1,899	2,189	2,876	5,848	1,009	3,391	2,264

3. Find the product in each of the following problems. Check each by the casting-out-9's check.

	a	b	c	d
I.	3.54 × .06	79.3 × .57	.807 × .24	369 × 3.1
II.	42.30 × 2.08	5.093 × .025	.0083 × 5.27	385.1 × 9.70
III.	59.25 × 8.364	.0952 × 73.49	5.003 × 6.048	798.5 × 80.09

4. Find the quotient in each of the following problems. Check each by the casting-out-9's check.

	a	b	c
I.	98.74 ÷ .56	6.243 ÷ 4.3	758.7 ÷ .68
II.	.5468 ÷ .94	3,887 ÷ .32	8,765.89 ÷ 1.24
III.	9.64532 ÷ 342	426.487 ÷ 62.1	67,787.3 ÷ .535
IV.	901,086 ÷ 87.6	96.4582 ÷ .0487	.0246581 ÷ 3.24

5. Find the sum in each of the following problems.

a	b	c	d	e
$5\frac{11}{12}$	$23\frac{1}{2}$	$13\frac{5}{6}$	$89\frac{1}{8}$	$92\frac{11}{16}$
$6\frac{7}{8}$	$87\frac{5}{6}$	$64\frac{1}{3}$	$23\frac{1}{4}$	$49\frac{5}{12}$
$8\frac{3}{4}$	$46\frac{3}{8}$	$85\frac{2}{3}$	$95\frac{1}{6}$	$55\frac{11}{24}$
$7\frac{5}{6}$	$54\frac{3}{4}$	$17\frac{1}{4}$	$38\frac{2}{3}$	$78\frac{1}{4}$

6. Find the difference in each of the following problems.

	a	b	c
I.	$\frac{7}{8} - \frac{2}{3}$	$\frac{5}{6} - \frac{3}{4}$	$\frac{4}{5} - \frac{2}{3}$
II.	$53 - \frac{1}{3}$	$216 - \frac{5}{6}$	$78 - \frac{6}{7}$
III.	$86 - 37\frac{7}{9}$	$24 - 13\frac{4}{7}$	$743 - 519\frac{6}{7}$

7. Find the product in each of the following problems.

	a	**b**	**c**
I.	$8\frac{1}{2} \times 10$	$6\frac{3}{4} \times 24$	$12\frac{2}{3} \times 8$
II.	$36 \times 5\frac{5}{6}$	$25 \times 6\frac{1}{2}$	$75 \times 4\frac{3}{8}$

8. Find the quotient in each of the following problems.

	a	**b**	**c**
I.	$7\frac{1}{2} \div 3$	$32\frac{2}{3} \div 16$	$53\frac{2}{3} \div 33$
II.	$25\frac{1}{3} \div \frac{4}{5}$	$32\frac{1}{4} \div \frac{3}{8}$	$73\frac{1}{3} \div \frac{5}{9}$

9. Change each of the following per cent values to a fraction.

	a	**b**	**c**	**d**	**e**
I.	20%	55%	36%	$5\frac{1}{2}\%$	$8\frac{3}{4}\%$
II.	300%	250%	125%	$4\frac{1}{4}\%$	$15\frac{2}{3}\%$

10. Change each of the following per cent values to a decimal.

	a	**b**	**c**	**d**	**e**
I.	46%	93%	158%	$8\frac{1}{2}\%$	$\frac{3}{4}\%$
II.	16.8%	5%	2.3%	$5\frac{3}{4}\%$	$17\frac{1}{5}\%$

11. Change each of the following numbers to its equivalent per cent value.

	a	**b**	**c**	**d**	**e**
I.	$.57$	$.24$	$.05$	$5\frac{1}{2}$	$3\frac{3}{8}$
II.	$\frac{3}{5}$	$\frac{5}{9}$	$\frac{7}{25}$	$1\frac{3}{4}$	$.425$

12. Approximately 48% of the population of a certain country are males. If the total population of the country is 14,375,423, how many males are there?

13. An article was purchased for $18.50 and sold for $25.90. What per cent of the cost was the markup?

14. George Riker sold all but $5\frac{1}{2}$ acres of his land to a development company. If this is only 2% of what he originally owned, how much land did Mr. Riker own before the sale?

15. Mr. Evans purchased a set of tires for his car at $28.50 each. Three years later, when he traded these tires in for new ones, he was allowed $2 for each tire. Using the straight-line method for computing depreciation,

    a. What was the annual depreciation on each of the tires?

    b. What was the annual rate of depreciation?

16. Find the amount of the Social Security tax that is taken from a salary of $106.75. Assume that the employee has not yet earned $4,200 during the year.

17. Using the income tax table on pages 172–173, find the income tax withheld from each of the following weekly salaries.

Salary	Exemptions	Income Tax
$ 65.20	2	$xxx
123.50	4	xxx
205.17	3	xxx

18. Complete the following payroll register. If necessary, use the Social Security table on pages 168–169 and the income tax table on pages 172–173.

Payroll Register										
Employee	Exemp-tions	M T W T F	Reg. Hrs.	Reg. Rate	Gross Salary	Soc. Sec.	Income Tax	Total Deduc.	Net Pay
F. Clem	2	8 8 8 8 8	$xxx	$1.83	$xxx	$xxx	$xxx	$xxx	$xxx
T. Burke	4	8 7 8 6 6	xxx	2.56	xxx	xxx	xxx	xxx	xxx

19. A bookcase that lists at $72.50 can be bought at a 40% discount. What is the net price?

20. The catalogue price of a spinet is $742. The manufacturer, however, allows a trade discount of 20% and 15%. What is the net price of the spinet to the dealer?

21. The Park Bedding Company received an invoice dated June 27, 19—, for merchandise amounting to $273.28. The terms of the invoice were 2/10, 1/30, n/60. If the bill was paid on July 2, how large was the payment?

22. Ryan's of Trenton purchased women's travel robes at $6.80 each and sold them at $8.50 each.

    a. What was the per cent of markup based on the cost?

    b. What was the per cent of markup based on the selling price?

23. At the end of the winter season, C. Crane and Sons had on hand 9 men's overcoats, which they marked down 30%. The original price on each coat was $79.50. What was the total reduction for the entire group of coats?

24. Oranges that ordinarily sell for 60 cents a dozen were reduced to 2 for 5 cents.

    a. How much would a buyer save on the purchase of 2 dozen oranges?

    b. What discount rate was the purchaser receiving?

25. A merchant sells men's shirts at $3.95 each. If his markup is 40% of the cost, what is the maximum price he should pay for these shirts?

26. Find the interest on each of the following loans.

    a. $500 @ 4% for 2 years   **e.** $540 @ $6\frac{1}{2}$% for 9 months

    b. $350 @ $5\frac{1}{2}$% for 3 years   **f.** $275 @ $5\frac{1}{3}$% for 7 months

    c. $425 @ $4\frac{1}{4}$% for $1\frac{1}{2}$ years   **g.** $250 @ 5% for 90 days

    d. $600 @ 6% for 4 months   **h.** $325 @ $4\frac{1}{2}$% for 75 days

27. Using the bankers' 60-day interest method, find the interest on each of the following loans.

    a. $720 @ 6% for 120 days   **c.** $654 @ 6% for 36 days

    b. $532 @ 6% for 20 days   **d.** $225 @ 6% for 87 days

28. Find the number of days between the following dates.

    a. June 15 to September 23   **c.** May 14, 1957, to March 10, 1958

    b. February 12 to July 5   **d.** January 18, 1957, to May 3, 1958

29. Using the simple-interest table on page 250, find the interest on each of the following loans.

    a. $600 @ 4% for 24 days   **b.** $950 @ $6\frac{1}{2}$% for 62 days

30. $500 was borrowed from a bank on October 17, 1958, at a discount rate of $5\frac{1}{2}$%. If the term of the note was 3 months, what were the proceeds on the note?

31. How much did Robert Fredericks receive on a 4-month non-interest-bearing note for $438 dated September 7 if he discounted the note on October 14 at 5%?

32. Vincent Haskins sold $527.60 worth of merchandise. He received in payment a note dated April 4, due in 5 months, with interest at 4%. What were the proceeds on this note if he discounted it on June 17 at 6%?

33. Barton's Appliance Store offered to sell a $259.95 refrigerator for 10% down and 24 monthly installments of $11.09 each. Find the installment charge if the refrigerator is purchased on the installment plan.

34. What rate of interest is charged if each of the following articles is purchased on the installment plan?

	Article	Cash Price	Installment Terms		
			Down Payment	Number of Payments	Monthly Payments
a	*Sofa*	$260.00	$60.00	20	$10.95
b	*Storm windows*	157.00	17.00	12	13.25
c	*Dishwasher*	189.95	9.95	9	21.50

35. John Dickson financed the purchase of a new car at 6% interest rate over a period of 24 months. If the amount that Mr. Dickson still owed after using his old car as a down payment was $3,200, what were his monthly payments?

36. The following advertisement appeared in a newspaper.

Blow Away Your Money Worries		
Arrange a personal loan through the Friendly Finance Company		
Cash You Get	20 Payments	6 Payments
$200	$12.56	$36.07
$500	29.98	88.74

Using the $200 loan for 20 months, answer the following questions.
  a. What is the total amount that was repaid to the loan agency?
  b. How much interest was paid on this loan?
  c. What yearly rate of interest was paid on the decreasing balance?

Note: In order to solve Problems 37–44 it will be necessary to refer to the tables in Chapter 13.

37. Find the premium on each of the following fire insurance policies if the insurance was purchased for the period indicated. (See pages 314–315.)

No.	Amt. of Insurance	Community	Structure	Period in Years	Premium
a	$15,000	A	Frame	1	$xxx
b	16,500	D	Brick	2	xxx
c	12,700	G	Brick	3	xxx

38. Find the premiums on the following short-term fire insurance policies. (See pages 317–318.)
  a. Annual premium: $35.56; period of policy: 45 days
  b. Annual premium: $74.29; period of policy: 237 days
39. The merchandise in a store was insured for $35,000 from April 14 to October 23 of the same year. If the annual fire insurance rate was $.96 per $100, what was the amount of the premium paid?
40. In each of the following cases, find the indemnity paid by the fire insurance companies under a policy that contained an 80% clause.
  a. Property value: $14,000; face value of policy: $8,000; fire loss: $6,000
  b. Property value: $26,500; face value of policy: $16,000; fire loss: $20,000
41. Find the total premium on each of the following automobile insurance policies. (See page 327.)

No.	Coverage		Class	Territory	Premium		Total
	Bodily Injury	Property Damage			Bodily Injury	Property Damage	
a	5-and-10	$ 5,000	1B	3	$xxx	$xxx	$xxx
b	10-and-20	5,000	1A	2	xxx	xxx	xxx
c	50-and-100	10,000	1C	4	xxx	xxx	xxx

42. How much more will a Class 1C driver pay for a $10,000 property damage policy if he lives in Territory 2 rather than in Territory 4?

43. As a Halloween prank, boys damaged the aerial of Mr. Tracey's car radio. The cost of repairing the damage was $12.75.

    a. What type of automobile insurance would have covered Mr. Tracey for this loss?

    b. How much of the loss would the insurance company have paid?

44. A man purchased a $10,000 30-year endowment policy at age 20.

    a. If he lived the entire 30 years, what was the total of his annual premiums?

    b. How much did he receive from the insurance company at the end of the 30 years?

    c. How much more did he receive from the insurance company than he paid in premiums?

45. In order to meet its expenses for the coming year, a city will have to raise $3,000,000 in taxes. If the total assessed value of the property in the city is $85,000,000, what will the tax rate in dollars per $100 have to be?

46. In the town of Bound Brook, property is assessed for 30% of its market value. If the tax rate is $57.40 per $1,000, what is the tax on a house that can be sold for $28,500?

47. Using the tax table on pages 360–361, find the tax due the Government by each of the following taxpayers. If the person is married, assume that he and his wife are filing a joint return.

    a. Adjusted gross income: $4,600; married and has one child

    b. Adjusted gross income: $3,925; married and caring for two dependent parents

48. The taxable income on line 5, page 2, of the 1040 return is shown by the figures below. Compute the tax due in each case by using the tax rate table on page 366.

    a. Taxable income: $3,650; joint return

    b. Taxable income: $8,243; single return

49. Find the primary benefit for Social Security on each of the following salaries.

    a. Average monthly salary: $160

    b. Average monthly salary: $85

50. When Mr. Edgerton applied for his Social Security benefits, it was found that his average monthly salary was $226.40. If his wife was over 65 at the time, what were their total family benefits?

51. Howard Langley died, leaving a wife and a daughter aged 5 years. His primary benefit was computed to be $92.60.

    a. What death benefit will the family receive?

    b. How large will his wife's monthly benefit be?

    c. How large will his daughter's monthly benefit be?

    d. For how many years will his wife and daughter receive these benefits?

52. Benjamin West purchased 200 shares of $5\frac{1}{2}\%$ preferred stock at $87\frac{1}{4}$. If the par value of the stock was $100 a share, what semiannual dividend did West receive?

53. Using the stock quotations that appear on pages 395–396, find the cost of each of the following purchases.

    a. 200 shares of Dow Chemical Company purchased at the low price.

    b. 500 shares of Flintkote purchased at the opening price.

54. Find the rate of return on each of the following stock purchases.

No.	Price per Share	Yearly Dividend	Rate of Return
a	$58	$2.40	xxx
c	$12\frac{3}{4}$	.85	xxx

55. Find the rate of return on each of the following preferred stock purchases.

No.	Price per Share	Par Value	Dividend Rate	Rate of Return
a	$82	$100	5%	xxx
b	$19\frac{1}{4}$	25	$4\frac{1}{2}\%$	xxx

56. If the profits of a company are to be divided in accordance with the investment of each partner, how much will each receive in the following partnerships?

No.	Investment of Each Partner	Total Profit
a	$12,000; $18,000	$8,400
b	$6,000; $8,000; $10,000	$7,500

57. Using the bond quotations on pages 422–423, find the interest received by the owners of the following bonds. Assume that the companies are paying interest on their bonds.

No.	Company	Par Value	Number of Bonds	Period	Interest
a	Armour	$1,000	3	annually	$xxx
b	R C A	1,000	2	semian.	xxx
c	Alcoa	1,000	4	quarterly	xxx

58. Find the accrued interest to the sales date in each of the following bond transactions.

No.	Par Value	Interest Rate	Interest Dates	Sales Date	No. of Bonds	Accrued Interest
a	$1,000	5%	May 1 and Nov. 1	July 12	1	$xxx
b	500	$4\frac{1}{4}\%$	Feb. 1 and Aug. 1	July 8	2	xxx

59. The number of billions of barrels of crude oil that was produced during a recent year is given by the following figures:

United States	2.4	Russia	.6
Middle East	1.2	Rest of world	.55
Venezuela	.8		

Construct a circle graph presenting these data. (See page 468.)

60. Using the table on page 482, find the cost of shipping the following articles by freight train from Newark, New Jersey.

No.	Destination	Class	Weight in Lbs.	Cost
a	*Effner, Indiana*	100	6,000	$xxx
b	*Lancaster, Pa.*	95	8,375	xxx

61. Find the cost of shipping the following articles by parcel post. Use the tables on pages 485 and 486 to compute your answer.

No.	Weight	Distance in Miles	Insurance	Parcel-Post Fee	Insurance Fee	Total
a	12 lbs.	200	None	$xxx	$xxx	$xxx
b	14 lbs. 3 oz.	628	$ 75	xxx	xxx	xxx
c	$18\frac{1}{4}$ lbs.	2,340	125	xxx	xxx	xxx

62. Find the postage on each of the following airmail deliveries. Use the table on page 487 to compute your answer.

No.	Weight	Distance	Cost
a	8 lbs.	Zone 5	$xxx
b	11 lbs. 7 oz.	840 miles	xxx
c	$12\frac{1}{2}$ lbs.	1,638 miles	xxx

63. Using the water-rate table on page 495, find the bill for the quarterly periods shown below.

No.	Meter Reading at Beginning of Period	Meter Reading at End of Period	No. of Gallons Consumed	Cost
a	349,000	371,000	xxx	$xxx
b	528,300	662,300	xxx	xxx

64. Mrs. Edwards purchased a wall-to-wall carpet for her living-room floor at a cost of $17.95 per square yard. If the dimensions of the floor are 24 feet by 14 feet, what was the cost of the carpeting?

DENOMINATE NUMBERS—THE ENGLISH AND METRIC SYSTEMS

Systems of measurements are essential in order that modern business may be carried on efficiently. Everyone, consumer as well as merchant, should know the common measures of the English and the metric systems and understand how to use them. Nearly all the nations of the world except the United States and England use the metric system. These two countries use the English system.

The metric system is used in scientific research in the United States. This system of weights and measures has one advantage over the English system. All the metric tables use a scale of 10; that is, ten of one denomination is equal to one of the next higher denomination. In linear measure, the scale is 10; in square measure, 100; and in cubic measure, 1,000. When a change is made from one measure to another, it is necessary only to move the decimal point either to the right or to the left.

A. The English System. Tables of weights and measures have been established by law and custom. These units of measurement are concrete numbers commonly referred to as *denominate numbers*.

TABLES OF WEIGHTS AND MEASURES

Linear (Line or Long) Measure
U. S. and British Standard

Used in measuring distances and lengths, widths, or thicknesses.

12 inches (in.)	= 1 foot (ft.)
3 feet	= 1 yard (yd.)
$5\frac{1}{2}$ yards, or $16\frac{1}{2}$ feet	= 1 rod (rd.)
40 rods	= 1 furlong (fur.)
8 furlongs, or 320 rods	= 1 mile (mi.)

The unit of length is the yard.
1 hand = 4 inches (used in measuring the height of horses).
1 fathom (marine measure) = 6 feet (used in measuring depths at sea).
1 knot = $1.152\frac{2}{3}$ miles (nautical or geographical mile).
1 league = 3 knots (3×1.15 miles).

Square (Surface) Measure
U. S. and British Standard

Used in measuring areas of surfaces.

144 square inches (sq. in.)	= 1 square foot (sq. ft.)
9 square feet	= 1 square yard (sq. yd.)
$30\frac{1}{4}$ square yards	= 1 square rod (sq. rd.)
160 square rods	= 1 acre (A.)
640 acres	= 1 square mile (sq. mi.)

The unit in measuring land is the acre, except for city lots.
A square, used in roofing, is 100 square feet.
The unit in measuring other surfaces is the square yard.

Solid or Cubic Measure
U. S. and British Standard

Used in measuring the volume of a body or a solid as well as the contents or capacity of hollow bodies.

1,728 cubic inches (cu. in.)	= 1 cubic foot (cu. ft.)
27 cubic feet	= 1 cubic yard (cu. yd.)
231 cubic inches	= 1 gallon (gal.)
$24\frac{3}{4}$ cubic feet	= 1 perch (P.) of stone
128 cubic feet	= 1 cord (cd.) of wood
1 cubic foot	= $7\frac{1}{2}$ gallons

1 cubic yard of earth = 1 load.
A cord of wood (128 cubic feet) is a pile 8 feet long, 4 feet wide, and 4 feet high.
1 cubic foot of water weighs $62\frac{1}{2}$ pounds (avoirdupois).

Circular or Angular Measure
U. S. and British Standard

Used in measuring angles or areas of circles.

60 seconds (")	= 1 minute (')	30 degrees = 1 sign ($\frac{1}{12}$ of a circle)
60 minutes	= 1 degree (°)	60 degrees = 1 sextant ($\frac{1}{6}$ of a circle)
360 degrees	= 1 circle (cir.)	90 degrees = 1 quadrant ($\frac{1}{4}$ of a circle)

A 90° angle is a right angle.

Liquid Measure
U. S. and British Standard

Used in measuring the liquid capacity of vessels or containers of all liquids except medicine.

4 gills (gi.)	= 1 pint (pt.)	63 gallons	= 1 hogshead (hhd.)
2 pints	= 1 quart (qt.)	2 barrels	= 1 hogshead
4 quarts	= 1 gallon (gal.)	$7\frac{1}{2}$ gallons	= 1 cubic foot
$31\frac{1}{2}$ gallons	= 1 barrel (bbl.)		

The unit of liquid measure is the United States gallon of 231 cubic inches.
1 gallon of water weighs $8\frac{1}{3}$ pounds (avoirdupois).

Dry Measure
U. S. and British Standard

Used in measuring the volume of the contents of containers of solids, such as produce, seed, fruits, and the like, that are not sold by weight.

2 pints (pt.)	= 1 quart (qt.)	4 pecks	= 1 bushel (bu.)
8 quarts	= 1 peck (pk.)	$2\frac{3}{4}$ bushels	= 1 barrel

Avoirdupois Weight
U. S. and British Standard

Used in weighing heavy, coarse articles, such as coal, iron, grain, hay, and the like.

$27\frac{11}{32}$ grains	= 1 dram
16 drams	= 1 ounce (oz.)
16 ounces	= 1 pound (lb.)
100 pounds	= 1 hundredweight (cwt.)
20 hundredweights	= 1 ton (T.)
2,000 pounds	= 1 ton
2,240 pounds	= 1 long or gross ton
7,000 grains (gr.)	= 1 pound avoirdupois

The United States Government uses the long ton of 2,240 pounds in fixing the duty on merchandise that is taxed by the ton.

Coal and iron sold at the mine are also weighed by the long ton.

Troy Weight

Used in weighing precious minerals, and by the United States Government in weighing coins.

24 grains	= 1 pennyweight (pwt.)
20 pennyweights	= 1 ounce
12 ounces	= 1 pound
240 pennyweights	= 1 pound
5,760 grains	= 1 pound troy
3,168 grains	= 1 carat

The unit of weight in the United States is the troy pound.

Pure gold is 24 carats fine. Gold marked 14 carats is $\frac{14}{24}$ pure gold by weight and $\frac{10}{24}$ alloy by weight.

Apothecaries' Dry Weight and Liquid Measure

Used by druggists and physicians in weighing and measuring drugs and chemicals, and in compounding dry and liquid medicines.

Dry Weight		Fluid Measure	
20 grains	= 1 scruple (sc.)	60 minims (m.)	= 1 fluid drachm, or dram
3 scruples	= 1 dram (dr.)		(f ℥)·
8 drams	= 1 ounce (oz.)	8 fluid drachms	= 1 fluid ounce (f ℥)
12 ounces	= 1 pound (lb.)	16 fluid ounces	= 1 pint (O.)
		8 pints	= 1 gallon (Cong.)

Avoirdupois weight, however, is used when drugs and chemicals are bought and sold wholesale.

Time Table

60 seconds (sec.)	= 1 minute (min.)		52 weeks	= 1 year (yr.)
60 minutes	= 1 hour (hr.)		12 months	= 1 year
24 hours	= 1 day (da.)		365 days	= 1 year *
7 days	= 1 week (wk.)		100 years	= 1 century (C.)
30 days	= 1 month (mo.) *			

* January, 31 days; February, 28 days (29 days in February in a leap year of 366 days); March, 31 days; April, 30 days; May, 31 days; June, 30 days; July, 31 days; August, 31 days; September, 30 days; October, 31 days; November, 30 days; December, 31 days.

Counting Table

20 units	= 1 score
12 units	= 1 dozen
12 dozen	= 1 gross (gro.)
12 gross	= 1 great gross (gr. gro.)

Paper Measure

24 sheets	= 1 quire (qr.)
20 quires	= 1 ream (rm.)
2 reams	= 1 bundle (bdl.)
5 bundles	= 1 bale (bl.)

Measures of Value

French Money

10 millimes (m.)	= 1 centime (c.)
10 centimes	= 1 decime (dc.)
10 decimes	= 1 franc (F.)

The unit of measure is the franc.

English Money

4 farthings (far.)	= 1 penny (d.)
12 pence	= 1 shilling (s.)
20 shillings	= 1 pound sterling (£)

The unit of measure is the pound sterling.

Commodity Weights

Beef, barrel	200 lbs.	Nails, keg	100 lbs.
Butter, firkin	56 lbs.	Pork, barrel	200 lbs.
Flour, barrel	196 lbs.	Salt, barrel	280 lbs.

Bushel Weights

The following weights are used in a bushel in most of the states:

Barley	48 lbs.	Corn (shelled)	56 lbs.	Potatoes	60 lbs.
Beans	60 lbs.	Corn meal	48 lbs.	Rye	56 lbs.
Buckwheat	48 lbs.	Oats	32 lbs.	Sweet potatoes	54 lbs.
Clover seed	60 lbs.	Onions	57 lbs.	Timothy seed	45 lbs.
Corn (ear)	70 lbs.	Peas	60 lbs.	Wheat	60 lbs.

B. The Metric System. The metric system of weights and measures is a decimal system. The three principal units are:

1. The meter, which is the unit of length.
2. The liter, which is the unit of capacity.
3. The gram, which is the unit of weight or mass.

The basic unit of the metric system is the meter, on which the other units are based. The length of the meter, which is 39.37 inches, was originally determined by taking one ten-millionth of the distance from the equator to the pole.

METRIC TABLES
Linear Measure

```
10 millimeters (mm.) = 1 centimeter (cm.)
10 centimeters       = 1 decimeter (dm.)
10 decimeters        = 1 meter (m.)
10 meters            = 1 dekameter (Dm.)
10 dekameters        = 1 hektometer (Hm.)
10 hektometers       = 1 kilometer (Km.)
10 kilometers        = 1 myriameter (Mm.)
```

The unit of measures of length is the meter.

Liquid and Dry Measure

```
10 milliliters (ml.) = 1 centiliter (cl.)     10 dekaliters  = 1 hektoliter (Hl.)
10 centiliters       = 1 deciliter (dl.)      10 hektoliters = 1 kiloliter (Kl.)
10 deciliters        = 1 liter (l.)           10 kiloliters  = 1 myrialiter (Ml.)
10 liters            = 1 dekaliter (Dl.)
```

The unit of capacity for liquids and solids is the liter.

Weight Table

```
10 milligrams (mg.) = 1 centigram (cg.)
10 centigrams       = 1 decigram (dg.)
10 decigrams        = 1 gram (g.)
10 grams            = 1 dekagram (Dg.)
10 dekagrams        = 1 hektogram (Hg.)
10 hektograms       = 1 kilogram (Kg.)
10 kilograms        = 1 myriagram (Mg.)
10 myriagrams       = 1 quintal (Q.)
10 quintals         = 1 tonneau (T.)
```

The unit of weight is the gram.

METRIC AND ENGLISH EQUIVALENTS
Linear-Measure Equivalents

```
1 in. = 2.54 cm.          1 cm. =  .3937 in.
1 ft. =  .3048 m.         1 dm. =  .328 ft.
1 yd. =  .9144 m.         1 m.  = 1.0936 yds.
1 rd. = 5.029 m.          1 Dm. = 1.9884 rds.
1 mi. = 1.6093 Km.        1 Km. =  .6214 mi.
```

Liquid- and Dry-Measure Equivalents

```
1 dry qt.     = 1.101 l.        1 l.  =  .908 dry qt.
1 liquid qt.  =  .9463 l.       1 l.  = 1.0567 liquid qt.
1 liquid gal. =  .3785 Dl.      1 Dl. = 2.6417 liquid gal.
1 pk.         =  .881 Dl.       1 Dl. = 1.135 pk.
1 bu.         =  .3524 Hl.      1 Hl. = 2.8377 bu.
```

Weight-Measure Equivalents

1 qt. Troy	=	.0648 g.	1 g.	=	15.432 gr. Troy
1 oz. Troy	=	31.104 g.	1 g.	=	.03215 oz. Troy
1 oz. Avoir.	=	28.35 g.	1 g.	=	.03527 oz. Avoir.
1 lb. Troy	=	.3732 kg.	1 kg.	=	2.679 lbs. Troy
1 lb. Avoir.	=	.4536 kg.	1 kg.	=	2.2046 lbs. Avoir.
1 T. (short)	=	.9072 t.	1 t.	=	1.1023 T. (short)

LEARNING EXERCISES

A. Solve the following problems based on the *English* system.

1. Express 360 square rods as acres.
2. Find the number of gallons in 462 cubic inches.
3. How many barrels are needed to hold 1,287 bushels?
4. What is the difference in ounces between 34 pounds troy and 34 pounds avoirdupois?
5. A sterling silver knife weighs 3 oz. 6 pwt. 12 gr. Find the weight of a dozen knives.
6. Reduce 79 rods 3 yards $1\frac{1}{4}$ feet and 5 inches to inches.
7. Express 24 square yards and 15 square feet in square inches.
8. A gold bar weighs 5 pounds 9 ounces 3 pennyweights and 7 grains. What is it worth at $35 an ounce?
9. 72 gallons of grape juice are purchased at $1.02 a gallon and sold at 15 cents a glass. If each glass contains 2 gills, what is the total gain?
10. Garden apartments are to be constructed on a plot of ground 38 rods by 16 rods. How many acres in the plot?

B. Solve the following problems based on the *metric* system.

1. Find the number of inches in 877.56 centimeters.
2. Express as kilograms: 29 pounds (troy); 29 pounds (avoirdupois).
3. Find the number of kilometers in 725 miles.
4. How many millimeters in 317 meters?
5. Express 7 dekaliters as: pecks, liquid gallons.
6. Reduce $28\frac{1}{2}$ kilograms to pounds.
7. How much will 575 dekaliters of grain cost at $1.75 a bushel?
8. The distance between two cities is 892 miles. Express in metric measurement.
9. How much is gained on 350 meters of material that costs 89 cents per meter and sells for $1.15 a yard?
10. Butter is purchased at 64 cents a pound. How many kilograms would be received for $9.75?

THE LANGUAGE OF BUSINESS MATHEMATICS

A comprehensive vocabulary of business terms is essential to a thorough understanding of the principles and problems presented in this text and will be of inestimable value in the study of other subjects in the commercial curriculum.

The student should make each business term a part of his vocabulary.

TERMS USED IN BUSINESS TRANSACTIONS

Acceptance. The agreement to pay a draft or bill of exchange when it is due.

Account. A record or report of business dealings.

Accrued interest. Interest that has accumulated or has been earned, but is not yet due.

Ad valorem. Based on value; an import duty or tax on merchandise at a certain per cent of its value at the shipping point.

Agent. A person authorized to act for another, called the principal.

Aggregate. Sum or total; that which has been collected.

Amortization. The reduction of a debt by periodic payments on the principal amount.

Amount. The total or sum; the sum of the principal plus the interest.

Annuity. A sum of money payable annually; an investment yielding a fixed annual income.

Appraise. To estimate the value of property.

Assessment. A valuation of property for purposes of taxation.

Asset. Anything of value owned by a person or business.

Average. Midway between two extremes; the result obtained by dividing the sum of several items by the number of items.

Balance. The difference between the increases and the decreases of an account.

Balance sheet. A statement showing the assets, debts, and present worth of a business.

Bank balance. The amount on deposit in a bank at any given time.

Bank discount. A deduction made by a bank when a note is paid before maturity.

Bank draft. An order on a bank to pay money.

Bankrupt. A person whose debts exceed his assets.

Base. The sum on which the percentage is calculated.

Bear. One who sells stocks, bonds, and other securities that he does not own, for future delivery, believing that there will be a fall in the market price of the securities.

Beneficiary. One who receives a benefit; the person who is entitled to receive the face value of an insurance policy or the income from an estate.

Bill of exchange. A draft; a written order from one person to another to pay a certain sum of money at a designated time.

Bill of lading. A written memorandum of freight or goods to be shipped, issued by the shipper.

Bill of sale. A written agreement transferring ownership to property, usually under seal; a contract for the sale of goods.

Board foot. A unit (foot long, foot wide, inch thick) used in measuring lumber.

Bond. An obligation in writing and under seal, issued by a corporation or government, bearing interest and promising the repayment of a loan at a definite time.

Bonus. A special allowance over and above what is due; extra wages.

Broker. An agent who buys and sells goods for others.

Brokerage. A percentage or commission charged by a broker for his services.

Budget. An estimate of probable income and expenses.

Bull. One who buys stocks, bonds, and other securities, believing that there will be a rise in the market price of the securities, or in order to cause a rise in price to take place.

Capital. The assets of a business; the amount of money or property belonging to a person.

Carload lot. A shipment occupying an entire freight car.

Carrying charge. Interest and other expenses borne by a borrower in connection with a loan, a mortgage on a house, installment-plan purchase, and the like.

Cash discount. A deduction allowed from the net amount due on a bill for prompt payment.

Clearinghouse. An institution through which banks exchange checks and drafts.

Commission. The sum paid an agent for doing business for another.

Commodity. Something bought and sold.

Compound interest. Interest computed on the principal plus the interest earned and accrued during a previous period.

Consignment. The sending of goods to another to be sold.

Co-operative. An organization permitting joint operation for mutual benefit, as a co-operative store, a consumer co-operative, and so on.

Corporation. An organization, created by law, with the legal rights of an individual, representing an association of persons.

Credit. Obtaining money or goods on the promise to pay for them at some future date.

Credit memorandum. A paper sent to a customer showing the amount of allowance made for returned goods, defective merchandise, or for other reasons.

Cumulative. Becoming larger by successive additions. Applied to dividend, interest, and the like, which, if not paid when due, is added to what is to be paid in the future.

Customs. Duties or taxes levied by the government on imports.

Deed. A written statement, under seal, by which ownership is transferred.

Default. Failure to pay what is due or to perform what has been promised.

Deficit. A shortage in funds or income.

Demurrage. The amount charged the one to whom freight is consigned, as a penalty for not unloading goods from the boat or freight car within a specified time.

Depreciation. A fall in value.

Disbursements. Amounts paid out.

Discount. A deduction from the gross amount of a debt, usually made in consideration of prompt or cash payment.

Dishonor. Failure to pay a note or draft when it matures; failure to accept a draft when it is presented for acceptance.

Dividend. Money, representing a part of the profits of a corporation, distributed among its stockholders.

Draft. An order directing the payment of money from one person to another.

Duplicate. An exact reproduction.

Earnest. A sum paid to bind a verbal contract.

Embezzlement. Unlawful use of property intrusted to one's care.

Exact time. The number of calendar days between dates.

Exchange. The charge made for collecting a draft or other commercial paper; a place where trading is carried on, as the stock exchange, cotton exchange, and so on.

Expiration. The natural end of anything, such as a lease.

Exports. Articles sent to another country.

Facsimile. An exact copy of the original, giving every detail.

Fee. Charge made for services.

Fiscal year. A period of one year, not necessarily beginning and ending with the calendar year.

Fixed charges. Charges that become due at stated intervals; for example, taxes, rent, bond interest.

Fluctuate. To vary irregularly in price, cost, or value.

Foreclosure. The sale of property to satisfy the debt secured by a mortgage on the property.

Forgery. The making or changing of a document with the intent to defraud.

Franchise. A special privilege granted by the government to a person or a corporation.

Good will. The money value of the reputation of a firm as held by the public.

Great gross. Twelve gross, 12 × 144 (1,728 articles).

Gross. Twelve dozen, 12 × 12 (144 articles).

Gross income. Total income before deducting expenses.

Guaranty. An undertaking to answer for the payment of a debt, or the performance of an obligation by another if he defaults.

Honor. To accept and pay a business paper, as a check, draft, trade acceptance, and the like, when due.

Imports. Articles brought into a country from other countries.

Indemnify. To secure against financial loss; to reimburse.

Indorse. To agree to; to guarantee payment; to write on the back of, as on a note, check, or other business paper.

Injunction. A court order requiring a person to do or not to do a particular act.

Insolvent. One whose assets are not sufficient to pay all debts.

Installment buying. A method of purchasing by partial payments; that is, payment on account to be made over a period of time.

Insurable interest. A legal right of a person to receive the benefit from an insurance contract.

Interest. The sum or the rate paid for the use of money.

In transit. On the way; on the road.

Inventory. An itemized list of the articles of merchandise on hand at any particular time.

Investment. Money used in an enterprise with the expectation of making a profit.

Invoice. An itemized statement, including quantity, description, prices, and shipping charges of merchandise sold or consigned.

Itemized statement. A paper sent to a customer showing in detail his purchases and payments.

Jobber. A person who buys from the importer or the manufacturer and sells to the retailer; the wholesaler; the middleman.

Job lot. An odd assortment of merchandise; an irregular quantity.

Journal. A book of original entry in which the first complete record of every business transaction is recorded chronologically.

Lease. A contract whereby the use of land, buildings, or other property is transferred for a term of years for rent or other income.

Ledger. A book in which all the transactions recorded in the journals are summarized and grouped in appropriate accounts.

Legal tender. Any form of money that the Government authorizes as acceptable in payment of money obligations.

Lessee. A person to whom a lease is given.

Lessor. A person who gives a lease to another.

Letter of credit. A letter issued by a bank authorizing its correspondent banks to honor the requests for money by the holder up to a specified amount.

Liability. A debt owed by a person or corporation.

Lien. A legal claim on real or personal property for the payment of a debt.

Liquidate. To pay off debts, or clear up and settle accounts.

List price. The price of an article as given in a list or catalogue. That price is often subject to trade discounts.

Long (buying long). An expression used to describe a purchase of merchandise or stocks in expectation of an increase in price.

Manifest. A schedule or list of the cargo on a ship.

Margin. The profit to be derived from the sale of an article; a part of the cost of stock deposited with the stockbroker by a customer.

Markup. Profit on sale of goods.

Maturity. The due date of a note or other business paper.

Merchandise. Goods that have been bought for sale.

Mortgage. A conditional transfer of title to personal property or real estate as security for the payment of a debt.

Negotiable. Capable of being transferred by indorsement or otherwise.

Negotiable paper. Any business paper payable to bearer or order, as promissory notes, bills of exchange, checks, certificates of deposit, and so on, title to which can be transferred by indorsement, assignment, or delivery.

Net profit. The difference between the selling price and cost price minus the cost of running the business.

Notary public. A public officer appointed by law, authorized to administer oaths, certify deeds and other paper, and protest notes.

Note (negotiable). A written promise to pay a stated sum of money at a definite or determinable time in the future, to the order of a definite person or to the bearer.

Option. The right to buy or sell property at a stated price within a given time.

Overdraw. To write checks or drafts for amounts greater than the balance on deposit.

Overhead. A word commonly used to mean the expense of running a business.

Par value. Full or face value.

Per annum. A Latin phrase meaning "by the year."

Petty cash. Small amounts of money paid out or received.

Policy. A written contract of insurance against financial loss due to the death of the insured or due to the destruction of property.

Power of attorney. A paper by which one person appoints another to act for him.

Premium. The amount paid as consideration for the contract of insurance.

Prime cost. Actual cost of goods before any expenses of delivery or commission.

Principal. The sum on which interest is paid; the person for whom another acts.

Proceeds. The amount of money received from a business transaction.

Proxy. An agent, representative, or substitute.

Quotation. The market price of a security or of merchandise.

Rebate. A return of part of a sum already paid; an allowance or credit.

Rectangle. A plane figure of four sides and four right angles. Its opposite sides are equal.

Remittance. A payment of money on account.

Requisition. A formal list of articles that are wanted.

Reserve. Funds accumulated for future use.

Retailer. One who sells goods in small quantities as opposed to a wholesaler or a jobber who sells in large quantities.

Revenue. Income.

Sales return. Merchandise returned by a customer.

Security. Anything of value given as a guarantee or pledge that a debt will be paid or an agreement kept.

Short (selling short). An expression used to describe a sale of merchandise or stocks not possessed by the seller at the time of the sale, to be delivered at some specified time in the future. The seller expects to buy the merchandise or stocks at a price lower than that quoted at the time of the sale.

Sight draft. An order to pay at once.

Sinking fund. Money set aside periodically from income to provide a fund with which to pay an existing debt when due.

Solvent. Able to pay one's debts.

Speculation. Anything bought or sold with the expectation of making a profit by a change in the market price.

Stock. Certificates representing ownership in a corporation; the merchandise used in a business.

Stock exchange. An organization of stockbrokers formed for the purpose of trading in stocks and bonds.

Surtax. A tax levied on income or property in addition to the regular tax.

Tare. An allowance made for the weight of a container.

Tariff. A table of fixed charges or taxes levied by the Government on exports and imports.

Time draft. An order to pay after a definite period of time.

Trade acceptance. A draft payable at a definite time, drawn by the seller of merchandise, on the buyer, for the amount of the sale, and accepted by him.

Trade discount. A deduction made from the list price of an article to bring this price into agreement with the market price.

Turnover. The act of selling a stock of goods and replacing it with a new supply of the same or similar goods.

Unit price. Cost or price of a single item.

Upkeep. The cost or act of keeping in repair or of maintaining.

Valuation. Estimated worth.

Voucher. Any written proof of the payment of money; a receipt.

Waybill. A statement containing a description and shipping directions of goods, sent by a railroad or steamship.

Yield. The return for services or money invested.

ABBREVIATIONS USED IN BUSINESS TRANSACTIONS

A.	Acre	**d.**	Pence	**km.**	Kilometer
A 1.	First grade	**da.**	Day	**KWH.**	Kilowatt-hour
agt.	Agent	**Dec.**	December	**L.**	Liter
amt.	Amount	**dept.**	Department	**lb.**	Pound
ans.	Answer	**dft.**	Draft	**L.C.L.**	Less than car
Apr.	April	**disc.**	Discount		lots
a/s.	Account sales	**do.**	Ditto	**l.p.**	List price
Aug.	August	**doz.; dz.**	Dozen	**ltd.**	Limited
av.	Average	**Dr.**	Doctor;	**L.S.**	Place for the
bg.	Bag		debtor		seal (locus sig-
bal.	Balance	**E.**	East		illi)
bbl.	Barrel	**ea.**	Each	**m.**	Mill; meter
bdl.	Bundle	**e.g.**	For example	**Mar.**	March
b.f.c.	Bill for collec-	**e.o.e.**	Errors and	**mdse.**	Merchandise
	tion		omissions	**Messrs.**	Gentlemen;
bkt.	Basket		excepted		Sirs
B/L.	Bill of lading	**etc.**	And so forth	**mi.**	Mile
B/O.	Back order	**ex.**	Example; ex-	**min.**	Minute
bot.	Bought		press	**mo.**	Month
bu.	Bushel	**exch.**	Exchange	**mos.**	Months
bx.	Box	**exp.**	Expense	**Mr.**	Mister
car.	Carton	**far.**	Farthing	**Mrs.**	Mistress
cd.	Cord; card	**Feb.**	February	**N.**	North
cg.	Centigram	**f.o.b.**	Free on board	**no.**	Number
ch.	Chain; chest	**frt.**	Freight	**N.S.F.; N/S.**	Not suf-
chg.	Charge	**fr.**	Franc		ficient funds
c.i.f.	Carriage and	**ft.**	Foot; feet	**Nov.**	November
	insurance free;	**fwd.**	Forward	**Oct.**	October
	cost, insur-	**gal.**	Gallon	**o/d.**	On demand
	ance, freight	**gi.**	Gill	**O.K.**	Correct
ck.	Check	**gr.**	Grain	**oz.**	Ounce
C. L.	Car lots	**gro.**	Gross	**p.**	Page
cm.	Centimeter	**guar.**	Guarantee	**payt.**	Payment
cml.	Commercial	**hf.**	Half	**pc.**	Piece
Co.	Company;	**hf. cht.**	Half chest	**pd.**	Paid
	county	**hhd.**	Hogshead	**per.**	By; by the
c/o.	Care of	**H.P.; h.p.**	Horsepower	**per cent.**	By the hun-
C. O. D.	Collect on de-	**hr.**	Hour		dred
	livery	**i.e.**	That is	**pf.**	Preferred
coll.	Collection	**in.**	Inch; inches	**pk.**	Peck
com.	Commission	**inc.**	Inclosure; in-	**pkg.**	Package
consg't.	Consignment		corporated	**pp.**	Pages
cr.	Creditor;	**ins.**	Insurance	**pr.**	Pair
	crate; credit	**inst.**	Instant; the	**pt.**	Pint
cs.	Case		current month	**prox.**	The following
csk.	Cask	**int.**	Interest		month
cu. ft.	Cubic foot	**I.; inv.**	Invoice	**pwt.**	Pennyweight
cu. in.	Cubic inch	**inv't.**	Inventory	**qr.**	Quire
cu. yd.	Cubic yard	**Jan.**	January	**qt.**	Quart
cwt.	Hundred-	**K.**	Carat	**rd.**	Rod
	weight	**kg.**	Kilogram	**recd.**	Received

552

rect.	Receipt	sig.	Signed; signa-	ult.	Last month
rm.	Ream		ture	via.	By way of
s.	Shilling	sq. ch.	Square chain	viz.	Namely; to
S.	South	sq. ft.	Square foot		wit
sec.	Second; secre-	sq. mi.	Square mile	vol.	Volume
	tary	sq. rd.	Square rod	vs.	against (ver-
sec'y.	Secretary	sq. yd.	Square yard		sus)
Sept.	September	T.	Ton	wk.	Week
set.	Settlement	tb.	Tub	wt.	Weight
ship.	Shipped	tr.	Transfer	yd.	Yard
shipt.	Shipment	treas.	Treasurer	yds.	Yards
				yr.	Year

SYMBOLS USED IN BUSINESS TRANSACTIONS

a/c	Account	"	Inch; seconds
a/s	Account sales	<	Less than
+	Addition; plus	×	Multiplication; times
()	Aggregation	#	Number (when written before
&	And		a figure). Pounds (when writ-
...	And so on		ten after a figure)
@	At; to; each	o/d	On demand
c/o	Care of	$1^1., 1^2., 1^3.$	One and one-fourth; one
¢	Cent		and one-half; one and three-
√	Correct; check mark		fourths
°	Degree	%	Per cent; hundredths
÷	Division	£	Pounds sterling
$	Dollar	:	Ratio
=	Equals; is equal to	∵	Since
/	Fraction (3/4)	√	Square root of
'	Foot; minutes	—	Subtraction; minus
>	Greater than	∴	Therefore
C	Hundred	M	Thousand

Index